G000269834

FOR SIXTH TER*
EXAMINATION
PAPER.

S. T. E. PAPERS
AND 'A' LEVEL
ETC.

A SHORTER INTERMEDIATE MECHANICS
SI EDITION

By D. HUMPHREY

INTERMEDIATE MECHANICS. Edited by J. Topping
Vol. I. *Dynamics.*
Vol. II. *Statics.*

REVISION MATHEMATICS FOR SCHOOL
CERTIFICATE. With Diagrams

By D. HUMPHREY and E. A. BAGGOTT

ELEMENTARY MECHANICS WITHOUT
HYDROSTATICS. With Frontispiece and
Illustrations

ELEMENTARY MECHANICS WITH
HYDROSTATICS. With Frontispiece and
Illustrations

A SHORTER INTERMEDIATE MECHANICS

SI EDITION
WITH DIAGRAMS

D. HUMPHREY, B.A., B.Sc.
Late Director of Education, The Polytechnic, London

J. TOPPING, M.Sc., Ph.D., D.I.C., F.INST.P., F.I.M.A.
Vice Chancellor and Principal, Brunel University, Uxbridge

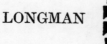

LONGMAN GROUP LIMITED
LONDON
Associated companies, branches and representatives throughout the world

SI edition © Longman Group Ltd 1971

All rights reserved. No part of this publication may be reproduced, stored in a retrieval system or transmitted in any form or by any means — electronic, mechanical, photocopying, recording or otherwise — without the prior permission of the copyright owner.

First published 1949
SI edition 1971
Eleventh impression 1980

ISBN 0 582 32236 7

Printed in Singapore by
Huntsmen Offset Printing Pte Ltd

PREFACE

MR D. HUMPHREY, before his death in December 1945, had planned to combine his two volumes on Intermediate Mechanics, with the intention that the one book would cover the requirements of students preparing for the Intermediate Science and Engineering examinations of the University of London, or for the ordinary papers in applied mathematics of the Higher School Certificate examinations.

I have tried to complete this plan in accordance with his wishes, being guided by his unfinished work, but I have been free to alter the contents as I thought fit. Parts of the book have been rewritten, and other parts have been removed completely; several of the diagrams have been altered, the examples have been graded where necessary, and a few have been placed more appropriately. In addition, the more difficult examples of scholarship standard have been deleted, and more elementary examples have been introduced, particularly at the beginning of the dynamics, to make the book more suitable for beginners. A new feature is a collection of revision examples at the end of the book; many of these are taken from recent examination papers. It is hoped that in these ways the few blemishes in the original volumes have been removed, and that the new book will be more suitable for those for whom it is designed.

As it is probably preferable to start the course with dynamics the contents have been grouped in the order, dynamics, statics, and hydrostatics, and a student with a little preliminary knowledge of the subject could read the book straight through. But others are recommended to omit Chapters 7, 8, and 9 until they have read Chapters 10, 11, and 12, which deal with statics. In Chapter 10, however, there is a sufficient account of the basic principles to suit those who would prefer to start with statics. As before, the calculus is used throughout, but little knowledge of it is necessary.

It is a pleasure to express thanks to the Syndics of the Cambridge University Press, the University of London, the

v

Oxford and Cambridge Schools Examination Board, the Joint Matriculation Board, and the Central Welsh Board for permission to use questions. The source of these questions is indicated.

I am indebted to Professor V. C. A. Ferraro, of University College, Exeter, who read part of the manuscript and made a number of suggestions. I am also grateful to Mr A. E. Chapman and Mr R. Newson who have helped with the correction of the proofs and assisted in other ways. For any correction of text or examples, or suggestions for improvement, I shall be very grateful.

THE POLYTECHNIC, W.1   J. TOPPING
1948

PREFACE TO THE SI EDITION

WITH the adoption by Britain of the system of SI units the text and the examples throughout the book have been appropriately modified. In many of the examples the changes have been made to keep the arithmetic as simple as possible and in others to bring the problem up-to-date. The newton has been used exclusively as the unit of force; it has been thought best not to introduce any other, and consequently the unit equal to the weight of a body of mass 1 kilogram, sometimes called the kilogram-force and denoted by 1 kgf, has not been used at all.

The other main change is that the chapters on hydrostatics have been removed in keeping with the changes in teaching in schools and the content of present examination syllabuses.

A short chapter on vectors has been introduced; it collects together the vector algebra used throughout and develops it further.

The chapter on Elementary Statistics has been retained because of the increasing importance these days of some knowledge of statistics and statistical techniques.

It is a pleasure to express my thanks again to the teachers and students who have written to me from time to time. I am glad that the book continues to be widely used.

BRUNEL UNIVERSITY, UXBRIDGE   J. TOPPING
1971

CONTENTS

CHAPTER   PAGE

1. DYNAMICS OF A PARTICLE. SPEED AND VELOCITY   1
Speed   1
Space–time curve   6
Displacement   14
Law of vector addition   16
Velocity   22
Parallelogram of velocities   24
Triangle and polygon of velocities   28
Relative velocity   34
Angular velocity   41

2. ACCELERATION   48
Acceleration   48
Relative acceleration   49
Motion with uniform acceleration   50
Vertical motion under gravity   58
Motion down a smooth inclined plane   63
Space–time and other curves for variable acceleration   67

3. FORCE, MOMENTUM, LAWS OF MOTION   79
Mass   80
Momentum   81
Newton's Laws of Motion   81
Newton's Law of Gravitation   82
Units of force   85
Weight and mass   85
Parallelogram of forces   87
Principle of linear momentum   88
Friction   89
Motion of connected particles   97
Attwood's machine   107

REVISION EXAMPLES A   117

4. WORK, POWER, AND ENERGY   122
Work   122
Power   123
Energy   131
Principle of conservation of energy   133
Variable forces   141
Force–space and indicator diagrams   142

CHAPTER   PAGE

Tension in an elastic string   145
Gravitational potential energy   149
Units and dimensions   153

5. IMPULSIVE FORCES. IMPACT OF
   ELASTIC BODIES   158

Impact of two bodies   159
Motion of a shot and gun   160
Impact of water on a surface   161
Impulsive tensions in strings   169
Impact of elastic bodies   177
Direct impact of two spheres   179
Impact on a fixed smooth plane   189
Oblique impact of two spheres   194

6. PROJECTILES   202

Time of flight   203
Range on a horizontal plane   204
Range on an inclined plane   214
The path of a projectile is a parabola   226
Problems involving impacts of projectiles   229

        REVISION EXAMPLES B   233

7. MOTION IN A CIRCLE   241

Normal acceleration   241
The conical pendulum   246
Governors of steam-engines   247
Motion of a railway carriage on a curved track   253
Motion in a vertical circle   263

8. SIMPLE HARMONIC MOTION   277

Definition and fundamental equation   277
Simple harmonic motion in a straight line   278
Particle on a smooth table attached to a spring   290
Particle suspended by a spring or elastic string   291
The simple pendulum   300

9. DYNAMICS OF A RIGID BODY   307

Kinetic energy of a rotating body   307
Moment of inertia and radius of gyration   308
Moment of inertia of a rod   308

CHAPTER   PAGE
Moment of inertia of a rectangular lamina   309
Moment of inertia of a circular ring   310
Moment of inertia of a circular disc   311
Moment of inertia of a solid sphere   311
Theorem of parallel axes   312
Perpendicular axis theorem   313
Moment of inertia of a rectangular prism   315
Moment of inertia of a circular cylinder   316
Velocity acquired by a rigid body rotating about a fixed
    axis under gravity   319
Moment of inertia of a flywheel   321
Angular momentum of a rigid body   324
Equation of motion of a body rotating about a fixed axis 325
Compound pendulum   327
Centre of oscillation   328
General motion of a rigid body in two dimensions   340
Translation and rotation   341
Angular momentum and kinetic energy of a rigid body
    moving in two dimensions   342
Equations of motion of a rigid body   342

REVISION EXAMPLES C   351

10. STATICS OF A PARTICLE   358
Force   358
Basis of statics   359
Parallelogram of forces   360
Smooth bodies   363
Tension of a string   363
Resolution of a force   365
Triangle of forces   369
Lami's Theorem   371
Polygon of forces   380
Resultant of any number of forces acting at a point 380
Conditions of equilibrium for a particle   388
Laws of Friction   392
Particle on rough horizontal plane   394
Particle on rough inclined plane   396

11. STATICS OF A RIGID BODY—PARALLEL
    FORCES—MOMENTS—COUPLES   403
Resultant of two like parallel forces   403
Resultant of two unlike parallel forces   404

CONTENTS

CHAPTER   PAGE

Centre of parallel forces and centre of gravity   406
Centre of gravity of a thin uniform rod   407
Centre of gravity of a lamina in the shape of a parallelo-
    gram   408
Centre of gravity of a triangular lamina   408
Moment of a force   411
Varignon's Theorem   412
Moment of a couple   415
Application of the principle of moments   415
The lever   422
The balance   422
The common steelyard   427

12. FORCES IN A PLANE ACTING ON A RIGID BODY   431
    Rigid body subject to three forces   431
    Rigid body subject to more than three forces   445
    Reduction of coplanar forces to a force or a couple   446
    Conditions of equilibrium for more than three forces   447
    Jointed rods   458
    Further examples on coplanar forces   472
    Composition of couples   484
    Reduction of coplanar forces to a force and a couple   491
    Line of action of resultant   493
    Conditions of equilibrium, other forms   493
    Moment of force about an axis   502
    Work done by a couple   504

    REVISION EXAMPLES D   507

13. GRAPHICAL CONSTRUCTIONS   513
    Force and funicular polygons   513
    Bow's notation   516
    Parallel forces   516
    Loaded frameworks   522

14. FRICTION   539
    Equilibrium of a single rigid body   540
    Conditions for sliding or tilting   553
    Equilibrium of jointed bodies   556
    Further worked examples   559

CHAPTER   PAGE

15. MACHINES   566

Mechanical advantage—velocity ratio   567
Efficiency   568
Systems of pulleys   569
Weston differential pulley   577
The wheel and axle   578
Overhauling   580
The screw   581
The differential screw   582

16. CENTRE OF GRAVITY   587

Three rods forming a triangle   587
Tetrahedron   588
Pyramid and solid cone   589
Curved surface of a cone   590
Centre of gravity of a number of particles, general formulae 590
Centre of gravity of a compound body or remainder   594
Quadrilateral lamina   605
Stability of equilibrium   610
Uniform circular arc   617
Sector of a circle   618
Segment of a circle   619
Solid hemisphere   621
Thin hollow hemisphere   622

REVISION EXAMPLES E   627

17. VECTORS   636

Addition and subtraction of vectors   637
Components of vectors   642
Areas as vectors   648

18. ELEMENTARY STATISTICS   655

Some terms and definitions   657
Mean   658
Working mean   659
Median   661
Cumulative frequency   662
Mean deviation   668
Standard deviation   669

CONTENTS

	PAGE
Checks and corrections	674
Other terms and definitions	680
Binomial distribution	690
Poisson distribution	693
Normal distribution	696
Standard error of the mean	698
ANSWERS TO EXAMPLES	706

THE following abbreviations are used to denote the source from which examples are taken:

B.Sc.	London University. B.Sc. Examination.
C.A.	G.C.E. Advanced Level. Cambridge University.
C.S.	College Scholarships. Cambridge University.
C.W.B.	Central Welsh Board. Higher Certificate.
Ex.	Exhibitions. London University.
H.C.	Oxford and Cambridge Higher Certificate.
H.S.C. & H.S.D.	Higher Schools. London University.
I.A.	Intermediate Arts. London University.
I.C.	Imperial College. Entrance and Scholarship Examination.
I.E.	Intermediate Engineering. London University.
I.S.	Intermediate Science. London University.
L.A.	G.C.E. Advanced Level. London University.
N.U.	Joint Matriculation Board. Northern Universities. Higher Certificates.
Q.E.	Qualifying Examination. Mechanical Sciences Tripos, Cambridge.
S.	Scholarships Examination. London University.

CHAPTER ONE

DYNAMICS OF A PARTICLE

SPEED AND VELOCITY

1.1. Mechanics is the science which deals with the action of forces on bodies. It is therefore concerned with much that we meet in everyday life—the motion of engines, the flight of aeroplanes and projectiles, the stresses in bridges and frameworks, the forces acting on a ship or a buoy floating in the sea, and many similar problems. Such problems, as we shall constantly note, have to be simplified and somewhat idealised to make them capable of solution by simple mathematics, but this simplification is a necessary preliminary to any more detailed or profound attack.

Under the influence of forces, bodies may be either in motion or at rest, relative to some assigned system or frame of reference. The part of mechanics which deals with the motion of solid bodies is called dynamics, and that concerned with solids at rest is called statics. The corresponding parts of the subject dealing with fluids are known as hydrodynamics and hydrostatics respectively. We shall first consider dynamics.

1.2. For simplicity, we shall assume to start with, that the dimensions of the solid body may be neglected compared with the other distances involved. We shall refer to such a body as a *particle*; it may be represented by a point.

When a particle is changing its position relative to some assigned origin O it is said to be in motion relative to O, and the curve drawn through all the successive positions of the particle is called its path relative to O.

The *speed* of a particle is the rate at which it describes its path. The speed expresses the rate of motion *without specifying the direction of motion*. Speed is therefore a quantity having magnitude only, and is defined completely when we know this magnitude, expressed, of course, in terms of some chosen units. For example, we can say that the speed is 10 metres per second; the number 10 specifies the speed completely. It involves, as we shall examine more carefully later, the unit of length, the metre, and the unit of time, the second.

Any quantity having magnitude and no direction is called a *scalar quantity*, so that speed is a scalar.

Similarly, a quantity having magnitude *and* direction, and thus requiring two magnitudes to specify it completely, is called a *vector quantity*.

All the quantities with which we shall have to deal will be either scalars or vectors; we shall define them carefully as they arise, for they obey different rules.

1.3. Units of speed

The English units of length and time formerly used were the foot and the second, and the unit of mass (see § 3.3) the pound. These units were called the foot–pound–second system, abbreviated to F.P.S. system.

The system in which the units are the centimetre, the gramme, and the second is known as the C.G.S. system.

International agreement between the standards authorities of the leading scientific countries has led to the adoption by Britain of a system of metric units, known as SI (le Système International d'Unités). In this system the unit of length is the metre (symbol m), the unit of mass the kilogramme (kg), and the unit of time the second (s). The unit of speed is therefore 1 metre per second, written $1 \, \mathrm{m \, s^{-1}}$.

We might note here that $1 \, \mathrm{kg} = 10^3 \, \mathrm{g}$, and that 1000 kg, which equals $10^6 \, \mathrm{g}$, is sometimes written 1 Mg, the symbol M (from mega) standing for 10^6.

1.4. Average speed

If a particle travels a distance s_1 m, from an assigned point in its path, in time t_1 s, and a distance s_2 m from the same point in time t_2 s, the average speed during the first t_1 s is $s_1/t_1 \, \mathrm{m \, s^{-1}}$, and during the first t_2 s it is $s_2/t_2 \, \mathrm{m \, s^{-1}}$.

Also since the particle travels $(s_2 - s_1)$ m in $(t_2 - t_1)$ s, its average speed in the interval t_1 to t_2 is $(s_2 - s_1)/(t_2 - t_1) \, \mathrm{m \, s^{-1}}$. In this way the average speed in any time-interval can be calculated; we merely divide the increment in distance by the corresponding increment in time.

EXAMPLE

A train is travelling from a station P *to a station* S, *stops at stations* Q *and* R *as shown in the following table. Find the average speed of the train between* P *and* Q, *between* R *and* S, *and for the whole journey.*

Station	Times	Distances from P
P depart	10.00	0 km
Q arrive	11.10	84 km
Q depart	11.15	84 km
R arrive	12.10	170 km
R depart	12.15	170 km
S arrive	13.10	247 km

$\therefore$ Average speed from P to Q $= \dfrac{\text{distance from P to Q}}{\text{time taken from P to Q}}$

$$= \frac{84 \text{ km}}{1\frac{1}{6} \text{ hours}} = 72 \text{ km h}^{-1}$$

$\therefore$ Average speed from R to S $= \dfrac{\text{distance from R to S}}{\text{time taken from R to S}}$

$$= \frac{77 \text{ km}}{55 \text{ min.}} = \frac{77 \times 60 \text{ km h}^{-1}}{55}$$

$$= 84 \text{ km h}^{-1}$$

$\therefore$ Average speed for whole journey $= \dfrac{\text{length of journey}}{\text{total time taken}}$

$$= \frac{247 \text{ km}}{3\frac{1}{6} \text{ hours}} = \frac{247 \times 6}{19} \text{km h}^{-1}$$

$$= 78 \text{ km h}^{-1}$$

1.5. As a further example, suppose a particle moves in such a way that its distance from some point in its path is 5, 10, 15, 20, 25, ... metres at the instants of time 1, 2, 3, 4, 5, ... s, so that the distance gone in each successive second is 5 m.

The average speed is 5 m s^{-1} in successive seconds. Indeed, the average speed is 5 m s^{-1} in any interval t_1 to t_2 where t_1 and t_2 may have any of the values 0, 1, 2, 3, 4, 5, e.g. $t_1 = 2$ and $t_2 = 4$. This is all we can deduce with certainty, but we might add that it is likely, though not inevitable, that the speed of the particle *throughout* the interval must have been 5 m s⁻¹.

It is useful to represent the data graphically. In Fig. 1.1 points are plotted corresponding to given values of the distance at the given times. These points obviously lie on a straight line through the origin, but this is not the only curve that can be drawn through them, as Fig. 1.2 shows.

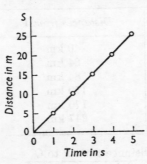

Fig. 1.1

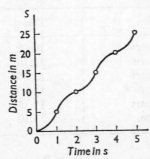

Fig. 1.2

The equation of the straight line shown in Fig. 1.1 is $s = 5t$, where s is the distance gone in time t. We only know that this equation is satisfied for the values $t = 0, 1, 2, 3, 4, 5$, but it is reasonable to assume that it is true for *all* values of t in this interval, for example, when $t = 1\cdot2$ or $2\cdot3$ or any other value between 0 and 5.

If this equation is satisfied for *all* values of t in the interval the speed is said to be *uniform*; otherwise, the speed is variable (cf. Fig. 1.2).

For instance, suppose the particle has travelled distances 5, 11, 14, 19, 25, . . . m at the instants 1, 2, 3, 4, 5, . . . s, the distances gone in successive seconds are unequal, being 6, 3, 5, 6 . . . m respectively, so that the *average* speed in these time-intervals is 6, 3, 5, 6, . . . m s⁻¹. It is clear that the speed is *not* uniform.

1.6. Uniform speed

Uniform speed may be defined as such that the particle moves through equal lengths of its path in equal times, however small these times may be. It is measured by the distance moved through in unit time.

If s is the distance moved through in time t, then the speed v, assumed uniform, is given by $v = s/t$ or $s = vt$.

The *average speed* of a particle in moving a certain distance in a given interval of time is therefore the speed with which it would have to move uniformly to describe the given distance in the given time. If the interval of time is at all large the speed will usually have varied from instant to instant throughout the interval. Hence the speed *at any instant* will not, in general, be equal to the average speed throughout the whole or part of the interval.

1.7. Speed at any instant

The speed at any instant t can, however, be found from the rate of motion during a very short interval of time including the instant t.

For, if s denotes the distance gone in time t, and $s+\delta s$ the distance gone in time $(t+\delta t)$, then $\delta s/\delta t$ measures the average speed of the particle during the time interval t to $t+\delta t$. If δt is small, $\delta s/\delta t$ will give *approximately* the speed at the instant t. The speed at the instant t can, in fact, be written as $\lim_{\delta t \to 0} (\delta s/\delta t)$, or ds/dt, in the notation of the differential calculus.

For example, if $s = 5t$, then $s+\delta s = 5(t+\delta t)$ and hence $\delta s = 5\delta t$

$\therefore$ $$\delta s/\delta t = 5.$$

Hence $ds/dt = 5$, so that the speed is 5 units at every instant in the interval for which the relation $s = 5t$ holds.

EXAMPLE

If the distance, s m, travelled by a particle in t s is $s = 4+6t-t^2$, find the average speed in the interval from $t = 2$ to $t = 2+\epsilon$ when $\epsilon = 0\cdot1, 0\cdot01$ and $0\cdot001$. Deduce the speed at $t = 2$.

Now the distance gone when $t = 2$ is $4+12-4 = 12$ m. Also the distance gone when $t = 2+\epsilon$ is

$$4+6(2+\epsilon)-(2+\epsilon)^2 = 12+2\epsilon-\epsilon^2 \text{ m}$$

$\therefore$ Distance gone from $t = 2$ to $t = 2+\epsilon$ is $(2\epsilon-\epsilon^2)$ m, and hence the average speed in this time-interval is $(2\epsilon-\epsilon^2)/\epsilon \text{ ms}^{-1}$, that is, $(2-\epsilon) \text{ ms}^{-1}$.

$\therefore$ In the interval $t = 2$ to $t = 2\cdot1$ the average speed is $1\cdot9$ m per sec. In the interval $t = 2$ to $t = 2\cdot01$ it is $1\cdot99 \text{ ms}^{-1}$, and in the interval $t = 2$ to $t = 2\cdot001$ it is $1\cdot999 \text{ ms}^{-1}$.

The average speed approaches 2 ms^{-1} as ϵ gets smaller and smaller; this is the speed *at the instant* $t = 2$.

It might be noted that if we had considered the time-interval $t = 2 - \epsilon$ to $t = 2$, we should have found the average speed to be $(2 + \epsilon)$ ms^{-1}, leading again to 2 ms^{-1} at the instant $t = 2$.

1.8. Space–time curve

If the values of s, the distance gone in time t, are plotted for different values of t the points will lie on a curve known as the *space–time curve*. Such a curve is APB in Fig. 1.3.

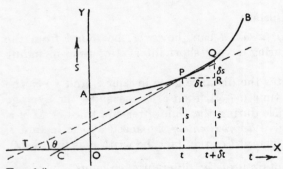

Fig. 1.3

If P is the point on the curve corresponding to the distance s and the time t and Q to the distance $s + \delta s$ and the time $t + \delta t$, then the average speed of the particle in the interval t to $t + \delta t$ is given by $\delta s/\delta t$, which equals the gradient of the chord PQ.

For if PR is drawn parallel to OX we have

$$\tan QPR = \frac{RQ}{PR} = \frac{\delta s}{\delta t}.$$

Also if QP produced meets OX at C, the angles QPR and PCX are equal, and hence

$$\tan PCX = \delta s/\delta t.$$

Now if δt is allowed to take smaller and smaller values Q approaches nearer and nearer to P, and as δt tends to zero the chord QPC becomes the tangent to the space–time curve at P. Hence if the tangent PT at P makes an angle θ with the time-axis OX, we have

$$\tan \theta = \lim_{\delta t \to 0} \tan PCX = \lim_{\delta t \to 0} \frac{\delta s}{\delta t} = \frac{ds}{dt}.$$

Thus *the speed at the instant t* equals tan θ, where θ is the angle the tangent PT at P makes with the axis of t.

It is clear that if the speed is uniform, the space–time curve is a straight line inclined at an angle θ to the axis of t, such that tan θ equals the value of the uniform speed.

If the space–time curve is *not* a straight line the speed of the particle must vary with time.

Thus an uninterrupted run of a train between two stations could be represented by a space–time curve similar to the curve OABC in Fig. 1.4.

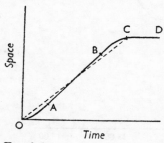

FIG. 1.4

The part OA, which is concave upwards, corresponds to the commencement of the journey with constantly increasing speed; the part AB, which is a straight line, corresponds to the train moving with uniform speed, and the part BC, which is concave downwards, to the slowing-down of the train until it is brought to rest again. It will be noted that the tangent to the curve at C is parallel to the time-axis, that is, its gradient is zero.

If the train ran the distance between the stations at uniform speed the space–time curve, of course, would be the straight line OC. Further, if the train stopped at the second station for some time the corresponding space–time curve would be the straight line CD parallel to the time-axis.

EXAMPLE (i)

Let us refer again to the example discussed in § 1.4.

Space–time curves for the journey are shown in Fig. 1.5.

The gradients of the dotted lines give the average speeds between the stations. The full lines represent uninterrupted runs between the stations, assuming uniform speed most of the time. It will be noted in the above example that if we were asked 'what was the speed of the train at 10.30?' we have not enough information to provide an answer. Actually it might have been pulled up at a signal at that instant, but on the assumption of an uninterrupted run between P and Q at approximately uniform speed most of the time, the speed at 10.30 is given by the gradient at A of the full line drawn in Fig. 1.5. This could be found approximately from a carefully drawn figure; it is equal to AC/BC (see Fig. 1.5).

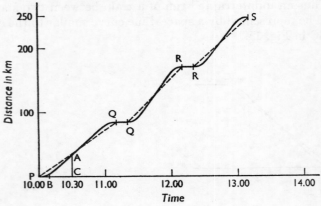

Fɪɢ. 1.5

It is clear that if we are given the distances gone at successive instants we can only find average speeds in the intervals between the instants. Anything more than this is mere conjecture. To find the speed at any instant we must know the distance gone at *every* instant in a time-interval including this instant. We can illustrate this by the following, rather idealised, example.

ᴇxᴀᴍᴘʟᴇ (ii)

The distances *s* gone by a particle at times *t* are as follows:

s (m)	0	1	4	9	15	21	27	33
t (s)	0	1	2	3	4	5	6	7

The average speeds in each successive second are therefore 1, 3, 5, 6, 6, 6, 6 ms^{-1}. This is all we can deduce with certainty.

But it is clear that during the first 3 s the speed is not uniform while afterwards the data suggest that the speed might be uniform and of magnitude 6 ms^{-1}.

In fact, we can easily verify that the data satisfy the relation $s = t^2$ for $t = 0, 1, 2, 3$, and the relation $s = 6t - 9$ for $t = 3, 4, 5, 6, 7$.

If we now make the assumption that the relation $s = t^2$ is satisfied for *all* values of t between 0 and 3, and the relation $s = 6t - 9$ is satisfied for *all* values of t between 3 and 7, we can find the speed at any instant. (The space–time curve corresponding to these relations is shown in Fig. 1.6.)

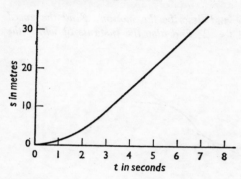

FIG. 1.6

For if
$$s = 6t - 9$$
then
$$s + \delta s = 6(t + \delta t) - 9$$
∴
$$\delta s = 6\delta t$$
∴
$$\delta s / \delta t = 6$$
and hence
$$ds/dt = 6.$$

Therefore the speed at every instant between $t = 3$ and $t = 7$ is 6 ms^{-1}.

Also if
$$s = t^2$$
then
$$s + \delta s = (t + \delta t)^2$$
∴
$$\delta s = (t + \delta t)^2 - t^2 = 2t \, \delta t + (\delta t)^2$$
∴
$$\delta s / \delta t = 2t + \delta t$$
∴
$$ds/dt = 2t.$$

Therefore the speed at any instant t between $t = 0$ and 3 is $2t \text{ ms}^{-1}$; that is, zero at $t = 0$; 2 ms^{-1} at $t = 1$; 3 ms^{-1} at $t = 1\frac{1}{2}$ and so on.

Thus an exact mathematical relation between s and t leads to an exact value of the speed at any time. In practice, such a relation between s and t is not usually known, and hence to find the speed at any time we must draw the tangent to the space–time graph at the appropriate point. This can usually only be done approximately.

EXAMPLE (iii)

The following table gives the distance s travelled by a particle in time t

t (in s)	0	1	2	3	4	5	6	7	8	9	10	11
s (in m)	0	4·9	7·8	9·4	9·9	10·0	10·1	10·6	12·2	14·0	14·4	14·5

Draw the space–time curve and describe the motion. Find the speed initially and at the instant t = 2; find also the instants at which the speed is 1·0 m s⁻¹.

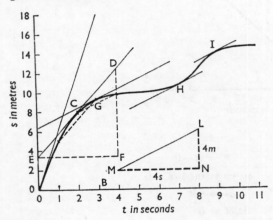

FIG. 1.7

The space–time curve is shown in Fig. 1.7. It is clear that from $t = 0$ to $t = 5$ the curve is concave downwards corresponding to decreasing speed, that at about $t = 5$ the speed begins to increase and later decreases again. Indeed, the average speeds in successive seconds are 4·9, 2·9, 1·6, 0·5, 0·1, 0·1, 0·5, 1·6, 1·8, 0·4, and 0·1, all expressed in metres per second (m s^{-1}). Thus the particle moves with decreasing speed until about $t = 5$, when it is practically at rest after which it accelerates until just after $t = 8$, when it begins to slow down again and at $t = 11$ it is almost stationary.

To find the initial speed we draw as accurately as possible the tangent OA to the space–time curve at the origin O; this has the gradient BA/OB which equals approximately 18 m/3 s, that is 6 m s^{-1}.

The speed at $t = 2$ is given by the gradient of the tangent to the curve at the point C; this equals approximately FD/EF, that is, $9·2 \text{ m}/4 \text{ s} = 2·3 \text{ m s}^{-1}$.

To find the instants at which the speed is 1·0 m s⁻¹ we have to find the points on the curve at which the tangents have the gradient

1·0 ms⁻¹. This gradient is shown in Fig. 1.7 by the triangle LMN; since NL = 4 m and MN = 4 s, the side ML has the gradient 1·0 ms⁻¹. We must now draw the tangents to the space–time curve which are parallel to ML. This can be done only approximately, but there are three points on the curve, shown as G, H, and I in Fig. 1.7, at which the tangents are parallel to ML. These points correspond approximately to the times $t = 3$, 7, and 9 respectively. At these instants roughly the speed is 1·0 ms⁻¹.

EXAMPLES 1.1

1. A train leaves London at 11.30 and reaches Southampton at 13.20 having covered 132 km. Find the average speed of the train in kmh⁻¹ per hour and ms⁻¹.

2. A man rows a boat downstream a distance of 3 km in 20 minutes, and rows back in 40 minutes. Find his average speed (i) downstream, (ii) upstream, and (iii) for the double journey.

3. Show that a *light-year*, defined as the distance traversed in a year by light travelling at the uniform speed of 3×10^8 ms⁻¹, equals $9·5 \times 10^{12}$ km. How long does light from the sun take to reach the earth, which is approximately 150 million km distant?

4. If sound travels in air at the uniform speed of about 335 ms⁻¹, show that the noise of an explosion at A will reach a point B 4 km distance from A in approximately 12 s. If the noise reaches two points C and D at exactly the same time, state where A must be relative to CD.

5. A radio signal is sent vertically upwards into the air and is reflected downwards from an ionised layer of the atmosphere. If the signal is received back $\frac{1}{500}$ s after it is sent out, find the height of the layer. (Radio waves travel at the uniform speed of 3×10^8 ms⁻¹.) If a signal were reflected from the moon, which is about 390,000 km from the earth, what time would elapse between the sending and the receiving of the signal?

6. The following tables give the distance s m described by a particle in t s. Draw a distance–time graph, and find the average speed in each successive second. Deduce a possible relation between s and t, and describe the corresponding type of motion in each case.

(a)	t	0	1	2	3	4	5
	s	0	4	8	12	16	20
(b)	t	0	1	2	3	4	5
	s	0	2	4	6	6	6

(c)

t	0	1	2	3	4	5
s	1	4	7	10	13	16

(d)

t	0	1	2	3	4	5
s	0	2	6	12	20	30

7. The following tables give the distance s m described by a particle in t s. Draw a distance–time graph, and find the average speed during the first 2 s, 5 s, 8 s respectively. Also obtain an estimate of the speed at the instants $t = 2, 5$, and 8 respectively.

(a)

t	0	1	2	3	4	5	6	7	8
s	0	3	6	9	9	9	11	13	15

(b)

t	0	1	2	3	4	5	6	7	8
s	0	0·5	2	4	6	8	10	11·5	12

8. A man starts at 10 a.m. from place A and walks at 6 km h^{-1} until he reaches place B 16 km distant, where he rests for half an hour. He then proceeds to place C, 10 km farther on, at the pace of 5 km h^{-1}. A motorist also starts from place A at 13.30 and travels towards B and C at a uniform speed of 32 km h^{-1}. Draw the space–time curves for the man and the motorist and from them find (a) the time and the distance of the man from A when the motorist passes him, (b) the time when the man is 5 km ahead of the motorist, and (c) if the motorist stopped 2 km from C, how long would he have to wait before the man caught him up?

9. The motion of a car is found to be as given in the following table, in which the distance s m corresponding to a given time t s is recorded:

t	3	4	5	6	7	8
s	17	22	27	35	43	52

Find the value of the average speed during the 4th, 5th, 6th, and 7th second. Plot the values of s against the values of t, and draw a smooth curve to represent the space–time graph. Determine from this curve the speed of the car at the end of the 4th, 5th, 6th, and 7th second.

10. The following table gives the distance s km described by a car in t h. Draw a graph of s against t and from it find a value of the speed of the car at the times $t = 2, 4$, and 6 respectively.

t	0	1	2	3	4	5	6	7	8
s	0	64	120	146	160	184	205	240	290

11. Define the speed of a moving particle and explain how it is obtained from the distance–time graph of the motion. A car travels s km in t min where

t	0	15	30	45	60	75	90	105	120
s	0	8	26	50	66	77	85	91	96

Draw the distance–time graph and find (i) the average speed, (ii) the maximum speed, and (iii) the instants at which the speed is 64 km h^{-1}.

12. Obtain an expression for the speed at time t s of a particle moving in a straight line such that its distance (s m) from a fixed point O at time t s is (i) $s = 4t+3$, (ii) $s = 2t^2+3$. Find the initial speed in each case.

13. A particle is thrown vertically upwards with a speed of 30 m s^{-1}, and its height s m after t s is given by $s = 30t-5t^2$. (a) Find the average speed during the interval δt measured from the instant t s from the start; (b) find an expression for the speed at any instant t; (c) find when the particle reaches its highest point, and its height then.

14. A particle moves along a straight line such that its displacement, s m, from a fixed point O at time t s is given in the following tables. Draw a graph of s against t, and deduce a value of the speed at the instants $t = 2$, 4, and 6 respectively. Describe the motion in each case.

(a)

t	0	1	2	3	4	5	6	7
s	0	2	4	6	6	6	3	0

(b)

t	0	1	2	3	4	5	6	7	8
s	0	7	12	15	16	15	12	7	0

(c)

t	0	1	2	3	4	5	6	7	8
s	0	7	10	7	0	-7	-10	-7	0

15. A particle moves in a straight line from rest so that its distance, s cm, from its starting-point at time t s, is given by the following table:

t	0	1	1·5	2	2·5	3	3·5	4	4·5	5	6
s	0	18	29	37	43	45	40	30	25	22	20

Draw the space–time graph for the motion and determine the speed of the particle when $t = 4·5$. Show that the particle also had this speed in the opposite direction at some instant between $t = 0$ and $t = 3$, and find the distance of the particle from its starting-point at that moment.

16. A walker and a cyclist start together from a place A at the speeds of 5 kmh⁻¹ and 16 kmh⁻¹ respectively. When the cyclist reaches a place B 32 km distant he rests for half an hour, and then returns towards A at 12 kmh⁻¹. Assuming that the speeds are uniform throughout, draw the distance–time curves and find from them (a) the time and distance from A where the walker and cyclist meet, and (b) the times when they are 16 km apart.

17. A body X moves from A to B in a straight line for 30 min with uniform velocity of 30 kmh⁻¹. It remains at B for 10 min and then travels 30 km further to C at 48 kmh⁻¹. After staying at C for 10 min, it returns to A at a uniform speed of 60 kmh⁻¹. Draw a graph showing the position of X at any time, and from it determine at what time a body Y leaving A at the same time as X will meet X on its return journey 20 km from A. At what uniform speed must Y move?

18. The distance s m moved by a particle in t s is given by $s = 1 \cdot 5t^2 - t$. Find its speed after t s. Find the instant at which the particle comes instantaneously to rest, and describe the motion.

19. The distance s m moved by a particle in t s is given by $s = 12t - t^2$. Find its initial speed, and the instants at which its speed is 8 ms⁻¹. Check your results by drawing the distance–time graph.

20. The distance s m moved by a particle in t s is given by $s = 2t^2$ from $t = 0$ to $t = 4$, $s = 16t - 32$, from $t = 4$ to $t = 8$ and $s = 80t - 4t^2 - 288$ from $t = 8$ to $t = 10$. Draw the distance–time graph. Find the speed of the particle in each of these time-intervals and describe the motion.

1.9. Displacement

If a particle is at some point P at time t its displacement relative to O is represented by OP in magnitude and direction. Displacement is a *vector* quantity, for it has magnitude and direction and hence requires two magnitudes to specify it completely.

We can specify OP, or alternatively, we can fix the position of P with respect to O, in two ways.

Firstly, let OX, OY (Fig. 1.8) be two fixed straight lines such that OP lies in their plane, and let PM be drawn parallel to OY to meet OX in M, and let PN be drawn parallel to OX to meet OY in N. Then the lengths of PN and PM (or OM and ON) will determine the position of P.

These lengths are the cartesian coordinates (x, y) of P referred to the axes OX, OY. Usually the axes are taken at right angles to each other.

Secondly, the position of P is also determined if we know the length of the line OP and the angle XOP (Fig. 1.9).

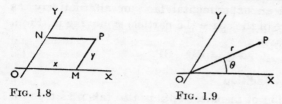

FIG. 1.8   FIG. 1.9

These are the polar coordinates (r, θ) of P, referred to O as pole and OX as initial line.

There are, of course, relations between x, y and r, θ which involve the angle between OX and OY.

If the axes OX and OY are at right angles, as shown in Fig. 1.10, then $x = r \cos \theta$ and $y = r \sin \theta$.

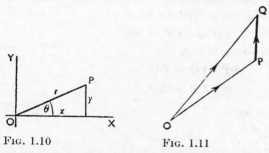

FIG. 1.10   FIG. 1.11

1.10. The displacement OP is denoted by **OP**. Accordingly, the displacement PO, which has the direction from P to O but the same magnitude as the displacement OP, is denoted by **PO** and we write

$$\mathbf{OP} = -\mathbf{PO}.$$

It is therefore very important to write the order of the letters correctly. The length OP equals the length PO, but the displacement **OP** is equal and opposite to the displacement **PO**.

If a particle moves from P (Fig. 1.11) to Q the change of position of the particle, or the displacement of Q with respect to P, is represented by the vector **PQ**.

Since the displacement from O to P followed by the displacement from P to Q is equivalent geometrically to the displacement from O to Q, we write

$$\mathbf{OP} + \mathbf{PQ} = \mathbf{OQ}. \tag{1}$$

This is the fundamental law of addition of displacements; it may be taken as an experimental fact, or alternatively, as defining the nature of the space the particle is moving in. From equation (1) we have

$$\mathbf{PQ} = \mathbf{OQ} - \mathbf{OP}. \tag{2}$$

1.11. Law of vector addition

This law of addition of displacements is also taken as true for *all* vectors, whatever their nature, and we shall refer to it as the *law of vector addition*. It states that *the sum of any two vector quantities of the same kind represented by* **OP** *and* **PQ** *is a vector represented by* **OQ**. We note that the addition can always be done graphically, that is, by drawing the triangle OPQ (Fig. 1.12).

Two vectors* are said to be *equal* if they have the same magnitude and the same direction. Thus, if (Fig. 1.12) we complete the parallelogram OPQR we have

$$\mathbf{OR} = \mathbf{PQ} \text{ and } \mathbf{OP} = \mathbf{RQ}.$$

But by the law of vector addition

$$\mathbf{OP} + \mathbf{PQ} = \mathbf{OQ}.$$

Hence, $$\mathbf{OP} + \mathbf{OR} = \mathbf{OQ} \tag{3}$$

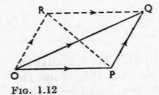

Fig. 1.12

which is a form of the law of vector addition *alternative* to equation (1). We shall refer to it as the *parallelogram law*, which may be stated thus: *the sum of two vectors* **OP** *and* **OR** *drawn from any point* O *is represented by the diagonal* **OQ** *of the parallelogram* OPQR *having* OP *and* OR *as adjacent sides*.

The difference of two vectors may also be found.

---

* We are only concerned here with 'free' vectors, not vectors localised in a line.

Since $$\mathbf{OP}+\mathbf{PR} = \mathbf{OR}$$
it follows that $$\mathbf{PR} = \mathbf{OR}-\mathbf{OP} \qquad (4)$$
and hence $$\mathbf{RP} = \mathbf{OP}-\mathbf{OR}.$$

Thus the diagonal **RP** represents the *difference* of the vectors **OP** and **OR**. We therefore have the important result that the two diagonals of a parallelogram represent the *sum* and *difference* of the vectors represented by the adjacent sides. We shall constantly use it.

The sum **OQ** of the vectors **OP** and **PQ** is sometimes called the *resultant* of the two vectors. Conversely, the vectors **OP** and **PQ** are known as the *components* of the vector **OQ**. Clearly **OQ** can be split up into two components in an infinite number of ways, for if OQ is given an infinite number of triangles OPQ can be drawn.

1.12. We note that $\mathbf{OP}+\mathbf{OP}$, which can be written 2**OP**, is a vector of magnitude 2OP parallel to **OP**. Similarly, if m is any scalar quantity, $m\mathbf{OP}$ is a vector of magnitude mOP parallel to **OP**. Further, if a and b are any two vectors, then

$$m(a+b) = ma+mb.$$

For if OP (Fig. 1.13) represents a, then $\mathrm{OP}_1 = m\mathrm{OP}$ represents ma; also if PQ represents b, then $\mathrm{P}_1\mathrm{Q}_1$ drawn parallel to PQ and

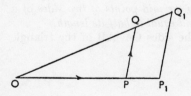

FIG. 1.13

of length mPQ represents mb. Thus $\mathrm{OP}_1/\mathrm{OP} = \mathrm{P}_1\mathrm{Q}_1/\mathrm{PQ} = m$, and hence Q_1 lies on OQ produced and is such that $\mathrm{OQ}_1/\mathrm{OQ} = m$.

$\therefore \qquad\qquad \mathrm{OQ}_1 = m\mathrm{OQ}.$

$\therefore \qquad\qquad \mathrm{OP}_1+\mathrm{P}_1\mathrm{Q}_1 = m(\mathrm{OP}+\mathrm{PQ}),$

that is, $\qquad\qquad ma+mb = m(a+b).$

EXAMPLE (i)

If OAB is any triangle show that $m\mathbf{OA}+n\mathbf{OB} = (m+n)\mathbf{OC}$, *for all values of m and n provided C is the point in AB such that* $m \times AC = n \times CB$.

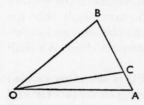

FIG. 1.14

If C is *any* point in AB.

$$m\mathbf{OA}+n\mathbf{OB} = m(\mathbf{OC}+\mathbf{CA})+n(\mathbf{OC}+\mathbf{CB})$$
$$= (m+n)\mathbf{OC}+m\mathbf{CA}+n\mathbf{CB}.$$

Since **CA** and **CB** are in the same straight line but in opposite directions, $m\mathbf{CA}+n\mathbf{CB}$ will be zero provided $m \times AC = n \times CB$, which proves the result.

Note. If $m = n$, we have

$$\mathbf{OA}+\mathbf{OB} = 2\mathbf{OC}$$

provided C is the mid-point of AB.

EXAMPLE (ii)

Prove vectorially that the line joining the mid-points of two sides of a triangle is parallel to the third side and equal to half its length.

If E, F are the mid-points of the sides CA, AB of the triangle ABC, then

$$\mathbf{FE} = \mathbf{FA}+\mathbf{AE}$$
$$= \tfrac{1}{2}\mathbf{BA}+\tfrac{1}{2}\mathbf{AC}$$
$$= \tfrac{1}{2}(\mathbf{BA}+\mathbf{AC}),$$

∴　　　　$\mathbf{FE} = \tfrac{1}{2}\mathbf{BC}$, that is, $FE = \tfrac{1}{2}BC$ and FE is parallel to BC.

1.13. Addition of any number of vectors

It is clear that *any number* of vectors can be compounded into a single vector, by repeated application of the addition law for two vectors.

For instance, suppose we wish to find the sum of the three

vectors, **P**, **Q**, and **R** (Fig. 1.15). We draw (Fig. 1.16) **OA** to represent **P** and **AB** to represent **Q**. Then **OB** represents **P**+**Q**. If we now draw **BC** to represent **R**, then

$$OC = OB + BC$$
$$= (P+Q)+R.$$

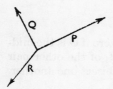

FIG. 1.15

It should be noted that the order in which the vectors are added does *not* affect the final result.

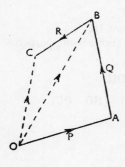

FIG. 1.16

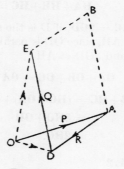

FIG. 1.17

For if **P** and **R** are added first, by drawing (Fig. 1.17) **OA** to represent **P** and **AD** to represent **R**, then **OD** represents **P**+**R**. If now **DE** is drawn to represent **Q**, then

$$OE = OD + DE$$
$$= (P+R)+Q.$$

It is clear from the geometry of the figures that OE and OC are equal and parallel, and therefore

$$OC = OE = P+Q+R.$$

OC (or **OE**) represents the *sum* of the vectors **P**, **Q**, and **R**.

EXAMPLE (i)

Find a point O *in the plane of a quadrilateral* ABCD *such that*
$OA+OB+OC+OD = 0$.

Now, $\qquad\qquad$ $OA+OB = 2OE$ if E is the mid-point of AB

and $\qquad\qquad$ $OC+OD = 2OF$ if F is the mid-point of CD

$\therefore\quad$ $OA+OB+OC+OD = 0$ if $OE+OF = 0$.

that is, if O is the mid-point of EF.

Similarly, the sum of the four given vectors is zero if O is the mid-point of the line joining the mid-points, G and H, of the other pair of opposite sides, BC and DA. Thus EF and GH bisect one another, as can easily be proved by simple geometry.

EXAMPLE (ii)

If H *is the orthocentre of the triangle* ABC *and* O *the circumcentre, show that*

$$OA+OB+OC = OH,$$

and $\qquad\qquad$ $HA+HB+HC = 2HO.$

Now, $OB+OC = 2OD$, if D is the mid-point of BC.

But, $2OD = AH$, since OD is parallel to AH (both being perpendicular to BC) and $2OD = AH$

$\therefore\qquad\qquad OA+OB+OC = OA+AH = OH$

Also, $\quad HA+HB+HC = (HO+OA)+(HO+OB)+(HO+OC)$

$$= 3HO+OH$$

$$= 2HO.$$

EXAMPLES 1.2

1. A boy walks from a place O a distance 3 km due east, and then 4 km due south. Show that he is 5 km from O in a direction $\tan^{-1}(\frac{4}{3})$ south of east. How far due west must he now walk in order to reach a position south-west of O?

2. A car starts from A and travels 10 km due west, 20 km north-west, and 30 km due north. Find its distance and bearing from A. How long will it take to return to A direct at an average speed of 50 km h^{-1}?

3. Two aeroplanes start from an airfield. One leaves at 10.00 and flies due north at an average speed of 400 km h^{-1}. The other leaves at 10.15 and flies on a course 60° west of north at an average speed of 480 km h^{-1}. Find their distance apart at 11.30 and the bearing of the first with respect to the second.

4. A vessel A is 100 km in a north-east direction from a port P, and a vessel B is also 100 km from P in a direction 15° north of east. If A is stopped, find how soon B can reach A if its maximum speed is 50 km h⁻¹. In what direction must it proceed?

5. A particle describes a circle of radius a with uniform speed v. If it starts from a point A, show that its displacement from A in time t equals $2a \sin (vt/2a)$ at an angle $vt/2a$ radians with the tangent at A to the circle.

6. The displacement of a body A with respect to a point O is:

   (a) 9 km north-east.   (c) 12 km 30° north of west.
   (b) 9 km 30° east of north.   (d) 12 km south-west.

   Find the component displacements of A measured in the easterly and northerly directions.

7. Find the sum of the displacements (a) and (b), (b) and (c), (a) and (d), where (a), (b), (c), and (d) are given in question 6 above.

8. Find the difference of the displacements (a) and (b), (b) and (c), (a) and (d), where (a), (b), (c), and (d) are given in question 6 above.

9. A vector of magnitude 10 units makes an angle of 45° with OX. Find the components of the vector along OX and the line that makes an angle of 75° with OX.

10. Two vectors have magnitude 2 and 3 respectively. The sum of their components along OX is 1 and the sum of their components along OY is 3, and OX and OY are perpendicular. Give a graphical construction for the directions of the vectors and show there are two solutions. Measure the angles which the vectors make with OX, and check the results numerically.

11. Vectors of magnitudes 4, 10, and 6 units are inclined at angles of 45°, 90°, and 135° respectively to a given direction. Find the sum of the vectors.

12. Vectors of magnitude 4, 3, 2, and 1 unit respectively are directed along AB, AC, AD, and AE, where angle BAC = 30°, angle CAD = 30°, and angle DAE = 90°. Find the magnitude of the sum of the vectors and the inclination of its direction to AB.

13. If the components parallel to the axes of x and y of the displacement a are 4 and 3 units, of the displacement b are 1 and -1 units, and of the displacement c are -2 and -3 units, find the magnitude and direction of the displacement:

   (i) $a+b$, (ii) $a-c$, (iii) $a+b+c$, (iv) $a-b-c$, (v) $2a-b$, and (vi) $a-3b+4c$.

14. If a, b, c are the displacements given in question 13, find the values of the constants m and n such that (i) $a+mb$ is parallel to the axis of x, (ii) $a+nc$ is parallel to the axis of y, (iii) $a = mb+nc$.

15. If D, E, F are the mid-points of the sides BC, CA, AB of the triangle ABC, show that   (i) $\mathbf{AB}+\mathbf{BC}+\mathbf{CA} = 0$,
    (ii) $2\mathbf{AB}+3\mathbf{BC}+\mathbf{CA} = 2\mathbf{FC}$,   (iii) $\mathbf{AD}+\mathbf{BE}+\mathbf{CF} = 0$.

16. If D, E, F are the mid-points of the sides of the triangle ABC and O is any point, show that $\mathbf{OA}+\mathbf{OB}+\mathbf{OC} = \mathbf{OD}+\mathbf{OE}+\mathbf{OF}$.

17. If the sides of the quadrilateral ABCD represents the vectors a, b, c, d, find the vectors represented by the sides of the quadrilateral EFGH, where E, F, G, H are the mid-points of the sides AB, BC, CD, DA respectively. Deduce that EFGH is a parallelogram.

18. If ABCD is any quadrilateral, show that $\mathbf{AD}+\mathbf{BC} = 2\mathbf{EF}$, where E, F are the middle points of AB and DC respectively, and that $\mathbf{AB}+\mathbf{AD}+\mathbf{CB}+\mathbf{CD} = 4\mathbf{XY}$, where X, Y are the middle points of the diagonals AC and BD respectively.

19. Find the position of the point O within a triangle ABC such that $\mathbf{OA}+\mathbf{OB}+\mathbf{OC} = 0$.

20. X and Y are the points of intersection of the medians of the two triangles ABC and PQR. Show that $\mathbf{AP}+\mathbf{BQ}+\mathbf{CR} = 3\mathbf{XY}$.

1.14. Velocity

The velocity of a moving particle relative to an assigned point O is the rate of change of its displacement relative to O. Velocity therefore possesses both magnitude and direction, and is a vector quantity.

The velocity of a particle is said to be *uniform* when the particle is moving in a fixed direction with uniform speed, that is, when both the direction and the magnitude of the velocity are uniform. Thus, if the particle is moving in a straight line with uniform speed its velocity is uniform, but if the particle is moving in a curve, e.g. a circle, its velocity is *not* uniform, even though its speed may be uniform, for the direction of its velocity is continually changing.

When uniform, the velocity of a moving particle is measured by its displacement in unit time. A particle is moving with a uniform velocity of v ms^{-1}, if, in t s, it describes a distance s m *along a straight line*, given by $s = vt$, for all values of t.

1.15. When the velocity of a moving particle is *variable* its velocity at any instant is understood to mean the displacement it would undergo in the next unit of time if it continued to move with the velocity which it had at the instant considered.

1.16. The velocity of a particle at any instant may be found as follows. Suppose the particle moves in a plane from a point P to a point Q (Fig. 1.18) in time t. Since the displacement in this

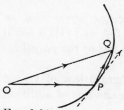

FIG. 1.18

time interval is $\mathbf{OQ-OP} = \mathbf{PQ}$, the average velocity during this interval is

$$\frac{\mathbf{OQ-OP}}{t} = \frac{\mathbf{PQ}}{t}.$$

We note that this quotient is a vector in the direction PQ having the magnitude of PQ/t. The average velocity is therefore parallel to PQ.

If t is small, $\mathbf{PQ}/t$ gives *approximately* the velocity of the particle when it is at the position of P. Thus, taking the interval of time indefinitely small, the velocity of the particle at P can be written as $\lim_{t \to 0} \mathbf{PQ}/t$.

This is a vector quantity having the magnitude $\lim_{t \to 0} PQ/t$ and having as direction the limiting position of the chord PQ, that is, the direction of the tangent at P to the path of P (Fig. 1.18).

1.17. The unit of velocity is the velocity of a particle which undergoes a displacement equal to unit distance in unit time.

Numerically this is the same as the unit of speed, and the magnitude of the velocity of a particle is the same as the magnitude of its speed. To express completely the velocity we must add a statement as to the direction of motion, e.g. $v \text{ m s}^{-1}$ in a north-east direction.

1.18. A particle or body may have several different velocities simultaneously, e.g. a person walking on the deck of a ship in motion. The single velocity which is equivalent to several other velocities is called their *resultant*, and the several velocities are called the *components* of this resultant.

Velocities, like all vector quantities, can be compounded by the parallelogram law.

1.19. The parallelogram of velocities

If an article possesses simultaneously velocities represented in magnitude and direction by the straight lines OA *and* OB *it has a resultant velocity represented by the diagonal* OC *of the parallelogram* OACB.

This follows at once from the parallelogram law of vector addition (§ 1.11), or it can be deduced from the law of addition of two displacements as follows.

If OA (Fig. 1.19) represents a velocity of magnitude u, and OB a velocity of magnitude v, we may imagine the particle to move along OA with speed u, while the line OA moves parallel to itself so that its end O describes the line OB with speed v. In unit time the particle will have moved along OA to A, and the line OA will have moved into the position BC, so that the moving particle will be at C.

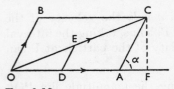

Fig. 1.19

At any intermediate time t the particle will have moved a distance ut along OA to D, say, while the line OA will have moved a distance vt parallel to itself.

If DE is drawn parallel to AC to meet OC in E,

$$\frac{DE}{OD} = \frac{AC}{OA} = \frac{v}{u}$$

∴ $$DE = OD \times \frac{v}{u} = ut\frac{v}{u} = vt$$

∴   DE is the distance moved by the line OA.

∴   the particle will be at E.

Hence OC is the path described by the particle, and OC represents in magnitude and direction the velocity which is equivalent to OA and OB, i.e. it represents their resultant.

If the angle AOB $= \alpha$, and CF is drawn perpendicular to OA, we have

$$OC^2 = OF^2 + FC^2$$
$$= (OA + AC \cos \alpha)^2 + (AC \sin \alpha)^2$$
$$= OA^2 + 2OA \times AC \cos \alpha + AC^2.$$

Hence, if the resultant OC is V,

$$V^2 = u^2 + v^2 + 2uv \cos \alpha.$$

If the component velocities u and v are at right angles,

$$V^2 = u^2 + v^2.$$

1.20. Resolution of a velocity

We can use the parallelogram law to resolve a given velocity into two components. It is obvious that this can be done in an infinite number of ways, for we can describe any number of parallelograms on a given straight line as diagonal.

In practice, the directions of the components are given, and these directions are usually at right angles.

In the latter case the values of the component velocities are easily obtained as follows:

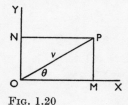

FIG. 1.20

Let OP (Fig. 1.20) represent the given velocity v, and suppose we wish to resolve it into two components, one along OX, and the other in a perpendicular direction OY.

Draw PM perpendicular to OX and PN perpendicular to OY.

Then OM, ON represent the components of v along OX and OY.

If the angle XOP $= \theta$,

$$OM = v \cos \theta, \text{ and } ON = v \sin \theta.$$

Hence a velocity v is equivalent to a velocity v cos θ along a line making an angle θ with its own direction, together with a velocity v sin θ perpendicular to the direction of the first component.

1.21. If x, y are the coordinates of a point A at any instant referred to axes OX, OY, then the component displacements of A at time t parallel to OX and OY are x and y respectively.

Hence the component velocities of A parallel to the axes are the rates of change of x and y, i.e.

$$dx/dt \text{ and } dy/dt.$$

These are often denoted by $\dot{x}$ and $\dot{y}$, i.e. $\dot{x} = dx/dt$, $\dot{y} = dy/dt$. By considering both components, we automatically take into account changes in the direction of motion of A.

This method of considering component velocities is of great importance when we have to deal with cases of motion where the path is not a straight line.

1.22. When we speak of the component of a velocity in a given direction it is understood that the other direction in which the velocity is to be resolved is perpendicular to this given direction.

If we do require the components of a velocity v in directions making angles α and β with it they can be found as follows:

Let OC (Fig. 1.21) represent v. Draw OA and OB, making angles α and β with OC, and through C draw parallels to complete the parallelogram OACB.

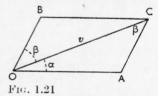

Fɪɢ. 1.21

Then OA and OB, or OA and AC represent the required components. From the triangle OAC, we have

$$\frac{OA}{\sin \beta} = \frac{OC}{\sin A} \text{ and } A = 180° - (\alpha + \beta)$$

$$\therefore \qquad OA = \frac{v \sin \beta}{\sin (\alpha + \beta)}.$$

Similarly, $\qquad OB = \dfrac{v \sin \alpha}{\sin (\alpha + \beta)}.$

EXAMPLES 1.3

1. Find the resultant of velocities of 8 m s^{-1} and 6 m s^{-1} at right angles.

2. Find the resultant of velocities of 8 m s^{-1} and 6 m s^{-1} inclined at an angle of 60°.

3. A railway carriage is travelling at 30 m s^{-1}, and a person rolls a ball across the floor of the carriage at right angles to the direction of motion of the train at 16 m s^{-1}. Find the resultant velocity of the ball.

4. A point is moving in a straight line with a velocity of 12 m s^{-1}; find the component of its velocity in a direction inclined at an angle of 30° to its direction of motion, when the other component makes an angle of (i) 60°, and (ii) 90° with the direction of motion.

5. A ball is moving at 20 m s^{-1} in a direction inclined at 60° to the horizontal; find the horizontal and vertical components of its velocity.

6. A man is walking in a north-westerly direction with a velocity of 5 km h^{-1}; find the components of his velocity in directions due north and due east respectively.

7. A cyclist rides at 16 km h^{-1} in a direction 30° east of north. Find the components of his velocity in directions due north and due east respectively.

8. A raindrop falls in still air at 3 m s^{-1}. Find its velocity if it falls through a current of air moving horizontally at a speed of 4 m s^{-1}.

9. A ship is steaming due west across a current which flows due south, and in half an hour travels 6 km in a direction 30° south of west. Find the speed of the current, and the rate at which the ship is steaming.

10. Resolve a velocity of 10 m s^{-1} into two components at angles of 30° and 45° respectively to the direction of the velocity.

11. Resolve a velocity of 10 m s^{-1} into two perpendicular components such that (i) the components are equal, and (ii) one component is twice the other.

12. Resolve a velocity of 15 m s^{-1} into two components such that one is at an angle of 30° to this velocity and has half the magnitude of the other component.

13. A particle travels along the line $y = 2x+1$ with the uniform

speed of 10 ms^{-1}. Find the components of its velocity parallel to the axes of x and y.

14. A particle moves in a straight line from the point $(1, 0)$ to the point $(6, 12)$ in 2 s. Find its average velocity between the two points, and the components parallel to the axes.

15. A particle describes a circle, centre O, of radius 18 m in 12 s. Find its speed, assumed uniform. If it passes through a point A at time $t = 0$, find the components of its velocity parallel and perpendicular to OA at time $t = 3$ s, 4 s, 8 s, and 11 s, respectively.

16. A particle describes a circle of radius 40 m with uniform speed in 8 s. Find its velocity at any instant. Also find the direction and magnitude of its average velocity during the time it takes to complete (a) one-quarter of the circle, (b) one-half of the circle, and (c) the whole circle.

17. A particle moves in a plane such that its (x, y) coordinates measured in metres are $(2t, t^2)$ at time t s. Sketch the path of the particle from $t = 0$ to $t = 4$, and find the components parallel to the axes of the average velocity of the particle (a) from $t = 1$ to $t = 2$, (b) from $t = 1$ to $t = 3$, and (c) from $t = 0$ to $t = 4$.

18. A particle moves in a plane such that its (x, y) coordinates measured in metres are $(2t, t^2)$ at time t s. Draw the distance–time graphs for motion parallel to the axis of x and the axis of y from $t = 0$ to $t = 5$, and deduce the components of the velocity parallel to these axes at times $t = 2$ and $t = 3$. Find also the resultant velocity at these instants.

19. A ball is thrown up into the air and moves such that its (x, y) coordinates measured in metres are $(15t, 10t - 5t^2)$ at time t s. Sketch the path of the particle from $t = 0$ to $t = 2$. Find the components parallel to the axes of the average velocity of the particle during this time-interval.

Find also the initial velocity of the ball, and the instant when it is moving parallel to the x-axis.

20. Find at what times the y-coordinate of the ball (in question 19) is 3·2 m, and the magnitude and direction of the velocity of the ball at these times.

1.23 Triangle of velocities

If a particle possesses simultaneously velocities represented by the two sides, AB, BC, of a triangle taken in order, it has a resultant velocity represented by AC.

This follows at once from the law of vector addition, or from the parallelogram of velocities.

The resultant of **AB** and **BC** (Fig. 1.22) is their vector sum, i.e. **AC**.

We write $\qquad\qquad$ **AB+BC = AC**.

AC can be found by drawing **AB** and **BC** to scale, or by calculation.

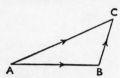

FIG. 1.22

1.24. Polygon of velocities

If a particle possesses simultaneously velocities represented by the sides AB, BC, CD, ... LM, *of a polygon taken in order, it has a resultant velocity represented by* AM.

For, by the triangle of velocities, the resultant of AB and BC (Fig. 1.23) is represented by AC, the resultant of AC and

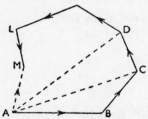

FIG. 1.23

CD is represented by AD, and so on; the resultant of all the velocities is therefore represented by AM.

It is obvious that this result also holds if the sides of the polygon are not in one plane.

We write **AB+BC+CD+ ... +LM = AM**.

AM can be found by drawing the polygon ABCD ... LM to scale.

1.25. When a particle possesses a number of given velocities we can also find their resultant by resolving each of them in two fixed directions OX, OY at right angles, adding the components in each of these directions to obtain a single velocity along OX and another along OY, and then compounding these two perpendicular velocities into a single one.

EXAMPLE

A particle has velocities of 2, $4\sqrt{2}$, 6, and 8 inclined at angles of 30°, 45°, 60°, and 120° respectively to a given direction. Find the magnitude and direction of their resultant.

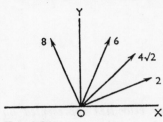

Fig. 1.24

Let OX (Fig. 1.24) be the given direction, and OY perpendicular to it.

The components along OX are

$$2\cos 30°,\ 4\sqrt{2}\cos 45°,\ 6\cos 60°,\ 8\cos 120°,$$

or $\sqrt{3}$,   4,   3, -4,

and their sum is

$$3+\sqrt{3}.$$

The components along OY are

$$2\sin 30°,\ 4\sqrt{2}\sin 45°,\ 6\sin 60°,\ 8\sin 120°,$$

or   1,   4, $3\sqrt{3}$, $4\sqrt{3}$,

and their sum is

$$5+7\sqrt{3}.$$

The velocities are therefore equivalent to a velocity of $3+\sqrt{3}$ along OX and a velocity of $5+7\sqrt{3}$ along OY.

If V is the resultant,

$$V^2 = (3+\sqrt{3})^2+(5+7\sqrt{3})^2$$
$$= 315{\cdot}632.$$

∴ $V = 17{\cdot}76.$

If θ is the angle this resultant makes with OX,

$$\tan \theta = \frac{5+7\sqrt{3}}{3+\sqrt{3}} = \frac{17\cdot124}{4\cdot732} = 3\cdot618$$

∴ $\theta = 74\frac{1}{2}°$ nearly.

We can also find the resultant velocity by adding the velocities vectorially, using the polygon of velocities.

Draw OA (Fig. 1.25) two units long at an angle of 30° to OX.

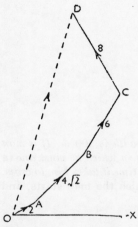

FIG. 1.25

Similarly, draw AB, BC, CD to represent the velocities $4\sqrt{2}$, 6, 8 respectively. Then **OD** represents the resultant velocity.

By measurement, OD = 17·8 and the angle DOX = 74°.

1.26. EXAMPLE (i)

A boat is rowed with a velocity of 8 kmh⁻¹ straight across a river which is flowing at 6 kmh⁻¹. Find the magnitude and direction of the resultant velocity of the boat. If the breadth of the river is 100 m, find how far down the river the boat will reach the opposite bank.

The component velocities of the boat are 4 kmh⁻¹ and 3 kmh⁻¹ at right angles. If v kmh⁻¹ is the resultant velocity

$$v = \sqrt{(6^2+8^2)} = \sqrt{(36+64)} = 10.$$

If θ (Fig. 1.26) is the angle the direction of this velocity makes with the bank

$$\cos \theta = \frac{6}{10}, \text{ or } \theta = \cos^{-1} 0\cdot6.$$

Now if A is the point from which the boat starts, and B is the point directly opposite on the other bank, C will be the point where the boat reaches the opposite bank.

But $BC/BA = \cot\theta = \tfrac{3}{4}.$

$\therefore$ $BC = \tfrac{3}{4}BA = \tfrac{3}{4}\times 100 \text{ m} = 75 \text{ m}.$

Hence the boat will be carried downstream a distance of 75 m.

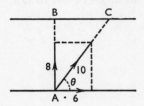

FIG. 1.26

EXAMPLE (ii)

A stream is running at 3 kmh⁻¹, and its breadth is 100 m. If a man can row a boat at 5 kmh⁻¹, find the direction in which he must row in order to go straight across the stream, and the time it takes him to cross.

Let A (Fig. 1.27) be the point from which the man starts, and AB perpendicular to the banks.

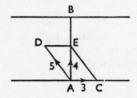

FIG. 1.27

Then the resultant of the stream's velocity of 3 km h⁻¹ in direction AC and the man's velocity of 5 km h⁻¹ has to be in the direction AB. If AC represents the velocity of the stream to scale, and AD the man's velocity to the same scale, then the diagonal AE of the parallelogram whose adjacent sides are AC and AD must lie along AB.

Now $AE = \sqrt{(5^2-3^2)} = 4$, and hence $\cos DAE = \tfrac{4}{5}$, i.e. the man must row in a direction making an angle $\cos^{-1}\tfrac{4}{5}$ with AB.

Also his resultant velocity is 4 km h⁻¹

$\therefore$ the time to cross $= \dfrac{100}{4000} \text{ h} = \dfrac{60\times 60}{40} \text{ s} = 90 \text{ s.}$

EXAMPLES 1.4

1. A boat is rowed with a velocity of 5 kmh⁻¹ and directed straight across a river flowing at 3 kmh⁻¹. If the breadth of the river be 120 m, find how far down the river the boat will reach the opposite bank.

2. A man wishes to go straight across a river; if he can row his boat with three times the velocity of the current, find at what inclination to the current he must keep the boat pointed.

3. A boy is riding a bicycle at 20 kmh⁻¹; in what direction must he throw a stone with a velocity of 10 ms⁻¹ so that its resultant motion may be at right angles to his own direction.

4. A boat is moored at a place where a current is flowing eastwards at 2 kmh⁻¹. Two buoys are also moored, each 50 m from the boat, one due north, the other due east of it. Two equally fast swimmers, each capable of a speed of 4 kmh⁻¹ in still water, start from the boat at the same time to swim one to each buoy and back to the boat. Which will reach the boat again first, and how much sooner?

5. A point which has velocities represented by 8, 9, and 13 is at rest; find the angle between the directions of the two smaller velocities.

6. A point has velocities of 3, 5, 4, and 6 in directions east, north-east, north, and north-west respectively; find the magnitude and direction of its resultant velocity.

7. A point has equal velocities in two given directions; if one of these velocities be halved, the angle which the resultant makes with the other is halved also. Show that the angle between the velocities is 120°.

8. If a point has two velocities, u_1 and u_2, inclined at such an angle that the resultant velocity $V = u_1$, show that if u_1 be doubled, the new resultant is at right angles to u_2.

9. A man who swims at 5 kmh⁻¹ in still water wishes to cross a river 150 m wide, flowing at 8 kmh⁻¹. Indicate graphically the direction in which he should swim in order to reach the opposite bank (i) as soon as possible, (ii) as little downstream as possible. How long will he take to cross, and how far will he be carried downstream in each case?

10. A ship is steaming on a course 30° east of north at a speed of 18 kmh⁻¹, and a man walks backwards and forwards across the deck in a direction perpendicular to the ship's course at a speed of 1 ms⁻¹. Find the actual directions in which the man moves.

(H.C.)

11. A particle has velocities of 4, 9, 12 ms^{-1} inclined at angles of 120° to one another. Calculate the resultant velocity, and check by drawing a polygon of velocities.

12. A particle has velocities represented by **OA** and **OB**, where AB is a diameter of a circle and O any point on the circumference. Show that the resultant velocity is represented by the diameter through O.

13. A particle has velocities of 3, 4, and 8 kmh^{-1} inclined at angles of 0°, 90°, and 120° respectively to the axis of x. Find the magnitude and direction of the resultant velocity (a) by drawing a polygon of velocities, and (b) by calculation.

14. A particle has velocities which can be represented in magnitude and direction by the sides AB, AF and the diagonal AD of the regular hexagon ABCDEF of side v. Find the resultant velocity.

What additional velocity parallel to EA must the particle be given in order that it might move parallel to AC?

15. A particle has velocities v, $2v$, $3\sqrt{3}v$, and $4v$ inclined at angles of 0°, 60°, 150°, and 300° respectively to the axis of x. Find the resultant velocity.

1.27. Relative Velocity

All velocities, as we have constantly emphasised, are relative velocities, that is, velocities relative to some assigned system of reference. The velocities with which we are most familiar are velocities relative to the earth. When we say that a train has a velocity of 40 kmh^{-1} in a certain direction we mean 40 kmh^{-1} relative to the earth. The earth itself is moving relative to the sun, so that the velocity of the train relative to the sun has a value which may be deduced from the velocity of the train relative to the earth and the velocity of the earth relative to the sun, as we shall now explain.

If the velocity of a particle P relative to some assigned point O, or some system of reference associated with O, is v_1, and the velocity of Q relative to O is v_2, *then the velocity of P relative to Q is the vector difference of v_1 and v_2, that is, $v_1 - v_2$.*

The velocity of Q relative to P is $v_2 - v_1$.

Of course, if P and Q are moving in parallel directions the velocity of P relative to Q is parallel to the velocities of P and Q and of magnitude equal to the algebraic difference of the velocities. Thus, if two trains P and Q are running on parallel rails with speeds of 40 kmh^{-1} and 35 kmh^{-1} respectively the speed of P relative to Q is $(40-35)$ km h^{-1} = 5 km h^{-1} if the trains are travelling in the same direction, but $(40+35)$ km h^{-1} = 75 km h^{-1} if the trains are travelling in opposite directions.

If **OA** (Fig. 1.28), of magnitude v_1, and **OB**, of magnitude v_2, represent the velocities of P and Q the velocity of P relative to

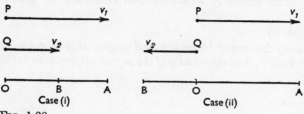

Case (i)   Case (ii)

FIG. 1.28

Q is represented by **OA**—**OB**, which equals **BA**, a vector of magnitude v_1-v_2 in case (i) and v_1+v_2 in case (ii), parallel to the velocity of P. Similarly, the velocity of Q relative to P is represented by **OB**—**OA** = **AB** = —**BA**.

Generally, if the velocities of P and Q are *not* parallel the same construction for the vector difference of their velocities may be used. From any point O (Fig. 1.29) draw **OA**, of mag-

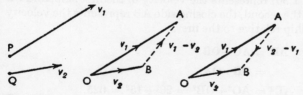

FIG. 1.29

nitude v_1, parallel to the velocity of P, and from the same point draw **OB**, of magnitude v_2, parallel to the velocity of Q.

Since $$\mathbf{OB}+\mathbf{BA} = \mathbf{OA}$$
we get $$\mathbf{BA} = \mathbf{OA}-\mathbf{OB} = v_1-v_2.$$
Therefore **BA** represents in magnitude and direction the velocity of P relative to Q. Similarly, the velocity of Q relative to P is represented completely by **AB**.

Thus the relative velocity of any two particles moving with given velocities can be found by drawing a simple vector triangle, such as the triangle OAB in Fig. 1.29. The closing side AB or BA represents the required relative velocity.

Similarly, if v_2, the velocity of Q relative to O, and v_1-v_2 the velocity of P relative to Q, are known, v_1, the velocity of P relative to O, can be found by using the same vector triangle OAB. It is only necessary to draw **OB** to represent v_2 and **BA** to represent the velocity of Q relative to P, and then **OA** represents v_1. And similarly whatever two velocities are given.

1.28. EXAMPLE (i)

A ship is steaming due east at 15 $km\,h^{-1}$, and another ship is steaming due south at 20 $km\,h^{-1}$; find the velocity of the second ship relative to the first.

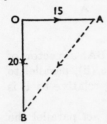

FIG. 1.30

If **OA** (Fig. 1.30) represents the velocity of the first ship, and **OB** the velocity of the second, the closing side AB represents the velocity of the second ship relative to the first.

For
$$\mathbf{AB} = \mathbf{AO} + \mathbf{OB}$$
$$= \mathbf{OB} - \mathbf{OA}.$$

Also
$$AB^2 = AO^2 + OB^2 = 20^2 + 15^2 = 625.$$

∴
$$AB = 25.$$

The relative velocity is therefore 25 $km\,h^{-1}$, and its direction makes an angle west of south whose tangent is $\frac{3}{4}$.

EXAMPLE (ii)

A train is travelling along a horizontal rail at 54 $km\,h^{-1}$, and rain is falling vertically with a velocity of 5 ms^{-1}. Find the apparent direction and velocity of the rain to a person travelling in the train.

The velocity of the train is 15 ms^{-1}.

Let **OB** (Fig. 1.31) represent the actual velocity of the rain. Draw OA horizontal to represent the magnitude and direction of the velocity of the train to the same scale. Complete the triangle OAB.

Then **AB** represents the relative or apparent velocity of the rain.

Also, $\tan ABO = \dfrac{AO}{OB} = \dfrac{15}{5} = 3.$

The magnitude of the relative velocity is

$$\sqrt{(15^2 + 5^2)} = 5\sqrt{(9 \times 1)} = 5\sqrt{10} \text{ m s}^{-1}.$$

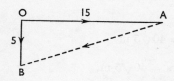

FIG. 1.31

EXAMPLE (iii)

At a given instant two cars are at distances 300 and 400 m from the point of intersection O of two straight roads crossing at a right angle and are approaching O at uniform speeds of 20 and 40 m s⁻¹ respectively. Find the shortest distance between the cars and the time taken to reach this position.

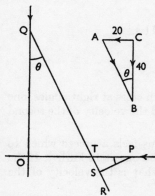

FIG. 1.32

Let P, Q (Fig. 1.32) be the positions of the two cars at the given instant. OP = 300 m and OQ = 400 m. Since their relative positions subsequently are required, we shall assume P remains at rest and Q moves with its velocity relative to P.

Draw **CA**, 20 units long, to represent the velocity of P, and **CB**, 40 units long, to represent the velocity of Q. Then **AB** represents the velocity of Q relative to P. Also $AB^2 = 20^2 + 40^2 = 2000.$

Draw QR parallel to AB; then QR represents the path of Q relative to P, and hence the perpendicular PS represents the shortest distance apart of P and Q.

Now $OT = 400 \tan \theta$ m $= 200$ m

$\therefore$ $TP = 100$ m

and hence

$$PS = TP \cos \theta$$

$$= 100 \times \frac{2}{\sqrt{5}} \text{ m} = 40\sqrt{5} \text{ m}$$

$\therefore$ Shortest distance between cars $= 40\sqrt{5}$ m.

Also, time to reach this position $= \dfrac{QS}{\text{velocity of Q relative to P}}$

but, $QS = QT + TS = (400 \sec \theta + 100 \sin \theta)$ m

$$= (200\sqrt{5} + 20\sqrt{5}) \text{ m}$$

$$= 220\sqrt{5} \text{ m}.$$

Also, velocity of Q relative to P $= \sqrt{2000} \text{ m s}^{-1} = 20\sqrt{5} \text{ m s}^{-1}$.

$\therefore$ Time for cars to reach the positions where they are the shortest distance apart

$$= \frac{220\sqrt{5} \text{ m}}{20\sqrt{5} \text{ m s}^{-1}} = 11 \text{ s}.$$

EXAMPLES 1.5

1. Two trains are travelling on lines which cross at right angles, one at 40, and the other at 50 km h^{-1}. Find the velocity of the second train relative to the first.

2. A passenger on the top of an omnibus feels a breeze which to him appears to blow directly across the bus at 16 km h^{-1}. If the omnibus is travelling at 24 km h^{-1}, what is the velocity of the wind?

3. Raindrops are falling through the air with a velocity of 3 m s^{-1}. If a north wind blows at 18 km h^{-1}, find the direction in which the drops appear to fall to a person walking north at 6 km h^{-1}. With what velocity would they hit his umbrella?

4. A steamship is travelling north at the rate of 16 km h^{-1}, and there is a north-east wind blowing at the rate of 32 km h^{-1}. In what direction will the smoke from the funnel appear to move to an observer on the ship?

5. One ship is sailing due east at 24 km h^{-1}, and another ship is sailing due north at 32 km h^{-1}; find the velocity of the second ship relative to the first.

6. A steamer going north-east at 20 km h^{-1} observes at noon a cruiser 16 km away and south-east of her, which is going north-north-east at 40 km h^{-1}. Draw a diagram of the cruiser's course as it appears from the steamer. At what time are the vessels nearest to one another, and how far are they then apart?

7. Two ships are steaming in opposite directions at 32 and 40 km h^{-1} respectively, and when they are directly abeam a shot is fired from one. If the gun at rest gives a muzzle velocity of 800 m s^{-1}, find the direction in which it must be fired to hit the other ship, gravity being neglected.

8. Two roads cross at right angles at P; a man A, walking along one of them at 4·5 km h^{-1}, sees another man B, walking on the other road at 6 km h^{-1}, at P when he is 50 m off. Find the velocity of A relative to B, and show that they will be nearest together when A has walked 18 m.

9. Two motor cars are proceeding, one on each road, towards the point of intersection of two roads which meet at an angle of 60°. If their speeds are 20 and 32 km h^{-1}, and they are respectively 70 and 40 m from the cross-roads, find their relative velocity, and the distances from the cross-roads when they are nearest together.   (I.E.)

10. To an observer on a ship travelling due west at 28 km h^{-1} another ship 2 km due south appears to be travelling north-east at 21 km h^{-1}. Find the magnitude and direction of the true velocity of the second ship, and the distance apart of the two ships when nearest to each other.   (I.S.)

11. A battleship is steaming 25 km h^{-1} due north; a cruiser, which steams at 40 km h^{-1}, is 8 km south-west, and is ordered to line up 2 km astern. Find graphically, or otherwise, the course the cruiser should steer to line up as quickly as possible.   (I.E.)

12. If a ship is moving north-east at 20 km h^{-1}, and a second ship appears to an observer on the first to be moving due east at 10 km h^{-1}, determine the actual direction and magnitude of the velocity of the second.   (I.S.)

13. From their point of intersection two straight roads lie respectively due east, and 60° north of east. At the same instant that a car travelling at 56 km h^{-1} due east is at the crossing, a second car is 8 km from it, and is travelling at 48 km h^{-1}

towards it from 60° north of east. Find by a graphical construction (or by calculation) the relative velocity of the first to the second car. Find also when they will be at their shortest distance apart.   (I.E.)

14. Two ships are sailing at speeds of 16 and 20 kmh⁻¹ along parallel lines in the same direction. When they are opposite one another and 3 km apart the faster ship turns its course through 30° in the direction of the other. Find how close they get to one another.   (I.E.)

15. A ship A is steering south at the rate of 12 kmh⁻¹, and a ship B is steering east at 16 kmh⁻¹, the distance AB being 2000 m and the line AB making an angle of 30° towards the west with the direction of motion of A. Calculate their relative velocity, and find how long it will be before they are closest together. (H.S.D.)

16. A man can swim at 3 kmh⁻¹ in still water. Find the time he would take to swim between two directly opposite points on the banks of a river 300 m wide flowing at 1·5 kmh⁻¹.   (H.S.D.)

17. A batsman is at the wicket W and a fieldsman is in the outfield at F. The batsman strikes the ball in a direction making 30° with the line WF with a speed 1½ times that with which the fieldsman can run. If the fieldsman starts off at once, at top speed, so as to field the ball as soon as possible, determine, graphically or otherwise, the direction in which he must run; and show that, if in doing this he has run 20 m, he was standing about 39 m from the wicket. (Assume that the ball travels along the ground with no diminution of speed.)   (H.S.D.)

18. A destroyer, steaming north 30° east, at 48 kmh⁻¹, observes at noon a steamer which is steaming due north at 20 kmh⁻¹, and overtakes the steamer at 12.45. Find the distance and bearing of the steamer from the destroyer at noon.   (H.C.)

19. Find the true course and the true speed of a steamer travelling through the water at 20 kmh⁻¹ and steering due north by the compass through a current of 5 kmh⁻¹ which sets south-east. Find also the direction in which the steamer should steer in order to make its true course due north, and the true speed on that course.   (H.C.)

20. A cruiser which can steam at 48 kmh⁻¹ receives a report that an enemy vessel, steaming due north at 32 kmh⁻¹, is 46 km away in a direction 30° north of east. Show (i) graphically, (ii) by calculation, that the cruiser can overtake the vessel in almost exactly 2 h.

21. Two motor cars, A, B, are travelling along straight roads at right angles to one another, with uniform velocities of 30 $km\,h^{-1}$ and 40 $km\,h^{-1}$, respectively, towards C, the point at which the roads cross. If AC is 0·75 km when BC is 1·2 km, find the shortest distance between the cars during the subsequent motion. (C.S.)

1.29. Angular velocity

If a particle P be in motion in a plane, and if O be a fixed point in the plane and OA a fixed straight line through O, the angular velocity of P about O is defined as the rate at which AOP increases.

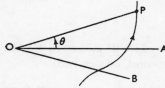

Fig. 1.33

It will be noted that if any other fixed line OB (Fig. 1.33) through O had been taken as initial line instead of OA the angular velocity about O would be given by the rate at which ∠BOP increases. This is, of course, the same as the rate at which ∠AOP increases, since ∠AOB is fixed. The angular velocity about O is thus independent of the line through O used as initial line.

Angular velocity is measured in *radians per second*, abbreviated as $rad\,s^{-1}$. When uniform, angular velocity is measured by the number of radians in the angle turned through by OP in 1 s. When variable, its value at any instant is measured by the angle through which OP would turn in 1 s if it continued to turn at the same rate as at the instant considered.

If θ is the angle between OP and OA at any instant the angular velocity is $d\theta/dt$ or $\dot\theta$.

1.30. *If a particle P describes a circle with O as centre with uniform speed its angular velocity about O is equal to its speed divided by the radius of the circle.*

Let P (Fig. 1.34) be the position of the particle at any time, Q its position 1 s later. The angular velocity equals the number of radians in the angle POQ.

But the number of radians in POQ $=$ arc PQ/OP. Also, the arc PQ is described in 1 s, and is therefore equal to the speed v.

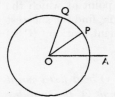

Fig. 1.34

Hence, if ω be the angular velocity, and r the radius of the circle,

$$\omega = v/r,$$
$$\therefore \qquad v = r\omega.$$

If n is the number of revolutions which P makes in 1 s the angular velocity is $2\pi n$ radians per second, or $2\pi n$ rad s^{-1}.

1.31. Suppose we consider a body of finite size (as distinct from a particle) rotating about a fixed axis CD (Fig. 1.35). We shall

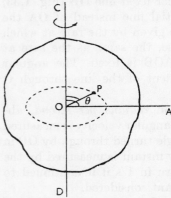

Fig. 1.35

assume that the body is rigid, that is, it does not change in shape or size.

We can fix the angular velocity of the body as follows:

Suppose P is *any* elementary particle of the body, and PO is drawn perpendicular to the axis of rotation CD. Then as the body rotates P describes a circle of radius PO about the axis. The angular velocity of P about O is the angular velocity of the body.

If OA is drawn perpendicular to CD and regarded as fixed in space the angular velocity equals the rate at which $\angle$AOP increases.

It is clear that for a rigid body this angular velocity is the same for every particle P whatever its position in the body. Of course, the *linear* speed, v, of such a particle P depends upon its distance from the axis, and is given by

$$v = \omega r$$

where ω = angular velocity, and r = OP = distance of P from the axis of rotation.

The rate at which a body is rotating is often given in revolutions per minute (abbreviated to rev min^{-1}).

1.32. *To find the velocity of any point of a vertical circular disc which is rolling uniformly, without sliding, on a horizontal plane.*

Let O (Fig. 1.36) be the centre and r the radius of the disc, A its point of contact with the plane AX, and let v be the velocity with which O moves.

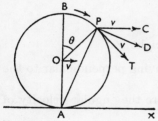

Fig. 1.36

Now as the centre moves forward uniformly in a straight line the disc turns uniformly about the centre; and since each point of the rim in succession touches the ground, it is clear that each point of the rim describes the perimeter relative to the centre while the centre moves forward a distance equal to the perimeter. Hence the velocity of any point on the rim relative to the centre is equal in magnitude to the velocity v of the centre.

The angular velocity (ω) of the disc about its centre is therefore equal to v/r.

If B is the highest point of the disc its velocity relative to O is v horizontally, and in the same direction as the velocity of O.

$\therefore$ velocity of B = $v+v = 2v$.

The velocity of A relative to O is also v, but in the opposite direction to the velocity of O.

$$\therefore \qquad \text{velocity of A} = v - v = 0,$$

i.e. the point A is instantaneously at rest.

If P is a point on the rim, such that the angle BOP $= \theta$, the resultant velocity of P is obtained by compounding together its velocity relative to O, v along the tangent PT, and the velocity of O, i.e. v horizontally along PC.

Now $\angle \text{CPT} = \theta$, and if V is the resultant velocity of P,

$$V^2 = v^2 + v^2 + 2v^2 \cos \theta$$
$$= 2v^2 (1 + \cos \theta) = 4v^2 \cos^2 \tfrac{1}{2}\theta$$
$$\therefore \qquad V = 2v \cos \tfrac{1}{2}\theta.$$

The direction of this velocity is along PD bisecting the angle CPT, since the two components are equal.

If AP is joined we see that

$$\angle \text{OPA} = \tfrac{1}{2}\theta,$$
$$\text{also } \angle \text{TPD} = \tfrac{1}{2}\theta,$$
$$\therefore \qquad \angle \text{APD} = \angle \text{OPT} = \text{a right } \angle.$$

Hence each point of the rim is moving perpendicular to the line joining it to A, the lowest point.

Also $AP = 2r \cos \tfrac{1}{2}\theta$, and therefore the angular velocity of P about A is

$$\frac{2v \cos \tfrac{1}{2}\theta}{2r \cos \tfrac{1}{2}\theta} = \frac{v}{r}$$

$$= \text{the angular velocity of the disc.}$$

Since the disc is rigid, all points in AP must have the same angular velocity about A, and it follows that all points on the disc are at this instant turning about A with angular velocity ω equal to that of the disc about its centre.

The point A is called the *instantaneous centre of rotation*.

1.33. EXAMPLE (i)

An engine is travelling at 108 $km\,h^{-1}$, and its driving wheel is 1·8 m in diameter; find the velocity and direction of motion of each of the two points of the wheel which are at a height of 1·35 m above the ground.

Let C (Fig. 1.37) be the centre of the wheel, A the point of contact with the rail, B the highest point, and D, E the points at a height of 1·35 m. Then, $\angle BCE = 60°$. The velocity of E is composed of its

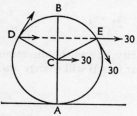

FIG. 1.37

velocity relative to C, i.e. 30 ms⁻¹ perpendicular to CE downwards, and the velocity of C, i.e. 30 ms⁻¹ horizontal. These are inclined at an angle of 60°, and the resultant velocity V bisects the angle between them, i.e. it is inclined at 30° below the horizontal.

Also $\quad V = \sqrt{\{30^2+30^2+2(30^2)\} \cos 60°\}} = 30\sqrt{3} \text{ ms}^{-1}$
$$= 108\sqrt{3} \text{ km h}^{-1}.$$

The component velocities of D are 30 ms⁻¹ horizontal, and 30 ms⁻¹ perpendicular to CD and upwards. The resultant is $30\sqrt{3}$ ms⁻¹ as for E, but it is inclined at an angle of 30° *above* the horizontal.

EXAMPLE (ii)
Explain how to find the angular velocity of the line joining two points whose velocities are given.

Let A and B (Fig. 1.38) represent the two points. Now it is

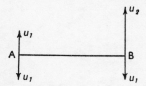

FIG. 1.38

evident that any component velocities of A and B parallel to AB will not affect the direction of AB, but the components perpendicular to AB will alter the direction of AB unless they happen to be equal and in the same direction.

To find the angular velocity of AB we therefore proceed as follows:

Resolve the velocities of A and B along and perpendicular to AB. Let u_1, u_2 be the components for A and B respectively perpendicular to AB.

Compound with each of these a velocity equal and opposite to that of one of them, say, u_1.

Then A is reduced to rest and B has a velocity of $u_2 - u_1$ perpendicular to AB,

$$\therefore \qquad \text{the angular velocity of AB} = \frac{u_2 - u_1}{\text{AB}}.$$

This is only the *instantaneous* angular velocity, for as the direction of AB changes the components perpendicular to AB will change and so will the length AB.

EXAMPLE (iii)

Two small marbles A and B are moving in a clockwise direction in concentric circular grooves of 20 cm and 30 cm radii respectively. The velocity of A in its groove is 20 cm s^{-1}, and that of B is 90 cm s^{-1}. At a given instant the marbles are 10 cm apart; what time will elapse before the distance between them is 50 cm?

Let O (Fig. 1.39) be the common centre of the grooves. The marbles can only be 10 cm apart when they are on a common diameter and on the same side of the centre as at A and B. They will be 50 cm apart when they are on a common diameter, but on opposite sides of the centre as at A', B', and then B will have described 180° more than A.

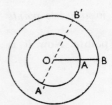

FIG. 1.39

It is easier to consider the *angular* velocities of the marbles than their linear speeds.

Since A's speed is 20 cm s^{-1}, it describes 360° or 2π radians in $2\pi \times 20/20 = 2\pi$ s. Hence its angular velocity is 1 rad s^{-1}.

B describes 360° in $2\pi \times 30/90 = \frac{2}{3}\pi$ s, and its angular velocity is therefore 3 rad s^{-1}.

$\therefore \qquad$ B's angular velocity *relative* to A is 2 rad s^{-1};

$\therefore \qquad$ the time B takes to gain 180° or π radians is $\pi/2$ s;

$\therefore \qquad$ they will be 50 cm apart after $\frac{1}{2}\pi$ or 1·57 s.

EXAMPLES 1.6

1. A wheel is making 300 rev min^{-1} about its centre; calculate the angular velocity of any point on the wheel about the centre. Also find the speed of a point at a distance of 2 cm from the centre.

2. A point moves in a circle with uniform speed; show that its angular velocity about any point on the circumference of the circle is constant.

3. A train is travelling at 64 km h^{-1}, and the diameter of one of the wheels of the engine is 1·5 m. Find the velocities of the two points on this wheel which are at a height 1·2 m above the ground.

4. A body travelling at right angles to the plane of a flywheel 75 cm in diameter, making 480 rev min^{-1}, makes a mark across the rim of the wheel. The mark is found to make an angle of 60° with the edge of the rim. Calculate the speed of the body.

5. Compare the velocities of the extremities of the hour and minute hands of a clock, their lengths being 2 and 3 cm respectively.

6. A wheel of 2·4 m diameter is rolling along the ground with a velocity of 6 m s^{-1}; find the angular velocity of the wheel and the magnitudes and directions of the velocities of the points at the extremities of the horizontal diameter.

7. The wheels of a bicycle are 76 cm in diameter, each crank is 19 cm long, and is geared so as to make one revolution while the wheels make two. Find the actual velocity of the ends of the crank (i) when at the highest, (ii) when at the lowest point of its path, when the bicycle is travelling at 16 km h^{-1}. Work out the same problem supposing that two revolutions of the crank correspond to one of the wheels.

8. A circular ring moves uniformly in a straight line in its own plane, and a point on the ring moves uniformly round the ring. Find the actual velocity of the point when the line joining it to the centre of the ring makes angles of (i) 90°, (ii) 45°, (iii) 0° with the direction of motion of the ring. (N.B. There is not necessarily any connection between the velocity of the ring and the velocity of the point.)

9. A bicycle wheel is 70 cm in diameter and the pedal crank is 17·5 cm long. If the pedals make one revolution to three revolutions of the wheels, and the speed of the bicycle is 24 km h^{-1}, find the velocity of each pedal when the top of the crank makes an angle θ with the vertical in a forward direction.   **(Q.E.)**

CHAPTER TWO

ACCELERATION

2.1. Change of velocity

Since a velocity has both magnitude and direction, it will be changed if we alter either of these or both.

Thus, suppose AB (Fig. 2.1) represents the velocity of a particle at any instant, and AC its velocity at a later instant. Then we know by the triangle of velocities that BC represents in magnitude and direction the change of velocity during the interval considered.

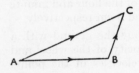

FIG. 2.1

If AC = AB, then the *speed* has remained the same, but there has still been a change of *velocity* represented by BC. In dealing with motion in a straight line we have only to consider changes of speed, but when the path is a curve we must remember that the direction of the velocity is continually changing, although the speed may remain constant. This case will be dealt with in a later chapter.

2.2 Acceleration

This term is used to denote the rate at which the velocity is changing. It is a vector quantity, and it may be either uniform or variable. *If a particle moves so that the changes of velocity in any equal times, however small, are the same in direction and equal in magnitude the acceleration is said to be uniform. The change of velocity in each unit of time measures the magnitude of the acceleration.*

If the acceleration is uniform the particle must be moving in a straight line or describing a parabola (see § 6.12. later).

2.3. When the changes of velocity in equal times are unequal in magnitude or not in the same direction the acceleration is said to be variable. When variable, the acceleration at any instant is measured by the change of velocity which would occur in the next unit of time if the acceleration remained constant in magnitude and direction during that interval. The path of the particle may be a straight line, but in general it is any curve.

2.4. The magnitude of the unit of acceleration is the acceleration of a particle which moves so that its velocity changes by the unit of velocity in each unit of time, e.g., 1 metre per second every second, usually written 1 metre per sec^2, 1 m/s^2, or 1 m s^{-2}.

2.5. Parallelogram of accelerations

If a particle has two accelerations represented in magnitude and direction by the straight lines OA, OB *it has a resultant acceleration represented by the diagonal* OC *of the parallelogram* OACB.

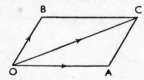

Fig. 2.2

This theorem follows at once from the law of vector addition, or from the parallelogram of velocities. Accelerations can therefore be compounded and resolved in the same way as velocities, and propositions similar to the Triangle and Polygon of Velocities are true for accelerations.

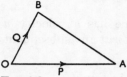

Fig. 2.3

2.6. Relative acceleration

If **OA**, **OB** (Fig. 2.3) represent the accelerations of two particles P and Q at any instant, the relative acceleration of one with respect to the other is the vector difference between **OA** and **OB**.

The acceleration of P relative to Q is

$$\mathbf{OA} - \mathbf{OB} = \mathbf{BA},$$

and the acceleration of Q relative to P is

$$\mathbf{OB} - \mathbf{OA} = \mathbf{AB}.$$

The relative acceleration can thus be obtained, as in the case of relative velocity, by drawing the triangle OAB.

If two particles have accelerations which are equal in magnitude and in the same direction their relative acceleration is zero and their relative motion is the same as if neither of them had any acceleration.

This often enables us to simplify a problem on the motion of bodies subject to a common acceleration by ignoring this acceleration.

It should be noticed that a particle at instantaneous rest may have acceleration, and that two particles whose velocities at any instant are equal and parallel (i.e. they have no relative velocity) may have relative acceleration with respect to each other.

MOTION IN A STRAIGHT LINE

2.7. We shall now consider the case of a particle moving with uniform acceleration in a straight line.

If the velocity is increasing the acceleration is said to be positive; if the velocity is decreasing the acceleration is negative.

A negative acceleration is, of course, the same as a retardation.

2.8. Motion with uniform acceleration

If a particle moving along a straight line has a velocity u initially (that is, at time $t = 0$) its velocity v at any subsequent instant t is given by

$$v = u + \text{the increase in velocity in time } t.$$

If the acceleration is uniform and equal to a the increase in velocity in time t is at, and hence

$$v = u + at. \tag{i}$$

Further, if s denotes the distance of the particle at time t from the point at which it starts, so that $s = 0$ when $t = 0$, we have

$$s = \text{average velocity} \times t.$$

Now if the acceleration is uniform the velocity is increasing at a constant rate, and hence the average velocity in any time-interval 0 to t will equal the velocity at the instant $\frac{1}{2}t$, that is, the mean of the velocities at the beginning and end of the time interval.

$\therefore \qquad\qquad s = \frac{1}{2}(u+v)t = \frac{1}{2}(u+u+at)t$

$\therefore \qquad\qquad s = ut + \frac{1}{2}at^2. \qquad\qquad\qquad\qquad\textbf{(ii)}$

From (i) and (ii) we can eliminate t as follows:

$$v^2 = u^2 + 2uat + a^2t^2 = u^2 + 2a\ (ut + \frac{1}{2}at^2)$$
$$= u^2 + 2as \qquad\qquad \textbf{from (ii)}$$

$\therefore \qquad\qquad\qquad v^2 = u^2 + 2as. \qquad\qquad\qquad\textbf{(iii)}$

These relations can also be derived as follows.

In the notation of the calculus, we have

$$\frac{\mathrm{d}^2 s}{\mathrm{d}t^2} = a.$$

$\therefore$ integrating $\quad \dfrac{\mathrm{d}s}{\mathrm{d}t} = at + A$, as a is constant.

Since $\qquad\qquad \dfrac{\mathrm{d}s}{\mathrm{d}t} = u$ when $t = 0$, $A = u$.

$\therefore \qquad\qquad \dfrac{\mathrm{d}s}{\mathrm{d}t} = u + at.$

But $\dfrac{\mathrm{d}s}{\mathrm{d}t} = v$, the velocity at time t, and hence

$$v = u + at \qquad\qquad\qquad\text{(i)}$$

Integrating again, $\qquad s = ut + \frac{1}{2}at^2 + B,$

and since $\qquad\qquad s = 0$ when $t = 0$, we have $B = 0$

$\therefore \qquad\qquad\qquad s = ut + \frac{1}{2}at^2. \qquad\qquad\qquad\textbf{(ii)}$

These three relations (i), (ii), and (iii) apply to the motion of a particle moving in a straight line with uniform acceleration. They do *not* apply in cases where the acceleration is variable.

It should be noticed that each relation contains a and three of the four quantities u, v, t, s, one of these being absent from each equation. These relations are of fundamental importance, and must be remembered. Only two of them are independent; from any two of them the third can be derived. In working problems we select the relations which contain the quantities we are given and the one we want to find.

It is, however, sometimes convenient to use the relation $s = \frac{1}{2}(u+v)t$, which was proved above in deriving relation (ii).

We collect these relations together for reference.

$$v = u+at$$
$$s = ut+\tfrac{1}{2}at^2$$
$$v^2 = u^2+2as$$
$$\text{and } s = \tfrac{1}{2}(u+v)t.$$

EXAMPLE (i)

A train which is moving with uniform acceleration is observed to take 20 and 30 s to travel successive 400 metres. How much farther will it travel before coming to rest if the acceleration remains uniform?

We do not know what the initial velocity of the train is, but we are given two distances and two times.

The train goes 400 m in 20 s.

$$\therefore \qquad\qquad 400 = 20u+\tfrac{1}{2}a \times 400 \qquad\qquad\qquad \text{(i)}$$

where u ms^{-1} is the velocity at the beginning of the first 400 m, and a ms^{-2} is the acceleration.

It also goes 800 m in 50 s.

$$\therefore \qquad\qquad 800 = 50u+\tfrac{1}{2}a \times 2500 \qquad\qquad\qquad \text{(ii)}$$
$$\therefore \qquad\qquad 2u+20a = 40$$

and $\qquad\qquad 5u+125a = 80$

whence $\qquad\qquad a = -4/15$

and $\qquad\qquad u = 68/3$.

We can now find the whole distance (including the two 400 m) travelled before coming to rest, for if this is s m

$$0 = \frac{68^2}{9} - \frac{8}{15}s$$
$$\therefore \qquad\qquad s = \frac{68^2 \times 15}{72} = 963 \cdot 3$$

∴ the further distance travelled is

$$963 \cdot 3 - 800 = 163 \cdot 3 \text{ m}.$$

Note.—In cases like this, where the times taken to travel successive distances are given, write down one equation for the first distance, and the second equation for the *sum* of the two distances. If we consider the second 400 m separately we have to use a different value for the initial velocity from that at the beginning of the first 400 m.

EXAMPLE (ii)

A train moves 3·6 km from rest to rest in 3 min. The greatest speed is 90 km h⁻¹, and the acceleration and retardation are uniform. Find the distance travelled at full speed.

It must be noticed that we are not told that the acceleration and retardation are *equal*.

Let s_1, t_1 be the distance and time for which the acceleration is a_1.

Let s_2, t_2 be the distance and time for which the retardation is a_2.

Let s, t be the distance and time at uniform speed.

Using km and h as units we get

$$90 = a_1 t_1 \text{ and } s_1 = \tfrac{1}{2} a_1 t_1^2.$$

Similarly,
$$90 = a_2 t_2 \text{ and } s_2 = 90 t_2 - \tfrac{1}{2} a_2 t_2^2$$
$$= 90 t_2 - 45 t_2$$
$$= 45 t_2.$$

Also
$$s = 90t.$$

∴ $$s_1 + s + s_2 = 45 t_1 + 90 t + 45 t_2 = 3 \cdot 6$$

∴ $$t_1 + 2t + t_2 = 0 \cdot 08.$$

Also $$t_1 + t + t_2 = 0 \cdot 05 \text{ since } 3 \text{ min} = 0 \cdot 05 \text{ h}.$$

∴ $$t = 0 \cdot 03$$

∴ the distance travelled at full speed $= 90 \times 0 \cdot 03$ km

$$= 2 \cdot 7 \text{ km}.$$

The data do not enable us to find t_1, t_2, etc., separately.

EXAMPLE (iii)

If an express train reduced speed from 96 km h⁻¹ to 24 km h⁻¹ in 0·8 km, for how long were the brakes applied, and how much longer would it take to come to rest?

We must, of course, assume that the retardation due to the brakes is uniform; let this be a km s⁻².

Using $\qquad v^2 = u^2 + 2as$

we get $\qquad 24^2 = 96^2 + 1\!\cdot\!6\ a$

$\therefore \qquad a = -\dfrac{96^2 - 24^2}{1\!\cdot\!6} = -\dfrac{120 \times 72}{1\!\cdot\!6} = -5400.$

Using $\qquad v = u + at$

we get $\qquad 24 = 96 - 5400t$

$\therefore \qquad t = \dfrac{72}{5400}\text{h} = 48 \text{ s.}$

To find the additional time t' h taken to come to rest, we have

$$0 = 24 - 5400t'$$

$\therefore \qquad t' = \dfrac{24}{5400} = \dfrac{4}{900}.$

$\therefore \qquad$ Additional time $= \dfrac{4}{900}\text{ h} = 16 \text{ s.}$

EXAMPLE (iv)

A cyclist riding at 18 *kmh*$^{-1}$ *passes a motor car just as it begins to move in the same direction. The car maintains an acceleration of* 0·4 *ms*$^{-2}$ *for* 20 *s, and then moves uniformly. How far will it have run before overtaking the cyclist?*

The distance moved by the car during the 20 s is given by

$$s = \tfrac{1}{2} \times 0\!\cdot\!4 \times 400 = 80 \text{ m}$$

The velocity at the end of this time is given by

$$v = 0\!\cdot\!4 \times 20 = 8 \text{ ms}^{-1}$$

The speed of the cyclist is $18 \times 10^3/3600 \text{ ms}^{-1} = 5 \text{ ms}^{-1}$

and the distance moved by the cyclist in this time is therefore 100 m.

The velocity of the car relative to the cyclist is 3 ms^{-1}

$\therefore$ to gain 20 m on the cyclist it takes $\dfrac{20}{3}$ s, and in this time it will have gone $\dfrac{160}{3}$ m, or $133\tfrac{1}{3}$ m altogether.

EXAMPLES 2.1

1. A train starts from rest at a station, and travels with uniform acceleration 1·2 ms^{-2}. What is the speed of the train after 30 s, and how far has it travelled?

2. A body starts from rest with uniform acceleration, and in 10 s acquires a speed of 15 ms^{-1}. What is its acceleration and how far has the body travelled in the 10 s?

3. A motor car travelling at 54 kmh^{-1} is brought to rest with uniform retardation in 5 s. Find its retardation and the distance it travelled in this time.

4. A body has an initial velocity of 100 ms^{-1} and is subject to a retardation of 2 ms^{-2}. At what time will its velocity be zero, and how far will it then have travelled?

5. A motor car, starting from rest and moving with uniform acceleration, goes 9·5 m in the 10th s after starting. Find the acceleration of the car, and the distance covered during 5 s from the start.

6. A body moves with uniform acceleration for 3 s and describes 27 m; it then moves with uniform velocity and during the next 5 s describes 60 m. Find its initial velocity and its acceleration.

7. A car increases its speed from 18 kmh^{-1} to 72 kmh^{-1} in a distance of 50 m, the acceleration being uniform. Find the acceleration and the speed when the car has covered 25 m of the distance.

8. A train approaching a station does two successive half-kilometres in 16 and 20 s respectively. Assuming the retardation to be uniform, find the further distance the train runs before stopping.

9. A train is uniformly accelerated and passes successive kilometre marks with velocities 10 kmh^{-1} and 20 kmh^{-1} respectively. Calculate the velocity when it passes the next kilometre mark, and the times taken for each of these two intervals of 1 km.

(H.S.D.)

10. A train is timed between successive posts A, B, and C, each 2 km apart. If it takes 100 s to travel from A to B and 150 s from B to C, find the retardation of the train, assuming that it remains uniform after the point A. Find also how far beyond C the train travels before it stops.

11. A particle moves in a straight line, with an initial velocity and a uniform acceleration. Find how far it travels in 12 s, given that it travels 48 m in the first 6 s and 32 m in the last 2 s. Find also the initial velocity.

12. A particle starts from rest and moves in a straight line with uniform acceleration. In a certain 4 s of its motion it travels 12 m and in the next 5 s it travels 30 m. Find (i) its acceleration, (ii) its velocity at the start of the timing, (iii) the distance it then had travelled.

13. A cage goes down a mine shaft 675 m deep in 45 s. For the first quarter of the distance only, the speed is being uniformly accelerated, and during the last quarter uniformly retarded, the acceleration and retardation being equal. Find the uniform speed of the cage while traversing the centre portion of the shaft. (I.A.)

14. A train, starting from rest, is uniformly accelerated during the first $\frac{1}{2}$ km of its run, then runs 1·5 km at the uniform speed acquired, and is afterwards brought to rest in $\frac{1}{4}$ km under uniform retardation. If the time for the whole journey is 5 min, find the uniform acceleration and the uniform retardation.

15. A particle starts from rest with a constant acceleration which ceases after an interval. It then moves uniformly at 5 m s^{-1} for 10 s, after which it is uniformly retarded and is brought to rest. If the whole motion occupies 16 s, find the distance traversed. The initial acceleration being 1·5 m s^{-2}, find the final retardation.

16. A body, moving in a straight line with constant acceleration, passes over distances a, b, and c in equal consecutive intervals of time t. Find (i) the relation between a, b, and c; (ii) the acceleration of the body; (iii) its velocity at the start of the part a of its path. (H.S.D.)

17. The cage of a pit performs the first part of its descent with uniform acceleration a and the remainder with uniform acceleration $2a$. Prove that, if h is the depth of the shaft, and t the time of descent, $h = \frac{1}{3}at^2$. (I.E.)

18. A particle moving in a straight line with uniform acceleration a passes a certain point with velocity u. Three seconds afterwards another particle, moving in the same straight line with constant acceleration $\frac{4}{3}a$, passes the same point with velocity $\frac{1}{3}u$. The first particle is overtaken by the second when their velocities are respectively 8·1 and 9·3 m s^{-1}. Find the values of u and a, and also the distance travelled from the point. (I.S.)

19. The brakes of a train are able to produce a retardation of 1·2 m s^{-2}. If the train is travelling at 90 km h^{-1}, at what distance from a station should the brakes be applied, if it is desired to stop at the station? If the brakes are put on at half this distance, with what speed will the train pass the station? (H.S.D.)

20. A cyclist A riding at 16 km h^{-1} is overtaken and passed by B riding at 20 km h^{-1}. If A immediately increases his speed with uniform acceleration, show that he will catch B when his speed is 24 km h^{-1}. If, when he has increased his speed to 22 km h^{-1}, he continues to ride at this speed and catches B after he has gone 200 m, find his acceleration. (I.E.)

21. Two points P and Q move in the same straight line, being initially at rest and Q being 18 m in front of P. Q starts from rest with an acceleration of 3 m s^{-2}, and P starts in pursuit with a velocity of 10 m s^{-1} and an acceleration of 2 m s^{-2}. Prove that P will overtake and pass Q after an interval of 2 s and that Q will in turn overtake P after a further interval of 16 s.

22. A lift ascends with constant acceleration a, then with constant velocity, and finally stops under a constant retardation a. If the total distance ascended is s, and the total time occupied is t, show that the time during which the lift is ascending with constant velocity is $\{t^2-(4s/a)\}^{\frac{1}{2}}$.   (H.S.D.)

23. A point moving in a straight line describes 16 m in the 2nd s of its motion, 28 m in the 5th s, 52 m in the 11th s. Prove that these distances are consistent with the supposition that the motion of the point is uniformly accelerated; also find the whole distance described in 10 s from the beginning of the motion.   (H.C.)

24. A point moving in a straight line covers 12 m, 18 m, and 42 m in successive intervals of 3 s, 2s, and 3 s. Prove that these distances are consistent with the supposition that the point is moving with uniform acceleration.   (I.A.)

25. A body starts with velocity u and moves in a straight line with constant acceleration a.

     If when the velocity has increased to $5u$ the acceleration is reversed in direction, its magnitude being unaltered, prove that when the particle returns to its starting-point its velocity will be $-7u$.   (I.A.)

26. The two ends of a train moving with constant acceleration pass a certain point with velocities u and v. Find in terms of u and v what proportion of the length of the train will have passed the point after a time equal to half that taken by the train to pass the point.   (I.E.)

27. A particle is moving in a straight line, and is observed to be at a distance a from a marked point initially, to be at a distance b after an interval of n s, to be at a distance c after $2n$ s, and at a distance d after $3n$ s. Prove that if the acceleration is uniform

$$d-a = 3(c-b),$$

and that the acceleration is equal to

$$\frac{c+a-2b}{n^2};$$

find also the initial velocity.   (I.S.)

28. A train starts from A with uniform acceleration $0\cdot15$ m s^{-2}. After 2 min the train attains full speed, and moves uniformly for 11 min. It is then brought to rest at B by the brakes producing a constant retardation $1\cdot5$ m s^{-2}. Find the distance AB.

(H.C.)

29. A particle traverses a distance of 300 m in a straight line at an average speed of 4 m s^{-1}, starting from rest and finishing at rest. It moves with a uniform acceleration for the first 10 s, and is brought to rest by a uniform retardation in the last 20 s of its motion, and moves at a uniform speed during the rest of its motion. Find the acceleration and retardation. (H.C.)

30. Prove that, if a particle moves with a uniform acceleration, the spaces described in consecutive equal intervals of time are in arithmetical progression.

   It is observed that a particle describes $396\cdot9$ m in 3 s, $392\cdot0$ m in the next 4 s, and $269\cdot5$ m in the next 5 s. Show that this is consistent with the particle moving with uniform retardation and find the time before it comes to rest. (I.S.)

31. A train starting from rest travels the first part of its journey with constant acceleration a, the second part with constant speed v, and the third part with constant retardation a', being brought thereby again to rest. If the average speed for the whole journey is $\frac{7}{8}v$, show that the train is travelling at constant speed for three-quarters of the total time. Find also what fraction of the whole distance is described with constant speed. (I.S.)

32. A train passes another on a parallel track; the first is running at a uniform speed of 60 km h^{-1}, and the second is running at a speed of 15 km h^{-1}, with an acceleration of $0\cdot15$ m s^{-2}. How long will it be before the second train catches the first again, and how far will the trains run in the interval? (Q.E.)

2.9. Acceleration of falling bodies

When a heavy body is falling towards the earth it is well known that its speed increases as it falls, or that it moves with an *acceleration*.

It has been shown by numerous experiments that, if the body is free from air resistance, this acceleration is uniform.

The earliest experiments were carried out by Galileo (1564–1642), who laid the basis of the science of dynamics. His work was continued and developed by Newton (1642–1727), who put forward the theory of gravitation to account for not only the motion of a body near the earth's surface but also for the motion of the moon about the earth, and of the earth and other planets about the sun.

The acceleration of a body falling freely (that is, air resistance neglected) near the earth's surface is now known as the 'acceleration due to gravity', and is denoted by g. At any given place its value is the same for *all* bodies, whatever their size and chemical composition, but it varies with altitude and from place to place over the earth's surface.

Its numerical value in metre-second units in the latitude of London is about 9·81. At the equator it is about 9·78.

In centimetre-second units the value in London is about 981, and at the equator about 978.

(In numerical examples, unless otherwise stated, the value of g may be taken as 980 cm s^{-2} or 9·8 m s^{-2}; the motion may be supposed to be *in vacuo*.)

2.10. Vertical motion under gravity

When a body is projected vertically upwards we regard the upward direction as the positive direction, and the body will experience a retardation or negative acceleration g. We shall, for simplicity, assume that g is constant, that is, we shall neglect the variation of g with height, and also the resistance of the atmosphere. If u is the initial velocity of projection the equations for motion with uniform acceleration thus become

$$v = u - gt \tag{i}$$
$$s = ut - \tfrac{1}{2}gt^2 \tag{ii}$$
$$v^2 = u^2 - 2gs. \tag{iii}$$

2.11. At the highest point it is clear that the velocity v must be zero, so that by putting $v = 0$ in equation (i) we get the time taken to reach the highest point;

$$0 = u - gt \text{ or } t = u/g.$$

If t is greater than u/g, v is negative and as t increases v increases numerically, that is, after reaching the highest point the body begins to descend, and its speed increases.

Equation (iii) gives the greatest height, for putting $v = 0$ we get:

$$0 = u^2 - 2gs \text{ or } s = u^2/2g.$$

∴   The greatest height attained is $u^2/2g$.

2.12. The velocity on returning to the point from which it was projected is given by putting $s = 0$ in equation (iii), and then

$$v^2 = u^2$$

i.e. $\hspace{4cm} v = \pm u.$

The $+$ sign gives the velocity on starting, and the $-$ sign the velocity on returning to the point of projection. The magnitude is the same as that of the velocity of projection, but the body is now moving downwards.

2.13. The time of flight is obtained by putting $s = 0$ in equation (ii), and this gives

$$0 = ut - \tfrac{1}{2}gt^2$$

$\therefore \hspace{3cm} t = 0 \text{ or } t = 2u/g.$

There are two values of t corresponding to the height $s = 0$; the value $t = 0$ obviously refers to the time of projection, while the value $2u/g$ gives the time required to return to the point of projection, i.e. the time of flight.

Notice that this is twice the time to the greatest height.

For any given height (less than the greatest) above the point of projection equation (ii) will give two values of t, one the time taken to reach that height on the way up, the other the time on the way down.

2.14. If we require the time taken to reach a point *below* the point of projection (when the body is projected upwards) we need not find the time up and down to the point of projection, and then the time taken to reach the point below. We simply substitute the distance below the point of projection for s in equation (ii), giving it a negative sign, as in the following example:

A body is projected vertically upwards with velocity 21 ms^{-1}: *how long will it take to reach a point* 280 *m below the point of projection?*

Using $\hspace{3cm} s = ut - \tfrac{1}{2}gt^2$

$\hspace{1cm}$ and $\hspace{2.5cm} s = -280, u = 21, g = 9{\cdot}8$

$\therefore \hspace{2.5cm} -280 = 21t - 4{\cdot}9t^2$

$\therefore \hspace{1.5cm} 4{\cdot}9t^2 - 21t - 280 = 0$

$$\therefore \qquad\qquad 7t^2 - 30t - 400 = 0$$
$$\therefore \qquad\qquad (t-10)(7t+40) = 0$$
$$\therefore \qquad\qquad t = 10 \text{ or } t = -40/7.$$

The latter value is obviously impossible, and the required time is 10 s.

2.15. *Velocity due to falling a given vertical distance from rest.*

The positive direction is now taken downwards, and the equation of motion is

$$v^2 = u^2 + 2gs.$$

Since the body starts from rest $u = 0$, and hence the velocity acquired in falling a distance h is given by

$$v^2 = 2gh$$
$$\therefore \qquad\qquad v = \sqrt{(2gh)}.$$

This is also the velocity required to take the body to a height h when projected vertically upwards.

EXAMPLES 2.2.

1. A body is projected vertically upwards with a velocity of 17·5 $\mathrm{m\,s^{-1}}$; find (i) how high it will go; (ii) what times elapse before it is at a height of 10 m.

2. A body is projected vertically upwards with a velocity of 24·5 $\mathrm{m\,s^{-1}}$; find (i) when its velocity will be 4·9 $\mathrm{m\,s^{-1}}$; (ii) how long it takes to return to the point of projection; (iii) at what times it will be 19·6 m above the point of projection.

3. A body falls from rest; find (i) how far it will fall in 10 s; (ii) how long it takes to fall 100 m; (iii) its velocity after falling 100 m.

4. A body is projected vertically downwards from the top of a tower with a velocity of 40 $\mathrm{m\,s^{-1}}$, and takes 3 s to reach the ground. What is the height of the tower?

5. A body is projected vertically upwards with a velocity of 35 $\mathrm{m\,s^{-1}}$. Find (i) how long it takes to reach its highest point; (ii) the distance it ascends during the 3rd s of its motion.

6. A body falls from rest from the top of a tower, and during the last second it falls $\frac{9}{25}$ of the whole distance. Find the height of the tower.

7. A body is projected vertically upwards with a certain velocity, and it is found that when it is 400 m from the ground it takes 8 s to return to the same point again. Find the velocity of projection and the whole time of flight.

8. A block falls from a mast-head, and is observed to take $\frac{2}{5}$ s in falling from the deck to the bottom of the hold, a distance of 7·5 m. Calculate the height of the mast-head above the deck.

(I.S.)

9. If a stone falls past a window 2·45 m high in 0·5 s, find the height from which the stone fell. (H.C.)

10. A ball is thrown vertically upwards with a velocity of 21 ms⁻¹; find its height when it is moving at the rate of 14 ms⁻¹, and find the time between the instants at which it is at this height. (H.C.)

11. A particle projected vertically downwards descends 100 m in 4 s. Show that it describes the last 30 m in about 0·7 s.

12. A particle is projected vertically upwards and at the same instant another is let fall to meet it. Show that, if the particles have equal velocities when they impinge, one of them has travelled 3 times as far as the other. (H.C.)

13. A ball is thrown vertically upwards with a speed of 42 ms⁻¹. Find where it is after 5 s, and the total distance it has actually travelled. If it falls past the point of projection into a well of depth 70 m, find when it strikes the bottom. (N.U.3)

14. A body is projected vertically upwards with an initial velocity of 28 ms⁻¹. Find the height to which the body rises.

Another body is projected vertically upwards 2 s after the first with an initial velocity of 21 ms⁻¹; find when the two bodies are at the same height, and find also the velocity of each body at this instant.

15. A particle is projected vertically upwards, and t s afterwards another particle is projected vertically upwards with the same initial velocity. Prove that their velocities when meeting will be each $\frac{1}{2} gt$. (H.S.D.)

16. A particle is projected vertically upwards with a velocity of u ms⁻¹, and after t s another particle is projected upwards from the same point and with the same initial velocity. Prove that the particles will meet after a lapse of

$$\left(\frac{t}{2} + \frac{u}{g} \right) \text{s}$$

from the instant of projection of the first particle. (H.S.D.)

17. A particle is projected vertically upwards with a velocity of u ms^{-1}, and after an interval of t s another particle is projected upwards from the same point and with the same initial velocity. Prove that they will meet at a height of

$$\frac{4u^2 - g^2t^2}{8g} \text{ m.}$$ (I.E.)

18. A man on the top of a tower of height 35 m holds his arm over the side of the tower and throws a stone vertically upwards with a speed of 14 ms^{-1}. Find (i) the height above the ground or the highest point reached by the stone, (ii) the speed of the stone when it reaches the ground, (iii) the time that the stone was in the air.

2.16. Motion down a smooth inclined plane

Let ABC (Fig. 2.4) represent the vertical section of a smooth plane inclined at an angle α to the horizontal, and P a particle on the plane.

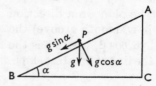

FIG. 2.4

The line AB represents a line of greatest slope on the plane. The acceleration g of a particle falling freely can be resolved into two components:

(i) an acceleration $g \sin \alpha$ down the plane;
(ii) an acceleration $g \cos \alpha$ perpendicular to the plane.

It is obvious that the plane prevents motion perpendicular to itself, so that the particle P must move down the plane with acceleration $g \sin \alpha$.

If l is the length of the plane AB the speed acquired in sliding from rest from A to B is obtained from the equation

$$v^2 = u^2 + 2as$$

by putting $u = 0$, $a = g \sin \alpha$, and $s = l$.

$\therefore$ $v^2 = 2g \sin \alpha \times l = 2gh$, where $h = $ AC.

$\therefore$ $v = \sqrt{(2gh)}.$

It is therefore the same as the speed acquired in falling freely through a vertical height equal to that of the plane. The time taken to slide down AB is *not* the same, however, as that taken to fall freely through AC.

The time taken to slide down AB is obtained from the equation

$$s = ut + \tfrac{1}{2}at^2$$

by putting $\qquad s = l,\ u = 0,\ a = g \sin \alpha.$

$\therefore \qquad\qquad l = \tfrac{1}{2}g \sin \alpha \times t^2$

$\therefore \qquad\qquad t = \sqrt{(2l/g \sin \alpha)}.$

The time taken to fall from A to C is given by

$$h = \tfrac{1}{2}gt^2 \text{ or } t = \sqrt{(2h/g)} = \sqrt{\{(2l \sin \alpha)/g\}}.$$

If the particle is projected up the plane we simply use the ordinary equations of motion and put $a = -g \sin \alpha$.

If the particle is made to slide down the plane in a direction inclined to a line of greatest slope (e.g. in a smooth groove) the acceleration is no longer $g \sin \alpha$, but $g \sin \alpha \cos \beta$, where β is the inclination of the direction of motion to the line of greatest slope.

EXAMPLE

A particle is projected (a) *upwards,* (b) *downwards, on a plane inclined to the horiozntal at 30°; if the initial velocity be 5 m s⁻¹ in each case, find the distances described and the velocities acquired in 4 s.*

(*a*) For motion *up* the plane we have

$$v = u - g \sin 30° \, t$$

and $\qquad\qquad s = ut - \tfrac{1}{2}g \sin 30° \, t^2$

$\therefore \qquad\qquad v = 5 - \tfrac{1}{2}(9 \cdot 8)4 = -14 \cdot 6$

and $\qquad\qquad s = 5 \times 4 - \tfrac{1}{2}(9 \cdot 8) \times \tfrac{1}{2} \times 16 = -19 \cdot 2$

i.e. the body is moving *down* the plane with a speed of 14·6 m s⁻¹, and is 19·2 m below the point from which it started.

(*b*) For motion *down* the plane

$$v = u + g \sin 30° \, t$$

and $\qquad\qquad s = ut + \tfrac{1}{2}g \sin 30° \, t^2$

$\therefore \qquad\qquad v = 5 + \tfrac{1}{2}(9 \cdot 8)4 = 24 \cdot 6$

and $\qquad\qquad s = 5 \times 4 + \tfrac{1}{2}(9 \cdot 8) \times \tfrac{1}{2} \times 16 = 59 \cdot 2$

i.e. the body is moving down the plane with a speed of 24·6 ms⁻¹ and has gone 59·2 m down the plane.

2.17. *The time taken by a body to slide down any smooth chord of a vertical circle, starting from the highest point, or ending at the lowest point of the circle, is constant.*

Let AB (Fig. 2.5) be a diameter of a vertical circle, of which A is the highest point and AC any chord.

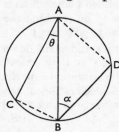

FIG. 2.5

Let $\angle BAC = \theta$, and $AB = d$, then $AC = AB \cos \theta = d \cos \theta$.

The acceleration down AC is $g \cos \theta$, and the time t taken to slide down AC from rest is obtained from

$$s = ut + \tfrac{1}{2}at^2$$

by putting $\quad s = d \cos \theta, u = 0, a = g \cos \theta$

$\therefore \qquad d \cos \theta = \tfrac{1}{2}g \cos \theta \times t^2$

$\therefore \qquad \qquad t^2 = 2d/g$

$\therefore \qquad \qquad t = \sqrt{(2d/g)}.$

Now, this is independent of θ, and is the same as the time taken to fall vertically from A to B.

The time taken to slide down all chords of the circle from A is therefore the same.

Let DB be any chord ending at B, and $\angle ABD = \alpha$.

The length of BD is $d \cos \alpha$, and the acceleration down BD is $g \cos \alpha$.

The time taken to slide down DB from rest is therefore given by

$$d \cos \alpha = \tfrac{1}{2}g \cos \alpha \times t^2$$

$\therefore \qquad \qquad t^2 = 2d/g$

$\therefore \qquad \qquad t = \sqrt{(2d/g)},$

the same value as before.

EXAMPLES 2.3

1. A particle is projected with a velocity of 20 m s^{-1} up a smooth inclined plane of inclination 30°; find the distance described up the plane, and the time that elapses before it comes to rest.

2. A particle sliding down a smooth plane, 3·6m long, acquired a velocity of 6 m s^{-1} from rest; find the inclination of the plane.

3. A particle slides from rest down a smooth inclined plane which is 12 m long and 2·7 m high. What is its velocity on reaching the bottom of the plane, and how long does it take to get there?

4. Two particles start together from a point O and slide down smooth straight wires inclined at angles 30°, 60° to the vertical, and in the same vertical plane and on the same side of the vertical through O. Show that the relative acceleration of the second particle with respect to the first is vertical and equal to $g/2$.   (I.S.)

5. A smooth inclined plane of length l and height h is fixed on a horizontal plane. Find the velocity with which a particle must be projected down the plane from the top in order that it may reach the horizontal plane in the same time as a particle let fall vertically from the top.

6. A long hollow straight tube AB, smooth inside, lies fixed on an inclined plane at an angle β with the lines of greatest slope, these being at an angle α to the horizontal. A smooth particle is put in at the upper end A and allowed to slide down. Find the distances it travels in t s, and the locus of all such points for different values of β, the end A always remaining at the same place.

                                                                (H.S.C.)

7. A right-angled triangle is placed with the side BC horizontal, and the side BA pointing vertically down; give a geometrical construction for finding the line of quickest descent from B to the hypotenuse AC.   (H.S.C.)

8. A particle slides down a smooth chord of a vertical circle ending in the lowest point. Show that the velocity acquired varies as the length of the chord.

9. A particle slides down a smooth chord of a vertical circle, starting from one end of the horizontal diameter. Show that the time taken varies as the square root of the tangent of the inclination of the chord to the vertical.

10. Show how to divide a line of greatest slope of a smooth inclined plane into three parts, so that a particle started from rest at the top may traverse them in equal times.

2.18. Motion in a straight line with variable acceleration

When the acceleration is *variable*, but follows some known law, we can obtain the equation of motion in the same way as for the simple case of uniform acceleration, i.e. by equating d^2s/dt^2 to the expression for the acceleration. The integration required to obtain the solution may be simple; in other cases only an approximate solution may be possible.

In some cases, especially those where, instead of a definite law, we are given a series of values of distances and times, or velocities and times, graphical methods may be used. We plot graphs connecting the quantities given, and obtain from them the other quantities associated with the motion.

There are several graphs which can be used in this way.

2.19. Space–time curve

We have shown earlier (1.8) that if we plot successive intervals of time along one axis, and the corresponding distance from some fixed point parallel to the other, we obtain a curve, known as the space–time curve (Fig. 1.3).

From this curve the distance gone in any time-interval can be read off directly, but further, the slope of the curve at any point P equals the speed at the instant corresponding to P.

Hence, by finding the slopes at different points on the curve we obtain the speeds at different times.

If we then plot the speed and time as in the next paragraph we get the speed–time curve, and we shall show that we can find from this the acceleration and the distance travelled.

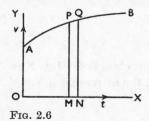

FIG. 2.6

2.20. Speed–time curve

If we plot successive intervals of time along OX (Fig. 2.6) and the corresponding speeds parallel to OY we shall obtain a curve APB, known as the speed–time curve.

If PM is the ordinate at P, then PM represents the speed at the time represented by OM.

Further, the slope of the curve APB at any point gives dv/dt, and hence equals the acceleration at the instant corresponding to that point.

When the acceleration is uniform the curve is a straight line, and conversely.

If we take a point Q (Fig. 2.6) very close to P and draw the ordinate QN so that MN $= \delta t$, then the area of the strip PMNQ is very nearly PM $\times \delta t = v\delta t$, where v is the value of the speed at P, and this product represents the space described in the interval δt.

Hence, the space described between any two times t_1 and t_2 equals the area under the curve APB between the ordinates at t_1 and t_2, and can be written $\int_{t_1}^{t_2} v \, dt$.

The units of this area are clearly speed $\times$ time, which equals distance.

Further, the magnitude of this area divided by (t_2-t_1) gives the average speed throughout this interval.

When the acceleration is uniform and equal to a the curve AB is a straight line (Fig. 2.7), and the space described in time

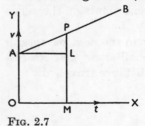

FIG. 2.7

$t (= \text{OM})$ is the area OMPA $= \triangle$PAL$+$rectangle OMLA. Now OA $= u$, the initial speed, and PL $= at$, the increment in speed in time t.

$\therefore$ $$\triangle PAL = \tfrac{1}{2}at \times t$$

and $$\text{area OMLA} = ut$$

$\therefore$ $$\text{space} = ut + \tfrac{1}{2}at^2$$

in agreement with formula (ii), 2.8.

Thus from the speed–time curve can be found:

(i) the *speed* at any instant by direct reading;

(ii) the *acceleration* at any instant by finding the gradient of the tangent to the curve corresponding to this instant; and

(iii) the *distance* gone in any time-interval by finding the area under the curve between the two ordinates corresponding to the beginning and the end of the interval.

2.21. Acceleration–time curve

If we plot time along OX (Fig. 2.8) and the corresponding values of the acceleration parallel to OY we get the acceleration–

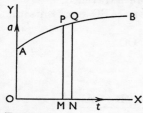

FIG. 2.8

time curve APB. The ordinate PM gives the value of the acceleration a at time $OM = t$. If we take a point Q on the curve close to P and draw the ordinate QN so that $MN = \delta t$, then the area PMNQ is very nearly equal to $a\,\delta t$, and this represents the change in speed in the interval δt.

The change in speed between any two times t_1 and t_2 is therefore the area under the curve APB between the ordinates at t_1 and t_2, and can be written

$$\int_{t_1}^{t_2} a\,\mathrm{d}t.$$

In the case of uniform acceleration, the acceleration–time curve is a straight line parallel to the time-axis. Any other curve corresponds to variable acceleration.

2.22. EXAMPLE (i)

Draw the speed–time graph of a point describing a straight line with uniform acceleration, and deduce the formula $v^2 = u^2 + 2as$.

If OA (Fig. 2.9) represent the initial speed, then, since the increments in speed during equal intervals of time are the same, the graph is a straight line AB.

The height of any point P above A is equal to the acceleration multiplied by the time represented by OM.

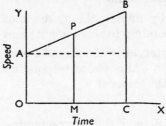

FIG. 2.9

The area under the graph gives the distance travelled.

If BC represents speed v, then the area OABC represents the distance s.

Now $\qquad$ area $\text{OABC} = \frac{1}{2}(\text{OA}+\text{CB}) \times \text{OC}$

and $\qquad\qquad \text{CB}-\text{OA} = a \times \text{OC}$

$\therefore \qquad\qquad\qquad \text{OC} = \dfrac{\text{CB}-\text{OA}}{a}$

$\therefore \qquad\qquad\quad s = \frac{1}{2} \times \dfrac{(\text{CB}+\text{OA})(\text{CB}-\text{OA})}{a}$

$\qquad\qquad\qquad\quad = \frac{1}{2}\dfrac{(\text{CB}^2-\text{OA}^2)}{a} = \frac{1}{2}\dfrac{v^2-u^2}{a}$

$\therefore \qquad\qquad\quad v^2 = u^2+2as.$

EXAMPLE (ii)

A train starts from a station A *to reach another station* B, *at a distance* c *from* A; *the motion is at first uniformly accelerated for a given time* t; *the velocity then remains constant for a given time* t'; *and is then uniformly retarded for a time* t''. *Represent the motion in a diagram, and by means of the diagram find the values of the acceleration and the retardation.*

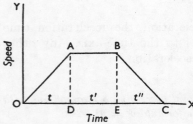

FIG. 2.10

Let OABC (Fig. 2.10) represent the speed–time graph; then AB is horizontal.

Draw AD, BE perpendicular to OX.

Then $\qquad c = \text{area OABC}$

$$= \text{AD}t' + \tfrac{1}{2}\text{AD}(t+t'')$$

$$= \tfrac{1}{2}\text{AD}(t+t''+2t')$$

$$\therefore \qquad \text{AD} = \frac{2c}{t+t''+2t'}.$$

Now the acceleration = the slope of OA

$$= \frac{\text{AD}}{\text{OD}}$$

$$= \frac{2c}{t(t+t''+2t')}.$$

The retardation = the slope of BC

$$= \frac{\text{BE}}{\text{EC}}$$

$$= \frac{2c}{t''(t+t''+2t')}$$

EXAMPLE (iii)

The speed–time graph of the motion of a car is shown in Fig. 2.11. Find the accelerations of the car during the given interval. Also find the average speed throughout the interval.

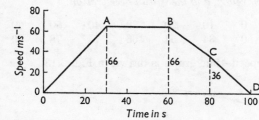

FIG. 2.11

Since OA is a straight line, the acceleration of the car in the first 30 s is uniform and of magnitude $66/30$ m s^{-2}.

For the next 30 s the speed is 66 m s^{-1} throughout and the acceleration is therefore zero.

From the instant $t = 60$ to the instant $t = 80$ the speed falls from 66 to 36 m s^{-1}, and the acceleration is uniform and of magnitude $(36-66)/20 = -1.5$ m s^{-2}.

For the last 20 s the acceleration is again uniform but of magnitude $-36/20$ ms^{-2}.

The acceleration–time graph of the motion is shown in Fig. 2.12.

Now the average speed throughout the interval is the total distance gone divided by 100 s.

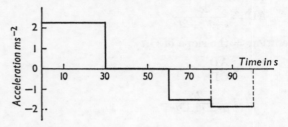

FIG. 2.12

The total distance gone is represented by the area under the speed–time curve, and hence equals

$$30 \times 33 + 30 \times 66 + 20 \times \tfrac{1}{2}(66+36) + 20 \times 18$$

that is, 4350 m.

∴   average speed throughout the interval $= 43\cdot5$ ms^{-1}.

EXAMPLE (iv)

The speed of a car on a track is found to be as given in the following table. Find the distance travelled, and the initial acceleration.

Time in s	0	10	20	30	40	50	60
Speed in kmh^{-1}	0	34	54	66	74	78	80

The corresponding speed–time graph is drawn in Fig. 2.13.

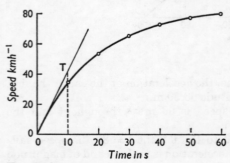

FIG. 2.13

The area under the curve equals the distance travelled, and this can be calculated, using Simpson's rule, as shown in the following table:

Time	Speed	Factor	Product
0	0	1	0
10	34	4	136
20	54	2	208
30	66	4	264
40	74	2	148
50	78	4	312
60	80	1	80
Sum		18	1048

$\therefore$ Distance travelled in 60 s.

$$= 60 \times \tfrac{1048}{18} \text{ units (s km h}^{-1})$$

$$= 60 \times \frac{1048}{18} \times \frac{1}{3600} \text{ km}$$

$$= 0.97 \text{ km, approximately.}$$

The initial acceleration may be obtained by drawing the tangent to the speed–time graph at the origin and finding its gradient. The tangent is shown as the line OT in Fig. 2.13, and its gradient equals 42 km h^{-1} per 10 s.

$$\therefore \quad \text{Initial acceleration} = \frac{42\,000}{3600 \times 10} \text{ m s}^{-2}$$

$$= 1.2 \text{ m s}^{-2} \text{ approximately.}$$

This result is only approximate, for the tangent to the curve cannot be drawn accurately.

EXAMPLE (v)

Draw the speed–time curve for a body which moves in a straight line such that its speed, v m s^{-1}, at time t s is given by $v = 4t - t^2$. Describe the motion of the body, and find its acceleration when $t = 1, 2,$ and 4. Find also its greatest distance from the starting-point measured in the direction in which it started.

The values of v for $t = 0, 1, 2, 3, 4, 5$ are plotted in Fig. 2.14, and the speed–time curve drawn. It is clear that the speed is initially zero, increases to 4 m s^{-1} at $t = 2$, then decreases to zero at $t = 4$, after which it continues to decrease indefinitely. Thus the body goes forward until $t = 4$, when it returns with constantly increasing speed.

To find the acceleration at time t we write:

$$v = 4t - t^2.$$

The speed at time $(t + \delta t)$ is given by

$$v + \delta v = 4(t + \delta t) - (t + \delta t)^2.$$

$\therefore \qquad\qquad \delta v = 4\delta t - 2t\delta t - (\delta t)^2.$

$\therefore \qquad\qquad \delta v/\delta t = 4 - 2t - \delta t.$

Hence, $\qquad\qquad \mathrm{d}v/\mathrm{d}t = 4 - 2t.$

Hence the acceleration at $t = 1$ is 2 ms^{-2}, at $t = 2$ is zero and at $t = 4$ is -4 ms^{-2}.

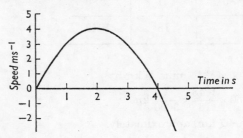

Fig. 2.14

Since the speed v is zero at $t = 4$ and negative afterwards, the body must begin to return towards the starting-point at the instant $t = 4$. Hence the greatest distance travelled in the direction in which it started is the distance gone in the interval $t = 0$ to $t = 4$, and is represented by the corresponding area under the speed–time curve.

This area, using Simpson's rule, is given by

$$\frac{0 + 4(3) + 2(4) + 4(3) + 0}{1 + 4 + 2 + 4 + 1} \times 4,$$

that is, $32 \times \frac{4}{12} = 10\frac{2}{3}$.

$\therefore$ The greatest distance required is $10\frac{2}{3}$ m.

Alternatively, using the calculus, we can write the distance gone in the interval $t = 0$ to $t = 4$ as

$$\int_0^4 v\mathrm{d}t = \int_0^4 (4t - t^2)\mathrm{d}t$$
$$= [2t^2 - \tfrac{1}{3}t^3]_0^4$$
$$= 32 - \tfrac{64}{3}$$
$$= 10\tfrac{2}{3}.$$

EXAMPLE (vi)

The acceleration of a particle t s after starting from rest is $(2t-1)$ m s^{-2}. Prove that the particle returns to the starting-point after $1\frac{1}{2}$ s, and find the distance of the particle from the starting-point after a further $1\frac{1}{2}$ s. Find also at what time after starting the particle attained a speed of 20 m s^{-1}.

If we draw the acceleration–time curve, which in this case is a straight line, the area under the curve from $t = 0$ to any instant gives the speed at that instant. Alternatively, we can use the calculus.

If the speed at time t s is v m s^{-1} the acceleration is dv/dt m s^{-2}, so that

$$dv/dt = 2t-1.$$

Hence,
$$v = t^2-t+A$$

where A is a constant.

Since $v = 0$ when $t = 0$, it follows that $A = 0$.

If we denote the distance gone at time t s by s m we have

$$ds/dt = v = t^2-t.$$

Hence,
$$s = \tfrac{1}{3}t^3-\tfrac{1}{2}t^2+B$$

where B is a constant. B is zero, since $s = 0$ when $t = 0$.

We note that the particle is at the starting-point, that is, $s = 0$ when

$$\tfrac{1}{3}t^3-\tfrac{1}{2}t^2 = 0.$$

$$\therefore \qquad t = 0 \text{ or } \tfrac{3}{2}.$$

Therefore the particle returns to the starting-point after $1\frac{1}{2}$ s.

The value of s after a further $1\frac{1}{2}$ s, that is, when $t = 3$, is given by

$$s = \tfrac{1}{3}(3)^3-\tfrac{1}{2}(3)^2 = 4\tfrac{1}{2}.$$

Hence the particle is 4·5 m from the starting-point.

Again, the speed of the particle is 20 m s^{-1} when

$$t^2-t = 20$$

$$\therefore \qquad t^2-t-20 = 0$$

$$\therefore \qquad (t-5)(t+4) = 0$$

$$\therefore \qquad t = 5 \text{ or } -4.$$

Hence the particle has a speed of 20 m s^{-1} after 5 s from the start. (The value $t = -4$ has no physical significance.)

EXAMPLES 2.4

1. Explain how the acceleration and the space covered may be obtained from the velocity–time diagram of a particle moving in a straight line.

   The velocity–time diagram consists of two straight lines AB, BC, where the coordinates of A, B, C are (0, 10), (10, 10), (20, 25), the first coordinate in each case being the time in seconds and the second coordinate the velocity in metres per second. Describe the motion of the particle and find the total distance covered.
   (H.C.)

2. If a sprinter can start with a velocity of 6 ms⁻¹, and run with uniform acceleration, find, graphically, the greatest speed attained in running 90 m in 10 s, and the necessary acceleration.
   (I.A.)

3. A train approaching a station does two successive half-kilometres in 16 and 20 s respectively. Assuming the retardation to be uniform, draw a graph to show the variation of the velocity with the time during this interval of 36 s.
   (H.C.)

4. The distance between two stations is 1800 m. An electric train starts from rest at one station with a uniform acceleration of 0.5 ms⁻²; it comes to rest at the other station with a uniform retardation of 0.75 ms⁻², and the speed for the intermediate portion of the journey is constant. Sketch the general form of the velocity–time graph, and find what the constant speed must amount to if the journey is to be completed in 3 min.
   (Q.E.)

5. A car is running steadily at 10 ms⁻¹; it then accelerates in such a way that for 200 m the velocity increases by 1 ms⁻¹ for each 10 m traversed. The acceleration then ceases. Draw curves showing the relation of v to s and a to s. What does the area of the latter curve denote?
   (Q.E.)

6. A train starts from rest with an acceleration of 0.3 ms⁻², which decreases uniformly with the time until the train is travelling at full speed after 3 min. The train is then pulled up with a uniform retardation, and is stationary after a further 1.2 min. Plot the acceleration–time, velocity–time, and distance–time graphs. Record the values of the retardation and distance from the starting-point at the instant when the brakes are applied.
   (Q.E.)

7. A train starts from a station, and for the first km moves with a uniform acceleration, then for the next 2 km with a uniform

speed, and finally for another km with uniform retardation, before coming to rest in the next station. The journey takes 4 min. Draw a graph showing how the speed varies with the time, and from it find the maximum value of the speed.

8. The speed of a train for the first minute of its motion is given by the following table:

Time in s	0	5	10	20	30	40	50	60
Speed in m s^{-1}	0	8·5	14·6	23	29·2	33·6	37	39

Find the distance travelled in the first minute and also the time in which the train travels the first half of that distance.

(Q.E.)

9. The relation between the velocity and the distance for a car starting from rest is given in the following table:

Velocity in m s^{-1}	0	6	11	15	18	20·5	22·3	23·8	24·8	25·5	26
Distance in m	0	15	30	45	60	75	90	105	120	135	150

Plot the velocity–distance curve, and show how to obtain the acceleration–distance curve from it. What is the acceleration in metre-second units at the mean distance? (Q.E.)

10. The relation between distance and time for a car starting from rest is given in the table:

Time in s	0	10	20	30	40	50	60	70
Distance in m	0	36	160	395	660	880	1040	1160

Plot a distance–time curve, and deduce the speed–time and acceleration–time curves for the first 60 s.

11. A car starts from rest, and its velocity at the end of intervals of 10 s during the first minute is 13, 20·5, 25, 28, 29·5, and 30 m s^{-1} respectively.

Plot the velocity–time graph and derive the velocity–distance graph. Thence obtain the mean values of the velocity during the first minute (i) with respect to time, (ii) with respect to distance.

(Q.E.)

12. The speed of a train at intervals of 1 min in a journey of 8 min are 0, 22, 42, 56, 60, 60, 52, 30, 0 km h^{-1} respectively. Draw the velocity–time graph, and estimate in kilometres the total distance travelled. Find the retardation in m s^{-2} at the end of the journey.

13. The velocity, v m s^{-1} of a car decreases with the time, t s, according to the formula

$$v = 40 - t^2.$$

Draw a velocity–time graph from $t = 0$ to $t = 7$. Find by graphical methods the distance travelled from $t = 3$ to $t = 6$ and the mean retardation in the same interval of time.   (N.U.3)

14. A train travelling at $37 \cdot 5$ m s^{-1} has steam shut off and brakes applied; its speed in m s^{-1} after t s is given by the formula

$$v = 37 \cdot 5 - t + 0 \cdot 005t^2.$$

Draw a time–speed graph from $t = 0$ to $t = 50$. Find the mean retardation during the 50 s and the instantaneous retardation at $t = 0$.   (N.U.3)
[The following examples may be best solved by using the calculus.]

15. The coordinate x m of a moving particle A at time t s is given by

$$x = t^3 - 2t^2 + 3t - 4.$$

Find the velocity and the acceleration of A at the instant $t = 4$.

16. The acceleration a of a particle P is given by $a = 3t - 2$. P starts from rest at the origin O at time $t = 0$. Find its velocity and its distance from O at time $t = 4$.

17. While a train is travelling from its start at A to its next stop at B its distance x km from A is given by $x = 90t^2 - 45t^3$, where t hours is the time taken. Find in terms of t its velocity and its acceleration, after time t.
    Hence find (i) the time taken in travelling from A to B, (ii) the distance AB, (iii) the greatest speed attained.

18. A particle is travelling along a straight line with a speed given by $(3t^2 - 4t + 3)$ m s^{-1}, where t s is the time measured from the instant when the particle is 2 m in the positive direction from a fixed point O on the line. Find its distance from O after 1 s and also after 3 s. Find also its minimum speed.

19. The acceleration of a car t s after starting from rest is $(75 + 10t - t^2)/20$ m s^{-2} until the instant when this expression vanishes. After this instant the speed of the car remains constant. Find (i) the maximum acceleration, (ii) the time taken to attain the greatest speed, and (iii) the greatest speed.

20. A particle is moving in a straight line and its distance, s m from a fixed point in the line after t s is given by

$$s = 12t - 15t^2 + 4t^3.$$

Find (i) the speed and acceleration of the particle after 3 s, and (ii) the distance travelled between the two times when the speed is instantaneously zero.

CHAPTER THREE

FORCE, MOMENTUM, LAWS OF MOTION

3.1. In the last chapter we dealt with motion without considering the cause of it. We have now to consider the cause of motion and changes of motion, and this introduces the idea of force. We recognise forces by the effects they produce, such as the tendency to alter the state of rest or uniform motion of bodies. It is this effect with which we are concerned in Dynamics, and we start from the following definition:

3.2. *Force is any cause which produces or tends to produce a change in the existing state of rest of a body, or of its uniform motion in a straight line.*

We are familiar in everyday life with examples of bodies in motion under the action of forces. A garden roller at rest on the lawn can be moved by pulling at the handle; the application of this force accelerates the roller, and its speed can be changed at will by varying the magnitude of the force. The roller can, of course, be brought to rest again by applying a force opposite to the direction of motion. It is clear that a force has magnitude and direction, and is therefore a *vector* quantity.

Many other examples of the effects of forces suggest themselves. If a football is kicked it begins to move in the direction of the kick; the harder the kick, the greater the immediate speed of the ball. Or again if the ball is merely let fall it drops to the ground and bounces back; what force controls the downward and upward motions? Or if the ball is placed on the ground so as to remain at rest, what forces then act on it?

We note that in all these examples two bodies are involved, i.e. the roller and the person pulling at the handle, the football and the kicker's boot, the ball and the earth. In each case the bodies are acted upon by mutual forces; we say that there is an *action* on one of them and a *reaction* on the other. If we are considering only one of the bodies we say that the force acting

on it is *external* or *impressed*; if we are considering both bodies
we refer to the forces (action and reaction) as *internal* forces.
Usually the bodies are in contact, but in some cases, as with
the ball falling towards the earth or the moon moving around
the earth, they are at a distance.

It is therefore necessary to consider (i) how a body A will
move when left to itself; (ii) how the motion is affected by the
action of an external force; (iii) if this external force is due to
another body B, how the action of B on A is related to the
reaction of A on B.

The answer to these questions is given in Newton's Laws
of Motion, but before enunciating these we require one or two
definitions.

3.3. *The Mass of a body is the quantity of matter in the body.*

It is clear that this definition, used by Newton himself, is
not satisfactory. What do we understand by 'quantity of
matter'? Matter we are all familiar with and we can take it as
a basic concept, not requiring definition, but 'quantity', which
does *not* mean 'volume', is more difficult to appreciate.

However, by the 'quantity of matter' in a body or its 'mass'
is meant a fundamental physical property of the body which we
encounter when we attempt to change the motion of the body,
that is, when we apply a force to it. We shall see later (3.11)
that Newton's fundamental postulates, known as Newton's
Laws of Motion, lead to a method of comparing the masses of
two bodies. In fact, it will be shown that the ratio of their
masses is the same as the ratio of their weights. Thus if
the mass of one is known, which may be taken as the fundamental unit of mass, the mass of any other body may be
found.

The fundamental unit of mass in the old British system,
known as the Imperial Standard *Pound* (1 lb), is of platinum
and in the form of a cylinder of height approximately equal to
its diameter. The SI unit of mass is that of the International
Prototype *Kilogramme*, which is made of platinum–iridium and
is also of simple geometrical form. This replaces the earlier
standard kilogramme, which was defined as the mass of a cubic
decimetre of water at a given temperature and pressure. The
symbol for kilogramme is kg.

It should be noted that mass has magnitude only; it is a *scalar* quantity.

3.4. *The* **Linear Momentum** *of a particle is the product of the mass of the particle and its velocity.*

Often this will be referred to simply as its momentum.

If m is the mass of the particle and v its velocity the (linear) momentum is mv. There is no special name for the unit of momentum; if m is in kg and v in $m\,s^{-1}$ we say that the momentum is mv SI units of momentum or mv kg-ms^{-1}.

It should be noticed that momentum is a vector quantity, it possesses both magnitude and direction, i.e. mv in the direction of v. If v has components v_1 and v_2 parallel to the axes OX and OY the component momenta parallel to these axes are mv_1 and mv_2. Similarly, if there are several particles the total momentum of the particles is the vector sum of the separate momenta. Thus, if we consider a body of finite size as a collection of particles the linear momentum of the body is given by the vector sum of the linear momenta of the separate particles. In the simplest case of a *motion of translation* of the body, that is, *when all the particles of the body are moving in parallel straight lines with equal velocities v*, the linear momentum of the body equals the product of the total mass of the body and its velocity v.

In general, of course, the motion of a body is not one of translation; there is often a motion of rotation superposed. In this case another quantity, known as the *angular momentum*, is used to represent the rotational motion; we shall deal with this later. For the present, if the body can *not* be regarded as a particle we shall assume it is not rotating, so that its momentum will be taken as the product of its mass and its velocity of translation.

3.5. Newton's Laws of Motion may be stated as follows:

1. *Every body continues in a state of rest or of uniform motion in a straight line, except in so far as it be compelled to change that state by external impressed forces.*

2. *Change of momentum per unit time is proportional to the impressed force, and takes place in the direction of the straight line in which the force acts.*

3. *To every action there is always an equal and opposite reaction; or the mutual actions of any two bodies are always equal and oppositely directed.*

For the first two of these laws we owe much to Galileo, and several of Newton's contemporaries, particularly Huyghens, contributed to their development, but Newton was the first to put them into formal shape in his *Principia*, published in 1686. His own contributions were outstanding.

No strict proof of these laws, experimental or otherwise, can be given.

They are the basic postulates or assumptions on which the science of Newtonian Dynamics is based, and like other scientific laws, they are justified only in so far as they lead to results in agreement with observation.

Of course, common experience confirms their truth in a general way, but the stricter test of careful experiment and observation must be applied.

For example, assuming the laws to be true, the motions of the moon and the planets can be calculated and then compared with observation. The positions of planets, the time of eclipses, etc., are worked out and published in the Nautical Almanac several years beforehand. The predicted places and times are found to agree with observations remarkably well, and thus provide excellent confirmation of these fundamental laws.

3.6. In many of these astronomical calculations another law enunciated by Newton is assumed. This is called *Newton's Law of Gravitation*, and can be stated as follows:

Every particle of matter attracts every other particle of matter with a force which varies directly as the product of the masses of the particles and inversely as the square of the distance between them.

Thus the gravitational force F acting between two particles of masses m_1 and m_2 at a distance r apart is given by

$$F = Gm_1m_2/r^2,$$

where G is a constant, known as the *Constant of Gravitation*. G is found experimentally to be $6 \cdot 670 \times 10^{-11}$ in SI units.

Numerous experiments have been made to verify this law directly, but the chief argument for its truth is again the agreement with observation of the various calculations based on it.

It is of interest to note that certain astronomical observations which could not be accounted for by Newton's laws, including the law of gravitation, have received an explanation on the *Theory of Relativity* first put forward by Einstein in 1905. From this a new mechanics, starting from postulates quite different from Newton's, has been built up. The mathematical expression of the laws of motion in this Relativity Mechanics only differ appreciably from the corresponding expressions in Newtonian Mechanics when the velocity of the particle is very large, that is, comparable with the velocity of light;* for ordinary velocities such as we commonly have to deal with the two formulae agree closely, and the Newtonian system of Dynamics, as we shall now develop it, is adequate. That this is so is clear from the progress of physics in the two centuries between Newton and Einstein.

Similarly, Newton's Law of Gravitation is a good enough approximation in most cases.

It should be noted that the force which acts on a body due to the gravitational attraction of the earth is called its *Weight*. This is a vector quantity; it acts vertically downwards.

3.7. The first law of motion

This law is essentially a definition of force. It tells us that force *accelerates* a body, and that only if there is no resultant force acting on the body will it continue to move with uniform velocity, that is, with uniform speed in a straight line.

This notion of force as held today is due to Galileo; it is not by any means self-evident, otherwise we should not have had to wait for its formulation until the seventeenth century, some two thousand years after the heyday of Greek science.

Returning to the example of the garden roller mentioned in 3.2, let us consider what happens when we cease to pull at the handle. If the lawn is level the roller, of course, slows down and ultimately stops. The rate at which it slows down depends upon various factors, for instance, on how well lubricated the roller is and how soft or wet the lawn is, but in any case the roller slows down as the result of certain frictional forces acting at the axle and at the surface of contact with the lawn. These forces are always present while the roller is in motion, so that

* The velocity of light *in vacuo* is $2 \cdot 997\ 925 \times 10^8$ ms^{-1}.

the force applied to the handle, *less* these frictional forces, is the force effectively moving the roller forward. The acceleration or retardation of the roller can be changed at will by altering the force applied, and when the force applied just balances the frictional forces the roller will continue to move with uniform speed. This helps us to appreciate why it is easier to keep a roller moving with uniform velocity than to start it, which involves giving the roller an acceleration.

Similarly, if a body is at rest on a horizontal table the resultant force on it must be zero, that is, its weight vertically downwards must be balanced by the thrust of the table on it exerted over the surface of contact.

This first law is really a special case of the second law, as we shall now examine.

3.8. The second law of motion

The second law enables us to define units of force and establish the fundamental equation of dynamics. Let a force whose measure is F acting on a mass m produce an acceleration a in the mass.

Then, by the second law,

$$F = k \text{ (rate of change of momentum)}$$

where k is some constant.

$$\therefore \quad F = k \text{ (rate of change of } mv)$$
$$= km \times \text{rate of change of } v \text{ (assuming } m \text{ is constant)}$$
$$= kma.$$

$$\therefore \quad F = kma, \text{ where } k \text{ is some constant.}$$

It is convenient to choose our unit of force so that k is equal to unity, i.e. $F = 1$ when $m = 1$ and $a = 1$, and if we do this our unit of force will be as follows:

The unit of force is that force which, acting on unit mass, generates in it unit acceleration.

The fundamental equation then becomes

$$F = ma.$$

We note that when $F = 0$, $a = 0$ as stated in the first law.

Further $F = ma$ is really a vector equation, i.e. the acceleration **a** is in the same direction as **F**, as stated in the second part of the second law (cf. 3.12). It should therefore be written

$$\mathbf{F} = m\mathbf{a}.$$

3.9. When the unit of mass was the pound, and the associated units of length and time the foot and second, the unit force was called a *Poundal* (abbreviated to pdl).

Similarly if the unit of mass is the gram, and the units of length and time are the centimetre and second, the unit force is called *a Dyne*.

In the SI system of units with the metre as the unit of length, the kilogramme as the unit of mass and the second the unit of time, the unit of force is known as the *Newton*.

Thus the newton (symbol N) *is that force which acting on a mass of* 1 *kg produces an acceleration of* 1 ms^{-2}.

$$F \text{ (newtons)} = m(\text{kg}) \, a \, (\text{m s}^{-2}).$$

3.10. The unit of force formerly used by engineers was the *Pound-weight* (lb-wt.), i.e. the force with which the earth attracts a pound of matter. This unit is not constant, but has different values at different parts of the earth's surface.

It is known that bodies fall to the earth with an acceleration denoted by g (cf. 2.9). This has different values in different places, but in this country the value of g is about 9·8 in metre-second units.

Since the weight of 1 kilogramme produces an acceleration of 9·8 ms^{-2}, the weight of 1 kg must equal 9·8 N. Alternatively, the newton is equal to the weight of 0·102 kg.*

3.11. We have pointed out earlier (2.9) that it is found by experiment that, at the same place, bodies of different masses fall in a vacuum with the same acceleration g.

Hence, if W_1 and W_2 be the weights of masses m_1 and m_2 at the same place, using $F = ma$ we get

$$W_1 = m_1 g$$

and

$$W_2 = m_2 g.$$

$$\therefore \qquad W_1/W_2 = m_1/m_2,$$

i.e. the weights of bodies at the same place are proportional to their masses.

* As someone has said, about the weight of a standard apple.

This enables us, as Newton showed, to compare masses by comparing their weights with an ordinary balance (see 3.3). If we take the same set of standard masses or weights to different places the mass of any given body will be found to have the same value at all these places.

On the other hand, a spring balance measures the strength of the earth's attraction on a body, i.e. its weight, and such a balance will give different readings in different places with the same body attached to it.

Thus mass is a fundamental constant of the body, the same at all places, whereas the weight of the body varies from place to place.

3.12. The second part of the second law implies the principle of the *Physical Independence of Forces*. The change of momentum produced by any force takes place in the direction of the straight line which the force acts. If several forces act on a particle each will produce its own change of momentum quite independently of the others; the *resultant* change of momentum will be the resultant of the separate changes produced by the individual forces.

For example, if two forces $\mathbf{F}_1$ and $\mathbf{F}_2$ act on a body of mass m they will produce acceleration $\mathbf{a}_1$ and $\mathbf{a}_2$ given by the equations

$$\mathbf{F}_1 = m\mathbf{a}_1$$

and

$$\mathbf{F}_2 = m\mathbf{a}_2.$$

Adding $\mathbf{F}_1 + \mathbf{F}_2 = m(\mathbf{a}_1 + \mathbf{a}_2)$, that is, $\mathbf{F} = m\mathbf{a}$, where $\mathbf{F}$ is the resultant of the forces $\mathbf{F}_1$ and $\mathbf{F}_2$, and $\mathbf{a}$ is the resultant of the accelerations $\mathbf{a}_1$ and $\mathbf{a}_2$.

It is clear that $\mathbf{a}$ must be in the same direction as $\mathbf{F}$. This can be shown geometrically as follows:

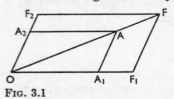

FIG. 3.1

Draw OA_1 and OA_2 to represent $\mathbf{a}_1$ and $\mathbf{a}_2$ respectively (Fig. 3.1). Then the diagonal OA of the parallelogram $OA_1\,AA_2$

represents **a**. Suppose F_1 is the point in OA_1 or OA_1 produced such that $OF_1 = m(OA_1)$; then OF_1 represents $m\mathbf{a}_1$, that is, $\mathbf{F}_1$. Similarly, if F_2 is the point in OA_2 or OA_2 produced such that $OF_2 = m(OA_2)$, then OF_2 represents $m\mathbf{a}_2$, that is, $\mathbf{F}_2$. If the parallelogram OF_1FF_2 be completed and the diagonal OF drawn, then OF represents completely $m\mathbf{a}_1+m\mathbf{a}_2$, that is, $\mathbf{F}_1+\mathbf{F}_2$ or $\mathbf{F}$.

But from the geometry of similar triangles, we can show that the diagonals OA and OF must lie in the same straight line and that OF equals $m(OA)$, that is $\mathbf{OF} = m\mathbf{OA}$ or $\mathbf{F} = m\mathbf{a}$.

We have really shown here, on the basis of Newton's second law, that since accelerations are compounded by vector addition, so are forces. This result is often stated as the *Parallelogram of Forces*, which may be expressed as follows:

If two forces represented in magnitude and direction by two straight lines OA, OB *act on a particle placed at* O, *their resultant is represented in magnitude and direction by the diagonal* OC *of the parallelogram* OACB.

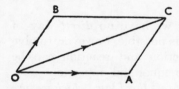

FIG. 3.2

This is the fundamental theorem of Statics (see 10.5), which, we note, has here been derived from Newton's laws of motion. It was, in fact, first clearly formulated in this manner by Newton himself.

3.13. The third law of motion

This law asserts that if two bodies B and C act on each other, the action of B on C is equal and opposite to the reaction of C on B.

Thus if a weight B is placed on a horizontal table C the weight exerts a force *downwards* on the table, which we will denote (Fig. 3.3) by A, *the action of* B *on* C. Similarly, the weight B experiences a force *upwards* due to the table C, which we will denote (Fig. 3.3) by R, *the reaction of* C *on* B.

Newton's third law states that $A = R$.

We note that the only other force acting on B is its weight W vertically downwards. The other forces acting on the table C are not specified, but there will certainly be vertical forces acting upwards on the legs where they were in contact with the floor. (If two bodies are involved it is always wise to use two figures, indicating the forces acting on each body separately.)

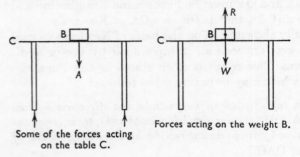

Some of the forces acting on the table C.

Forces acting on the weight B.

FIG. 3.3

In this as in most other cases we have no *direct* way of proving that A and R are equal. It is possible, however, to give a hydrostatical example where action and reaction can be directly measured and shown to be equal and opposite.

For the present we emphasise that this third law, which we owe to the genius of Newton, is justified in that the results based on it agree with observation.

An interesting example of action and reaction is provided by the motion of the moon about the earth. The action of the earth on the moon is a gravitational pull which is responsible for the moon moving about the earth in an approximately circular path; the reaction of the moon on the earth is an equal and opposite gravitational pull which is responsible for producing tides in the oceans. Another example of action and reaction is the jet-propelled aeroplane. Air drawn in is compressed and heated, and ejected through a nozzle. This backward jet produces an equal and opposite reaction on the aeroplane, which is thus propelled forwards.

We might note here that we shall deduce later, on the basis of Newton's third law, a very important principle in dynamics known as the *Principle of Linear Momentum*. It may be stated:

In any system of mutually attracting or impinging particles the linear momentum in any fixed direction remains unaltered unless there is an external force acting in that direction.

This principle will be used in dealing with impulsive forces in the next chapter.

3.14. In the equation $F = ma$, the force F and consequently the acceleration a may be either constant or variable.

For the present we shall consider cases where they are constant, and where the motion takes place in a straight line.

3.15. Friction

In many problems it is assumed that the surface on which the body is resting is *smooth*, that is, there is no force between the surface and the body tending to prevent motion along the surface. The only force acting on the body due to its contact with the surface is normal to the surface. It is called the *normal reaction*. This is, of course, an ideal case; in all actual cases when a body is moved over a surface a force known as *friction* is called into play which tends to prevent the body moving. It is found by experiment that, when one body is moved over another in contact with it, the force of friction tending to prevent motion bears a constant ratio to the normal reaction between the two surfaces, the value of this ratio depending only on the nature of the surfaces in contact. This constant ratio is called the *coefficient of dynamical friction* for the given surfaces. If R is the normal reaction between the surfaces, F the force of friction,

$$F/R = \mu \text{ or } F = \mu R$$

where μ is the coefficient of dynamical friction.

This result is true whatever the area of the surface in contact. We shall apply it to a particle.

If a body or a particle is moving on a horizontal surface (Fig. 3.4), and not acted on by any other force inclined to the horizontal the normal reaction

$$R = mg$$

and then $$F = \mu mg.$$

If a particle is moving on an inclined plane of slope α, and not acted on by other forces except in directions parallel to the plane, the reaction between the plane and the particle is

$$mg \cos \alpha$$

and then $F = \mu mg \cos \alpha.$

If there is any force, such as the tension of a string, tending to pull the particle away from the surface, this reduces the normal reaction and consequently the friction. Similarly the friction is increased if the particle is acted upon by forces tending to push it into the surface.

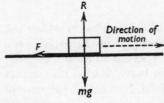

FIG. 3.4

3.16. EXAMPLE (i)

What force will give a mass of 9 kg a velocity of 25 km h⁻¹ in 1 min?

We must find the acceleration necessary to produce this velocity of 25 000/3600 ms⁻¹ in 60 s.

Using $v = u + at$

$$\frac{25\ 000}{3600} = 60a$$

∴ $a = \frac{25}{216}$ ms⁻².

The mass acted on is 9 kg, and the force required to produce the acceleration a is therefore

$$F = 9 \times \frac{25}{216} \text{ N}$$

$$= \frac{25}{24} \text{ N}.$$

EXAMPLE (ii)

An engine and train weigh 203 Mg, and the engine can exert a pull equal to the weight of 3·77 Mg. The resistance to the motion of the train is ¹⁄₁₀₀ of its weight, and the brake power equals one-fifth of its weight.

The train starts from rest and moves uniformly till it acquires a velocity of 40 kmh⁻¹; steam is then shut off and the brakes are put hard on. Find the whole distance the train will have run before it comes to rest and the whole time taken.

While the engine is pulling, the tractive force is $3·77 \times 1000$ g N, since 1 Mg = 1000 kg, and the resistance is 203×10 g N.

∴ the resultant accelerating force is $(3770-2030)$g N = 1740 g N.

∴   the acceleration $= \dfrac{1740 \times 9·8}{203 \times 1000}$ ms⁻²

$$= 0·084 \text{ ms}^{-2}.$$

Since $40 \text{ kmh}^{-1} = \dfrac{40\,000}{3600}$ ms⁻¹, we have to find how far the train goes in acquiring a velocity of $\dfrac{100}{9}$ ms⁻¹ with an acceleration of $0·084$ ms⁻².

Using $v^2 = u^2 + 2as$ we get

$$\left(\frac{100}{9}\right)^2 = 0·168 \, s$$

∴ $s = 10^4/81 \times 0·168$

$$= 734·7 \text{ m}.$$

To find the time taken we use $v = u + at$ and get

$$\frac{100}{9} = 0·084 \, t$$

∴ $t = 132·3$ s.

The retarding force is $\left(\dfrac{1}{100} + \dfrac{1}{5}\right)$ of the weight of the train, and therefore the retardation is $0·21 \times 9·8$ ms⁻².

To find the distance s travelled in losing the velocity of $\dfrac{100}{9}$ ms⁻¹, we have

$$0 = \left(\frac{100}{9}\right)^2 - 2 \times 0·21 \times 9·8 \, s$$

$$s = 10^4/81 \times 0·42 \times 9·8$$

$$= 30·0 \text{ m}.$$

To find the time to come to rest we have

$$0 = \frac{100}{9} - 0\cdot21 \times 9\cdot8\, t$$

$$t = \frac{100}{9 \times 0\cdot21 \times 9\cdot8} = 5\cdot4 \text{ s.}$$

The whole distance run $= 764\cdot7$ m.
The whole time $= 137\cdot7$ s.

Note. When a train is running with uniform velocity the resultant force acting on it is zero, i.e. the pull of the engine must be just equal to the resistances. If the pull is greater than the resistances the train will accelerate.

If a body slides down an incline with uniform velocity the component of its weight down the incline must be equal to the resistance.

EXAMPLE (iii)

A train travelling uniformly on the level at the rate of 48 *km h⁻¹ begins an ascent of* 1 *in* 75. *The tractive force that the engine exerts during the ascent is the same as that exerted on the level. How far up the incline will the train go before coming to rest? Assume that the resistance due to friction, etc., is the same on the incline as on the level.*

Since the train is moving uniformly on the level, the pull of the engine is equal to the resistances.

On coming to the incline these forces still balance, but there is now the component of the weight of the train down the slope retarding it.

If m kg is the mass of the train the component of weight down the slope is $mg/75$ N, and as this is the resultant force acting parallel to the slope the retardation will be $g/75$ m s⁻². The initial velocity is 48 km h⁻¹, that is, 48 000/3 600 m s⁻¹ = 40/3 m s⁻¹.

The distance s (in metres) travelled before losing this velocity is given by

$$0 = \left(\frac{40}{3}\right)^2 - \frac{2 \times 9\cdot8}{75} s$$

$$\therefore \qquad s = \frac{1600 \times 75}{9 \times 19\cdot6} = 680.$$

$\therefore \qquad$ Distance travelled $= 0\cdot68$ km.

EXAMPLE (iv)

An engine of mass 110 *Mg is coupled to and pulls a carriage of mass* 30 *Mg; the resistance to the motion of the engine is* $\frac{1}{100}$ *of its weight;*

the resistance to the motion of the carriage is $\frac{1}{150}$ of its weight. Find the tension in the coupling if the whole tractive force exerted by the engine is equal to the weight of 3 Mg.

We must first find the acceleration produced in the engine and carriage.

The total resistance	$= \left(\dfrac{110}{100}+\dfrac{30}{150}\right) 10^3 \times 9\cdot 8$ N
	$= 1300 \times 9\cdot 8$ N.
The accelerating force	$= (3000 - 1300)\, 9\cdot 8$ N
	$= 1700 \times 9\cdot 8$ N.
The total mass	$= 140 \times 10^3$ kg
$\therefore$ the acceleration	$= \dfrac{1700 \times 9\cdot 8}{140\ 000}$ m s^{-2}
	$= 0\cdot 119$ m s^{-2}.

$\therefore$ The accelerating force on the carriage is

$$30 \times 10^3 \times 0\cdot 119 \text{ N}$$
$$= 3570 \text{ N}.$$

But the accelerating force on the carriage = tension in coupling —resistance. The resistance to the carriage

$$= \frac{30}{150} \times 10^3 \times 9\cdot 8 \text{ N} = 1960 \text{ N}$$

$\therefore$ the tension in the coupling

$$= (3570 + 1960) \text{ N} = 5530 \text{ N}.$$

EXAMPLE (v)

A body, of mass m kg, is placed on a horizontal plane which is moving with an upward vertical acceleration a m s^{-2}. Find the reaction between the body and the plane.

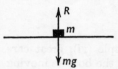

FIG. 3.5

Let R N be the reaction between the body and the plane. Since the body is moving upwards with an acceleration, it is evident that R is greater than the weight mg.

The resultant upward force acting on the body is $(R-mg)$ N.

$$\therefore \qquad R-mg = ma$$
$$\therefore \qquad R = m(g+a).$$

If the plane be moving downwards with acceleration a the weight mg is now greater than R. The resultant downward force acting on m is $(mg-R)$ N, and

$$mg-R = ma$$
$$\therefore \qquad R = m(g-a).$$

If in the latter case $a = g$, then $R = 0$, i.e. there is no reaction between the body and the plane.

EXAMPLE (vi)

A rifle bullet passes through two planks in succession, and the average resistance of the second plank is 50 per cent more than that of the first. The initial velocity is 800 ms^{-1}, and the bullet loses 160 ms^{-1} in passing through each plank. Show that the thickness of the planks are as 27 : 14.   (I.E.)

Since the resistance of the second plank is 50 per cent more than that of the first, it will produce $1\frac{1}{2}$ times the retardation produced by the first.

Let a ms^{-2} be the retardation produced by the first, then $\frac{3}{2}a$ is the retardation produced by the second.

Let s_1, s_2 m be their thicknesses, then we have

$$640^2 = 800^2 - 2as_1$$
and
$$480^2 = 640^2 - 3as_2$$
$$\therefore \qquad 2as_1 = 1440 \times 160$$
and
$$3as_2 = 1120 \times 160$$
$$\therefore \qquad \frac{2s_1}{3s_2} = \frac{144}{112} = \frac{9}{7}$$
$$\therefore \qquad \frac{s_1}{s_2} = \frac{27}{14}.$$

Note. In problems similar to that in Example (vi), great care must be taken to distinguish the cases (*a*) when the body is moving horizontally, and (*b*) vertically.

In (*a*) if u is the initial velocity, m the mass, s the distance penetrated, R the average resistance, and a the retardation

$$0 = u^2 - 2as, \text{ or } a = u^2/2s.$$

Hence, $R = ma = mu^2/2s$.

In (b) the first equation is the same,

$$0 = u^2 - 2as,$$

but now the weight of the body mg is acting vertically downwards, so that the *resultant retarding force* is not R but $R - mg$, if the body is moving downwards, and hence

$$R - mg = ma.$$

The resistance is greater by the weight of the body than in the case where the motion is horizontal.

EXAMPLES 3.1

1. Find the acceleration produced when: (i) a force of 6 N acts on a mass of 12 kg; (ii) a force of 6 N acts on a mass of 12 g.

2. What force acting on a mass of 12 kg will generate in it a velocity of 15 km h^{-1} in 5 min.

3. A body of mass 100 kg is acted on by a force of 7 N. How long will it take to acquire a velocity of 15 km h^{-1}?

4. A ship of 10 000 Mg slows, with engines stopped, from 12 km h^{-1} to 10 km h^{-1} in a distance of 90 m; assuming the resistance to be uniform, calculate its value in newtons.

5. A truck is found to travel with uniform speed down a slope which falls 1 m vertically for every 112 m length of the slope. If the truck starts from the bottom of the slope with a speed of 18 km h^{-1}, how far up will it travel before coming to rest? (I.A.)

6. Find in newton per kilogramme the force exerted by the brakes of a train travelling at 60 km h^{-1} which will bring it to rest in half a km, and find the time during which the brakes act. (H.C.)

7. A force equal to the weight of 10 g acts on a mass of 218 g for 5 s. Find the velocity generated and the distance moved in this time.

8. Find the magnitude of the force which, acting on a mass of 1 kg for 5 s, causes the mass to move through 10 m from rest in that time.

9. The resistance to the motion of a train due to friction, etc., is equal to $\frac{1}{160}$ of the weight of the train. If the train is travelling on a level road at 72 km h^{-1} and comes to the foot of an incline of 1 in 150 and steam is then turned off, how far will the train go up the incline before it comes to rest? (H.S.D.)

10. A train travelling uniformly on the level at the rate of 80 km h^{-1} begins an ascent of 1 in 75. The tractive force that the engine exerts during the ascent is constant and equal to $\frac{1}{100}$ of the weight of the train, the resistance (due to friction, etc.) is constant, and equal to $\frac{1}{150}$ of the weight of the whole train. Show that the train will come to a standstill after climbing for 2·5 km.

11. A body of mass 25 g is observed to travel in a straight line through 369, 615, and 861 cm in successive seconds. Prove that this is consistent with a constant force acting on the body. What is the value of this force?

12. Some trucks, starting from rest on an incline of 1 in 140, acquired a speed of 25 km h^{-1} in 10 min. Calculate the resistance to the motion of the trucks in N per kg mass of the trucks.   (I.E.)

13. A force equal to the weight of 1 Mg acts for 3 s on a mass of 5 Mg. Find the velocity produced and the space passed over.

14. A mass of 10 kg rests on a horizontal plane which is made to ascend: (i) with a constant velocity of 5 ms^{-1}; (ii) with a constant acceleration of 5 ms^{-2}; find in each case the reaction of the plane.

15. A man, of mass 70 kg, stands on the floor of a lift. Find the reaction of the floor when the lift is (i) ascending, (ii) descending, with a uniform acceleration of 4 ms^{-2}.

16. A scale pan, on which rests a mass of 50 g, is drawn upwards with a constant acceleration, and the reaction between the mass and the pan is found to be 0·5 N; find the acceleration of the scale pan.

17. A body whose true weight was 13 N appeared to weigh 12 N when weighed by means of a spring balance in a moving lift. What was the acceleration of the lift at the instant of weighing?   (I.A.)

18. A train of mass 160 Mg starts from a station, the engine exerting a tractive force of $\frac{1}{64}$ of the weight of the train in excess of the resistances until a speed of 60 km h^{-1} is attained. This speed continues constant until the brakes, causing a retardation of 0·75 ms^{-2}, bring the train to rest 8 km away. Find the time taken: (i) during acceleration; (ii) during retardation; (iii) altogether.

19. The pull exerted by an engine is $\frac{1}{80}$ of the weight of the whole train, and the maximum brake force which can be exerted is $\frac{1}{30}$ of the weight of the train. Find the time in which the train travels from rest to rest up a slope of 1 in 240 and 4·8 km long, the brakes being applied when steam is shut off.   (H.S.C.)

20. In a lift, accelerated upwards at a certain rate, a spring balance indicates a weight to have a mass of 10 kg. When the lift is accelerated downwards at twice the rate the mass appears to be 7 kg. Find the actual mass, and the upward acceleration of the lift.

21. A vertical shield is made of two plates of wood and iron respectively, the iron being 2 cm, and the wood 4 cm thick. A bullet fired horizontally goes through the iron first and then penetrates 2 cm into the wood. A similar bullet fired with the same velocity from the opposite direction goes through the wood first and then penetrates 1 cm into the iron. Compare the average resistance exerted by the iron and the wood. (I.E.)

22. A 100-g bullet, travelling at 150 m s⁻¹, will penetrate 8 cm into a fixed block of wood. Find the velocity with which it would emerge, if fired through a fixed board 4 cm thick, the resistance being supposed uniform and to have the same value in each case. (H.S.D.)

23. A bullet of mass 30 g is fired into a fixed block of wood with a velocity of 294 m s⁻¹, and is brought to rest in $\frac{1}{150}$ s. Find the resistance exerted by the wood, supposing it to be uniform. (H.C.)

3.17. Motion of connected particles

In the last paragraph we considered the motion of a single mass. We shall now consider some simple cases of the motion of two masses connected by a light inextensible string. In such cases we apply the equation $F = ma$ to each of the masses, as in the following examples.

We note that a string connecting two masses in motion is in a state of tension, and that the string exerts forces on the masses equal to the tensions at its ends. If the string is light (that is, if its weight is neglected) the tension is the same throughout its length. On the other hand, if the string is heavy the tension will in general vary from point to point, depending upon the weight per unit length. If the string is extensible the tension will vary with the extension.

Also, if the string passes round a pulley the tension is only the same on the two sides if the pulley is smooth and the string is light; otherwise the tension in the string where it leaves the pulley depends upon the coefficient of friction and the length of string in contact.

For simplicity, we shall usually consider a *light, inextensible* string passing round a *smooth* pulley or peg. In such an ideal case the tension throughout the string will be constant.

EXAMPLE (i)

Two particles of masses m_1 and m_2 kg are connected by a light inextensible string passing over a small smooth fixed pulley. Find the resulting motion of the system and the tension in the string.

The tension is the same throughout the string; let this be T N, the masses m_1 and m_2 being in kg. Suppose m_1 greater than m_2,

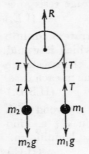

FIG. 3.6

then m_1 will move downwards and m_2 upwards, and, since the string is inextensible, the upward acceleration of m_2 is equal to the downward acceleration of m_1. Let this acceleration be a m s^{-2}.

Now, the forces acting on m_1 are m_1g downwards, and T upwards, ∴ the resultant force on m_1 is $m_1g - T$ downwards.

Hence, using $\qquad\qquad F = ma$

we get $\qquad\qquad m_1g - T = m_1a.$ (i)

The resultant force on m_2 is $T - m_2g$ upwards,

∴ $\qquad\qquad\qquad T - m_2g = m_2a.$ (ii)

We now solve equations (i) and (ii) to find a and T.

Adding, $\qquad\qquad (m_1 - m_2)g = (m_1 + m_2)a$

∴ $\qquad\qquad\qquad a = \dfrac{m_1 - m_2}{m_1 + m_2}g.$

From (i)
$$T = m_1(g - a)$$
$$= m_1\left(1 - \frac{m_1 - m_2}{m_1 + m_2}\right)g$$
$$= \frac{2m_1m_2}{m_1 + m_2}g.$$

If the parts of the string not in contact with the pulley hang vertically the force R on the pulley

$$= 2T = \frac{4m_1m_2}{m_1+m_2}g.$$

EXAMPLE (ii)

A mass m_2 kg is placed on a smooth horizontal table, and connected by a light inextensible string passing over a small smooth pulley at the edge to a mass m_1 kg hanging freely. Find the resulting motion and the tension in the string.

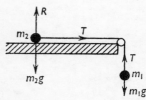

FIG. 3.7

The mass m_1 will move downwards and m_2 along the table. Since the string is inextensible, the accelerations of m_1 and m_2 are equal; let this acceleration be a m s^{-2}. Let T N be the tension in the string. The forces acting on m_1 are m_1g downwards and T upwards,

$\therefore$ the resultant force on m_1 is $m_1g - T$.

$\therefore$ using $F = ma$,

$$m_1g - T = m_1a. \tag{i}$$

Since m_2 is resting on a smooth horizontal surface, its weight has no effect as far as motion along the surface is concerned. The weight is balanced by the reaction R of the plane ($R = m_2g$). The resultant force tending to produce motion horizontally is therefore the tension T. Hence, for m_2, we have

$$T = m_2a. \tag{ii}$$

Adding (i) and (ii), $m_1g = (m_1 + m_2)a$

$\therefore$

$$a = \frac{m_1}{m_1+m_2}g.$$

Substituting in (ii)

$$T = \frac{m_1m_2}{m_1+m_2}g.$$

In this case the force on the pulley, P N, is the resultant of two equal forces T N at right angles,

$$\therefore \qquad P = \sqrt{(T^2+T^2)} = T\sqrt{2}$$
$$= \frac{\sqrt{2}m_1 m_2}{m_1+m_2}g.$$

EXAMPLE (iii)

A particle of mass m_2 kg rests on the surface of a smooth plane inclined at an angle α to the horizontal, and is connected by a light inextensible string, passing over a small smooth pulley at the top of the plane, to a mass m_1 kg hanging freely. Find the resulting motion and the tension in the string.

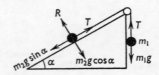

FIG. 3.8

The tension of the string is the same throughout; let this be T N. The accelerations of the masses are the same; let this be a m s^{-2}. The forces acting on m_1 are its weight $m_1 g$ vertically downwards and T vertically upwards. If m_1 moves downwards

$$m_1 g - T = m_1 a \qquad \text{(i)}$$

The forces acting on m_2 *parallel to the surface of the plane* are $m_2 g \sin \alpha$ down the plane and T up the plane; the resultant force tending to produce motion up the plane is therefore $T - m_2 g \sin \alpha$.

$$\therefore \qquad T - m_2 g \sin \alpha = m_2 a \qquad \text{(ii)}$$

Also since m_2 does not move perpendicular to the plane,

$$R - m_2 g \cos \alpha = 0.$$

Adding (i) and (ii) $g(m_1 - m_2 \sin \alpha) = (m_1 + m_2)a$

$$\therefore \qquad a = \frac{m_1 - m_2 \sin \alpha}{m_1 + m_2}g.$$

We note that $a > 0$, that is, m_1 moves downwards, if $m_1 > m_2 \sin \alpha$. T is obtained by substituting for a in (i).

Note. In working numerical examples similar to those above, the results there given must not be used as formulae for substituting the numerical values. Each question should be worked as shown in

Examples (i) to (iii), using the numbers given in the question instead of letters.

EXAMPLE (iv)

A particle slides down a rough inclined plane of inclination α. If μ be the coefficient of friction, find the motion.

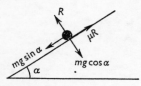

FIG. 3.9

Let m be the mass of the particle, and R the normal reaction of the plane; then the friction is μR.

Now as there is no motion perpendicular to the surface of the plane, the reaction of the plane must equal the component of the weight of the particle perpendicular to the plane,

∴ $$R = mg \cos \alpha.$$

The resultant force acting down the plane is

$$mg \sin \alpha - \mu R = mg \sin \alpha - \mu mg \cos \alpha.$$

The acceleration down the plane is

$$\frac{mg \sin \alpha - \mu mg \cos \alpha}{m} = g(\sin \alpha - \mu \cos \alpha)$$

which is positive, and hence $\sin \alpha > \mu \cos \alpha$, or $\tan \alpha > \mu$.

If $\sin \alpha < \mu \cos \alpha$, that is, $\tan \alpha < \mu$, there will be no acceleration down the plane, and as the particle obviously cannot move up the plane, this means that it will remain at rest. It will be noted that in this case the value of the frictional force must be $mg \sin \alpha$, which is less than when the body is in motion.

If the particle is projected up the plane the resultant retarding force down the plane is

$$mg \sin \alpha + \mu mg \cos \alpha.$$

EXAMPLE (v)

Two particles of masses m_1 and m_2 rest on the rough faces of a double inclined plane and are connected by a light inextensible string passing over a small smooth pulley at the vertex of the plane. If the faces of the plane are equally rough, find the resulting motion.

Let the inclinations of the faces on which m_1 and m_2 rest be α and β respectively, and suppose that m_1 moves downwards.

Let T be the tension in the string.

Since the particles do not move perpendicular to the faces, the reactions of the faces are equal to the components of the weights perpendicular to the faces, i.e. $m_1 g \cos \alpha$ for m_1, and $m_2 g \cos \beta$ for m_2.

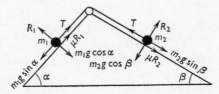

FIG. 3.10

Since m_1 moves *down*, the friction on it acts *up* the plane. Hence the total downward force on m_1 is

$$m_1 g \sin \alpha - T - \mu m_1 g \cos \alpha$$

and the total upward force on m_2 is

$$T - m_2 g \sin \beta - \mu m_2 g \cos \beta.$$

Hence, if a is the common acceleration,

$$m_1 g \sin \alpha - T - \mu m_1 g \cos \alpha = m_1 a \qquad \text{(i)}$$
$$T - m_2 g \sin \beta - \mu m_2 g \cos \beta = m_2 a. \qquad \text{(ii)}$$

Adding (i) and (ii),

$$a(m_1 + m_2) = g(m_1 \sin \alpha - m_2 \sin \beta - \mu m_1 \cos \alpha - \mu m_2 \cos \beta)$$

giving a.

T is obtained by substituting for a in either (i) or (ii).

EXAMPLE (vi)

Two masses 10 kg and 3 kg respectively are connected by a fine string which passes over a smooth pulley fixed at the head of a smooth inclined plane 5 m long and 1 m high. The heavier particle is on the plane and the lighter particle just hangs over the pulley, the string being 5 m long. Find the acceleration of the masses and the tension of the string. How long will it be after the 3 kg mass reaches the ground before the string is again taut?   (I.A.)

Let T N be the tension of the string, a ms^{-2} the common acceleration.

The resultant force downwards in N acting on the 3 kg mass is

$$3g - T$$

and the resultant force in N on the 10 kg mass acting up the plane is

$$T - 10 \times \tfrac{1}{5}g = T - 2g.$$

∴ The equations of motion are

$$3g - T = 3a$$

and

$$T - 2g = 10a.$$

Adding

$$13a = g$$

∴

$$a = g/13.$$

Hence,

$$T = 2g + 10a = 2g + \tfrac{10}{13}g = \tfrac{36}{13}g.$$

When the 3 kg mass reaches the ground the masses will have moved 1 m from rest with acceleration $g/13 = \dfrac{9 \cdot 8}{13} \ \text{m s}^{-2}$.

∴ their common velocity $v \ \text{m s}^{-1}$ is given by

$$v^2 = 2 \times \frac{9 \cdot 8}{13} \times 1 = \frac{19 \cdot 6}{13}$$

∴

$$v = 1 \cdot 22.$$

Now the 3 kg mass is stopped by the ground, the string becomes slack and the 10 kg mass moves on with velocity v, and subject to a retardation $g/5 = 9 \cdot 8/5 \ \text{m s}^{-2}$.

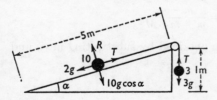

Fig. 3.11

The time t s taken to go up the plane and return to the point from which it began to move freely is given by

$$0 = 1 \cdot 22t - \tfrac{1}{2}(1 \cdot 96t^2)$$

∴

$$t = \frac{1 \cdot 22}{0 \cdot 98}$$

$$= 1 \cdot 25.$$

After this interval the string again becomes taut.

EXAMPLE (vii)

*A mass of M kg rests on a smooth horizontal table and is attached by
two inelastic strings to masses m, m' kg (m'>m), which hang over
smooth pulleys at opposite edges of the table. Find the acceleration of the
system and the tension in the strings.*

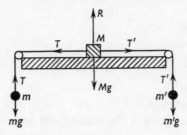

FIG. 3.12

If T N be the tension in the string connecting m and M, T' N
that in the other string, and a m s^{-2} is the acceleration, we have

for m',	$m'g - T' = m'a$	(i)
for m,	$T - mg = ma$	(ii)
for M,	$T' - T = Ma.$	(iii)

Adding the three equations

$$(m'-m)g = (m'+m+M)a$$

$$\therefore \qquad a = \frac{m'-m}{m'+m+M}g.$$

The values of T' and T are obtained by substituting in (i) and
(ii).

EXAMPLES 3.2

1. Two particles, of masses 6 and 10 kg, are connected by a light
   string passing over a smooth pulley. Find: (i) their common
   acceleration; (ii) the tension in the string; (iii) the force on the
   pulley.

2. Two particles, of masses 5 and 7 kg, are connected by a light
   string passing over a smooth pulley. Find their common acceleration and the tension in the string.

3. Two particles, of masses 7 and 9 g, are connected by a light
   string passing over a smooth pulley. Find their common acceleration and the tension in the string.

4. Two particles, of masses 20 and 30 g, are connected by a fine string passing over a smooth pulley. Find their common acceleration and the tension in the string.

5. A mass of 9 kg resting on a smooth horizontal table is connected by a light string, passing over a smooth pulley at the edge of the table, to a mass of 7 kg hanging freely. Find the common acceleration, the tension in the string, and the force on the pulley.

6. In the last question, if the 7 kg mass starts from the level of the edge, which is 2·1 m above the ground, and the string, which is 4·2 m long, is taut and perpendicular to the edge; find: (i) how long the 7 kg mass takes to reach the ground; (ii) how long after that the 9 kg mass takes to reach the edge of the table.

7. A mass of 5 kg is placed on a smooth horizontal table 1·8 m high at a distance of 5·4 m from the edge and connected by a light string 5·4 m long to a mass of 3 kg on the edge of the table. If the 3 kg mass is pushed gently over the edge, find: (i) how long it takes to reach the ground; (ii) how much longer the 5 kg mass takes to reach the edge.

8. A particle, of mass 5 kg, is placed on a smooth plane whose height is 4 m and length 20 m. The particle is connected by a light string passing over a smooth pulley at the top of the plane to a mass of 3 kg hanging freely. Find the common acceleration and the tension of the string.

9. If, in question 8, the 5 kg mass is initially at the bottom of the slope and the 3 kg mass hanging just over the pulley, find: (i) how long the 3 kg mass takes to reach the ground; (ii) the time that elapses after this happens before the string again becomes taut.

10. Two masses of $\frac{1}{4}$ kg and $7\frac{3}{4}$ kg connected by an inextensible string 1·5 m long, lie on a smooth table 0·75 m high. The string being straight and perpendicular to the edge of the table, the lighter mass is drawn gently just over the edge and released. Find: (i) the time that elapses before the first mass strikes the floor, and (ii) the time that elapses before the second mass reaches the edge of the table.   (I.S.)

11. A mass of 2 kg lies at the bottom of an inclined plane 9 m long and 3 m high. It is attached by a light cord 9 m long, which lies along the line of greatest slope of the plane, to a mass of 1 kg, which hangs just over the top of the plane. The system is allowed to move. Assuming that the hanging mass comes to rest when it reaches the ground, find the distance that the mass of 2 kg will travel before it first comes to rest.   (H.S.D.)

12. A particle of mass 5 kg, resting on a smooth plane of inclination 30°, is attached to a light string which passes over a smooth pulley at the highest point of the plane and carries a hanging weight of mass 2 kg. Calculate the acceleration of each weight, assuming that the whole motion takes place in the vertical plane through the pulley and the line of greatest slope. Find also the tension in the string.   (H.S.D.)

13. A mass of 5 kg rests on a rough horizontal table, and is connected by a light string with a mass of 3 kg hanging freely. If the coefficient of friction between the 5 kg mass and the table is $\frac{1}{3}$, find the resultant acceleration and the tension in the string.

14. A mass of 4 kg rests on a rough horizontal table (coefficient of friction $\frac{1}{2}$), and is connected by a light string with a mass of 3 kg hanging freely. Find the velocity acquired and the distance described by the masses in 7 s.

15. A particle slides down a rough inclined plane, whose inclination to the horizontal is 45°, and whose coefficient of friction is $\frac{3}{4}$; show that the time of descending any distance is twice what it would be if the plane were smooth.

16. Two rough planes, inclined at 30° and 60° to the horizontal and of the same height, are placed back to back; masses of 4 and 12 kg are placed on the faces and connected by a light string passing over a smooth pulley at the top of the planes; if the coefficient of friction is $\frac{1}{2}$, find the resulting acceleration.

17. A rough plane is 15 m long and 9 m high, the coefficient of friction is $\frac{1}{3}$, and a particle slides down the plane from rest at the highest point; find the velocity of the particle on reaching the bottom and the time taken.

18. A light inextensible string, passing over a small smooth fixed pulley, carries at one end a weight of mass 4 kg, and at the other two weights each of mass 3 kg. If the system is allowed to move, find the acceleration with which the mass of 4 kg ascends.

     If one of the 3 kg masses falls off after the 4 kg mass has ascended a distance of $2\frac{1}{2}$ m, how much farther will the 4 kg mass ascend?

19. An engine driver of a train at rest observes a truck moving towards him down an incline of 1 in 60 at a distance of 0·8 km. He immediately starts his train away from the truck at a constant acceleration of 0·15 ms^{-2}. If the truck just catches the train, find its velocity when first observed. Assume that friction opposing the truck's motion is $\frac{1}{160}$ of the weight of the truck.
                                                      (C.S.)

20. On a cable railway a car, of mass $2\frac{1}{2}$ Mg, is drawn up a slope of 1 in 10 from rest with an acceleration of 1 ms^{-2} against a constant frictional resistance of $\frac{1}{100}$ of the weight of the car. Find the tension in the cable. (H.S.C.)

3.18. Attwood's machine

In the simplest form of this machine two equal masses (M) are connected by a light cord passing over a light pulley P, as in Fig. 3.13.

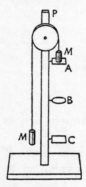

FIG. 3.13

The axis of the pulley is supported horizontally so that it can turn with very little friction.

If the masses are set in motion they will move with a velocity which is very nearly constant for a short time, and by measuring the time taken by one of the masses to describe a given distance the value of this velocity can be obtained.

The machine is used to verify the laws of motion and to obtain a rough value for g. The masses are set in motion by placing a small rider of known mass (m) on one of the large masses which can be released from a platform A, attached to the stand which supports the pulley.

A ring B is fixed to the stand vertically below A, and is of such size that M can pass through it, but the rider m remains on the ring. The masses will then move with uniform velocity and the time taken for the descending mass to go from B to a platform C at a known distance below B is measured by a stop-watch.

The distance from A to B is also known.

Now until the rider is removed the acceleration of the system is

$$\frac{mg}{2M+m}.$$

If AB $= h_1$ the velocity v on reaching the ring is given by

$$v^2 = 2\frac{mg}{2M+m}h_1.$$

If h_2 is the distance BC, and t the time taken for the mass to go from B to C

$$v = \frac{h_2}{t}$$

$$\therefore \qquad \frac{h_2{}^2}{t^2} = \frac{2mgh_1}{2M+m}$$

$$\therefore \qquad g = \frac{h_2{}^2}{2mh_1t^2}(2M+m).$$

3.19. The chief causes of inaccuracy in the experiment are as follows:

(1) The pulley, although light, requires some force to make it rotate. Allowance can be made for this, as explained in Chapter 9.

(2) There is some friction at the axle of the pulley. This can be reduced by supporting the axle of the pulley on the edges of four light wheels called friction wheels, or by attaching a small rider to the mass which carries the rider m. The mass of this extra rider is adjusted until the masses (without m) run uniformly when set in motion.

(3) The string may slip on the pulley, and, as this is not perfectly smooth, friction is introduced.

This cannot be avoided entirely, but can be partly allowed for as in (2) by means of an additional rider.

(4) It is difficult to measure accurately the time taken for the mass M to go from B to C.

The error in measuring the time can be reduced by the device used in what is called the 'ribbon' Attwood's machine.

In this type of machine the string supporting the masses is replaced by a tape. A fine brush is attached to the end of a spring, or vibrator, which is adjusted to make a given number of vibrations per second.

The brush, which is inked, is placed so that it touches the tape where the latter passes over the top of the pulley.

A lever is arranged so that, as it releases the mass with the rider from its platform, the vibrator is set in motion. The brush then traces a wavy line on the tape as it passes over the pulley. The distances between successive portions of the curve so traced are the actual distances moved by the masses, while the time taken to move any distance is known from the period of the vibrator.

3.20. The following examples are of a more difficult nature. If the accelerations of the various parts of the system are not the same it is essential to find what connections there are between them. The principle of the method, i.e. applying the equation $F = ma$ to each part of the system, is the same as before.

EXAMPLE (i)

To one end of a light string passing over a fixed pulley is attached a particle of mass 8 kg and to the other end a light pulley. Over this pulley passes a light string to the ends of which are attached particles of masses 5 and 3 kg respectively. Find the acceleration of the 8 kg mass and the tension in the string attached to it.

(I.S.)

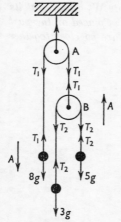

FIG. 3.14

In Fig. 3.14 A is the fixed pulley and B the light pulley.

Suppose the 8 kg mass moves *downwards* with acceleration A $\mathrm{ms^{-2}}$. Then pulley B moves *upwards* with acceleration A $\mathrm{ms^{-2}}$.

The 5 kg mass moves *downwards relative to* B with acceleration a ms^{-2}, say, and the 3 kg mass moves *upwards relative to* B with acceleration a ms^{-2}. Therefore the upward acceleration of these masses relative to the fixed pulley or the support are $(A-a)$ and $(A+a)$ ms^{-2} respectively.

If the tensions in the strings are T_1 and T_2 N, the forces acting on the various bodies are as shown in Fig. 3.14, and hence the equations of motion are as follows:

for 8 kg mass $\qquad\qquad\qquad 8A = 8g - T_1 \qquad\qquad$ (i)

for pulley B $\qquad\qquad\qquad\quad 0 = T_1 - 2T_2 \qquad\qquad$ (ii)

for 5 kg mass $\qquad\qquad 5(A-a) = T_2 - 5g \qquad\qquad$ (iii)

for 3 kg mass $\qquad\qquad 3(A+a) = T_2 - 3g. \qquad\qquad$ (iv)

From these four equations the four unknowns T_1, T_2, A, and a can be found.

Eliminating a from equations (iii) and (iv) we get

$$30A = 8T_2 - 30g.$$

But $\qquad\qquad\qquad 8A = 8g - 2T_2 \qquad\qquad$ from (i) and (ii)

$\therefore \qquad\qquad\qquad 62A = 2g.$

$\therefore \qquad\qquad\qquad A = g/31.$

Also $\qquad\qquad T_1 = 8g - 8A = 7\tfrac{23}{31}g.$

EXAMPLE (ii)

A_1 and A_2 *are two fixed pulleys in the same horizontal line. A light string is placed over* A_1 *and* A_2, *and carries weights* W_1 *and* W_2 *at its free ends. Another pulley* B *carrying a weight* W_3 *is placed on the part of the string between* A_1 *and* A_2. *If* A_1 *and* A_2 *are so close together*

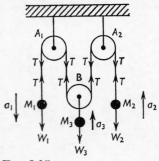

FIG. 3.15

that all the portions of the string not in contact with the pulleys are vertical, prove that when all the weights are in motion the tension in the string is

$$\frac{4}{W_1^{-1} + W_2^{-1} + 4W_3^{-1}}.$$

Prove also that the condition that W_3 *shall remain at rest while* W_1 *and* W_2 *are in motion is* $4W_1W_2 = W_3(W_1+W_2).$ (H.S.D.)

It is evident that the distance moved by B is equal to half the algebraic sum of the distances moved by W_1 and W_2. For if W_1 and W_2 both move downwards through distances x_1 and x_2, B will move up a distance $\frac{1}{2}(x_1+x_2)$; if W_1 moves down x_1 and W_2 up x_2, B will move *up* a distance $\frac{1}{2}(x_1-x_2)$.

Suppose that W_1 moves down with acceleration a_1, W_2 and W_3 move up with acceleration a_2 and a_3 respectively, and let T be the tension in the string.

Then
$$a_3 = \tfrac{1}{2}(a_1-a_2).$$
The equations of motion are:

For W_1,
$$W_1-T = M_1a_1 \tag{i}$$

for W_2,
$$T-W_2 = M_2a_2 \tag{ii}$$

for W_3,
$$2T-W_3 = M_3a_3 \tag{iii}$$

where $W_1 = M_1g$, $W_2 = M_2g$ and $W_3 = M_3g$.

But $2a_3 = a_1-a_2$, and hence from (i), (ii) and (iii);

$$2 \times \frac{2T-W_3}{M_3} = \frac{W_1-T}{M_1} - \frac{T-W_2}{M_2}$$

$$\frac{4T}{M_3} + \frac{T}{M_1} + \frac{T}{M_2} = 2g+g+g$$

$$\therefore \qquad T = \frac{4g}{M_1^{-1}+M_2^{-1}+4M_3^{-1}}$$

$$= \frac{4}{W_1^{-1}+W_2^{-1}+4W_3^{-1}}.$$

If W_3 is to remain at rest, a_3 must be zero.
Now, from (iii)

$$a_3 = \frac{2T}{M_3} - g$$

$$= \frac{8g}{\dfrac{W_3}{W_1}+\dfrac{W_3}{W_2}+4} - g$$

$$= \frac{4g - \dfrac{W_3}{W_1}g - \dfrac{W_3}{W_2}g}{\dfrac{W_3}{W_1}+\dfrac{W_3}{W_2}+4}$$

and this is zero if
$$\frac{W_3}{W_1}+\frac{W_3}{W_2} = 4$$

or
$$4W_1W_2 = W_3(W_1+W_2).$$

EXAMPLE (iii)

A particle of mass m slides down the face of a smooth wedge of mass M and slope α, free to move on a smooth horizontal table. Show that the acceleration of the wedge is mg sin α cos α/(M+m sin² α), and find the reaction between the particle and the wedge.

Figure 3.16A shows the forces acting on the mass m, namely, its weight mg and the reaction R perpendicular to the face of the wedge.

Figure 3.16B shows the forces acting on the wedge; a force R equal

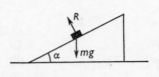

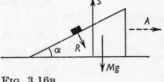

Fig. 3.16A   Fig. 3.16B

and opposite to the force acting on m, its weight Mg and the reaction S due to its contact with the smooth horizontal table.

The wedge will move horizontally with acceleration A, say, and the mass m will move down the face of the wedge with acceleration a, say, *relative to the wedge*. The acceleration of m relative to the fixed table is therefore the resultant of a down the wedge at an angle α to the horizontal and A horizontally, that is, $a \sin \alpha$ vertically downwards and $a \cos \alpha - A$ horizontally (to the left).

The equations of motion are:

For m $ma \sin \alpha = mg - R \cos \alpha$ (i)

and $m(a \cos \alpha - F) = R \sin \alpha.$ (ii)

For M $MA = R \sin \alpha$ (iii)

and $0 = S - R \cos \alpha - Mg$ (iv)

From equations (ii) and (iii)

$$m(a \cos \alpha - A) = MA$$

$\therefore$ $ma \cos \alpha = (M+m)A.$

From equations (i) and (iii)

$$(M+m)A \sin \alpha/\cos \alpha = mg - MA \cos \alpha/\sin \alpha.$$

$\therefore$ $(M+m)A \sin^2 \alpha = mg \sin \alpha \cos \alpha - MA \cos^2 \alpha$

$\therefore$ $(M+m \sin^2 \alpha)A = mg \sin \alpha \cos \alpha.$

Also from (iii) $R = MA/\sin \alpha$

$$= Mmg \cos \alpha/(M+m \sin^2 \alpha).$$

EXAMPLE (iv)

A man weighing 84 kg, and a weight of 70 kg, are suspended by a light rope over a smooth pulley. Find the acceleration of the man. If the man pulls himself up the rope so that his downward acceleration is only half this value, find the upward acceleration of the weight, and show that the upward acceleration of the man relative to the rope is $g/10$.

If a ms^{-2} is the acceleration when the man is not pulling, and T N the tension in the rope we get

$$84g - T = 84a$$
and
$$T - 70g = 70a$$
$$\therefore \qquad 154a = 14g, \text{ or } a = \tfrac{1}{11}g.$$

When the man is pulling on the rope we must consider the force F N he exerts on the rope. As an equal and opposite force F is exerted on the man, and his downward acceleration is now $\tfrac{1}{22}g$, we get

$$84g - F = 84 \times (g/22)$$
$$\therefore \qquad F = 84g - 84g/22.$$

If A ms^{-2} is the acceleration of the weight upwards

$$F - 70g = 70A$$
$$\therefore \qquad 12g - \tfrac{6}{11}g - 10g = 10A$$
$$\therefore \qquad A = \tfrac{8}{55}g.$$

The upward acceleration of the man relative to the rope is

$$\tfrac{8}{55}g - \tfrac{1}{22}g = \tfrac{1}{10}g.$$

EXAMPLES 3.3

1. A fine string passes over a smooth fixed pulley and carries at its ends masses of m and $5m$ kg respectively. Find the acceleration of the masses and the tension of the string, stating clearly the units you employ.

A string with one end fixed passes under a movable pulley A of mass m kg, over a fixed pulley and under a movable pulley B of mass $5m$ kg, its other end being attached to the axle of the pulley A, and all the hanging parts of the string being vertical. Show that the tension of the string is the same as that of the string in the first part of the question, that the acceleration of the pulley A is equal to that of the mass m, but that the acceleration of the pulley B is half that of the mass $5m$. (I.S.)

2. Two pulleys, of masses 12 kg and 8 kg, are connected by a fine string hanging over a smooth fixed pulley. Over the former is hung a fine string with masses 3 kg and 6 kg at its ends, and over the latter a fine string with masses 4 kg and x kg. Determine x so that the string over the fixed pulley remains stationary, and find the tension in it. (I.E.)

3. Masses of 5 kg and 2 kg are suspended from the ends of a string which passes over two fixed pulleys and under a movable pulley whose mass is m kg, the portions of the string not in contact with the movable pulley being vertical. Find the value of m in order that when the system is released the movable pulley may remain at rest, and find in this case the accelerations of the other masses and the tension of the string. (H.S.C.)

4. To one end of a light string passing over a smooth fixed pulley is attached a particle of mass M, and the other end carries a light pulley over which passes a light string to whose ends are attached particles of mass m_1 and m_2. Find the accelerations of the particles, and show that if $M = \dfrac{4m_1 m_2}{m_1 + m_2}$ the mass M will remain at rest or move with uniform velocity. (Ex.)

5. A particle of mass M on a smooth horizontal table is tied to one end of a string which passes over a fixed pulley at the edge and then under a movable pulley of mass m, its other end being fixed so that the parts of the string beyond the table are vertical. Show that m descends with acceleration $\dfrac{m}{4M+m}g$, and find the horizontal and vertical components of the acceleration of the centre of mass of M and m. (I.S.)

6. A string with one end fixed passes under a movable pulley A, of mass m kg, and then over a fixed pulley, and carries at its free end a mass B of $3m$ kg. Find the tension of the string and the accelerations of A and B, stating clearly the units that you employ. (All portions of the strings are to be regarded as vertical.) (I.S.)

7. A string is attached to a fixed point A. It passes round the lower part of a movable pulley B, to which a weight $2W$ is attached, then over a fixed pulley C, and a weight $W+w$ hangs from its extremity. The parts of the string not in contact with the pulleys are vertical. Neglecting friction and the mass of the pulleys, find the acceleration with which the system moves when left to itself. (I.S.)

8. Masses of 100 g and 60 g are attached to the ends of a fine string, which passes over a smooth fixed pulley. Find the acceleration of the masses and prove that the tension of the string is equal to the weight of 75 g. The pulley, whose mass is 50 g, is now detached from its fastening, and attached by means of another fine string to a mass of 100 g, which lies on a smooth table over whose edge the string passes. Prove that the pulley moves as if the original weights were removed and its own mass were increased by 150 g. (H.C.)

9. A, B are masses of 6 kg and 3 kg respectively, resting on two smooth tables, placed with their edges parallel. They are connected by a fine string, which hangs between the tables with its hanging parts vertical and carries in its loop a smooth pulley C of mass 4 kg. The string lies in a vertical plane and crosses the edges of the tables at right angles to the edges. Find the tension in the string: (i) when A and B are held fast; (ii) when B is held but A moves; (iii) when A and B move; and show that in the three cases the tensions are in the ratio 21 : 18 : 14. (H.C.)

10. A light string ABCD has one end fixed at A, and passing under a movable pulley of mass M at B and over a fixed pulley at C, carries a mass M' at D. The parts of the string are supposed vertical. Show that M descends with acceleration

$$\frac{M-2M'}{M+4M'}g.$$ (H.C.)

11. A string with one end fixed passes under a pulley A of mass M, then over a fixed pulley, then under a pulley B of mass M', and its other end is attached to the axle of A. The string is taut and its hanging parts are vertical. Find the ratio of the velocities of A and B when the system is in motion, and show that the acceleration of A is

$$\frac{4M-2M'}{4M+M'}g$$

downwards. (I.S.)

12. A particle of mass 2 kg is placed on the smooth face of an inclined plane of mass 7 kg and slope 30°, which is free to slide on a smooth horizontal plane in a direction perpendicular to its edge. Show that if the system start from rest the particle will slide down a distance of 5 m along the face of the plane in 1·3 s. (C.S.)

13. A wedge of mass M and angle α is placed on a rough horizontal plane, the coefficient of friction being μ. A smooth particle of

mass m is placed gently on the inclined face of the wedge. Show that, if the wedge moves, its acceleration will be

$$\frac{m \cos \alpha \ (\sin \alpha - \mu \cos \alpha) - \mu M}{m \sin \alpha \ (\sin \alpha - \mu \cos \alpha) + M} g. \qquad \text{(H.S.C.)}$$

14. On a smooth fixed inclined plane of angle α there is placed a smooth wedge of mass M and angle α, in such a way that the upper face of the wedge is horizontal; on this horizontal face is placed a particle of mass m. Prove that the resultant acceleration of the particle in the subsequent motion is

$$\frac{(M+m)g \sin^2 \alpha}{M+m \sin^2 \alpha},$$

and evaluate the pressure between the wedge and the plane.
(I.A.)

15. The angle of a smooth wedge of mass M is α. The wedge is placed with one face on a smooth horizontal table and a particle of mass m is allowed to slide down its face. Prove that a horizontal force $mg \sin \alpha \cos \alpha$ must be applied to the wedge to keep it from moving, and that the reaction between the wedge and the table is

$$(M+m \cos^2 \alpha)g. \qquad \text{(H.S.D.)}$$

16. A man of 60 kg and a weight of mass 48 kg are suspended by means of a light rope over a smooth pulley. If the man pulls himself up the rope so that his downward acceleration is $g/18$, find the acceleration of the weight, and the acceleration of the man relative to the rope.

17. A man of 72 kg lets himself down one portion of a light rope hanging over a smooth pulley with an acceleration of $0 \cdot 6$ ms^{-2}. Find with what uniform acceleration a man of 48 kg must pull himself up by the other portion so that the rope may remain at rest.

18. A wedge of mass M, whose section ABC is a triangle right-angled at A, is placed with the face BC on a smooth, horizontal table. The faces AB, AC are rough, the coefficient of friction being μ. Two masses m_1, m_2, connected by a light inextensible string passing over a light frictionless pulley at A, rest on the faces AB, AC, respectively, and m_1 moves down AB with acceleration a relative to the wedge. Write down the equations necessary to find a, and the acceleration A of the wedge. (Ex.)

19. A particle P of mass m rests on a rough horizontal table whose coefficient of friction is μ, and is attached to one end of a fine

inextensible string, which passes over a smooth fixed pulley A at the edge of the table. The string then passes under a smooth movable pulley B of mass m and over a smooth fixed pulley C, the other end of the string being attached to a particle D of mass m which hangs vertically. All the portions of the string not in contact with a pulley are horizontal and vertical. Prove that if $\mu > \frac{3}{5}$, P will not move, and that if $\mu < \frac{3}{5}$, D will move with acceleration $(3-\mu)g/6$.   (C.S.)

20. A smooth hemispherical bowl, of mass M, with centre C, lies rim downwards on a smooth table, and a particle, of mass m, is placed on it at a point A, whose angular distance from the vertex V of the bowl is α. Show that if a horizontal force of suitable magnitude is applied to the bowl in the plane VCA the particle will remain at rest relatively to the bowl as it moves.   (N.U.3)

REVISION EXAMPLES A

1. A man can row at a speed v through still water and wishes to cross a straight river flowing with speed u. Prove that he can reach the point A directly opposite to him if, and only if, $v > u$.

   If $v < u$ and he rows so as to reach a point B on the opposite bank as near as possible to A, find the ratio of AB to the width of the river.   (L.A.)

2. A ship is sailing due north at 32 kmh⁻¹. It observes at noon another ship, on a bearing N. 45° E. and at a distance of 8 km, sailing due west at 24 kmh⁻¹. At what time are the ships closest together and how far are they then apart?

   For how long a time is the distance between the ships less than 8 km?   (L.A.)

3. An aeroplane flies direct from a place A to another place B, due north of A, and back again. Throughout the journey there is a south-west wind blowing at 64 kmh⁻¹. If the speed of the aeroplane in still air is 320 kmh⁻¹ and the time taken for the whole journey is 7 hours, find the distance from A to B.   (L.A.)

4. A ship is steaming due north at speed u and the wind appears to blow from the direction θ east of north, where $0° < \theta < 45°$. The ship turns and steams due south at the same speed u and the wind now appears to blow from the direction θ south of east. Find the magnitude and direction of the true wind velocity.

                          (L.A.)

5. Explain what is meant by saying that velocity is a vector, and deduce the construction for the velocity of a point B relative to another point A when the velocities of A and B relative to an

observer are given. A bus is travelling at 20 kmh⁻¹ along a
straight road, and a man, running at 10 kmh⁻¹ along a perpendicular road, sees it when it is 200 m short of the junction and
he himself is 150 m short. Show that he can never get nearer
to the bus than $20\sqrt{5}$ m.   (C.W.B.)

6. If the velocity of A is known and the relative velocity of B with
respect to A is known, show how the velocity of B may be determined. To a cyclist moving due east at 16 kmh⁻¹ the wind
appears to be blowing from the north, and when moving due
north with the same speed it appears to be blowing from a
direction 30° west of north. Find the magnitude and the direction of the velocity of the wind.

7. Two straight roads OA, OB are inclined to each other at an acute
angle α; one car moves along OA, towards O, with uniform speed
u, while a second car moves along OB, away from O, with uniform speed v. If the first car is at a distance c from O when the
second car is at O, prove that, when the cars are at the least
distance apart, the ratio of their distances from O is

$$v+u \cos \alpha : u+v \cos \alpha.$$

Show also that the cars are at their least distance apart after
time

$$\frac{c(u+v \cos \alpha)}{u^2+v^2+2uv \cos \alpha}.$$ (C.W.B.)

8. A particle is accelerating uniformly along a straight line ABCD.
If it travels the successive distances AB $= a$, BC $= b$, CD $= c$
in equal intervals of time, prove that $c = 2b-a$, and that the
ratio of the speeds at D and A is

$$\frac{5b-3a}{3a-b}.$$ (L.A.)

9. A train, of length 64 m, has a speed of 80 kmh⁻¹ and an acceleration of 0·15 ms⁻² when it meets another train, of length 72 m,
travelling along a parallel line in the opposite direction with a
speed of 40 kmh⁻¹ and an acceleration of 0·3 ms⁻². Find the
time the trains take to pass and their relative speed at the end
of that time. What distance is covered by each engine during the
time of passing?   (L.A.)

10. (i) A train takes a time T to perform a journey from rest to rest.
It accelerates uniformly from rest for a time pT and retards
uniformly to rest at the end of the journey for a time qT; during

the intermediate time it travels uniformly with speed V. Prove that the average speed for the journey is

$$\tfrac{1}{2}V(2-p-q).$$

(ii) In travelling a total distance s a train accelerates uniformly from rest through a distance ps, then travels with uniform speed V, and finally retards uniformly to rest through a distance qs. Find the average speed for the whole journey.

(L.A.)

11. A train travelling at 72 km h^{-1} is checked by track repairs. It retards uniformly for 200 m, covers the next 400 m at constant speed, and accelerates uniformly to 72 km h^{-1} in a further 600 m. If the time at the constant slower speed is equal to the sum of the times taken in retarding and accelerating, find the total time taken. (L.A.)

12. A train left a station A at 16.00 for a station B, 30 km away, where it arrived at 16.40. At 16.15 the speed was 48 km h^{-1} and at 16.30 the speed was 72 km h^{-1}. The speed of 72 km h^{-1} was maintained until the brakes were applied, causing a uniform retardation under which the train came to rest at its destination. During the first and second 15 min intervals the accelerations were constant. At what time did the train reduce speed, and what was the retardation in metres per second per second? Draw the velocity–time graph. (I.S.)

13. The following table gives the speed of a motor car at minute intervals during a journey lasting 4 min:

t (min)	0	1	2	3	4
v (km h^{-1})	0	50	80	80	0

Assuming that the acceleration was uniform during these intervals, draw the velocity–time graph of the motion. From the graph, or otherwise, find: (i) the length of the journey in km; (ii) the time taken for the first 2 km; (iii) the time taken for the first 3 km.

14. A particle moves in a straight line with uniform acceleration α; its initial velocity is u; prove that the distance x travelled in time t is given by

$$x = ut + \tfrac{1}{2}\alpha t^2.$$

Two cars, A and B, are travelling along parallel straight paths. The cars are observed to be side-by-side when A is at a point P of its path and again when A is at another point Q. Assuming that A and B move with uniform accelerations α_1 and α_2, prove that, if their velocities at P are u_1 and u_2 respectively, the distance PQ is

$$\frac{2(u_1-u_2)(u_1\alpha_2-u_2\alpha_1)}{(\alpha_1-\alpha_2)^2}.$$
(C.W.B.)

15. Two particles P and Q describe coplanar concentric circles, of centre O and radii a and $2a$, in the same sense; the constant angular velocities of the radii OP and OQ are 4ω and ω and initially OPQ is a straight line. Prove that the angular velocity of PQ first becomes zero when POQ is the acute angle whose cosine is 4/5. Find also the tangent of the angle which at this instant the acceleration of P relative to Q makes with OQ.
(C.W.B.)

16. A string with one end fixed passes under a pulley A of mass m, then over a fixed pulley, and its other end is attached to the axle of a pulley B of mass m, the pulleys being small, and a second string passes over pulley B and carries masses m and m' at its ends. The hanging parts of the strings are all vertical, and in the subsequent motion from rest the mass m' does not move. Find m' in terms of m and find the acceleration of A. (L.A.)

17. A light string passes over a light smooth pulley fixed to the ceiling of a lift, and carries masses of 6 kg and 7 kg at its ends. The 7 kg mass is held in contact with the pulley and the 6 kg mass is hanging with the string vertical. If the 7 kg mass is now released, find the tension in the string while motion occurs, and the time that elapses before the 7 kg mass is 1 m below the pulley: (i) when the lift remains at rest; (ii) when the lift is rising vertically with constant acceleration $\frac{1}{8}g$. (I.S.)

18. One end of a light inextensible flexible string is attached to a mass of 9 kg, which is at rest on a smooth horizontal table. The string passes over the edge of the table and to its other end is attached a smooth light pulley. Over this pulley passes another similar string, to the ends of which are attached masses of 5 kg and 2 kg. If the system is released from rest with the hanging portions of the strings taut and vertical, show that the 9 kg mass moves along the table with acceleration $40g/103$. (L.A.)

19. A light inelastic string passes over a fixed smooth peg. At each end of the string is attached a scale-pan of mass 30 g. A 60 g weight is placed on one scale-pan and two 60 g weights, one on top of the other, are placed in the second scale-pan. The system is released from rest with the scale-pans hanging vertically.

Calculate the acceleration of the system, the tension in the string, the thrust the weights exert on each scale-pan, and the reaction between the two weights in the second scale-pan. (L.A.)

20. A particle is projected with velocity u straight up a rough plane inclined to the horizontal at an angle α. The angle of friction between the particle and the plane is $\epsilon(\epsilon < \alpha)$. Find the distance ascended and the velocity with which the particle returns to the point of projection, and prove that, if the times of ascent and descent are t_1 and t_2,

$$\frac{t_2^2 - t_1^2}{t_2^2 + t_1^2} = \frac{\tan \epsilon}{\tan \alpha}.$$

What happens when ϵ is greater than α? (H.C.)

CHAPTER FOUR

WORK, POWER, AND ENERGY

4.1. Work

When a force moves its point of application it is said to do
work. If the force is *constant* the work done by the force is
defined as the product of the force and the distance through
which the point of application moves *in the direction of the force*.
It is a scalar quantity.

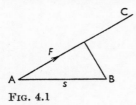

FIG. 4.1

Let a force F move its point of application from A to B
(Fig. 4.1), where the distance AB = s.

Then, if the force is in the direction AC, inclined at an angle
θ to AB, the work done is $F \times$ the projection of AB on AC,

$$= Fs \cos \theta.$$

This can also be written $F \cos \theta \times s$, which is the product of
the displacement s and the component of F in the direction
of the displacement.

Of course, if the force is in the direction of the displacement,
$\theta = 0$ and the work done equals Fs, the product of the force
F and the displacement s.

Further, if $\theta = 90°$, that is, if the force and the displacement
are perpendicular, the work done by the force in such a displacement is zero. Conversely, if the work done by a force is
zero, the force or the displacement must be zero, or the force
and the displacement must be perpendicular.

Again, if $\theta > 90°$ the work done *by* the force is negative, or
we say, work is done *on* or *against* the force.

If a number of forces F_1, F_2, ... F_n act on a particle the
total work done by the forces in any displacement of the

particle is simply the algebraic sum of the work done by F_1, $F_2, \ldots F_n$ separately.

Units of Work

4.2. The absolute unit of work in the F.P.S. system is the work done by a poundal in moving its point of application through 1 foot in the direction of the force.

This unit is called a *Foot-Poundal*.

The unit of work formerly used by engineers is called a *Foot-Pound*; it is the work done by a force of 1 pound (lb) weight in moving its point of application through 1 foot in the direction of the force, or the work done in raising a weight of 1 pound vertically through 1 foot.

4.3. The absolute unit of work in the C.G.S. system is the work done by a force of 1 dyne in moving its point of application through 1 centimetre in the direction of the force. This unit is called an *Erg*.

The work done by a force of 1 newton in moving its point of application through 1 metre in the direction of the force is defined as 1 *Joule*. It is written 1 J. It is the SI unit of work.

4.4. Power is the rate of doing work, i.e. the work done in unit time.

The SI unit of power is the *Watt*; it is 1 Joule per second and is written 1 W.

The British unit of power used earlier was the *Horse-Power*, and is equivalent to about 746 watts.

If a force of F newtons keeps its point of application moving in the direction of the force with uniform speed v metres per second, the work done per second is Fv joules, that is, the power is Fv watts.

In the case of a train running at a speed of v metres per second, the work done by the engine per second at any instant is equal to the pull multiplied by v, the speed at that instant. If the speed v is uniform, then the pull of the engine is equal to the resistance R due to friction, etc., and the power is equal to Rv.

If the train is accelerating the work done per second is not Rv, as work is also being done in accelerating the train.

The pull of the engine is not equal to R; it is greater than R when there is an acceleration and less than R when there is a retardation.

4.5. EXAMPLE (i)

The total mass of an engine and train is 200 Mg; what is the power of the engine if it can just keep the train moving at a uniform speed of 100 kmh⁻¹ on the level, the resistances due to friction, etc., amounting to $\frac{1}{200}$ of the weight of the train?

Since the speed is uniform, the pull of the engine is equal to the total resistance, i.e. $1000g$ N.

The speed is $\qquad 100 \ \text{kmh}^{-1} = 1000/36 \ \text{ms}^{-1}$

$\therefore \qquad$ the work per second $= 1000 \times 9 \cdot 8 \times 1000/36$ J

$\therefore \qquad\qquad\qquad$ power $= 10^5 \times 2 \cdot 72$ W

$\qquad\qquad\qquad\qquad\qquad = 272$ kW.

EXAMPLE (ii)

What power is required to take a train weighing 200 Mg at a uniform speed of 60 kmh⁻¹ up an incline of 1 in 100, the resistance due to friction, etc., being $\frac{1}{200}$ of the weight of the train?

The resistance $= 1000$ g N, and the component weight down the slope $= 2000$ g N. Since the speed is constant, the pull of the engine must be equal to the resistance plus the component of the weight.

$\therefore \qquad\qquad\qquad$ the pull $= 3000g$ N

Since the speed is $60\ 000/3600 = 100/6 \ \text{ms}^{-1}$,

and the work done per second $= 3000\text{g} \times 100/6$ J

$\therefore \qquad\qquad\qquad$ power $= 50\ 000g$ W

$\qquad\qquad\qquad\qquad\qquad = 490$ kW.

EXAMPLE (iii)

An engine of 280 kW is taking a train of mass 150 Mg up an incline of 1 in 250, and the resistance equals the weight of 350 kg. What is the maximum uniform speed of the train in km per hour?

The maximum work per second which can be done by the engine is 280×10^3 J.

The resistance is $350g$ N.

The component of weight down the slope

$$= \frac{150 \times 1000}{250} \, g \text{ N}$$

$$= 600g \text{ N}.$$

At uniform speed v ms^{-1} the pull of the engine must equal the resistance+component of weight.

$\therefore$ the pull $= 950g$ N

and the work per second $= 950gv$ J

$\therefore$ $950 \times 9 \cdot 8v = 280 \times 10^3$

$\therefore$ $v = \dfrac{280 \times 10^3}{950 \times 9 \cdot 8}$

Expressing this in kmh^{-1} we get:

$$\text{maximum speed} = \frac{280 \times 3600}{950 \times 9 \cdot 8} \text{ kmh}^{-1}$$

$$= 108 \text{ kmh}^{-1}.$$

EXAMPLE (iv)

A motor car whose mass is 750 kg starts from rest on a level road and is uniformly accelerated for 10 s until its speed is 18 kmh^{-1}. If the resistances to motion are 5 g N, find the power of the car 10 s after the start.

Since the car acquires a speed of 18 kmh^{-1} = 5 ms^{-1} in 10 s, its uniform acceleration is 0·5 ms^{-2}. If the driving force exerted by the car during this time is D N the equation of motion is

$$D - 5g = 750 \times 0 \cdot 5$$

$\therefore$ $D = 375 + 49 = 424.$

Therefore when the speed is 5 ms^{-1} the work done by the car per second $= 5 \times 424$ J.

$\therefore$ power $= 2 \cdot 12$ kW.

EXAMPLE (v)

A man is cycling at 18 kmh^{-1} up a slope of 1 in 30. If the man and machine have a mass of 84 kg, and frictional resistances are equivalent to the weight of 1 kg, find the rate at which the man is working. Assuming that the man exerts a constant vertical pressure on each pedal in its downward path, find this pressure when the cranks are 0·16 m long and the gear is 1·8 m.

The component of weight down the slope is $2 \cdot 8g$ N.

$\therefore$ the total force overcome $= 3 \cdot 8g$ N

$\therefore$ the work done per second $= 3 \cdot 8 \times 9 \cdot 8 \times 18\,000/3600$ J

$\therefore$ power $= 19 \times 9 \cdot 8$ W

                    $= 0 \cdot 186$ kW.

The gear being $1 \cdot 8$ m means that for each revolution of the crank the bicycle moves forward a distance of $1 \cdot 8\pi$ m.

The external work done in one revolution $= 3 \cdot 8 \times 9 \cdot 8 \times 1 \cdot 8\pi$ J.

In one revolution the man exerts a pressure P N through a distance of $4 \times 0 \cdot 16$ m $= 0 \cdot 64$ m,

$\therefore$ the work he does $= 0 \cdot 64\,P$ J

$\therefore$ $0 \cdot 64\,P = 3 \cdot 8 \times 9 \cdot 8 \times 1 \cdot 8\pi$

$\therefore$ $P = \dfrac{3 \cdot 8 \times 9 \cdot 8 \times 1 \cdot 8\pi}{0 \cdot 64} = 329.$

EXAMPLE (vi)

A fast cruiser is propelled at a speed of 60 $km\,h^{-1}$ by means of engines whose effective power is 30 000 kW. Calculate the resistance to the motion of the ship, and assuming that the resistance varies as the square of the speed, what power would be required for a speed of 72 $km\,h^{-1}$?   (Q.E.)

Let the resistance to the motion of the ship be D N. When the speed of the ship is uniform the effective force forward due to the engines must just balance the resistance, and hence when the speed is 60 km h^{-1} the work done per second is $D \times 60\,000/3600$ J and hence

$$D \times 60\,000/3600 = 30\,000 \times 10^3$$

$\therefore$ $D = 1800 \times 10^3.$

Now, if the resistance varies as the square of the speed its value when the ship is moving at 72 km h^{-1} will be $D \times 72^2/60^2$ N.

Therefore work done per second at this steady speed

$$= D \times \frac{72^2}{60^2} \times \frac{72\,000}{3600} \text{ J}$$

$\therefore$ power $= 1800 \times 10^3 \times \dfrac{36}{25} \times 20$ W

                    $= 51\,840$ kW.

4.6. Transmission of power by belts

Suppose a belt passes round a pulley which it turns without any slipping.

Let T_1, T_2 N be the tensions in the portions of the belt which are receding from and approaching the pulley ($T_1 > T_2$).

These tensions both act away from the pulley, and the total work done by them when the belt moves through any distance will be the product of the difference of the tensions and the distance.

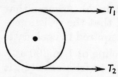

FIG. 4.2

If r m is the radius of the pulley, n the number of revolutions per second, then the distance moved by the belt in 1 s is $2\pi rn$ m.

The work done per second by the belt is therefore

$$2\pi rn(T_1 - T_2) \text{ J.}$$

and this is the amount of work transmitted per second. The power transmitted is

$$2\pi rn(T_1 - T_2) \text{ W.}$$

EXAMPLE

Power is transmitted from one shaft to another by means of a single belt running at 20 ms^{-1}. If the tensions in the two straight parts of the belt are in the ratio of 5 : 2, and if the greatest power that can be transmitted without breaking the belt is 15 kW, what is the tension which will just break the belt? (I.S.)

The actual tension on the tighter side is the limiting tension. If T_1, T_2 are the tensions on the two sides in newtons the work done per second is $(T_1 - T_2)20$ J.

$\therefore$ $\qquad\qquad\qquad (T_1 - T_2)20 = 15\ 000$

$\therefore$ $\qquad\qquad\qquad\qquad \frac{3}{5}T_1 = 750$

$\therefore$ $\qquad\qquad\qquad\qquad\ \ T_1 = 1250$ N.

A tension slightly over this will break the belt.

EXAMPLES 4.1

1. A crane lifts 22 packages, each of mass 100 kg through a height of 5 m. Find the work done by the crane.

2. A car is running on a level road at a uniform speed of 60 kmh^{-1} against resistances of 120 N. Find the work done per second.

3. A car is driven at a uniform speed of 48 kmh^{-1} up an incline of 1 in 8. If the total mass of the car is 800 kg, and resistances are neglected, calculate the power at which the car is working.

4. Calculate the least energy required to cycle 400 m at 20 kmh^{-1}: (i) on a level road, and (ii) up an incline of 1 in 20. Assume that the mass of the cycle and rider is 100 kg and that the resistances are 20 N at 20 kmh^{-1}. Find the least power required in each case.

5. A train whose mass is 250 Mg runs up an incline of 1 in 200 at a uniform rate of 32 kmh^{-1}; the resistance due to friction, etc., is equal to the weight of 3 Mg. At what power is the engine working? (I.S.)

6. A vessel of 30 000 Mg, whose engines are of 22 500 kW, is steaming at the rate of 24 kmh^{-1}. Find the resistance per Mg of the vessel's mass. (I.S.)

7. A motor car, of total mass 1500 kg is running on a level road at a uniform speed of 48 kmh^{-1}. On reaching a hill, which descends at a uniform gradient of 1 in 20, it is allowed to free-wheel, and the speed is observed to remain the same as before. Calculate the resistance of the road, and the power exerted on the level. (I.S.)

8. A train of mass 250 Mg is travelling up a slope of 1 in 140 at a constant speed of 48 kmh^{-1}. Taking the frictional resistances to be $\frac{1}{160}$ of the weight of the train, calculate the power which is being exerted.

Find also the maximum speed in kilometres per hour that 450 kW could maintain on the level, if the frictional resistances were then increased to $\frac{1}{150}$ of the weight of the train.

9. A train of mass 100 Mg acquires uniformly a speed of 48 kmh^{-1} from rest in 400 m. Assuming a resistance of 300 g N, find the tension in the coupling between the engine and the train, and the maximum power at which the engine is working during the 400-m run. The mass of the engine may be neglected. (I.S.)

10. A locomotive of 700 kW and mass 90 Mg is dragging a train of mass 120 Mg up a slope of 1 in 84. The frictional resistances amount to 36 g N per Mg. Find the maximum uniform speed at which the train can travel up the incline. (I.S.)

11. A train of total mass 250 Mg is drawn by an engine working at 420 kW. If at a certain instant the total resistance is $1750g$ N, and the speed is 48 kmh^{-1}, what is the train's acceleration measured in kilometres per hour per second?   (I.S.)

12. A load of mass 3 Mg is being hauled by a rope up a railway line which rises 1 in 140. There is a retarding force, due to friction, etc., of $20g$ N per Mg of load. At a certain instant the speed is 16 kmh^{-1} and the acceleration is 0·6 ms^{-2}. Find the pull in the rope, and the power exerted at that instant.   (I.A.)

13. A motor car of mass 2 Mg arrives at the bottom of a hill 0·8 km long, which rises 1 in 112, with a speed of 32 kmh^{-1}, and reaches the top of the hill with a speed of 16 kmh^{-1}. If there is a retarding force, due to friction, of 5 g N, calculate the work done by the engine in getting the car up the hill.   (I.A.)

14. A car of mass $2\frac{1}{2}$ Mg is accelerating at 0·6 ms^{-2} up an incline of 1 in 50, the resistance being $\frac{1}{75}$ of the weight of the train. Find the power exerted when the speed is 32 kmh^{-1}.   (I.S.)

15. A man with his bicycle has a mass of 100 kg. He begins to ascend an incline of 1 in 10, with a speed of 40 kmh^{-1}, and with uniform retardation. He has to dismount when his speed is not greater than 8 kmh^{-1}. If he works at an average of 75 W, how far will he ascend? How far would he have ascended if he had not worked at all?   (I.E.)

16. Find the uniform force that will move a 1 kg mass from rest through 1 m in 1 s. If this force is exerted while the mass moves through 100 m from rest, find the work done by the force and the maximum power attained.   (I.A.)

17. A train is running at 48 kmh^{-1} when it is at a distance of 0·4 km from a station. Steam is then shut off and the train runs against a uniform resistance equal to $\frac{1}{100}$ of the weight of the train. If the uniform brake force that can be exerted on the train provides a resistance equal to $\frac{1}{10}$ of the weight of the train in addition to the above resistance, find how far from the station the brake must be applied so that the train may be brought to rest at the station.   (I.A.)

18. A motor car engine, working at a uniform rate of 5·6 kW, can drive a car at a uniform speed of 30 kmh^{-1} against a uniform resistance. The car has a mass of 1500 kg. At what speed will the engine drive the car up a slope of 1 in 10, if it works at the same power and meets the same resistance?

19. A man and his cycle are of total mass m; he can work at a uniform power of H; his least speed consistent with remaining

on his machine is V. What is the inclination of the steepest hill he can ascend at a constant speed, assuming that there is a constant frictional resistance R to be overcome? What is the average pressure on his pedal at right angles to the crank if the gear multiplication is n? Find numerical results if $m = 70$ kg, $V = 6$ km h^{-1}, $H = \cdot 75$ W, $R = 2$ g N, $n = 10$.   (I.S.)

20. A bicycle is geared up to 1·8 m, and the length of the pedal crank is 16 cm. Calculate the velocity of the pedal (i) at its highest point, (ii) at its lowest point, when the bicycle is going at 18 km h^{-1}. If the bicycle and rider have a mass of 70 kg, find the force on the pedals in climbing a hill of 1 in 50.   (I.E.)

21. An engine draws a train of mass 250 Mg along a level track at a speed of 56 km h^{-1} against resistances which may be taken at $\frac{1}{200}$ of the weight of the train. Find the power necessary to draw the train at the same speed up an incline of 1 in 160.   (I.S.)

22. Find the power required to enable a 200-Mg train to travel up a slope of 1 in 80 at 48 km h^{-1}, frictional resistances being $\frac{1}{100}$ of the weight of the train. What is the maximum speed which it could maintain on the level?   (Ex.)

23. An engine draws a load of mass 500 kg out of a pit 90 m deep by means of a rope which cannot bear safely a load greater than the weight of 750 kg. Find the least time required to raise the load to rest at the surface, and the greatest power exerted by the engine.   (Ex.)

24. The mass of an engine and train is 250 Mg; what is the least power of the engine if it is capable of increasing the speed of the train from 32 km h^{-1} to 80 km h^{-1} in a distance of 800 m on the level? The total resisting force is $\frac{1}{100}$ of the weight of the train and the pull of the engine is assumed to be constant.   (H.S.C.)

25. A train of mass 250 Mg meets with a constant frictional and air resistance of $\frac{1}{140}$ of its weight. When the engine is doing 450 kW on the level and the train is running at 40 km h^{-1} what is the acceleration of the train? What would be the greatest possible speed for the train at this rate of working, if the resistances did not alter?   (H.S.D.)

26. A train travelling uniformly on the level at 100 km h^{-1} begins an ascent of 1 in 50. The tractive force due to adhesion has a maximum value equal to the weight of 3 Mg, the resistances due to friction, etc., equal the weight of 1·5 Mg, and the mass of the whole train is 200 Mg. Show that it cannot surmount the incline if this exceeds about 3·2 km in length, and find the power exerted by the engine, (i) just before beginning the ascent, (ii) just after.

27. The power developed by a locomotive going at 40 km h^{-1} is 15 kW, the mass is 40 Mg, and the resistance $\frac{1}{320}$ of the weight of the locomotive; if the acceleration be constant, find the tractive force, the time taken, and the distance gone from rest. The maximum power that can be developed being 25 kW, find the greatest distance that can be gone in 3 hours from rest. (I.E.)

28. A train of mass 300 Mg is ascending a slope of 1 in 120 with an acceleration of 0·15 m s^{-2}. At a speed of 24 km h^{-1} the power developed is 900 kW. Find the magnitude of the resistances, apart from gravity, acting on the train. (H.S.C.)

29. A pulley 45 cm in diameter receives 7·5 kW when revolving 180 times per minute, and the tension of the belt on the tight side is $2\frac{1}{2}$ times that on the slack. Find the tension on the tight side, and the width of the belt required if its thickness is 1·2 cm, and the greatest tension it can support is 250 N/cm^2 of cross-section.
(H.S.C.)

30. A train of mass M starts from rest at A and travels with uniform acceleration for a time t_1. Steam is then shut off, and the train comes to rest at B (without the brakes being touched). The distance from A to B is a, and total time taken is t. The resistance due to friction is k times the weight of the train. Prove that $t - t_1 = 2a/kgt$, and that the greatest rate of working of the engine during the journey is $2aMk^2g^2t/(kgt^2 - 2a)$. (H.C.)

31. A motor car of mass 1 Mg attains a speed of 64 km h^{-1} when running down an incline of 1 in 20 with the engine cut off. It can attain a speed of 48 km h^{-1} up the same incline when the engine is working. Assuming that the resistance varies as the square of the velocity, find the power developed by the engine. (C.S.)

32. An engine of mass 100 Mg is allowed to run down a bank, whose slope is 1 in 30, with steam shut off, and is observed to attain a maximum speed of 120 km h^{-1}, air and frictional resistances being assumed proportional to the square of the speed.

   If the engine can develop 750 kW show that its maximum speed up the bank, under its own steam, is about 64 km h^{-1}.
(Q.E.)

4.7. Energy

The energy of a body is its capacity for doing work. Since the energy of a body is measured by the work it can do, the units of energy are the same as those of work. The SI unit of energy is therefore the joule.

A body may possess energy owing to a variety of causes,

e.g. heat and electricity are forms of energy, which can be converted into mechanical work. In dynamics, however, we are concerned only with purely mechanical energy which may be of two kinds, *Kinetic* or *Potential*.

4.8. *The Kinetic Energy of a body is the energy it possesses in virtue of its motion, and is measured by the amount of work which it does in coming to rest.*

Consider a particle of mass m moving with velocity v, and suppose it is brought to rest by a constant force F which produces in it a retardation a, then $F = ma$.

Let x be the space described by the particle before it comes to rest, then

$$0 = v^2 - 2ax$$

$\therefore$ $ax = \tfrac{1}{2}v^2.$

$\therefore$ Now the work done by the particle is $Fx = max$

$\therefore$ the work done $= \tfrac{1}{2}mv^2$

$\therefore$ the kinetic energy of the body $= \tfrac{1}{2}mv^2.$

It should be noticed that $\tfrac{1}{2}mv^2$ gives the kinetic energy in joules if m is in kilogrammes and v in metres per second.

4.9. *The Potential Energy of a body is the work it can do in moving from its actual position to some standard position.*

Examples of potential energy are the energy of a weight above the ground (the standard position being the surface of the earth), compressed air (the standard position being the volume it would occupy at atmospheric pressure), a bent or compressed spring (the standard position being its natural shape).

The potential energy of a particle of mass m at height h above the surface of the earth is the work the particle can do in falling to the ground, and this is equal to the work done in raising it to a height h, viz. mgh.

4.10. *A particle of mass m falls from rest at a height h above the ground. Show that the sum of its potential and kinetic energies is constant throughout the motion.*

Let v be the velocity of the particle when it has fallen through a distance x to a point P.

Then
$$v^2 = 2gx$$

Its kinetic energy at $P = \frac{1}{2}mv^2 = mgx$

Its potential energy at $P = mg(h-x)$

therefore the sum of its kinetic and potential energies at P is

$$mgx + mgh - mgx = mgh$$

which is independent of x, and is therefore constant throughout the motion.

On reaching the ground the velocity V is given by

$$V^2 = 2gh$$

the kinetic energy $= \frac{1}{2}mV^2 = mgh$

$= $ potential energy at height h.

Hence, on reaching the ground, all the potential energy has been transformed into kinetic energy.

4.11. Principle of Conservation of Energy

The example in the last paragraph is a simple illustration of the *Principle of Conservation of Energy*. In its most general form this principle states that:

The total amount of energy in the universe is constant; energy cannot be created or destroyed, although it may be converted into various forms, e.g. heat, light, sound.*

In the example of the last paragraph, when the particle hits the ground it apparently loses all its energy. Actually the kinetic energy is converted into other forms of energy, mainly heat.

Similarly, when a body is projected along a rough horizontal

---

* The Principle of Conservation of Energy is one of the most important principles in science. In its most modern form it is known as the Principle of Mass-Energy, for Einstein has shown that mass (m) and energy (E), are interchangeable according to the equation $E = mc^2$, where c is the velocity of light. This transformation of mass into energy is the source of nuclear energy as used in the atomic bomb and in nuclear power stations. In Newtonian mechanics, however, mass and energy are regarded as two distinct physical quantities, and there are two conservation laws, one for mass and one for energy.

surface which reduces it to rest its kinetic energy is gradually transformed into heat. In dynamics we are not concerned with the energy once it has been transformed, but it must be remembered very carefully that in all cases where there are sudden jerks or impacts in a system, or where there is motion against friction of any kind, some mechanical energy is always apparently lost; it is actually converted to other forms.

If we exclude forces of this nature which cause conversion of energy to other forms we can use a restricted form of the general principle applicable to mechanical energy alone (i.e. apart from other forms), and often called the *Principle of Energy*.

In the case of forces such as gravity the work done in bringing a system from one position to another depends only on the initial and final positions and not on the manner in which the transition is made. Such forces are called *Conservative*, and the principle of energy so often used in dynamical problems may be stated as follows:

If a system of bodies in motion be under the action of a conservative system of forces the sum of the kinetic and potential energies of the bodies is constant.

4.12. The principle of energy is most commonly used when considering motion under gravity; it tells us that, in the absence of friction and impacts, for any loss in kinetic energy there must be an equal gain in potential energy, and *vice versa*.

Thus, for a body sliding down a *smooth* inclined plane the kinetic energy acquired is equal to the loss of potential energy, and depends only on the vertical distance descended.

The kinetic energy, and therefore the speed, acquired in sliding down the plane is the same as that acquired by falling vertically through the height of the plane (see p. 64).

If a ring threaded on a smooth vertical circle is projected up from the lowest point the speed at any point depends only on the vertical height of that point above the bottom of the circle. Similarly, for a particle sliding down any smooth curve; the speed at the bottom depends only on the vertical height descended.

Great care must be taken never to use this principle in problems where there is any friction, or any sudden jerk or impact. In such cases energy is nearly always converted.

4.13. EXAMPLE (i)

Find the power required to pump 4·5 m³ of water per minute from a depth of 15 m and deliver it through a pipe of 40 cm² cross-section. (Assume that 1 m³ of water has a mass of 10³ kg and neglect the effects of friction.) (H.S.C.)

Work done per minute in raising the water

$$= 4\cdot5 \times 10^3 \times 9\cdot8 \times 15 \text{ J}$$
$$= 66\cdot15 \times 10^4 \text{ J}.$$

This equals the gain in potential energy of the water per minute.

But the water is also given kinetic energy. If the velocity of the water is v ms⁻¹ a column v m long and 0·004 m² cross-section is discharged every second, so that

$$\text{Volume issuing per minute} = 0\cdot004v \times 60 \text{ m}^3$$
$$= 4\cdot5 \text{ m}^3$$
∴ $$0\cdot24v = 4\cdot5$$
∴ $$v = 18\cdot75 \text{ ms}^{-1}.$$

∴ Kinetic energy imparted to the water per min.

$$= \tfrac{1}{2} \times 4\cdot5 \times 10^3 \times 18\cdot75^2 \text{ J}$$
$$= 79\cdot10 \times 10^4 \text{ J}.$$

∴ Total gain in energy per minute $= 145\cdot25 \times 10^4$ J
∴ power $= 145\cdot25 \times 10^4/60$ W
$$= 24\cdot2 \text{ kW}.$$

EXAMPLE (ii)

A body of mass m is projected up a plane of inclination α with an initial velocity of V. Find how far up the plane the body goes, and the loss of mechanical energy during this motion.

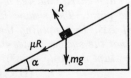

FIG. 4.3

The forces acting on the body are its weight mg, the reaction R normal to the plane, and the frictional force μR down the plane.

Therefore the acceleration a up the plane is given by

$$ma = -mg \sin \alpha - \mu R$$

and
$$0 = R - mg \cos \alpha.$$

$\therefore$
$$a = -g (\sin \alpha + \mu \cos \alpha).$$

Therefore if s is the distance the body goes up the plane before it comes to instantaneous rest we have

$$0 = V^2 + 2as$$

$\therefore$
$$s = V^2/2g(\sin \alpha + \mu \cos \alpha).$$

Now, the loss in kinetic energy of the body

$$= \tfrac{1}{2}mV^2$$

and the gain in potential energy of the body

$$= mg\, s \sin \alpha.$$

Therefore total loss of mechanical energy

$$= \tfrac{1}{2}mV^2 - mgs \sin \alpha$$

$$= \tfrac{1}{2}mV^2 - \tfrac{1}{2}mV^2 \frac{\sin \alpha}{\sin \alpha + \mu \cos \alpha}$$

$$= \tfrac{1}{2}mV^2 \frac{\mu \cos \alpha}{\sin \alpha + \mu \cos \alpha}.$$

We note that this is zero if $\mu = 0$, that is, there is *no* loss of mechanical energy if the plane is smooth.

EXAMPLE (iii)

A light inelastic string passes round small smooth pulleys A *and* B *in the same horizontal line at a distance* 2a *apart and carries masses* m_1 *at each end and a mass* m_2 *($<2m_1$) at its mid-point. The system is released from rest with* m_2 *at the mid-point of* AB. *By applying the principle of the conservation of energy, show that the system comes to instantaneous rest when* m_2 *has fallen a distance* $4am_1m_2/(4m_1^2 - m_2^2)$.

(H.C.)

Suppose m_2 falls a distance x before it comes to instantaneous rest; each mass m_1 will then have ascended $\sqrt{(a^2 + x^2)} - a$.

Hence since the pulleys are smooth, the gain in potential energy of the two masses m_1 must equal the loss in potential energy of the mass m_2.

$$\therefore \qquad 2m_1g\{\sqrt{(a^2+x^2)}-a\} = m_2gx.$$

$$\therefore \qquad 2m_1\sqrt{(a^2+x^2)} = m_2x+2m_1a$$

$$\therefore \qquad 4m_1{}^2(a^2+x^2) = (m_2x+2m_1a)^2$$

$$\therefore \qquad 4m_1{}^2x^2 = m_2{}^2x^2+4m_1m_2xa$$

$$\therefore \qquad x = \frac{4m_1m_2a}{4m_1{}^2-m_2{}^2}.$$

4.14. In problems where a mass loses velocity owing to the action of a retarding force, e.g. a bullet passing through a plank, or a train being pulled up by its brakes, we can obtain a measure of the retarding force in two ways:

(1) If we know the time during which the force acts, and the initial and final velocities u and v of the mass m, then if F is the average force,

$$Ft = m(u-v).$$

(2) If we know the distance s travelled during the retardation we can obtain the average force by equating the work done to the loss of kinetic energy,

$$Fs = \tfrac{1}{2}m(u^2-v^2).$$

It must be clearly understood that the measure of the force thus obtained is an *average* value. In the first case it is a time average, and in the second a space average.

If the force is constant the two methods will give the same value, but if the force is not constant the values will be different. For if

$$\frac{m(u^2-v^2)}{2s} = \frac{m(u-v)}{t}$$

we get
$$\frac{u+v}{2} = \frac{s}{t}$$

i.e. the average velocity (s/t) is equal to the means of the initial and final velocities. Now, this is not necessarily the case unless the acceleration is constant, i.e. unless the force is constant.

EXAMPLES 4.2

1. Find the ratio of (i) the momenta, (ii) the kinetic energies, of a mass of 80 g moving at 2·5 km/min, and a mass of 10 kg moving at 2 ms^{-1}. (I.A.)

2. A force equal to the weight of 5 kg acts on a mass of 30 kg, originally at rest, for 10 s. Find the distance travelled by the mass, and the kinetic energy generated in it. (H.C.)

3. Express the kinetic energy of 250 kg moving at 10 kmh^{-1}. A mass of 10 Mg is drawn up a slope of 1 in 96 against a resistance of $\frac{1}{120}$ of the weight of the train. If 32 kW is used, find the greatest speed that the mass can have. (I.A.)

4. Calculate the energy required to raise an 18 kg shot to a height of 2 m, and then project it with an initial velocity of 12 ms^{-1}. What is the power required for a motor car, which weighs 1400 kg and can travel at 48 kmh^{-1} against an air resistance equal to $\frac{1}{30}$ of its own weight? (I.A.)

5. A man lifts a stone weighing 300 g from the ground to a height of 2 m, and then throws it away horizontally with a velocity of 6 ms^{-1}. How much work has to be done on the stone? If the man does this 20 times per minute, find the average rate at which he is working, neglecting the work he does in moving himself. (I.A.)

6. Show that the velocity of water in a pipe of cross-section 100 cm^2 which delivers 0·1 m^{3}s^{-1} is 10 ms^{-1}.

   Calculate, correct to three significant figures, the power of an engine which raises the water in this pipe to a height of 12 m and then delivers it at this height at 0·1 m^{3}s^{-1}.

7. Find the power required to pump 2 m^3 of water per minute from a depth of 30 m, the water being delivered through a circular pipe 8 cm in diameter (neglect friction). (H.C.)

8. Find the power of an engine which can fill a cistern, 60 m above the level of a river, with 140 m^3 of water in 24 hours, assuming that only two-thirds of the work actually done by the engine is available for raising the water. (H.C.)

9. An engine is raising water from a depth of 18 m and discharging 0·75 m^{3}s^{-1} with a velocity of 14·5 ms^{-1}. Find the potential energy and the kinetic energy of the water discharged per second, and find the power at which the engine is working. (H.C.)

10. If a body moves in a straight line under the action of a constant force, prove that the increase in the kinetic energy of the body during any interval is equal to the work done by the force. A lift of mass 250 kg rises from rest through a height of 15 m in 5 s with a uniform acceleration. Find the average power exerted during this time. (H.S.D.)

11. What must be the power of an engine which is to fill a reservoir 500 m long and 300 m wide to a depth of 3·5 m by pumping water from a river 1·5 km away, and 150 m lower in level, in 15 days, working day and night. (I.S.)

12. An engine in 7 s has raised a load of 1 Mg through a height of 1 m, and has communicated to it a speed of 3 ms⁻¹. At what average power has it been working? (H.C.)

13. A cyclist and his machine together have a mass of 80 kg. In free-wheeling down a hill 200 m long, which falls a vertical distance of 8 m the cyclist increases his speed from 3 ms⁻¹ to 10 ms⁻¹. Calculate the change in the total kinetic energy of cycle and rider, and hence calculate the average value of the resistance to motion.

14. A dock 200 m long and 40 m wide, with a depth of water 12 m, has to be pumped dry in 6 hours, all the water being lifted to a level of 0·6 m above the original water level in the dock. If the useful power exerted by the pumping engines is constant, calculate what it must amount to, and find the time it takes to empty the last 2 m of water in the dock. (Q.E.)

15. A car of mass 1 Mg has climbed a height of 32 m in going 1·6 km; it started from rest and is proceeding at 60 kmh⁻¹ at the end. The frictional resistance of the road is the weight of 24 kg. What is the ratio of the gains of kinetic and potential energy, what fraction of the total work done is stored, and what is the average power exerted if the climb took 3 minutes? (Q.E.)

16. Three equal weights are attached to the middle and ends of a light cord which is placed over two smooth pulleys at the same level so that the central weight hangs symmetrically between the pulleys and the others hang vertically. If the central weight is pulled down until its connecting cord makes angles of 50° with the horizontal, and is then let go, find what the angles will be when next the weights come to momentary rest. (H.S.C.)

17. Two bodies, of mass 240 and 250 g respectively, are suspended by a light string on either side of a smooth peg. Find the loss of potential energy when the heavier mass has descended 160 cm from rest, and hence deduce the velocities of the two masses at

this moment. Verify your value for the velocities by making the calculation in another way.

18. Define 'work', and explain in what units it is measured. A mass of 100 kg was dragged to the top of a hill 300 m high along a road rising uniformly 0·3 m vertically for every 9 m measured on the map, and with a coefficient of friction $\frac{1}{10}$. After coming to rest at the top it slid straight down a slope at 45° to the horizontal with a coefficient of friction $\frac{1}{2}$. Calculate the total work done in dragging the weight to the top of the hill on the upward journey, and the amount of this total recovered as kinetic energy at the end. What was the total work done against friction?   (C.W.B.)

19. A particle is projected with velocity V directly up a rough plane of inclination α. Show that when it again has velocity V it will be at a distance

$$\frac{V^2}{g} \times \frac{\cos \alpha \sin 2\lambda}{\cos 2\lambda - \cos 2\alpha}$$

from the point of projection, λ being the angle of friction, which is less than α.   (H.S.D.)

20. Show how to estimate the difference of potential energy in a system, acted on by gravity only, in two different configurations. A particle of mass M is attached to two particles, each of mass m, by means of two light inextensible strings passing over two small smooth fixed pegs, distant $2c$ apart at the same level. Show that, when the mass M falls from a position in which the strings are each inclined to the vertical at an angle θ to the position in which they are each inclined to the vertical at an angle ϕ, there is a loss of potential energy of amount

$$Mgc(\cot \phi - \cot \theta) - 2mgc(\operatorname{cosec} \phi - \operatorname{cosec} \theta).$$

Deduce that, if there is equilibrium when the strings are each inclined to the vertical at an angle α, and the system is released from a position in which the strings are each inclined to the vertical at an angle θ, it will next come to instantaneous rest when the inclination is ϕ, where

$$\tan^2 \tfrac{1}{2}\alpha = \tan \tfrac{1}{2}\theta \tan \tfrac{1}{2}\phi.$$ (H.C.)

21. Explain briefly the terms kinetic energy, potential energy, conservation of energy. A light endless string of length $4na$ carries two equal smooth heavy beads P and Q threaded upon it. It rests over two smooth pegs A and B at the same level and a distance $2a$ apart, the beads P and Q being separated by the

pegs. Initially the system is at rest, P being held at the mid-point of AB, and then released. Show that the relative speed V of the beads as they collide is given by

$$V^2 = 8ga\sqrt{(n-1)}\{\sqrt{(n+1)} - \sqrt{n}\}$$ (H.S.C.)

4.15. Work done by a variable force

Suppose a particle is subject to a force F which is variable in magnitude and/or direction, and that the particle moves from the point o to the point c along the path $omnc$ (Fig. 4.4).

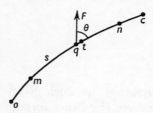

FIG. 4.4

If q is a point on this path at a distance s from o, measured along the curve, and t a neighbouring point at a distance $s + \delta s$, the work done by F as the particle moves from q to t is approximately $F \cos \theta \delta s$, where θ is the angle between F and qt. The total work done as the particle moves from m to n is given approximately by the sum of all these expressions $F \cos \theta \delta s$, that is, $\Sigma F \cos \theta \, \delta s$, the summation being taken from m to n.

This can be represented graphically (Fig. 4.5) by plotting $F \cos \theta$ against s. If PQ and OQ represents the values of $F \cos \theta$ and s corresponding to the point q of the path, then P lies on a curve APB known as the *force–space curve*. AM represents the value of $F \cos \theta$ at m, and OM $= om = s_1$. Similarly BN represents the value of $F \cos \theta$ at n, and ON $= on = s_2$.

If RT represents the value of $F \cos \theta$ at t, and OT $= s + \delta s$, then the area of the strip PQTR equals approximately $F \cos \theta \, \delta s$, and hence represents the work done by F as the particle moves from q to t.

Thus the work done by F as the particle moves from m to n is represented by the area ABNM, and is in fact given by the integral $\int_{s_1}^{s_2} F \cos \theta \, ds$.

The work done by F in any displacement can therefore be

found by calculating the area under the force–space curve, or by evaluating the corresponding integral.

We have assumed here that the curve AB is traced in the direction from A to B, i.e. that s is increasing. If it is traced in

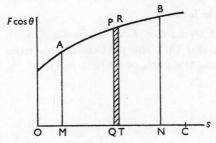

Fɪɢ. 4.5

the opposite direction, so that s is decreasing, the work given by the area ABNM is done *against* the force (by other forces) and we must then reckon it as negative work as far as the force F is concerned.

4.16. Suppose the force–space curve is closed, as in Fig. 4.6, and traced in the direction shown by the arrows.

Starting from A, the upper portion of the curve AP_1B represents the magnitude of the component of the force as its

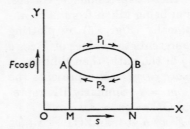

Fɪɢ. 4.6

point of application moves a distance represented by MN; and the area AP_1BNM represents the positive or useful work done *by* the force. The lower portion of the curve BP_2A represents the magnitude of the force as its point of application moves back through the distance represented by MN; the area AP_2BNM represents the work done *against* the force.

The total positive or useful work done by the force while its point of application has moved from M to N and back is represented by the *difference* between the areas AP_1BNM and AP_2BNM, i.e. by the area of the closed curve AP_1BP_2.

4.17. Indicator diagrams

To obtain a measure of the amount of work done by the steam pressure in a steam engine during a complete stroke of the piston an indicator is attached to the cylinder of the engine. The indicator consists of a small cylinder containing a light piston controlled by a spiral spring, so that the vertical displacement of the piston is proportional to the steam pressure in the main cylinder. The indicator piston actuates a pencil which traces a curve on a sheet of paper placed on a rotating drum.

The engine is thus made to trace its own force–space diagram. The curve is a closed one, and its area gives a measure of the work done by the engine at each stroke.

4.18. EXAMPLE (i)

A train of mass 260 Mg is drawn from rest up an incline of 1 in 200, the resistances to motion being $\frac{1}{130}$ of the weight of the train. The driving-force D in units of $10^3 g$ N at different distances s in m is as follows:

s	0	30	60	90	120	150	180	210	240	270	300
D	9·0	9·2	8·2	7·0	6·2	5·6	5·1	4·7	4·4	4·2	4·0

Find the speed of the train when it has gone 240 m, and the power of the engine at this point.

If we plot D against s the area under the curve as far as $s = 240$ equals the total work done by the engine after it has gone that distance. This may be found by simply counting squares, or by using Simpson's or some other rule, or by using a planimeter. It is approximately $6·6 \times 10^3 \times 9·8 \times 240$ J.

But the work done against the resistances $= 22 \times 10^3 \times 9·8 \times 240$ J.

Also, the work done in raising the train vertically a distance of $240/200$ m $= 1·2 \times 260 \times 10^3 \times 9·8$ J.

If the velocity of the train when it has covered 240 m is v m s^{-1}, the kinetic energy of the train $= \frac{1}{2} \times 260 \times 10^3 \times v^2$ J.

Hence by the principle of energy,

$$2 \times 10^3 \times 9·8 \times 240 + 1·2 \times 260 \times 10^3 \times 9·8 + 130 \times 10^3 \times v^2$$

$$= 6·6 \times 10^3 \times 9·8 \times 240$$

$$\therefore \quad v^2 = 59·7$$

$$\therefore \quad v \simeq 7·73.$$

Therefore speed of train is about 7.73 m s^{-1}.

Also, the work done per second by the engine when at a distance of 240 m $= 4.4 \times 10^3 \times 9.8 \times 7.73$ J

$$\therefore \qquad\qquad \text{power} = 333 \times 10^3 \text{ W}$$
$$= 333 \text{ kW}.$$

EXAMPLE (ii)

The speed of a train of mass 100 *Mg varies with time in accordance with the following table*:

Time in s	0	10	20	30	40	50	60
Speed in km h^{-1}	0	36	56	68	76	80	81

The train is running down an incline of 1 *in* 400. *Find the power being exerted by the engine at the end of the first half-minute if the frictional and air resistance to motion at that instant amounts to* $\frac{1}{200}$ *of the weight of the train.*

The component of the weight down the plane is 100×10^3 g/400 N and the resistance to motion is $\frac{1}{2} \times 10^3$ g N. Hence if the driving force at the end of the first half-minute is D in newtons and the acceleration at this instant is a in m s^{-2}, the equation of motion is

$$D + \tfrac{1}{4} \times 10^3 \times 9.8 - \tfrac{1}{2} \times 10^3 \times 9.8 = 100 \times 10^3 a$$
$$\therefore \qquad\qquad D = 10^5 a + 2.45 \times 10^3.$$

But a is given by the gradient of the speed–time curve at the instant $t = 30$, which is approximately 1 km s^{-1} = 1000/3600 m s^{-2}.

$$\therefore \qquad D = \frac{10^6}{36} + 2.45 \times 10^3 = 30.22 \times 10^3$$

$$\therefore \qquad\qquad \text{driving force} = 30.22 \times 10^3 \text{ N}.$$

But the speed at the end of the first half minute is 68 km h^{-1}.

$$= 68 \times \frac{10^3}{3600} \text{ m s}^{-1}$$

$$\therefore \qquad \text{Power at this instant} = \frac{30.22 \times 10^3 \times 68 \times 10^3}{3600} \text{W}$$

$$= 570 \text{ kW}.$$

EXAMPLE (iii)

A car of mass 6 *Mg starts from rest under the action of a force given by the following table*:

t in s	0	2	4	6	8	10	12	14	16	18	20
$\frac{1}{10}F$ in N	304	300	283	248	198	168	146	130	120	112	108

If the resistances to motion are equivalent to a constant force of $\frac{1}{60}$ of the weight of the car, draw the acceleration–time curve, and find the velocity of the car at the end of the time.

It is assumed that the car is travelling along a horizontal road. Hence the effective force forward is $F-10^2\times9\cdot8$ N, so that the acceleration, a in $\mathrm{m\,s^{-2}}$, at time t is given by

$$F-980 = 6\times10^3 a$$

∴ $$a = (F-980)/6000.$$

a can therefore be calculated from the tabulated values of F, and the acceleration–time curve can be drawn. The area under this curve gives the velocity of the car. It is found that the velocity at time $t = 20$ is approximately $3\cdot3$ m s^{-1}.

It might be noted that the velocity, v m s^{-1}, of the car at any instant can be found from this curve, and hence the power of the car at this instant can be calculated. The power at time $t = 20$ is $1080\times3\cdot3$ W $= 3\cdot56$ kW.

4.19. Tension in an elastic string

As an example of a variable force we will consider the tension in an elastic string.

It is found by experiment that the tension of an elastic string varies directly as the extension of the string beyond its natural length, provided the extension is small. This fact was discovered by Hooke (1635–1703), and is embodied in what is usually known as Hooke's Law. This may be stated as follows:

If l is the natural length of an elastic string, and l' the stretched length, then the tension T is given by

$$T = \frac{\lambda}{l}(l'-l)$$

where λ is a constant depending on the thickness and material of the string. λ is usually called the *Modulus of Elasticity of the String*.

It is obvious that λ is the tension required to stretch the string to double its natural length, and has the same units as T.

Young's Modulus E is the value of λ for a string of unit area cross-section; in fact, it equals λ divided by the area of the cross-section, and is expressed as E units of force per unit area.

4.20. Work done in stretching an elastic string

Let λ be the modulus and l the natural length, then for an extension x, the tension is

$$T = \lambda x/l.$$

This can be represented graphically (Fig. 4.7) by the straight line OAB inclined to the axis of x at an angle θ given by $\tan \theta = \lambda/l$.

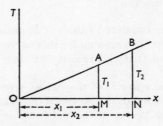

Fig. 4.7

The work done in increasing the extension from x_1 to x_2 is given by the area of the trapezium AMNB, and equals $\frac{1}{2}(T_1+T_2)(x_2-x_1)$, where $T_1 = \lambda x_1/l$ and $T_2 = \lambda x_2/l$.

Hence the work done is the product of the mean of the initial and final tensions and the extension.

Otherwise, using the calculus, we can say that the work done in increasing the extension from x by an amount dx, so small that T may be supposed constant, is Tdx or $(\lambda x/l)dx$.

Hence the work done in increasing the extension from x_1 to x_2 is

$$\int_{x_1}^{x_2}(\lambda x/l)dx = \frac{\lambda}{l}\left[\frac{x^2}{2}\right]_{x_1}^{x_2}$$

$$= \frac{\lambda x_2{}^2-x_1{}^2}{2l}$$

$$= \frac{\lambda}{2l}(x_2+x_1)(x_2-x_1),$$

$$= \frac{1}{2}(T_2+T_1)(x_2-x_1).$$

Hence the work done is the product of the mean of the initial and final tensions and the tension.

The potential energy of the string when it is extended an amount x is therefore $\frac{1}{2}\lambda x^2/l$.

EXAMPLE (i)
*An elastic string, of natural length 0·6 m, is stretched 8 cm by a weight
of 1 kg hanging on it. Find the work done in stretching it from a length
of 0·65 to 0·7 m.*

The fact that a weight of 1 kg stretches the string 8 cm enables us
to find λ, for

$$1 \times 9{\cdot}8 = \frac{\lambda}{0{\cdot}6} \times 0{\cdot}08.$$

The tension for an extension of 0·05 m is

$$T_1 = \frac{\lambda}{0{\cdot}6}(0{\cdot}05) = \frac{5}{8} \times 9{\cdot}8 \text{ N}.$$

The tension for an extension of 0·1 m is

$$T_2 = \frac{\lambda}{0{\cdot}6}(0{\cdot}1) = \frac{10}{8} \times 9{\cdot}8 \text{ N}.$$

Therefore the mean of the initial and final tensions is

$$\tfrac{1}{2}(T_1 + T_2) = \frac{7{\cdot}5}{8} \times 9{\cdot}8 \text{ N}$$

and the extension is 0·05 m.

$$\therefore \qquad \text{the work done} = \frac{7{\cdot}5}{8} \times 9{\cdot}8 \times 0{\cdot}05 = 0{\cdot}46 \text{ J}.$$

Note. Care must be taken in using Hooke's Law to keep all length
measurements in the same units.

EXAMPLE (ii)
*A mass of 5 kg is attached to one end of an elastic string of natural
length 1·2 m, whose other end is fixed at a point* A . *The modulus of the
string is such that the 5 kg mass hanging vertically would stretch the
string 15 cm. The mass is held at* A *and allowed to fall vertically. How
far below* A *will it come to rest?*

Since the 5-kg weight stretches the string 0·15 m,

$$5 \times 9{\cdot}8 = \frac{\lambda}{1{\cdot}2} \times 0{\cdot}15 \text{ or } \lambda = 392 \text{ N}.$$

When the mass has fallen 1·2 m its velocity is $\sqrt{(2g \times 1{\cdot}2)} \text{ ms}^{-1}$,
and its kinetic energy is $\tfrac{1}{2} \times 5 \times 2{\cdot}4 g$ J.

The mass now begins to stretch the string, and the extension
goes on until the work done in stretching is equal to the loss of
kinetic and potential energy of the 5-kg mass.

If the extension produced when the mass comes to rest is x m the final tension is $\lambda x/1\cdot2$ N, and the initial tension is zero. Hence the work done in stretching.

$$= \lambda x^2/2\cdot4 \text{ J}$$

$$= 392x^2/2\cdot4 = \frac{490}{3}x^2 \text{ J}.$$

The loss of kinetic energy of the mass is $6\times9\cdot8$ J and the loss of potential energy of the mass is $5\times9\cdot8x$ J.

$$\therefore \qquad \frac{490}{3}x^2 = (6+5x)9\cdot8$$

$$\therefore \qquad 100x^2 = 36+30x$$

$$\therefore \qquad x = 0\cdot755.$$

Hence the distance below A at which the mass comes to rest is 1·955 m.

Note (i). It is important to remember that as the mass descends and stretches the string it loses *both kinetic and potential energy.*

Note (ii). In solving the quadratic for x, the root with the negative sign in front of the radical can be ignored, as it would be negative.

Note (iii). After the mass comes to rest the string will contract and pull it up again, and, assuming that no energy is dissipated in the stretching, when it reaches the point 1·2 m below A it will have the same velocity as it had when going down, and this will be just sufficient to take it up to A again.

EXAMPLE (iii)

A ring of mass m can slide on a smooth vertical wire. It is attached by a light string of natural length l and modulus of elasticity $mg\sqrt2$ to a point at a distance l from the wire. Prove that, if the ring begins to move when the string is unstretched, it will descend until the length of the string is 3l before its velocity vanishes. (I.S.)

Suppose when the ring is again at rest that the length of the string is L.

$\therefore$ Increase in potential energy of the string $= \frac{1}{2}mg\sqrt2(L-l)^2/l$.

The ring will then have descended a distance $\sqrt{(L^2-l^2)}$, and hence the loss in potential energy of the ring $= mg\sqrt{(L^2-l^2)}$.

There is no change in kinetic energy.

Hence, since the wire is smooth,

$$\frac{1}{2}mg\sqrt2(L-l)^2/l = mg\sqrt{(L^2-l^2)}$$

$$\therefore \qquad (L-l)^2 = \sqrt2l\sqrt{(L^2-l^2)}.$$

Therefore squaring and dividing by $L-l$, we get

$$(L-l)^3 = 2l^2(L+l)$$

$\therefore$ $\qquad\qquad (L^2+l^2)(L-3l) = 0$

$\therefore$ $\qquad\qquad\qquad\qquad L = 3l.$

4.21. Gravitational potential energy

Another example of a variable force is the gravitational force due to the earth. The force acting on a mass m at the earth's surface is its weight mg, but at a height x above the earth's surface this has a different value, viz. $mgR^2/(R+x)^2$, where R is the radius of the earth, as the gravitational pull of the earth at points *outside* it varies inversely as the square of the distance from the centre.

Thus the work done in raising a mass m from the earth's surface to a height h is given by:

$$\int_0^h \frac{mgR^2}{(R+x)^2}\mathrm{d}x = mgR^2\left[-\frac{1}{R+x}\right]_0^h = mgR^2\left[-\frac{1}{R+h}+\frac{1}{R}\right]$$

$$= mghR^2 \times \frac{h}{R(R+h)}$$

$$= mgh/\left(1+\frac{h}{R}\right).$$

In most problems with which we have to deal h is small compared with R, and thus the work done is approximately mgh, the expression used earlier for the potential energy of a mass m at height h (4.9).

EXAMPLES 4.3

1. A force of P N moves a body of mass 16 kg from rest in its own direction. The value of P at a distance x from the starting-point is given by the table:

P N	7	90	207	290	225	180	0
x m	0	0·28	0·5	0·9	1·2	1·5	1·85

Plot P against x, and using the proposition that 'the change in kinetic energy equals the work done', draw a graph giving the velocity at any instant throughout the interval. (I.E.)

2. A truck starting from rest and of mass 15 Mg is drawn along the level against a constant resistance of $\frac{1}{75}$ of the weight of the train. The draw-bar pull is found to vary with the distance travelled according to the following table:

Distance travelled in m	0	10	20	30	40	50
Draw-bar pull in 10^2 N	36·0	35·6	34·8	32·9	30·5	27·2

Find (i) the work done by the force, (ii) the kinetic energy of the truck, (iii) the velocity of the truck, when the truck has travelled the first 50 m.

3. A mass of 1 Mg is drawn from rest up an incline of 1 in 200 by a force parallel to the ground and varying with the distance according to the following table:

Distance in m	0	50	100	150	200	250	300	350	400
Force in N	460	580	600	520	400	260	140	100	40

If the frictional resistance to the motion is 100 N, find the velocity of the body after passing over 400 m.

4. A car whose mass is 1000 kg starts from rest, and the resistance to the motion is equal to $\frac{1}{40}$ of its weight. When it has travelled a distance s m the force exerted by the engine is F N where

s	0	5	10	15	20	25	30
F	3220	3170	3110	3035	2935	2825	2685

Construct the acceleration–space graph of this (continuous) motion, and find the speed of the car when it has travelled 30 m.

5. A train of mass 500 Mg commences to climb a gradient at a speed of 40 km h^{-1}. The engine exerts a constant pull of $\frac{1}{100}$ of the weight of the train, and the total resistance R due to all causes, including gravity, rises with time in accordance with the following table:

R (10^3 N)	10	14	20	28	38	48	64
t (min)	0	0·5	1·0	1·5	2·0	2·5	3·0

Determine the speed of the train at the end of 3 minutes. (Q.E.)

6. State Hooke's law for an elastic string.

The ends of an elastic string of natural length $2a$ are fixed in a horizontal line and at a distance $2a$ apart. A particle of mass m attached to the string at its mid-point rests in equilibrium. If each half of the string is inclined to the vertical at an angle θ, find the modulus of the string.   (L.A.)

7. An elastic string, of natural length $2a$, is found to extend a distance b when a particle of weight W is suspended from a free end. The particle is now removed and attached to the mid-point of the string, the ends of which are then tied to two points A and B in the same vertical line at a distance apart greater than $2a$. Assuming that, in the equilibrium position, the lower part of the string remains taut, show that the displacement of the weight W from the mid-point of AB is $b/4$.   (L.A.)

8. The force required to compress a spring varies as the amount of compression or extension. If it requires a force of 20 N to hold a certain spring compressed 1 cm, find how much work is required to compress it another centimetre.   (H.S.C.)

9. A mass M is attached to a light elastic spring and produces an extension e when the spring is suspended from a fixed point. If in this position a small mass m is added to M and the combined mass is allowed to fall from rest, find the greatest extension produced in the spring.

10. An elastic string of natural length 3 m can be stretched to a length of 4 m by a weight of mass 10 kg. Its two extremities are fixed to two points A, B in the same horizontal line at a distance of 4 m apart, and a mass of 15 kg is attached to the mid-point. If this mass is released from rest while the string is horizontal find the velocity of the mass when it has descended a distance of 1·5 m.

11. A particle of mass m is attached by a light elastic string, of natural length a and modulus λ, to a fixed point O on a rough plane inclined at θ to the horizontal, the coefficient of friction being $\mu(<\tan\theta)$. Initially the string lies along a line of greatest slope of the plane with m below O. If m is released from rest when the string is just taut, find the distance it moves before it comes to rest again. Examine the subsequent motion, when $\mu = \frac{1}{4}\tan\theta$.

12. A spring whose weight can be neglected is fixed in a vertical position, and a weight W resting on it produces a compression a. Show that if the weight W is let fall on the spring from a height $\frac{3}{2}a$ above it, the maximum compression of the spring in the motion which follows is $3a$.   (H.S.D.)

13. A weight of mass 4 kg will compress a spring through 2·5 cm. A model truck, of mass 250 g, runs into the spring, used as a buffer, with a velocity of 90 cms^{-1}. How far will the spring be compressed before the truck is brought to rest?   (H.C.)

14. A particle, of mass m, is supported by two light elastic strings, each of natural length a and modulus of elasticity $15\ mg/16$, the other ends of which are fixed one at each of two points, A, B in the same horizontal line and at a distance $2a$ apart. Verify that, in the position of equilibrium, each string is inclined to the vertical at an angle of $\cos^{-1} 4/5$, and find how much work must be done to raise the particle to the mid-point of AB.   (H.C.)

15. Assuming that the acceleration due to gravity decreases uniformly in the magnitude from g at the earth's surface to zero at the earth's centre, show that the potential energy of a particle of mass m at a depth x below the surface may be written $-mgx + mgx^2/2R$, where R is the radius of the earth.

16. A particle is shot vertically upwards with a speed of $0 \cdot 8\ km\,s^{-1}$. Find how high it will go assuming that the acceleration due to gravity (i) is constant, and (ii) varies inversely as the square of the distance from the earth's centre. (Take the radius of the earth equal to 6400 km, and neglect resistance of the atmosphere.)

17. A weight of mass 100 kg hangs freely from the end of a rope. The weight is hauled up by means of a windlass. The pull in the rope starts at $150g$ N, and then diminishes uniformly at the rate of $1g$ N for every metre of rope wound in. Find the velocity of the weight after 50 m of rope has been wound. The weight of the rope may be neglected.   (Q.E.)

18. A car of mass 1 Mg starts from rest on a level road. The tractive force acting on it is initially $40g$ N, and this falls, the decrease being proportional to the distance travelled, until its value is $15g$ N at the end of 100 m, after which it remains constant. There is a constant frictional resistance of $15g$ N. Find the speed of the car at the end of the 100 m, and plot a curve, on a distance base showing the gradual rise of the speed from the start.   (Q.E.)

19. A mass is suspended from a fixed point O by an elastic string of natural length a, and when the mass is hanging freely the length of the string is $5a/3$. Show, by the principle of energy, that if the mass be allowed to fall from rest at O, the greatest length of the string in the subsequent motion is $3a$.

Find also the speed with which the mass is moving when it is at a distance $2a$ from O.   (C.W.B.)

20. A body of mass M kg moves from rest under the action of a constant horizontal force F N. At the same instant another body of the same mass moves from rest under the action of a force in a fixed horizontal direction, which does work at a constant rate

P Js^{-1}. If after T s the bodies have the same speed V ms^{-1} show that $P = \frac{1}{2}FV$.

Find the ratio of the speeds of the bodies when they have been moving for $4T$ s. (L.A.)

4.22. Units and dimensions

The units of mass, length, and time are called *fundamental units*, since the units of other quantities, such as speed, force, etc., can be expressed in terms of them. The unit of speed is a speed of unit distance in unit time, e.g. 1 ms^{-1}; the unit of acceleration is an increase of unit speed in unit time, e.g. 1 ms^{-2}. The unit of force is the product of unit mass and unit acceleration.

If we denote the units of length, mass, and time by L, M, T the

unit of speed will be $\qquad \dfrac{L}{T} = LT^{-1}$

the unit of acceleration $\qquad = \dfrac{\text{unit of speed}}{\text{unit of time}} = \dfrac{L}{T^2} = LT^{-2}$

the unit of force $\qquad = \dfrac{ML}{T^2} = MLT^{-2}$

the unit of work $\qquad = \text{unit of force} \times \text{unit of distance}$

$$= \dfrac{ML^2}{T^2} = ML^2T^{-2}.$$

Now the unit of area is the product of two unit lengths or L^2, and is said to be of two dimensions in length. A volume is said to be of three dimensions in length.

This idea of dimensions is extended to include mass and time, and the powers to which the fundamental units are raised to produce the unit of any quantity are called the *dimensions* of that quantity. Thus the dimensions of speed are said to be 1 in length and -1 in time, those of work are 1 in mass, 2 in length, and -2 in time.

4.23. The dimensions of any physical quantity are easily obtained by considering the way in which the quantity is defined, and by writing down the formula for its unit in terms of M, L, and T as above.

Momentum is defined as the product of mass and velocity and its dimensional formula is therefore

$$\frac{ML}{T} = MLT^{-1}.$$

Angular velocity is obtained by dividing an angle in radians (which is merely a ratio of lengths and independent of units) by time, and its dimensional formula is

$$\frac{1}{T} = T^{-1}.$$

Power is obtained by dividing work by time, and its dimensional formula is therefore

$$\frac{ML^2}{T^3} = ML^2T^{-3}.$$

There are two important uses of dimensions which will now be considered.

4.24. In any equation between physical quantities each term must be of the same dimensions in the fundamental units. Just as it is impossible in ordinary arithmetic to add, say, pence and metres, so it is impossible to add any two terms of different dimensions. This often gives a useful check as to whether a formula is a possible one.

Thus, take the equation of motion

$$v^2 = u^2 + 2as,$$

the dimensions of v^2 are $\qquad L^2/T^2$

the dimensions of u^2 are $\qquad L^2/T^2$

the dimensions of $2as$ are $\qquad (L/T^2) \times L = L^2/T^2$

so that all the terms are of the same dimensions, namely, L^2/T^2.

In 3.17 we obtained a formula for the tension in a string over a pulley connecting two masses,

$$T = \frac{2m_1 m_2}{m_1 + m_2} g.$$

The dimensions of the right-hand side are that of a mass multiplied by an acceleration or ML/T^2, and are therefore those of a force, as they should be.

If the formula had only one mass in the numerator it could not represent a force, as its dimensions would be L/T^2 those of an acceleration.

In 3.20, Example (iii), we obtained an expression for the acceleration of a wedge

$$\frac{mg \sin \alpha \cos \alpha}{M+m \sin^2 \alpha}.$$

Now the dimensions of a trigonometrical ratio are zero, and as each term in the numerator and denominator contains a mass, the dimension in mass is zero. Hence the dimensions of the whole expression are those of g, an acceleration, and this is correct.

If the mass were missing from any one of the terms the expression could not represent an acceleration.

A result, such as V^2/g, where V is a velocity, is of dimensions

$$(L^2/T^2) \times (T^2/L) = L$$

and therefore represents a length.

V/g is of dimensions $(L/T) \times (T^2/L) = T$

and therefore represents a time.

4.25. Dimensional formulae can also be used to find the change in a unit due to changes in the fundamental units.

Let M, L, T be the units of mass, length, and time in one system, M', L', T' those in a second system.

Then if the units of, say, force in these two systems are F and F', we get

$$F : F' = \frac{ML}{T^2} : \frac{M'L'}{T'^2}$$

or

$$\frac{F}{F'} = \frac{MLT'^2}{M'L'T^2}.$$

Thus, if M, L, T are F.P.S. units, and M', L', T' are SI units, taking 1 lb = 0·453 kg and 1 ft = 0·305 m, we have

$$\frac{1 \text{ pdl}}{1 \text{ N}} = 0·453 \times 0·305 = 0·138$$

$\therefore$ 1 pdl = 0·138 N.

EXAMPLE

Taking 1 *lb* = 0·453 *kg*, 1 *ft* = 0·305 *m*, *and* g = 32 *ft s*$^{-2}$, *find the number of joules in a foot-poundal.*

The dimensions of work are

$$\frac{ML^2}{T^2}$$

$$\therefore \qquad \frac{1 \text{ ft pdl}}{1 \text{ J}} = \frac{ML^2 T'^2}{M'L'^2 T^2}$$

where M is 1 lb, L is 1 ft, and T is 1 s, and M', L', T' are 1 kg, 1 m, and 1 s respectively.

$$\therefore \qquad \frac{1 \text{ ft pdl}}{1 \text{J}} = 0·453 \times (0·305)^2$$

$$= 0·0421$$

$$\therefore \qquad 1 \text{ ft pdl} = 0·0421 \text{ J.}$$

EXAMPLES 4.4

1. If the units of mass, length, and time be 100 kg, 100 m, and 100 s respectively, find the units of force and work.

2. If the units of length, velocity, and force be each doubled, show that the units of time and mass will be unaltered, and that of energy will be increased in the ratio 1 : 4.

3. If a second be the unit of time, the acceleration due to gravity the unit of acceleration, and a kg the unit of mass, find the unit of energy.

4. If m is the mass of a body in kg, V its velocity in m s^{-1}, in what units is its kinetic energy expressed when we say that this energy is measured by $\frac{1}{2}mV^2$? If the units of length and mass be each multiplied by 10 and the unit of time divided by 10, how will the following units be affected: (i) acceleration; (ii) energy; (iii) force; (iv) power?   (I.S.)

5. Given that 1 kg = 2·204 lb, 1 m = 3·281 ft, 1 hp = 33,000 ft lb per min., g = 981 cm s^2, show that 3 hp is approximately 2·24 kW.

6. Taking 1 year of 365$\frac{1}{4}$ days to be the unit of time, the Earth's distance from the Sun (148·6 × 10^6 km) to be the unit of length, and the mass of the Earth to be the unit of mass, find the kinetic energy of the Sun relative to the fixed stars, its velocity relative to them being 17·6 km s^{-1}, and its mass 332 000 times that of the Earth.   (I.C.)

7. State the dimensions of *force, power, angular velocity, pressure at a point in a fluid.*

   If the force of attraction between two masses m and m_1, distant r apart, is $k\dfrac{mm_1}{r^2}$, find the dimensions of k, and its numerical value when SI units are employed. [$g = 9{\cdot}81$ ms^{-2}, radius of earth $= 6{\cdot}37 \times 10^3$ km, mass of earth $= 6{\cdot}14 \times 10^{24}$ kg.]   (H.S.C.)

8. Verify that the following equations are dimensionally correct:

   (i) $s = ut + \frac{1}{2}gt^2$.

   (ii) $T = 2\pi\sqrt{l/g}$, where T is the time of oscillation of a simple pendulum of length l.

   (iii) $E = \frac{1}{2}mv^2$ where $E =$ energy of a body of mass m moving with velocity v.

   (iv) $W = N\theta$ where $W =$ work done by a couple of moment N in turning a body through an angle θ.

9. If the time of oscillation, T, of the bob of mass m of a simple pendulum of length l is written as

$$T = Am^x l^y g^z$$

   where A, x, y, z are constants, find by considering the dimensions the values of $x, y,$ and z.

10. If the velocity v of sound in a gas of pressure p and density ρ is written as

$$v = Ap^x \rho^y,$$

   where A, x, y are constants, find x and y.

11. If the velocity v of waves on an ocean of density ρ is written as

$$v = Ag^x \rho^y \lambda^z,$$

   where A, x, y, z are constants, g is the acceleration due to gravity, and λ the wavelength, find from the consideration of dimensions the values of $x, y,$ and z.

12. A particle of mass m is projected vertically upwards with velocity u and reaches a height h. Show that u^2/gh is non-dimensional.

CHAPTER FIVE

IMPULSIVE FORCES
IMPACT OF ELASTIC BODIES

5.1. Impulse

The term *impulse of a force* is defined as follows:

When a force F is constant, the impulse is the product of the force and the time during which it acts, i.e. Ft.

But if the force F acts on a mass m it produces an acceleration a so that

$$Ft = mat = m(v - u)$$

where u and v are the initial and final velocities of m.

$\therefore$ *impulse of the force = change of momentum produced.*

When the force F is variable the impulse of F equals the integral of the force with respect to the time, i.e.

$$\int_o^t F \, \mathrm{d}t$$

where t is the time during which the force acts.

But $F = m\dfrac{\mathrm{d}v}{\mathrm{d}t}$, and therefore the impulse is

$$\int_o^t F \mathrm{d}t = \int_o^t m\frac{\mathrm{d}v}{\mathrm{d}t}\mathrm{d}t = \left[mv \right]_o^t$$
$$= m(v - u).$$

Hence generally

Impulse of force = change of momentum produced.

5.2. Impulsive forces

Suppose the force F is very large, but acts only for a short time. The body will move only a very short distance while the force is acting, so that the change of position of the body may be neglected. The total effect of the force is measured by its impulse, or the change of momentum it produces.

Such a force is called an impulsive force.

Theoretically the force should be infinitely great and the time during which it acts infinitely small. This is, of course, never realised in practice, but approximate examples are the blow of a hammer, the impact of a bullet on a target, the collision of two billiard balls.

5.3. Impact of two bodies

If two bodies A and B impinge, then, from Newton's third law, the action of A on B is, during their contact, equal and opposite to that of B on A.

Hence the impulse of A and B is equal and opposite to that of B on A. It follows that the changes in momentum of A and B are equal and opposite, and the sum of the momenta of the two bodies, measured in the same direction, is unaltered by their impact.

This is an example of the *Principle of Conservation of Linear Momentum* (3.13) which is used in dealing with problems in which impacts or impulsive forces occur.

Suppose a mass m, moving with velocity v, strikes a mass M at rest, which is free to move in the direction of m's motion, and the two move on as a single body. There is no loss of momentum; the gain in momentum of M equals the loss in momentum of m.

Now the momentum of the mass m before impact is mv. Hence, if V is the velocity of the two together after the impact,

$$(M+m)V = mv$$

$$\therefore \qquad V = \frac{m}{M+m}v.$$

The gain in momentum of M is MV, that is, $Mmv/(M+m)$, and the loss in momentum of m is $m(v-V)$, which equals MV.

It should be noted that, although there is no change in the total momentum due to the impact, *there is a loss of kinetic energy*.

The kinetic energy before impact is $\frac{1}{2}mv^2$.

The kinetic energy after impact is

$$\tfrac{1}{2}(M+m)V^2 = \tfrac{1}{2}\frac{m^2}{M+m}v^2$$

and this is obviously less than $\frac{1}{2}mv^2$, since $\dfrac{m}{M+m}$ is less than unity.

Since kinetic energy is lost in nearly all cases of impact, the principle of energy must never be used in dealing with cases where impulsive forces occur.

5.4. It is also most important to realise that the principle of momentum can be applied only in a direction in which there is no *external* impulsive force acting.

Thus, if a bullet strikes a fixed target perpendicularly all the momentum of the bullet is, of course, destroyed. If the bullet hits a *smooth* target obliquely the impulse it receives is perpendicular to the surface of the target, since it is smooth. Hence there is no change in momentum parallel to the surface of the target, but all momentum perpendicular to the target is destroyed.

If a bullet moving horizontally hits perpendicularly the face of a block whose section is CDEF (Fig. 5.1), resting on a smooth inclined plane AB, and becomes embedded in it, then the only direction in which we can apply the principle of momentum is

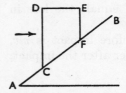

Fig. 5.1

parallel to the face of the inclined plane AB. The component of the bullet's momentum parallel to AB is shared between the bullet and the block. The component of momentum perpendicular to AB is destroyed by the impulsive reaction of the plane.

5.5. Motion of a shot and gun

When a gun is fired the explosive charge forms a large volume of gas at very high pressure. This pressure acts equally on the shot and gun in the direction of the barrel and drives the shot out.

If the gun is free to move in the direction of the barrel the forward momentum generated in the shot at the instant it leaves the barrel is equal to the backward momentum generated in the gun.

If the gun is placed on a smooth horizontal plane with the barrel horizontal we can say that the momenta of the shot and gun are equal and opposite (both will be horizontal). If, however (as is usually the case), the barrel of the gun is elevated we note that the horizontal momentum of the gun is equal and opposite to the horizontal momentum of the shot, but the vertical momentum imparted to the gun is at once destroyed by the impulsive pressure of the plane on which it stands.

Any apparatus (such as a spring) for preventing the horizontal recoil of the gun does not introduce an impulsive force at the instant of firing, and does not prevent the principle of momentum being applied. In such a case we calculate the momentum and velocity of recoil as if the spring were absent.

The spring does not exert any force until it is compressed, so that, neglecting the time taken for the shot to leave the gun, we consider the gun to start moving back with the velocity it would have if the spring were absent. The spring then gradually reduces the gun to rest.

In the same way the action of gravity is neglected in cases of impact; this again is not an *impulsive* force, and the impact is over before its effect is appreciable.

5.6. Impact of water on a surface

To find the pressure due to a jet of water impinging against a fixed surface, or a continuous fall of rain on the ground, we have only to calculate the amount of momentum destroyed per second. Here we are dealing with a succession of impacts or impulsive forces. The amount of momentum destroyed per second gives us the average force on the surface; this force acting for 1 s would produce or destroy the given amount of momentum.

5.7. EXAMPLE (i)

A bullet of mass 30 g is fired with a velocity of 200 ms^{-1} into a block of wood of mass 2 kg, and lying on a smooth table. Find the velocity with which the block and bullet move after the bullet has become embedded in the block.

(I.S.)

The momentum of the bullet before impact is 0.03×200 kg m s^{-1} units; no momentum is lost by the impact, as there is no external horizontal force acting, and as the total mass in motion is now 2.03 kg, the common velocity, V ms^{-1}, of the two is given by

$$2.03V = 6$$
$$\therefore \qquad V = 2.96.$$

EXAMPLE (ii)

A shot, of mass 100 kg, is fired with a velocity of 550 ms^{-1} from a gun of mass 50 Mg, which is free to recoil in the direction of the barrel; find the resulting velocity of the gun.

The forward momentum of the shot $= 100 \times 550$ kg m s^{-1} units. The backward momentum of the gun is equal to the forward momentum of the shot.

Hence, if V ms^{-1} is the velocity of the gun,

$$50 \times 10^3 V = 100 \times 550$$
$$\therefore \qquad V = 1.1.$$

EXAMPLE (iii)

If, in the last example, the gun is resting on an incline of 3 in 5, and the shot is fired horizontally, find the velocity of recoil of the gun.

In this case some of the horizontal momentum imparted to the gun is destroyed by the inclined plane on which it rests, and we can only say that the momentum of the gun parallel to the plane is equal to that of the shot parallel to the plane.

Now the momentum of the shot parallel to the plane is

$$100 \times 550 \times \text{the cosine of the slope} = 100 \times 550 \times \tfrac{4}{5}.$$

Hence, if V ms^{-1} is the velocity of recoil of the gun,

$$50 \times 10^3 V = 100 \times 440$$
$$\therefore \qquad V = 0.88.$$

EXAMPLE (iv)

A gun, of weight W, is mounted on a smooth railway, and is fired in the direction of the track. It fires a shell, of weight w, with velocity V relative to the ground. If the angle of elevation of the gun is α, prove that the initial direction of the motion of the shell is inclined to the ground at an angle

$$\cot^{-1}\left(\frac{W \cot \alpha}{W+w}\right).$$

(H.S.C.)

Let AB (Fig. 5.2) represent the barrel of the gun.

As the shot leaves the barrel the gun is moving backwards, and this imparts a backward horizontal component of velocity to the shot. The direction of the initial motion of the shot is therefore inclined to the horizontal at an angle greater than α. Let this angle be θ, and let the velocity of the gun be U.

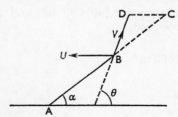

Fig. 5.2

The *horizontal* momentum of the gun is equal to the *horizontal* momentum of the shot, and hence $MU = mV\cos\theta$, where $W = Mg$ and $w = mg$.

$$\therefore \qquad\qquad WU = wV\cos\theta. \qquad\qquad\text{(i),}$$

Also V is the resultant of a velocity in the direction of the barrel AB, and the horizontal velocity of the gun U.

If BD represents V, then if DC is drawn horizontal to meet AB produced in C, CD will represent U by the triangle of velocities.

Angle DCB $= \alpha$, angle DBC $= \theta - \alpha$

and
$$\frac{\text{CD}}{\sin(\theta-\alpha)} = \frac{\text{BD}}{\sin\alpha}$$

$$\therefore \qquad\qquad \frac{\sin(\theta-\alpha)}{U} = \frac{\sin\alpha}{V}. \qquad\qquad\text{(ii)}$$

Multiplying this equation by (i)

$$W\sin(\theta-\alpha) = w\sin\alpha\cos\theta$$

$$\therefore \qquad W(\sin\theta\cos\alpha - \cos\theta\sin\alpha) = w\sin\alpha\cos\theta$$

$$\therefore \qquad W(\tan\theta\cos\alpha - \sin\alpha) = w\sin\alpha$$

$$\therefore \qquad\qquad \tan\theta\cos\alpha = \sin\alpha + \frac{w}{W}\sin\alpha$$

$$= \frac{W+w}{W}\sin\alpha$$

$$\therefore \qquad\qquad \tan\theta = \frac{W+w}{W}\tan\alpha$$

$$\therefore \qquad\qquad \cot\theta = \frac{W\cot\alpha}{W+w}.$$

EXAMPLE (v)

Water issues from a circular pipe of 8 cm diameter with a velocity of 5 ms⁻¹; find the mass of water discharged per minute. If the water impinges directly upon a plane, and its momentum is thereby destroyed, what is the pressure of the jet upon the plane?

The area of the cross-section of the pipe is $\frac{1}{4}\pi(0.08)^2$ m², and a column 5 m long is discharged every second.

The volume per minute

$$= \pi(0.0016) \times 5 \times 60 \text{ m}^3$$

and its mass

$$= 0.48\pi \times 10^3 \text{ kg}$$
$$= 1507 \text{ kg.}$$

The mass discharged per second

$$= 25.1 \text{ kg,}$$

and its velocity is 5 m s⁻¹.

Therefore the momentum destroyed per second

$$= 25.1 \times 5 \text{ kg m s}^{-1} \text{ units.}$$

The pressure

$$= 125.5 \text{ N.}$$

EXAMPLE (vi)

A pile driver of mass 3 Mg falls through a height of 5 m on to a pile of mass 1 Mg; if the pile is driven 24 cm into the ground, find the resistance of the ground (supposed uniform).

The velocity of the pile driver after falling 5 m is

$$\sqrt{(2 \times 9.8 \times 5)} = 9.9 \text{ m s}^{-1}$$

and its momentum is $3 \times 10^3 \times 9.9$ kg m s⁻¹.

After the impact the total mass in motion is 4 Mg, and if V m s⁻¹ is the common velocity of the driver and pile *immediately* after the impact

$$4 \times 10^3 V = 3 \times 10^3 \times 9.9$$

∴ $$V = 7.4.$$

Now this velocity is destroyed in 24 cm, and if a m s⁻², is the retardation, we get

$$0 = 7.4^2 - 2a(0.24)$$

∴ $$a = 7.4^2/0.48 = 114.1$$

and the retarding force is $4 \times 10^3 \times 114.1 = 4.56 \times 10^5$ N.

The resistance of the ground R must equal the retarding force plus the weight of the driver and pile,

$$\therefore \qquad R = 4 \times 10^3 \times 9\cdot8 + 4\cdot56 \times 10^5$$
$$= 4\cdot95 \times 10^5 \text{ N.}$$

EXAMPLES 5.1

1. A bullet of mass 30 g is fired with a velocity of 840 m s⁻¹ into a block of wood of mass 5 kg and resting on a smooth horizontal table. Find the common velocity of the bullet and block after the bullet has become embedded in the block.

2. A bullet of mass 20 g is fired with a velocity of 4020 cm s⁻¹ into a block of wood of mass 4 kg and resting on a smooth horizontal table. Find the common velocity of the bullet and block after the bullet has become embedded in the block.

3. A gun of mass 10 Mg free to recoil in the direction of the barrel, fires a shot of mass 100 kg with a velocity of 400 m s⁻¹. Find the velocity of recoil of the gun.

    If the recoil is resisted by a constant force so that the gun moves back only 12 cm, find the magnitude of this force.

4. A gun of mass 20 Mg resting on an inclined plane of slope 30°, fires a shot of mass 200 kg horizontally with a velocity of 630 m s⁻¹. Find the velocity of recoil of the gun, and the distance it moves up the incline before coming to rest.

5. Find the average pressure per square metre on the ground due to a rainfall of 1·2 cm in 2 hours. The velocity of the rain on striking the ground is equal to that acquired in falling freely through 270 m, and 1 m³ of rainwater has a mass of 1 Mg.

6. A pile driver of mass 5 Mg falls from a height of 3 m on to a pile of mass 1 Mg; if the pile is driven in 8 cm, find the average resistance of the ground.

7. An inelastic vertical pile of mass 0·5 Mg is driven 0·6 m into the ground by 30 blows of a hammer of mass 2 Mg, falling through 1·5 m. Find the resistance of the ground, supposed uniform.

    (I.S.)

8. A hammer of mass 1 kg, moving with a velocity of 6 m s⁻¹, drives a nail of mass 30 g, 2·5 cm into a fixed piece of wood. Find the common velocity of the nail and hammer just after impact, the percentage loss of energy, the time of motion of the nail, and the force of resistance of the wood assuming it to be constant.

    (I.E.)

9. A pile driver falls through h m on to a pile of mass W kg; if the resistance to penetration be R g N, and the desired penetration h cm, find the mass of the driver.

10. If a gun of mass M fires horizontally a shot of mass m, find the ratio of the energy of recoil of the gun to the energy of the shot. If a 500-kg gun discharges a 25-kg shot with a velocity of 300 m s^{-1}, find the uniform resistance necessary to stop the recoil of the gun in 15 cm.   (I.S.)

11. A shot of mass m is fired from a gun of mass M, placed on a smooth horizontal plane and inclined at an angle α to the horizontal. If v is the velocity of the gun's recoil at the instant when the shot leaves it, prove that the horizontal component of the impulsive pressure on the shot is Mv, and that the component at right angles to the gun's length is $mv \sin \alpha$. (It is assumed in each case that the impulsive pressure is resolved into two components at right angles.)

    Prove that the initial direction of the shot's motion is inclined at $\tan^{-1}\left[\left(1+\dfrac{m}{M}\right)\tan\alpha\right]$ to the horizontal.   (H.C.)

12. A shot of mass 8 kg is fired horizontally from a gun of mass 500 kg. If the muzzle velocity of the shot is 500 m s^{-1}, calculate that of the gun.

    Calculate the total kinetic energy produced (in the shot and gun); and, if the distance travelled along the bore of the gun is 2·1 m, find the average force applied to the shot. How far will the gun have moved when the shot leaves the muzzle?

13. A shot of mass m is fired from a gun of mass M, which is suspended by ropes of length l. If the total kinetic energy is the same as it would be if the shot left the muzzle of a fixed gun with velocity v, find the actual velocities of the shot and gun at the moment of separation, and find to what height the gun will rise at the recoil.   (H.C.)

14. In making a steel stamping a mass of 100 kg falls on to the steel through a distance of 1 m, and is brought to rest after traversing a further distance of 1·2 cm.

    Assuming that a uniform resistance is exerted by the steel, find the magnitude of this resistance.   (H.S.C.)

15. A bullet of mass m kg is fired horizontally with a velocity of v m s^{-1} into a block of wood of mass M kg suspended by a light cord. It is noted that the wood and embedded bullet swing until a height of h m above the original position is reached. Show that $mv = (M+m)\sqrt{(2gh)}$; it being given that the whole motion takes

place in one vertical plane. If an aeroplane rises vertically at 20 ms⁻¹ and drops an object of mass 10 kg from a height of 600 m, calculate the magnitude of the impulse with which the object strikes the ground, stating clearly the unit of impulse employed.   (H.S.D.)

16. A bullet of mass m, moving with velocity v, strikes a block of mass M, which is free to move in the direction of the motion of the bullet, and is embedded in it. Show that the loss of kinetic energy is $\frac{1}{2} Mmv^2/(M+m)$.

If the block is afterwards struck by an equal bullet moving in the same direction with the same velocity, show that there is a further loss of energy equal to

$$\frac{M^2mv^2}{2(M+2m)(M+m)}.$$ (I.S.)

17. A block of wood of mass 500 g is placed on a rough horizontal floor, the coefficient of friction between the block and floor being 0·4. A bullet of mass 40 g is fired with a velocity of 150 ms⁻¹ into the block. Find: (i) the velocity with which the block and bullet begin to move together after the impact; (ii) the distance which the block moves along the floor; (iii) the ratio of the energy lost during the impact to that lost through friction with the floor.   (I.S.)

18. From a gun of mass M, which can recoil freely on a horizontal platform, is fired a shell of mass m, the elevation of the gun being α. Show that the angle (ϕ) which the path of the shell initially makes with the horizontal is given by the equation

$$\tan \phi = (1+m/M) \tan \alpha;$$

and further, assuming that the whole energy of the explosion is transferred to the shell and the gun, show that the muzzle energy of the shell is less than it would be if the gun were fixed in the ratio $M : (M+m \cos^2 \phi)$.   (Q.E.)

19. A jet of water issues vertically at a speed of 10 ms⁻¹ from a nozzle 0·6 cm² section. A ball of mass 0·5 kg is balanced in the air by the impact of the water on its underside. Find the height of the ball above the level of the jet.

20. The penetration of a 15-g bullet, fired at 300 ms⁻¹, into a fixed block of wood is 7·5 cm.

If the bullet is fired at the same speed into a block of the same wood 5 cm thick (of mass 1·5 kg) which is free to move, prove that the block will be perforated; and find the velocity with which the bullet emerges.   (Q.E.)

21. A fire engine is directing a horizontal jet through a nozzle 2·5 cm in diameter fixed to the engine. It is delivering 1·6 m³ of water per minute. What is the reaction on the fire engine?
    (Q.E.)

22. A racing motor offers 1·5 m² of area to wind pressure. If the density of air is 1·25 kg m⁻³, calculate the power absorbed in overcoming wind resistance when the car is travelling at 100 km h⁻¹ against a head wind of 16 km h⁻¹.   (Q.E.)

23. A machine gun is fired backwards from the rear of an armoured car at the rate of 600 rounds per minute. The mass of each bullet is 15 g and the muzzle velocity 660 m s⁻¹. Find the driving force added to that of the car when the car is travelling at 60 km h⁻¹.
    (Q.E.)

24. A railway truck of mass 10 Mg moving with a velocity of 10 km h⁻¹ strikes, and is at the same moment coupled to, another truck of mass 5 Mg previously at rest. The second truck has its wheels locked by brakes, the coefficient of friction between the wheels and the rails being 0·2. Find how far the trucks move after the impact.   (Q.E.)

25. A pile of mass 1 Mg is being driven into the ground by blows from a mass of 500 kg which falls freely a distance of 2·5 m on to the pile without rebounding. The pile is driven in 15 cm by one blow. If the resistance of the ground is uniform, what is the amount of this resistance, and what is the time of penetration?
    (Q.E.)

26. Prove that if a horizontal jet of water could be made to issue through a nozzle of 6·4 cm² orifice at the rate of 4·8 m³ min⁻¹ it would exert a force about equal to the weight of 1 Mg against an obstacle placed in its path; and find the power required to produce the jet.   (H.S.C.)

27. A target of mass M is moving in a straight line with uniform velocity V. Shots of mass m are fired with velocity v in the opposite direction so as to strike the target, becoming embedded in it. Find how many shots must be fired in order to make the target begin to move back. Find also the kinetic energy lost when the first shot strikes the target.   (I.S.)

28. A train of trucks is being started from rest, and just before the last coupling becomes taut the front part has acquired a velocity of 24 km h⁻¹. If the part of the train now in motion has a mass of 72 Mg and the last truck has a mass of 6 Mg, find the jerk in the coupling.

29. A jet of water of cross-section 20 cm^2 and velocity 12 ms^{-1} impinges normally on a plane inelastic wall, so that the velocity of the water is destroyed on reaching the wall. Calculate the thrust on the wall. (I.S.)

5.8. Impulsive tensions in strings

Suppose two particles, A and B (Fig. 5.3), to be connected by an inextensible string and to lie on a smooth horizontal table.

FIG. 5.3

Then, if an impulse P is applied to one of them (say B) we cannot tell at once in what direction B will move (unless the direction of P is along or perpendicular to AB), as an impulsive tension is produced in the string and this also acts on B, which is therefore subject to *two* impulsive forces. We do know, however, that A is subject only to the impulsive tension in the string and must therefore start to move in the direction AB, and that its velocity is equal to the component of B's velocity in this direction.

We know also that the resultant momentum of A and B in the direction of the blow is equal to P, while the resultant at right angles to this direction is zero.

EXAMPLE

Two balls A and B, of masses 4 kg and 2 kg respectively, lie on a smooth horizontal plane and are connected by a taut inextensible string; B is due east of A. B is struck in such a manner that, if it were free, it would move north-east with a velocity of 21 ms^{-1}. Prove that B actually moves with a velocity of about 15·65 ms^{-1} in a direction about 71° 34′ north of east. Also compare the magnitude of the impulsive tension in the string with that of the blow. (I.E.)

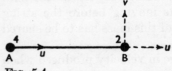

FIG. 5.4

The magnitude of the blow is 42 units of impulse, and its direction north-east. Let u, v ms^{-1} be the components of B's velocity along and perpendicular to AB (Fig. 5.4). The velocity of A is then u ms^{-1} along AB.

The momentum in the direction AB is equal to the component of the blow in that direction, i.e. $42/\sqrt{2}$ units.

$$\therefore \qquad 4u+2u = 42/\sqrt{2}$$

and the momentum perpendicular to AB is equal to the component of the blow perpendicular to AB, i.e. $42/\sqrt{2}$ units.

$$\therefore \qquad 2v = 42/\sqrt{2}$$
$$\therefore \qquad u = 7/\sqrt{2} \text{ and } v = 21/\sqrt{2}.$$

If V ms^{-1} is the resultant velocity of B.

$$V^2 = \tfrac{49}{2}+\tfrac{441}{2} = \tfrac{490}{2} = 245$$
$$\therefore \qquad V = 15{\cdot}65.$$

If θ is the angle the direction of V makes with the east,

$$\tan \theta = \frac{v}{u} = 3$$
$$\therefore \qquad \theta = 71° \ 34' \text{ nearly.}$$

The impulsive tension in the string generates a velocity u in A, i.e. a velocity of $7/\sqrt{2}$ ms^{-1} in a mass of 4 kg

$$\therefore \qquad \text{the tension is } 28/\sqrt{2} \text{ units of impulse.}$$
$$\therefore \qquad \frac{\text{impulsive tension}}{\text{blow}} = \frac{28}{42\sqrt{2}} = \frac{\sqrt{2}}{3} = 0{\cdot}47.$$

5.9. When two masses, connected by an inextensible string passing over a smooth pulley, are in motion, and the descending one is stopped, we know that the other goes on moving freely under gravity until the string again becomes taut. This was illustrated by examples in the last chapter. We have now to consider what happens *after* the string becomes taut again. The common velocity of the two masses after the jerk is less than that of the single mass which was moving before the string became taut, since the momentum of this mass has to be shared between the two.

We can also calculate the change in velocity produced when one of the masses picks up an extra mass previously at rest.

5.10. EXAMPLE (i)

Two masses of m and 2m are connected by a light inextensible string passing over a smooth pulley. Find the acceleration of the system.

If the mass 2m hits the ground (without rebounding) after the masses have been moving for 3 s, find how much time elapses from the instant this happens until the system is instantaneously at rest with the string taut.

If a be the common acceleration, and T the tension in the string, the equations of motion are

$$2mg - T = 2ma$$

and

$$T - mg = ma$$

$\therefore$

$$3ma = mg \text{ or } a = g/3.$$

After 3 s the common velocity v is given by

$$v = (g/3) \times 3 = g.$$

The mass m moves freely under gravity, starting with this velocity, and the time (t s) taken to go up and return to its initial position is given by

$$0 = gt - \tfrac{1}{2}gt^2$$

$\therefore$

$$t = 2.$$

When the string again becomes taut its velocity is again g, and its momentum is mg units.

Hence, if V is the common velocity after the jerk,

$$2mV = mg - mV$$

$\therefore$

$$V = \tfrac{1}{3}g.$$

The system starts moving with this velocity, but, as the heavier mass is moving upwards, there will be a retardation of $g/3$, equal to the original acceleration.

Hence the time t' s taken to come to rest is given by

$$0 = \frac{g}{3} - \frac{g}{3}\, t'$$

$\therefore$

$$t' = 1.$$

Hence the total interval between the impact of the $2m$ mass and the system coming to rest is

$$t + t' = 3 \text{ s.}$$

Note. If the masses are left to themselves the heavier one will descend and hit the plane again and the motion will be repeated indefinitely. The time taken for it to hit the plane the second time is, however, only $\frac{1}{3}$ of the original time, since it has only to acquire $\frac{1}{3}$ of the velocity it had in the first case. When the heavier mass is jerked up again the common velocity is again divided by 3, and so the time to rest will also be divided by 3. The interval from the instant when the heavier mass begins to descend until the system is again at rest in each repetition of the motion is $\frac{1}{3}$ of that in the preceding case. The total time until the heavier mass remains in contact with the ground is the sum of an infinite G.P. of common ratio $\frac{1}{3}$.

EXAMPLE (ii)

Two masses of 9 kg and 7 kg are fastened to the ends of a light thread which passes over a smooth pulley, the two portions of the string being vertical. The system is released from rest, and after moving for 2 s, a mass of 5 kg at rest is suddenly attached to the 7 kg mass. Find when the system will come to rest again. How far will the original masses have moved altogether?

(I.S.)

Let a m s^{-2} be the acceleration of the system, and T N the tension in the string, then

$$9g - T = 9a$$

and

$$T - 7g = 7a$$

$$\therefore \qquad 16a = 2g$$

$$\therefore \qquad a = \tfrac{1}{8}g.$$

After 2 s the velocity is v m s^{-1} where

$$v = \tfrac{1}{8}g \times 2 = 2{\cdot}45.$$

The momentum of the 9 kg mass is 22·05 units downwards and of the 7 kg mass is 17·15 units upwards.

If V m s^{-1} is the common velocity after picking up the 5 kg mass,

$$22{\cdot}05 - 9V = 12V - 17{\cdot}15$$

$$\therefore \qquad V = 39{\cdot}2/21.$$

The masses are now 9 and 12 kg, and if A m s^{-2} is the retardation and T' N the tension in the string, we get

$$12g - T' = 12A$$

and

$$T' - 9g = 9A$$

$$\therefore \qquad 21A = 3g$$

$$\therefore \qquad A = \tfrac{1}{7}g.$$

The time, t s, taken for the system to come to rest is given by

$$0 = \frac{39 \cdot 2}{21} - \frac{g}{7} t$$

$$\therefore \quad t = \frac{39 \cdot 2}{21} \times \frac{7}{9 \cdot 8} = \tfrac{4}{3}.$$

During the first 2 s the original masses move s_1 m, where

$$s_1 = \tfrac{1}{2} \times \tfrac{1}{8} g \times 4 = 2 \cdot 45.$$

During the last $\tfrac{4}{3}$ s, they move s_2 m where

$$s_2 = \frac{39 \cdot 2}{21} \times \tfrac{4}{3} - \tfrac{1}{2} \times \frac{9 \cdot 8}{7} \times \tfrac{16}{9} = \frac{78 \cdot 4}{63} = 1 \cdot 24.$$

Hence the total distance moved is 3·69 m.

EXAMPLE (iii)

A body of weight W, moving due north with speed, is suddenly caused to move north-west at a speed of v. What is the blow or impulse it has received? If the change in velocity has been gradual under a constant force and had taken a time T to effect the change, find the acceleration, and show that, if $v = u/\sqrt{2}$ and x and y be the displacements north and west at any time, $(y+x)^2 = 4uTy$. (I.E.)

In this problem it will be best to consider the *components* of the impulse in directions north and west.

Let ON (Fig. 5.5) represent north and OW west.

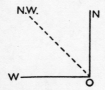

FIG. 5.5

The velocity v in direction north-west has components $v/\sqrt{2}$ north and $v/\sqrt{2}$ west.

The change in velocity in direction ON is $(v/\sqrt{2}) - u$, and in direction OW is $v/\sqrt{2}$.

Hence the components of impulse are

$$\frac{W}{g} \left(\frac{v}{\sqrt{2}} - u \right) \quad \text{and} \quad \frac{W}{g} \times \frac{v}{\sqrt{2}}.$$

The resultant impulse is

$$\frac{W}{g}\sqrt{\left(\frac{v^2}{2}+u^2-\frac{2uv}{\sqrt{2}}+\frac{v^2}{2}\right)}$$

$$=\frac{W}{g}\sqrt{\left(u^2+v^2-\frac{2uv}{\sqrt{2}}\right)}.$$

If F_1, F_2 are the components of the constant force along ON and OW respectively,

$$F_1 T = \frac{W}{g}\left(\frac{v}{\sqrt{2}}-u\right) \text{ and } F_2 T = \frac{W}{g}\times\frac{v}{\sqrt{2}}.$$

The component accelerations are

$$\frac{F_1 g}{W} \text{ and } \frac{F_2 g}{W}$$

or

$$\frac{1}{T}\left(\frac{v}{\sqrt{2}}-u\right) \text{ and } \frac{1}{T}\times\frac{v}{\sqrt{2}}.$$

The resultant acceleration is

$$\frac{1}{T}\sqrt{\left(\frac{v^2}{2}+u^2-\frac{2uv}{\sqrt{2}}+\frac{v^2}{2}\right)}$$

$$=\frac{1}{T}\sqrt{\left(v^2+u^2-\frac{2uv}{\sqrt{2}}\right)}.$$

At time t the displacements x and y are given by

$$x = ut+\tfrac{1}{2}\times\frac{1}{T}\left(\frac{v}{\sqrt{2}}-u\right)t^2.$$

and

$$y = \tfrac{1}{2}\times\frac{1}{T}\times\frac{v}{\sqrt{2}}t^2.$$

If

$$v = \frac{u}{\sqrt{2}} \text{ we get } x = ut-\frac{u}{4T}t^2.$$

and

$$y = \frac{u}{4T}t^2$$

$$\therefore \qquad y+x = ut$$

$$\therefore \qquad (y+x)^2 = u^2t^2 = 4uTy.$$

EXAMPLES 5.2

1. Two masses of 100 g and 80 g are connected by a light string passing over a smooth fixed pulley. The system starts from rest and the 80 g mass, after it has risen 9 cm, passes through a fixed

ring on which rests a bar of mass 40 g, and so carries the 40 g mass on with it. Show that the 40 g mass will be carried nearly 7·4 cm above the ring. (I.A.)

2. Two particles m_1 and m_2 $(m_1 > m_2)$, connected by a light inextensible string passing over a smooth fixed pulley, are left free. If the heavier particle reaches the ground after descending a distance d, after how many seconds will it be jerked off the ground, and with what velocity will it begin to rise? (I.S.)

3. Two masses, each of 2 kg connected by a string passing over a smooth pulley, are moving vertically with a velocity of 2 ms⁻¹. The ascending mass passes through a fixed ring without touching it, and removes from the ring a mass of 250 g which it carries with it. Find the height to which the 250-g mass is carried, and the time that elapses before it is again left on the ring. (I.A.)

4. Two masses $3M$ and M are connected by a cord passing over a pulley, and the whole is at rest with the former on the ground. A third mass M falls through a height h, strikes the second mass, adheres to it, and sets the whole in motion. Prove that the mass $3M$ will rise from the ground to a height $h/5$. (I.A.)

5. Two masses of 1·5 kg and 2·5 kg are tied to the ends of a string 4 m long. The string passes over a smooth peg 2·4 m above a horizontal table, the 2·5 kg mass lying on the table, the 1·5 kg mass being held close to the peg. If the 1·5-kg mass is allowed to fall, show that it will not reach the table.

Find also the greatest height reached by the 2·5-kg mass and the time it is in motion before it reaches the table a second time. (I.A.)

6. Two masses m and M are connected by a light string passing over a smooth weightless pulley vertically above a smooth inelastic horizontal plane, M being held so as to prevent motion. If M is released and takes t s to reach the plane, show that the system will first be at rest instantaneously (with the string taut) after a time

$$\frac{3Mt}{M+m},$$

and that the system will be finally at rest with M on the plane after a time $3t$. (Ex.)

7. Two particles of masses 90 g and 150 g are connected by an inextensible string of length 4·2 m which passes over a small smooth pulley at a height of 3 m above a table on which the heavier particle rests, vertically beneath the pulley. The other

particle is raised to the pulley and allowed to fall. Find the velocity of the system after the jerk, and the time at which it will first come to rest.   (I.S.)

8. Two masses of 2 kg and 3 kg are fastened to the ends of a light string of length 2 m, and placed on a smooth horizontal shelf 5 m above the ground. The 2 kg mass is placed at the edge of the shelf, and the 3 kg mass 1 m away from the edge, the line joining the two masses being perpendicular to the edge. If the 2 kg mass is gently pushed over the edge, find the time that elapses before the 3 kg mass reaches the end of the table.

9. Two equal masses (M) are connected by a light inextensible string which passes over a smooth peg, the masses hanging freely under gravity. A rider of mass m is placed on one of these masses. When this mass has descended through a distance h the rider is raised off the mass. At the same instant the other mass picks up from rest a precisely similar rider. Show that the system will next come to rest when the first mass has descended a further distance,

$$\frac{4M^2h}{(2M+m)^2}.$$ (H.S.C.)

10. Two particles of masses 4 kg and 3 kg are lying on a smooth table and are connected by a slack string. The first particle is projected along the table with a velocity of 21 m s^{-1} in a direction directly away from the second particle. Find the velocity of each particle after the string has become taut, and also find the difference between the kinetic energies of the system when the string is slack and when it is taut.

If the second particle is attached to a third particle of unknown mass by another slack string, and if the velocity of the system after both strings have become taut is 8 m s^{-1}, find the magnitude of the unknown mass.   (N.U.3)

11. Two particles A and B each of mass m are connected by a light inextensible string of length l, and rest on a smooth horizontal table at a distance $\frac{1}{2}l$ apart. The particle B receives a horizontal impulse $m\mu$ in a direction perpendicular to AB. Find the impulse in the string on tightening and the velocity of B immediately afterwards, if (i) A is held fixed and (ii) A is free to move.

Show that the loss of kinetic energy when A is fixed is twice the loss when A is free.

12. A particle of 60 g mass moving at 5 m s^{-1} in a given direction is struck by a blow which deflects its direction of motion through 60° and doubles its velocity. If a particle at rest, of 270 g mass,

were struck an equal blow, in what direction relative to the direction of the first particle, and with what velocity would it begin to move? Also, if velocity of the former particle were reversed before the blow, what would be its velocity and direction after the blow? (I.E.)

13. Three equal particles A, B, C of mass m are placed on a smooth horizontal plane. A is joined to B and C by light threads AB, AC, and the angle BAC is 60°.

An impulse I is applied to A in the direction BA. Find the initial velocities of the particles and show that A begins to move in a direction making an angle $\tan^{-1}\frac{\sqrt{3}}{7}$ with BA. (C.S.)

14. Three small bodies of masses 40, 50, 60 g respectively lie in order in a straight line on a large smooth table, the distance between consecutive bodies being 15 cm. Two slack strings, each 60 cm in length, connect the first with the second, and the second with the third. The third body is projected with a speed of 4·5 ms⁻¹ directly away from the other two. Find the time which elapses before the first begins to move and the speed with which it starts. Find also the loss of kinetic energy. (H.C.)

15. What do you understand by the statement 'momentum is a vector'? In a square ABCD the mid-point of CD is X. Bodies whose masses are 3, 2, 4, 1 kg moving along AX, BX, CX, DX respectively with speeds 5, 6, 3, 8 ms⁻¹ collide simultaneously at X and remain united. Determine, preferably by graphical methods, the new velocity and also the loss of kinetic energy.

If only the first three bodies remain united after the collision and the fourth moved off in the direction BD with a speed of 6 ms⁻¹, find the final velocity of the composite body. (N.U.4)

5.11. Impact of elastic bodies

When two spheres of any hard material collide they separate again, and in many cases, as when they are moving in opposite directions before impact, the velocity of one of them is reversed.

The spheres are slightly compressed, and, as they generally tend to return to their original shape, they rebound.

The time during which they are in contact may be divided into two parts: (i) the period of compression, and (ii) the period of restitution, during which they are recovering their shape. The property which causes bodies to recover their shape and here causes the rebound after collision is called *Elasticity*. If a body does not tend to recover its shape it will cause no force of restitution, and such a body is said to be *Inelastic*.

In dealing with the impact of elastic bodies we shall suppose that they are smooth, so that the only mutual action they can have on each other will be along the common normal at the point where they touch.

Usually the bodies are considered to be smooth spheres, and the mutual action between them is then along the line joining their centres.

When the direction of motion of each body is along the common normal at the point where they meet the impact is said to be *direct*.

When the direction of motion of either, or both, is not along the common normal the impact is said to be *oblique*.

Suppose two bodies of masses m_1 and m_2, moving with velocities u_1 and u_2 respectively, impinge directly.

If v_1 and v_2 are the velocities after impact the principle of momentum gives us the equation

$$m_1 v_1 + m_2 v_2 = m_1 u_1 + m_2 u_2. \qquad \text{(i)}$$

In the cases dealt with previously the bodies have kept together after impact, so that $v_1 = v_2$, and one equation is sufficient to determine this velocity.

When the bodies separate after impact this one equation is not sufficient to determine v_1 and v_2.

This is only to be expected, as the values of v_1 and v_2 will depend on the material of the bodies, and the principle of momentum takes no account of this.

There is no way of calculating the effect of the elasticity of the bodies, and we have to fall back on the results of experiments. Newton investigated the rebound of elastic bodies experimentally, and the result of these experiments is embodied in the following law.

5.12. Newton's experimental law

When two bodies made of given substances impinge directly the relative velocity after impact is in a constant ratio to the relative velocity before impact, and in the opposite direction. If the bodies impinge obliquely the same result holds for the component velocities along the common normal.

Hence, in the case of direct impact, if u_1, u_2 be the velocities before, and v_1, v_2 the velocities after impact, *all measured in the same direction along the direction of the impact*,

$$\frac{v_1 - v_2}{u_1 - u_2} = -e$$

where e is a positive constant depending on the material of which the bodies are made, and is called the *coefficient of restitution* (sometimes called the *coefficient of elasticity*).

This law, therefore, gives us a second equation,

$$v_1 - v_2 = -e(u_1 - u_2) \qquad \text{(ii)}$$

and by means of this and equation (i) (5.11) we can find v_1 and v_2.

The value of e differs considerably for different bodies; for two glass balls it is about 0·9; for ivory 0·8; while for lead it is about 0·2.

Bodies for which e is zero are said to be inelastic, while for *perfectly elastic* bodies $e = 1$.

Note. Newton's Law, like many experimental laws, is not accurately true. The value of e for given bodies does alter slightly for very large velocities, and in any case the law must be regarded only as an approximate one.

5.13. Direct impact of two spheres

Let m_1, m_2 be the masses, u_1, u_2 the velocities before impact, v_1, v_2 the velocities after impact, and e the coefficient of restitution.

The directions of the velocities are shown in Fig. 5.6.

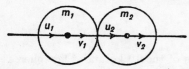

FIG. 5.6

We then have as above,
by the principle of momentum,

$$m_1 v_1 + m_2 v_2 = m_1 u_1 + m_2 u_2 \qquad \text{(i)}$$

by Newton's Law,

$$v_1 - v_2 = -e(u_1 - u_2) \qquad \text{(ii)}$$

Multiplying (ii) by m_2 and adding

$$(m_1+m_2)v_1 = (m_1-em_2)u_1+m_2(1+e)u_2.$$

Multiplying (ii) by m_1 and subtracting

$$(m_1+m_2)v_2 = m_1(1+e)u_1+(m_2-em_1)u_2.$$

These equations give v_1 and v_2.

If one sphere, say m_2, is moving originally in a direction opposite to that of m_1 the sign of u_2 will be negative in each of the equations (i) and (ii).

It is most important to specify the directions of v_1 and v_2 carefully. We fix on the direction we are going to call positive, usually from left to right, and then assume that both v_1 and v_2 are in this direction.

If either of them is really in the opposite direction the value obtained for it will have a negative sign.

In writing down equation (ii) great care must be taken to subtract the velocities in the same order on both sides. It is best to draw a diagram showing clearly the positive direction and the directions of the velocities of both bodies.

EXAMPLE (i)

A ball of mass 10 kg, moving at 5 m s⁻¹, overtakes another of mass 4 kg, moving at 2 m s⁻¹ in the same direction. If e = ½, find the velocities after impact.

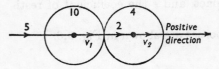

Fɪɢ. 5.7

Let v_1, v_2 m s⁻¹ be the velocities of the 10 kg and 4 kg spheres respectively after impact. By the principle of momentum

$$10v_1+4v_2 = 10\times5+4\times2 = 58$$

and by Newton's Law

$$v_1-v_2 = -\tfrac{1}{2}(5-2) = -\tfrac{3}{2}$$

$$\therefore \qquad 14v_1 = 52 \text{ or } v_1 = 3\tfrac{5}{7}$$

and $$14v_2 = 73 \text{ or } v_2 = 5\tfrac{3}{14}.$$

EXAMPLE (ii)

If the 4-kg ball in the previous question be moving in a direction opposite to that of the 10-kg ball, find the velocities after impact.

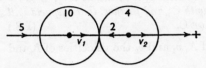

FIG. 5.8

The equations now become

$$10v_1 + 4v_2 = 10 \times 5 - 4 \times 2 = 42$$

and

$$v_1 - v_2 = -\tfrac{1}{2}(5+2) = -\tfrac{7}{2}$$

$\therefore$

$$14v_1 = 28 \text{ or } v_1 = 2$$

and

$$14v_2 = 77 \text{ or } v_2 = 5\tfrac{1}{2}.$$

EXAMPLE (iii)

A ball of mass 8 kg, moving with a velocity of 10 ms^{-1}, impinges directly on another of mass 24 kg, moving at 2 ms^{-1} in the opposite direction. If $e = \tfrac{1}{2}$, find the velocities after impact.

The equations here are

$$8v_1 + 24v_2 = 8 \times 10 - 24 \times 2 = 32$$

and

$$v_1 - v_2 = -\tfrac{1}{2}(10+2) = -6$$

$\therefore$

$$32v_1 = 32 - 144 = -112$$

$\therefore$

$$v_1 = -\tfrac{112}{32} = -3\tfrac{1}{2}.$$

Also

$$32v_2 = 32 + 48 = 80$$

$\therefore$

$$v_2 = \tfrac{80}{32} = 2\tfrac{1}{2}.$$

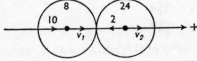

FIG. 5.9

The negative sign of v_1 shows that the direction of motion of the 8-kg ball is *reversed*, as we took the direction left to right as positive, and assumed v_1 to be in this direction. Since v_2 is positive, the 24-kg sphere moves from left to right after impact, so that its direction of motion is also reversed.

EXAMPLE (iv)

Three smooth spheres, A, B, C, of masses $3m$, m, $2m$ respectively, lie on a smooth table with their centres in a straight line. A is projected to impinge on B; show that, if the coefficient of restitution is $\frac{1}{2}$, B is reduced to rest after its first impact with C; and further, that impacts will cease with the second impact of B on C.   (I.S.)

Let u be the initial velocity of A, v_1 and v_2 the velocities of A and B after impact, then

$$3mv_1 + mv_2 = 3mu$$

and
$$v_1 - v_2 = -\tfrac{1}{2}u$$

$\therefore$
$$4v_1 = 2\tfrac{1}{2}u \text{ or } v_1 = \tfrac{5}{8}u.$$

Also
$$4v_2 = \tfrac{9}{2}u \text{ or } v_2 = \tfrac{9}{8}u.$$

B moves on faster than A, and strikes C. If v_2', v_3' be the velocities of B and C after impact, we get

$$mv_2' + 2mv_3' = \tfrac{9}{8}mu$$

and
$$v_2' - v_3' = -\tfrac{1}{2} \times \tfrac{9}{8}u$$

$\therefore$
$$3v_2' = 0$$

i.e. B is reduced to rest.

Also
$$3v_3' = (\tfrac{9}{8} + \tfrac{9}{16})u = \tfrac{27}{16}u$$

$\therefore$
$$v_3' = \tfrac{9}{16}u.$$

After the first impact A moves on with velocity $\tfrac{5}{8}u$, and strikes B again after the latter has been reduced to rest. If V_1, V_2 be the velocities of A and B after impact

$$3mV_1 + mV_2 = 3m \times \tfrac{5}{8}u,$$

and
$$V_1 - V_2 = -\tfrac{1}{2} \times \tfrac{5}{8}u.$$

These equations give

$$V_1 = \tfrac{25}{64}u$$

and
$$V_2 = \tfrac{45}{64}u.$$

The latter is greater than the velocity of C ($\tfrac{9}{16}u$), so that B overtakes C again; if V_2', V_3' be their velocities after impact, we get

$$mV_2' + 2mV_3' = \tfrac{45}{64}mu + \tfrac{9}{16}2mu = \tfrac{117}{64}mu$$

and
$$V_2' - V_3' = -\tfrac{1}{2}(\tfrac{45}{64} - \tfrac{9}{16})u = -\tfrac{9}{128}u.$$

These equations give

$$V_2' = \tfrac{36}{64}u \text{ and } V_3' = \tfrac{81}{128}u.$$

The velocities of A, B, C are now

$$\tfrac{25}{64}u \text{ or } \tfrac{50}{128}u, \tfrac{36}{64}u \text{ or } \tfrac{72}{128}u, \text{ and } \tfrac{81}{128}u,$$

in the same direction, and no more impacts can occur.

5.14. Loss of kinetic energy due to direct impact

Let m_1, m_2 be the masses, u_1 and u_2, v_1 and v_2 their velocities before and after impact, and e the coefficient of restitution.

We have, as before,

$$m_1v_1+m_2v_2 = m_1u_1+m_2u_2 \tag{i}$$

and

$$v_1-v_2 = -e(u_1-u_2). \tag{ii}$$

Square both equations, multiply the square of the second by m_1m_2 and add the results; we get

$$(m_1{}^2+m_1m_2)v_1{}^2+(m_2{}^2+m_1m_2)v_2{}^2 = (m_1u_1+m_2u_2)^2 \\ +e^2m_1m_2(u_1-u_2)^2$$

$$\therefore m_1(m_1+m_2)v_1{}^2+m_2(m_2+m_1)v_2{}^2 = (m_1u_1+m_2u_2)^2 \\ +m_1m_2(u_1-u_2)^2+e^2m_1m_2(u_1-u_2)^2-m_1m_2(u_1-u_2)^2$$

$$\therefore (m_1+m_2)(m_1v_1{}^2+m_2v_2{}^2) = (m_1+m_2)(m_1u_1{}^2+m_2u_2{}^2) \\ -m_1m_2(u_1-u_2)^2(1-e^2)$$

$$\therefore \tfrac{1}{2}m_1v_1{}^2+\tfrac{1}{2}m_2v_2{}^2 = \tfrac{1}{2}m_1u_1{}^2+\tfrac{1}{2}m_2u_2{}^2-\tfrac{1}{2}\frac{m_1m_2}{m_1+m_2}(u_1-u_2)^2(1-e^2).$$

Now

$$\tfrac{1}{2}m_1v_1{}^2+\tfrac{1}{2}m_2v_2{}^2$$

is the kinetic energy after impact, while

$$\tfrac{1}{2}m_1u_1{}^2+\tfrac{1}{2}m_2u_2{}^2$$

is the kinetic energy before impact.

$\therefore$ the loss in kinetic energy is

$$\tfrac{1}{2}\frac{m_1m_2}{m_1+m_2}(u_1-u_2)^2(1-e^2).$$

We see that there is always a loss unless $e = 1$, when this expression vanishes.

In many numerical examples it is easier to find the velocities after impact, and subtract the kinetic energy after impact from that before. The above is the shortest way of obtaining the value for the loss in the general case.

EXAMPLE (i)

A sphere of mass 1 kg, moving at 10 ms^{-1}, overtakes another sphere of mass 5 kg moving in the same line at 3 ms^{-1}. Find the loss of kinetic energy during impact, and show that the direction of motion of the first sphere is reversed. (Coefficient of restitution = 0·75.)   (H.S.C.)

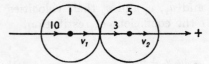

Fig. 5.10

If v_1 and v_2 ms^{-1} be the velocities of the 1 kg and 5 kg spheres after impact,

$$v_1 + 5v_2 = 10 + 15 = 25$$

and
$$v_1 - v_2 = -\tfrac{3}{4}(10-3) = -\tfrac{21}{4}$$

∴
$$6v_1 = 25 - \tfrac{105}{4} = -\tfrac{5}{4} \text{ or } v_1 = -\tfrac{5}{24}$$

and
$$6v_2 = 25 + \tfrac{21}{4} = \tfrac{121}{4} \text{ or } v_2 = \tfrac{121}{24}.$$

The value of v_1 is negative, showing that the direction of motion of the first sphere is reversed.

It must be remembered that the direction of motion does not affect the value of the kinetic energy. Algebraically, the value of v^2 is the same whether v is positive or negative.

The kinetic energy before impact is

$$\tfrac{1}{2} \times 1 \times 10^2 + \tfrac{1}{2} \times 5 \times 3^2 = 50 + \tfrac{45}{2} = 72 \cdot 5 \text{ J}.$$

The kinetic energy after impact is

$$\tfrac{1}{2} \times 1 \times \frac{25}{24^2} + \tfrac{1}{2} \times 5 \times \frac{121^2}{24^2} = \frac{5}{2 \times 24^2}(5 + 14\ 641) = 63 \cdot 6 \text{ J}.$$

The loss of energy

$$= 72 \cdot 5 - 63 \cdot 6 = 8 \cdot 9 \text{ J}.$$

EXAMPLE (ii)

Two masses, m and n, are moving in the same straight line; prove that their kinetic energy is

$$\tfrac{1}{2}(m+n)V^2 + \tfrac{1}{2}\frac{mn}{m+n}v^2,$$

where V is the velocity of their centre of mass, and v is their relative velocity.

If there is a direct impact between the masses, prove that their loss of kinetic energy is

$$\tfrac{1}{2}\frac{mn}{m+n}(1-e^2)v^2$$

where e is their coefficient of restitution.

(I.S.)

If u_1 and u_2 are the velocities of m and n, the velocity V of their centre of mass is given by

$$V = \frac{mu_1+nu_2}{m+n}$$

and their relative velocity $v = u_1-u_2$.

If E is their kinetic energy

$$E = \tfrac{1}{2}mu_1{}^2+\tfrac{1}{2}nu_2{}^2$$

$\therefore \qquad (m+n)E = \tfrac{1}{2}m^2u_1{}^2+\tfrac{1}{2}n^2u_2{}^2+\tfrac{1}{2}mn(u_1{}^2+u_2{}^2)$

$$= \tfrac{1}{2}(mu_1+nu_2)^2+\tfrac{1}{2}mn(u_1{}^2+u_2{}^2)-mnu_1u_2$$

$$= \tfrac{1}{2}(mu_1+nu_2)^2+\tfrac{1}{2}mn(u_1-u_2)^2$$

$\therefore \qquad (m+n)E = \tfrac{1}{2}(m+n)^2V^2+\tfrac{1}{2}mnv^2$

$\therefore \qquad E = \tfrac{1}{2}(m+n)V^2+\tfrac{1}{2}\dfrac{mn}{m+n}v^2.$

Now the velocity of the centre of mass is unaffected by impact between the masses, and hence the first term remains unaltered. By Newton's Law the relative velocity v is multiplied by e and reversed, i.e. it becomes $-ev$.

Hence, the second term becomes, after the impact,

$$\tfrac{1}{2}\frac{mn}{m+n}e^2v^2$$

and the loss in kinetic energy is

$$\tfrac{1}{2}\frac{mn}{m+n}v^2(1-e^2).$$

EXAMPLES 5.3

1. A sphere of mass 6 kg, moving at 4 ms^{-1}, overtakes another sphere of mass 4 kg, moving in the same direction with velocity 2 ms^{-1}. If $e = \tfrac{1}{4}$, find the velocities after impact.

2. A ball of mass 10 kg, moving at 8 ms^{-1}, overtakes another of mass 8 kg, moving in the same direction at 5 ms^{-1}. If $e = \tfrac{1}{2}$, find the velocities after impact.

3. A ball of mass 10 kg, moving at 8 m s^{-1} impinges directly on a ball of mass 8 kg, moving in the opposite direction at 4 m s^{-1}. If $e = \frac{1}{3}$, find their velocities after impact.

4. A ball of mass m, moving at 7 m s^{-1}, overtakes another of mass $2m$, moving in the same direction at 1 m s^{-1}. If $e = \frac{3}{4}$, show that the first ball will remain at rest after impact.

5. If two perfectly elastic spheres, of equal mass and moving in opposite directions, impinge directly, show that they will exchange velocities.

6. Two spheres of masses m and m', and coefficient of restitution e, impinge directly. Prove that the momentum transferred from one sphere to the other is

$$\frac{mm'}{m+m'}(1+e) \text{ (relative velocity before impact).} \qquad \text{(I.S.)}$$

7. A ball of mass m_1, moving with velocity v_1, impinges directly on a ball of mass m_2 lying at rest, and the second ball then impinges directly upon a third ball of mass m_3, which is also at rest. If the coefficient of restitution of the first pair is e, and that of the second pair is e', find the velocities of all three balls immediately after these impacts.   (I.E.)

8. Two spheres of masses 60 and 90 g are moving in their line of centres towards each other with velocities of 8 m s^{-1} and 10 m s^{-1}, and their coefficient of restitution is $\frac{3}{4}$. Find their velocities after impact, and the amount of kinetic energy transformed in the collision.   (I.A.)

9. If the velocities of two spheres before direct impact are given, show that the impulse which each sphere receives varies as

$$\frac{(1+e)mm'}{m+m'},$$

where e is the coefficient of restitution, and m, m' are the masses of the spheres.   (I.A.)

10. Two particles are moving in the same straight line. Express their kinetic energy in terms of their masses, their relative velocity, and the velocity of their centre of gravity; and hence, or otherwise, show that, if the particles are inelastic, kinetic energy is always lost by their impact. Two particles of masses m and $14m$ are moving with velocities $6u$ and u respectively, and the coefficient of restitution between them is $0\cdot5$. Show that, after impact, the kinetic energy gained by one equals half that lost by the other.   (I.S.)

11. A mass of 4 kg, moving at 20 ms⁻¹, overtakes a mass of 3 kg, moving in the same direction at $15\frac{1}{3}$ ms⁻¹. Five seconds after the impact the 3 kg mass encounters a fixed obstacle, which reduces it to rest. Assuming the coefficient of restitution between the masses to be $\frac{1}{2}$, find the further time that will elapse before the 4 kg mass strikes the 3 kg mass again.   (H.S.D.)

12. 1 truck of mass 10 Mg, moving at 2·4 ms⁻¹, impinges on another truck at rest of mass 5 Mg, and after impact the speed of the second truck relative to the first is 0·6 ms⁻¹. Determine the loss of kinetic energy due to the impact.   (I.E.)

13. A sphere of mass 3 kg, moving with a velocity of 7 ms⁻¹, impinges directly on another sphere, of mass 5 kg, at rest; after the impact the velocities of the spheres are in the ratio of 2 : 3. Find the velocities after impact and the loss of kinetic energy.
                                                                      (H.S.C.)

14. Three balls, A, B, C, of masses $3m$, $2m$, $2m$, and of equal radii, lie on a smooth table with their centres in a straight line. Their coefficient of restitution is $\frac{1}{4}$. Show that, if A is projected with velocity V to strike B, there are three impacts, and that the final velocities are

$$\frac{(50,\ 57,\ 60)}{128}V.$$ (H.C.)

15. Two trucks, of mass 5 Mg and 3 Mg respectively are standing on the same level set of rails. If the heavier truck impinges on the lighter, which is at rest, with a speed of 1·5 ms⁻¹, and the velocity of the lighter relative to the heavier after they separate is 0·9 ms⁻¹, find the actual speeds of the two trucks after they separate, and calculate the kinetic energy lost by the impact.
                                                                      (H.C.)

16. A, B, C are three exactly similar small spheres at rest in a smooth horizontal straight tube. A is set in motion and impinges on B. Show that A will impinge on B again after B has impinged on C, and show that there will be no more impacts, if e, the coefficient of restitution between the spheres, is not less than $3-\sqrt{8}$.
                                                                      (H.C.)

17. Three small exactly similar spheres, A, B, C are at rest in a smooth straight horizontal tube. The coefficient of restitution between any two of the spheres is 0·5. A is projected towards B with a velocity u.

     Determine the velocities of the three spheres after B has impinged on C, and A has impinged a second time on B, and show that there will be no more impacts.   (H.C.)

18. A truck of mass 5 Mg is moving on a set of level rails at the rate of 1·5 ms⁻¹, and impinges on a second truck of mass 10 Mg, which is standing at rest on the same rails. If after the impact the second truck moves on at the rate of 0·6 ms⁻¹, find the rate at which the first truck moves after the impact, and calculate the amount of kinetic energy lost by the impact. (H.C.)

19. The velocities of two spheres before impact are represented in magnitude and direction by lengths OP and OQ, those after impact by Op, Oq (the points O, P, Q, p, q, being in a straight line).

Prove that the ratio of Qq to Pp is equal to the ratio of the masses, and that the ratio of QP to qp is the coefficient of restitution. (I.S.)

20. Two spheres impinge on each other directly, and the impulse between them is R. Just before impact the velocity of their common centre of gravity is U, and the velocity of the faster-moving sphere relative to this centre of gravity is U_1. Show that the kinetic energy lost by this sphere is

$$\tfrac{1}{2}R[2U+(1-e)U_1],$$

where e is the coefficient of restitution between the spheres. (I.S.)

21. Two smooth spheres of masses m and m' impinge directly, their relative velocity just before impact being v, and the coefficient of restitution e.

Prove that the loss of kinetic energy due to the impact is

$$\tfrac{1}{2}\frac{mm'v^2(1-e^2)}{m+m'}.$$ (H.S.D.)

22. A ball overtakes another ball of m times its mass, which is moving with $1/n$th of its velocity in the same direction. If the impact reduces the first ball to rest, prove that the coefficient of restitution is

$$\frac{m+n}{mn-m},$$

and that m must be greater than $\dfrac{n}{n-2}$. (H.S.D.)

23. Two imperfectly elastic spheres, of weights W and $2W$, collide directly. Just before the impact the lighter sphere is moving with velocity 9 ms⁻¹, and the heavier with velocity 2 ms⁻¹ in opposite directions. The smaller sphere is brought to rest by the impact. Find the coefficient of restitution, and the velocity of the larger sphere after the impact. (H.S.D.)

24. Three spheres of equal mass lie in a straight line. If the first sphere be given a velocity u, show that the velocities of the spheres, after two impacts have taken place, are

$$\tfrac{1}{2}(1-e)u, \quad \tfrac{1}{4}(1-e^2)u, \quad \text{and} \quad \tfrac{1}{4}(1+e)^2u.$$

where e is the coefficient of restitution. (I.S.)

25. A ball is dropped, and after falling for 1 s meets another equal ball which is moving upwards with speed of 15 m s^{-1}. Calculate the velocity of each ball after the collision, given that the coefficient of restitution is $\tfrac{3}{4}$.

Find the percentage loss in kinetic energy due to the impact. (N.U.)

26. Two spheres of masses m_1 and m_2, travelling with velocities v_1 and v_2 in the same direction, collide directly and rebound. Determine the amount of momentum which is transferred between the spheres during the impact when the coefficient of restitution is e. If the velocities after impact are u_1, u_2, show that each sphere loses the same energy if

$$v_1 + v_2 + u_1 + u_2 = 0. \qquad \text{(C.W.B.)}$$

5.15. Impact of a smooth sphere on a fixed smooth plane

Let AB (Fig. 5.11) be the fixed plane, P the point at which the sphere impinges. Then if C is the centre of the sphere, CP is

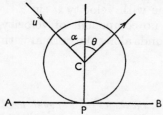

Fig. 5.11

the normal to the plane at P. Let the velocity of the sphere at impact be u, and the direction of motion of its centre make an angle α with CP. It rebounds at some angle θ to PC.

Since the plane and sphere are smooth, there is no impulse parallel to the plane; hence the component of the sphere's velocity in this direction, viz. $u \sin \alpha$, is unaltered.

By Newton's experimental law, the relative velocity *along the normal* after impact is $-e$ times that before impact measured in the same direction.

∴   if n is the normal velocity after impact

$$n - 0 = -e(u \cos \alpha - 0) \text{ or } n = -eu \cos \alpha$$

i.e. the normal velocity is reversed and multiplied by e.

The velocity after impact has therefore two components, $u \sin \alpha$ parallel to AB, and $eu \cos \alpha$ parallel to the normal PC.

The resultant velocity after impact $= u\sqrt{(\sin^2 \alpha + e^2 \cos^2 \alpha)}$. If θ be the angle between the direction of motion and the normal,

$$\tan \theta = \frac{u \sin \alpha}{eu \cos \alpha} = \frac{1}{e} \tan \alpha$$

or $\cot \theta = e \cot \alpha.$

The impulse on the plane due to the impact is measured by the change of momentum along the normal. If m is the mass of the sphere, this is

$$mu \cos \alpha + meu \cos \alpha = mu(1 + e) \cos \alpha.$$

If $e = 1$, the velocity after impact is u, and $\theta = \alpha$, the sphere after impact rebounds so that the angle of reflection is equal to the angle of incidence.

If $e = 0$ there is no velocity along the normal after impact, and the sphere slides along the plane with velocity $u \sin \alpha$.

If the impact be direct there is no component of velocity parallel to the plane, the sphere rebounds along the normal with velocity eu.

EXAMPLE (i)

A ball, moving with a velocity of 20 ms^{-1}, impinges on a smooth fixed plane in a direction making an angle of 30° with the plane; if the coefficient of restitution is $\frac{2}{5}$, find the velocity of the ball after the impact.

The component of velocity parallel to the plane is 20 cos 30°, or $10\sqrt{3}$ ms^{-1}, and this is unaltered by the impact.

The component of velocity perpendicular to the plane is 20 sin 30°, or 10 ms^{-1}, and this is reversed and multiplied by $\frac{2}{5}$.

The components of velocity along and perpendicular to the plane after impact are, therefore,

$$10\sqrt{3} \text{ and } 4 \text{ ms}^{-1}.$$

If V ms⁻¹ is the resultant velocity,

$$V^2 = 300 + 16 = 316$$

$$\therefore \qquad V = \sqrt{316} = 17 \cdot 7.$$

The direction makes an angle $\tan^{-1}(4/10\sqrt{3})$ or $\tan^{-1}(2\sqrt{3}/15)$ with the plane.

EXAMPLE (ii)

A particle falls from a height h upon a fixed horizontal plane; if e be the coefficient of restitution, show that the whole distance described before the particle has finished rebounding is $(1+e^2)h/(1-e^2)$ and that the whole time taken is

$$\frac{1+e}{1-e} \times \sqrt{\frac{2h}{g}}.$$

Let u be the velocity of the particle on first hitting the plane, so that

$$u^2 = 2gh.$$

The particle rebounds with velocity eu. The velocity when it hits the plane the second time is again eu, and the velocity after the second rebound is e^2u. Similarly, the velocities after the third, fourth, etc., rebounds are e^3u, e^4u, etc.

The height to which the particle rises after the first rebound is

$$\frac{(eu)^2}{2g}$$

and after the second

$$\frac{(e^2u)^2}{2g}$$

and so on.

Also $u^2 = 2gh$, so that these distances are e^2h, e^4h, etc. Hence the whole distance described is

$$h + 2(e^2h + e^4h + \dots \text{ to infinity})$$

$$= h + 2h\frac{e^2}{1-e^2} = h\frac{1+e^2}{1-e^2}.$$

The time of flight after the first impact is $2eu/g$, after the second $2e^2u/g$, and so on, and the time of falling originally is

$$\sqrt{\left(\frac{2h}{g}\right)}.$$

Hence, the whole time of motion

$$= \sqrt{\left(\frac{2h}{g}\right)} + \frac{2u}{g}(e + e^2 + e^3 + \ldots \text{ to infinity})$$

$$= \sqrt{\left(\frac{2h}{g}\right)} + 2\sqrt{\left(\frac{2h}{g}\right)}(e + e^2 + \ldots)$$

$$= \sqrt{\left(\frac{2h}{g}\right)}\left(1 + 2\frac{e}{1-e}\right) = \sqrt{\left(\frac{2h}{g}\right)} \times \frac{1+e}{1-e}.$$

EXAMPLE (iii)

A sphere of mass m lies on a smooth table between a sphere of mass
m' and a fixed vertical plane. It is projected towards the other sphere;
show that, if the coefficient of restitution between the two spheres and
between m and the plane is $\frac{3}{5}$ in both cases, m will be reduced to rest at
its second impact with m' if m' = 15m.   (I.S.)

Let u be the velocity of projection of m, and v_1, v_2 the velocities
of m and m' after impact, then

$$mv_1 + m'v_2 = mu$$

and
$$v_1 - v_2 = -\tfrac{3}{5}u$$

∴
$$(m + m')v_1 = u(m - \tfrac{3}{5}m')$$

and
$$(m + m')v_2 = \tfrac{8}{5}mu.$$

Putting $m' = 15m$, these become

$$16mv_1 = u(m - 9m) = -8mu \text{ or } v_1 = -\tfrac{1}{2}u$$

and
$$16mv_1 = \tfrac{8}{5}mu \text{ or } v_2 = \tfrac{1}{10}u.$$

The velocity of m is therefore reversed; it hits the plane with
velocity $\tfrac{1}{2}u$ and rebounds with velocity

$$\tfrac{3}{5} \times \tfrac{1}{2}u \text{ or } \tfrac{3}{10}u$$

which enables it to catch m' again.

If V, V' be the velocities of m and m' after their second impact,

$$mV + m'V' = \tfrac{3}{10}mu + \tfrac{1}{10}m'u$$

and
$$V - V' = -\tfrac{3}{5}(\tfrac{2}{10})u = -\tfrac{3}{25}u$$

∴
$$(m + m')V = \tfrac{3}{10}mu + \tfrac{1}{10}m'u - \tfrac{3}{25}m'u$$

or putting $m' = 15m$ we get

$$16mV = \tfrac{3}{10}mu + \tfrac{3}{2}mu - \tfrac{9}{5}mu$$
$$= 0.$$

∴ m is reduced to rest.

EXAMPLES 5.4

1. A particle falls from a height of 10 m upon a fixed horizontal plane, the coefficient of restitution being $\frac{1}{5}$. Find the height to which the particle rises after impact, and the time it takes to reach the plane again. What is the velocity after the second rebound?

2. A ball falls from a height of 10 m upon a fixed horizontal plane; if it rebounds to a height of 6·4 m, find the coefficient of restitution.

3. A ball moving at 12 ms^{-1} impinges on a smooth fixed plane so that its direction of motion makes an angle of 30° with the plane; if the coefficient of restitution is $\frac{1}{2}$, find the magnitude and direction of the velocity of the ball after impact.

4. A ball falls from a height of 10 m upon an inclined plane, the coefficient of restitution being $\frac{1}{5}$. Find the magnitude and direction of the velocity of the ball after impact, when the inclination of the plane is: (1) 45°; (2) 60°.

5. A billiard ball of mass 210 g strikes a smooth cushion when moving at 2·4 ms^{-1} in a direction inclined at 30° to the cushion. If the coefficient of restitution is $\frac{7}{8}$, find the loss of kinetic energy due to the impact.   (I.A.)

6. A marble dropped on a stone floor from a height of 4 m is found to rebound to a height of 3 m. Find the coefficient of restitution.

7. A billiard table is 1·8 m by 2·4 m. Find the position of a point in the shorter side and the direction of projection, such that a ball thus struck off will describe a rectangle and return to the same spot after rebounding at each of the other three cushions, the ball being smooth, and the coefficient of elasticity being $\frac{4}{9}$.   (I.S.)

8. A sphere of mass m moving with velocity u impinges on a fixed plane, the direction of motion making an angle α with the plane. If e is the coefficient of restitution between the sphere and the plane, find: (i) the magnitude and direction of the velocity of the sphere after impact; (ii) the loss of momentum; (iii) the loss of kinetic energy.   (I.S.)

9. A smooth elliptical tray is surrounded by a smooth vertical rim; prove that a perfectly elastic particle projected from a focus along the tray in any direction will after two impacts return to the focus.   (H.S.D.)

10. If sheets of paper are placed on a table the coefficient of restitution is reduced by an amount proportional to the thickness of

the paper. When a ball is dropped on to the bare table it rises after impact to three-quarters of the height of fall. When the thickness of the paper is 2·5 cm it rises to only one-half of the height of fall. What thickness of paper is required in order that the rebound shall be one-quarter of the height of fall?   (I.S.)

11. The line joining the centres of two equal smooth balls P and Q lying on a smooth table is perpendicular to a smooth vertical plane; the ball P farthest from the plane slides towards Q, which is at rest, with velocity u; after the impact Q meets the plane and a second impact occurs and so on. If e is the coefficient of restitution between the balls and e' that between Q and the plane, find the velocities of P and Q after the first impact of Q with the plane. Show that there will necessarily be a third impact of P and Q if $e' < \dfrac{(1-e)^2}{(1+e)^2}$.   (H.S.D.)

12. A bullet of mass 60 g is fired horizontally into a fixed block of wood, striking it with a speed 400 m s⁻¹. If the bullet penetrates to a distance 15 cm, find the average force of resistance of the wood to the motion.

   If the block were of metal, and the bullet rebounded instead of penetrating, find the kinetic energy which would be lost at the impact if the coefficient of restitution between the bodies were 0·3. State the units in which you give your result.   (N.U.)

5.16. Oblique impact of two spheres

Let C_1, C_2 (Fig. 5.12) be the centres of the spheres, m_1, m_2 their masses, and let their velocities u_1 and u_2 be inclined at angles α and β to the line of centres C_1C_2 at the moment of impact.

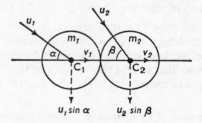

Fig. 5.12

The components of velocity perpendicular to C_1C_2 are $u_1 \sin \alpha$, $u_2 \sin \beta$, and these are unaltered by the impact.

Considering the motion along C_1C_2, if v_1 and v_2 are the components of the velocities along this line after impact we have, by the principle of momentum,

$$m_1 v_1 + m_2 v_2 = m_1 u_1 \cos \alpha + m_2 u_2 \cos \beta \qquad \text{(i)}$$

and by Newton's Law,

$$v_1 - v_2 = -e(u_1 \cos \alpha - u_2 \cos \beta). \qquad \text{(ii)}$$

These equations give

$$v_1 = \frac{(m_1 - em_2)u_1 \cos \alpha + m_2 u_2 (1+e) \cos \beta}{m_1 + m_2}$$

$$v_2 = \frac{m_1 u_1 (1+e) \cos \alpha + u_2 (m_2 - em_1) \cos \beta}{m_1 + m_2}.$$

The resultant velocity of each sphere and its direction of motion can be found from these components and the components perpendicular to $C_1 C_2$, viz. $u_1 \sin \alpha$ and $u_2 \sin \beta$.

If $m_1 = m_2$ and $e = 1$, then $v_1 = u_2 \cos \beta$ and $v_2 = u_1 \cos \alpha$, i.e. the spheres interchange their velocities in the direction of the line of centres.

In many problems one of the spheres is at rest. Now, if $u_2 = 0$, the equations (i) and (ii) above reduce to

$$m_1 v_1 + m_2 v_2 = m_1 u_1 \cos \alpha$$

and

$$v_1 - v_2 = -eu_1 \cos \alpha$$

$$\therefore \quad v_1 = \frac{(m_1 - em_2)u_1 \cos \alpha}{m_1 + m_2} \text{ and } v_2 = \frac{m_1 u_1 (1+e) \cos \alpha}{m_1 + m_2}.$$

The second sphere has no velocity perpendicular to the line of centres, so that it moves off along that line.

The sphere m_1 has velocity $u_1 \sin \alpha$ perpendicular to $C_1 C_2$, so that if θ is the angle made by its direction of motion with $C_1 C_2$

$$\tan \theta = \frac{u_1 \sin \alpha}{v_1} = \frac{(m_1 + m_2) \sin \alpha}{(m_1 - em_2) \cos \alpha}.$$

If also $m_1 = m_2$, the results simplify still further, and we have

$$v_1 = \tfrac{1}{2}(1-e)u_1 \cos \alpha, \quad v_2 = \tfrac{1}{2}(1+e)u_1 \cos \alpha$$

and

$$\tan \theta = \frac{2 \sin \alpha}{(1-e) \cos \alpha}.$$

5.17. Loss of kinetic energy in oblique impact

The velocities perpendicular to the line of centres are unaltered. The loss of kinetic energy is therefore the same as in the case of direct impact (5.14) if we substitute $u_1 \cos \alpha$ and $u_2 \cos \beta$ for u_1 and u_2 respectively.

The loss is therefore

$$\tfrac{1}{2} \frac{m_1 m_2}{m_1 + m_2} (u_1 \cos \alpha - u_2 \cos \beta)^2 (1 - e^2).$$

5.18. EXAMPLE (i)

A ball of mass 8 kg, moving with velocity 4 ms⁻¹, impinges on a ball of mass 4 kg, moving with velocity 2 ms⁻¹. If their velocities before impact be inclined at angles 30° and 60° to the line joining their centres at the moment of impact, find their velocities after impact when $e = \tfrac{1}{2}$.

Let C_1 and C_2 (Fig. 5.13) be the centres of the balls.

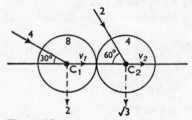

FIG. 5.13

The components of velocity perpendicular to $C_1 C_2$ are $4 \sin 30°$ and $2 \sin 60°$, or 2 and $\sqrt{3}$ ms⁻¹. These are unaltered by the impact.

If v_1 and v_2 be the components of the velocities along $C_1 C_2$ after impact we have by momentum equation

$$8v_1 + 4v_2 = 8 \times 4 \cos 30° + 4 \times 2 \cos 60° = 16\sqrt{3} + 4$$

and by Newton's Law

$$v_1 - v_2 = -\tfrac{1}{2}(4 \cos 30° - 2 \cos 60°) = -\tfrac{1}{2}(2\sqrt{3} - 1).$$

$$\therefore \qquad\qquad 2v_1 + v_2 = 4\sqrt{3} + 1$$

and

$$2v_1 - 2v_2 = -2\sqrt{3} + 1.$$

$$\therefore \qquad\qquad 3v_2 = 6\sqrt{3} \quad \text{or} \quad v_2 = 2\sqrt{3},$$

and

$$6v_1 = 6\sqrt{3} + 3 \quad \text{or} \quad v_1 = \frac{2\sqrt{3} + 1}{2}.$$

The velocity of the 8 kg sphere

$$=\sqrt{\left\{4+\left(\frac{2\sqrt{3}+1}{2}\right)^2\right\}}=\sqrt{\left(\frac{29+4\sqrt{3}}{4}\right)}\ \mathrm{m\,s^{-1}}$$

and if θ be the inclination to C_1C_2

$$\tan\theta=\frac{2\times2}{2\sqrt{3}+1}=\frac{4(2\sqrt{3}-1)}{11}.$$

The velocity of the 4 kg sphere

$$=\sqrt{(3+12)}=\sqrt{15}\ \mathrm{m\,s^{-1}}$$

and if ϕ be the inclination to C_1C_2

$$\tan\phi=\frac{\sqrt{3}}{2\sqrt{3}}=\tfrac{1}{2}.$$

EXAMPLE (ii)

A sphere of mass M, travelling with velocity u, impinges obliquely on a stationary sphere of mass M', the direction of the blow making an angle α with the line of motion of the impinging sphere. If the coefficient of restitution is e, prove that the impinging sphere is deflected through an angle β, such that

$$\tan\beta=\frac{M'(1+e)\tan\alpha}{(M-eM')+(M+M')\tan^2\alpha}.$$

Find the subsequent velocities if $u=10\ ms^{-1}$, $\alpha=30°$, $M'=2M$, and $e=0\cdot5$.   (Ex.)

Let C_1 and C_2 (Fig. 5.14) be the centres of M and M'.

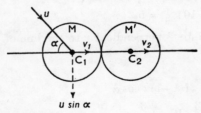

FIG. 5.14

The component velocities of M along and perpendicular to C_1C_2 are $u\cos\alpha$ and $u\sin\alpha$, and the latter is unaltered by the impact.

If v_1 and v_2 are the components of the velocities along C_1C_2 after impact

$$Mv_1+M'v_2=Mu\cos\alpha \tag{i}$$

and

$$v_1-v_2=-eu\cos\alpha \tag{ii}$$

$$\therefore \qquad (M+M')v_1 = u(M-eM')\cos\alpha$$

$$\therefore \qquad v_1 = \frac{(M-eM')u\cos\alpha}{M+M'}.$$

To find the angle of deflection we resolve v_1 and $u\sin\alpha$ perpendicular to and along the original direction of motion.

The sum of the components perpendicular to the original direction is

$$u\sin\alpha\cos\alpha - v_1\sin\alpha$$

$$= u\sin\alpha\cos\alpha - \frac{(M-eM')u\sin\alpha\cos\alpha}{M+M'}$$

$$= \frac{(1+e)M'u\sin\alpha\cos\alpha}{M+M'}.$$

The sum of the components along the original direction is

$$u\sin^2\alpha + v_1\cos\alpha = u\sin^2\alpha + \frac{(M-M'e)u\cos^2\alpha}{M+M'}$$

$$= \frac{u(M+M'\sin^2\alpha - eM'\cos^2\alpha)}{M+M'}$$

$$\therefore \qquad \tan\beta = \frac{(1+e)M'\,u\sin\alpha\cos\alpha}{u[M\sin^2\alpha + M'\sin^2\alpha + M\cos^2\alpha - eM'\cos^2\alpha]}$$

$$= \frac{M'\,(1+e)\tan\alpha}{(M+M')\tan^2\alpha + (M-eM')}.$$

If $u=10$, $\alpha=30°$, $M'=2M$, $e=0.5$, we get

$$v_1 = \frac{(M-\frac{1}{2}2M)u\cos\alpha}{M+2M} = 0$$

and
$$u\sin\alpha = 10 \times \tfrac{1}{2} = 5.$$

Therefore the velocity of M is 5 ms^{-1} perpendicular to the line of centres.

Also from (i) and (ii)

$$(M+M')v_2 = M(1+e)u\cos\alpha$$

$$\therefore \qquad v_2 = \frac{M(1+e)u\cos\alpha}{M+M'} = \frac{\frac{3}{2}\times 10 \times \frac{\sqrt{3}}{2}}{3} = \frac{5\sqrt{3}}{2}\ \text{ms}^{-1}.$$

EXAMPLE (iii)

A sphere is suspended from a fixed point by an inextensible string. A second sphere of small radius and equal mass m, moving downwards in a direction making an angle of 30° with the vertical, impinges directly on the first sphere with speed V. If the coefficient of restitution *between the spheres is $\frac{1}{2}$, prove that the initial velocity of the first sphere after impact is $\frac{3}{5}V$.*

Calculate also the impulsive force in the string at the moment of impact.   (H.S.D.)

In this problem, although the impact is direct, the suspended sphere is not free to move along the line of centres. It is only free to move perpendicular to the string, i.e. horizontally, and *we can apply the principle of momentum in this direction only.*

Newton's Law is applied, as usual, along the line of centres.

Let A (Fig. 5.15) be the point of suspension, and C the centre of the first sphere.

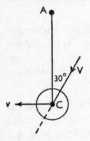

Fig. 5.15

Let v be the horizontal velocity of this sphere after impact, u the velocity of the impinging sphere after impact.

As the blow on the latter is along the line of centres, u is in the same straight line as the original direction of motion.

Equating horizontal momenta after and before impact,

$$mv + mu \cos 60° = mV \cos 60° \qquad \text{(i)}$$

From Newton's Law, along the line of centres,

$$u - v \cos 60° = -\tfrac{1}{2}V \qquad \text{(ii)}$$

$$\therefore \qquad v + \tfrac{1}{2}u = \tfrac{1}{2}V$$

and $$u - \tfrac{1}{2}v = -\tfrac{1}{2}V$$

$$\therefore \qquad \tfrac{5}{4}v = (\tfrac{1}{2} + \tfrac{1}{4})V = \tfrac{3}{4}V$$

$$\therefore \qquad v = \tfrac{3}{5}V.$$

Also $$\tfrac{5}{4}u = -\tfrac{1}{4}V \text{ or } u = -\tfrac{1}{5}V.$$

The vertical momentum before impact was $mV \cos 30° = \dfrac{\sqrt{3}m}{2}V.$

The vertical momentum after impact is

$$-\tfrac{1}{5}mV \cos 30° = -\dfrac{\sqrt{3}}{10}mV.$$

The impulsive tension in the string is equal to the change of momentum it produces, and is therefore

$$\frac{\sqrt{3}}{2}mV + \frac{\sqrt{3}}{10}mV = \frac{3\sqrt{3}}{5}mV.$$

EXAMPLES 5.5

1. A sphere of mass 2 kg moving at 10 ms⁻¹, impinges obliquely on a sphere of mass 4 kg which is at rest, the direction of motion of the first sphere making an angle of 60° with the line of centres at the moment of impact. Find the velocities of the spheres after impact, the coefficient of restitution being $\frac{1}{2}$.

2. A sphere of mass 8 kg moving at 6 ms⁻¹, impinges obliquely on a sphere of mass 4 kg which is at rest, the direction of motion making an angle of 30° with the line of centres. Find the velocities of the spheres after impact, the coefficient of restitution being $\frac{3}{4}$.

3. A sphere of mass 2 kg moving with velocity 8 ms⁻¹, impinges on a sphere of mass 4 kg, moving with velocity 2 ms⁻¹; if their velocities before impact be in like parallel directions and inclined at an angle of 30° to the line of centres at the moment of impact, find the velocities after impact, the coefficient of restitution being $\frac{1}{8}$.

4. If, in the last example, the spheres are moving in opposite parallel directions, find their velocities after impact.

5. Two equal balls, moving with equal speeds, impinge so that their directions of motion are inclined at 30° and 60° to the line of centres at the moment of impact; if the balls are perfectly elastic, find the directions of motion after the impact.

6. If, in question 5, the coefficient of restitution is $\frac{1}{2}$, find the velocities of the balls after impact.

7. A sphere of mass m impinges obliquely on a sphere of mass M, which is at rest. Show that, if $m = eM$, the directions of motion after impact are at right angles.

8. A smooth billiard ball impinges on another equal ball at rest in a direction that makes an angle α with the line of centres at the moment of impact, and e is their coefficient of restitution. Prove that the angle, through which the direction of motion of the impinging ball is deviated, is $\tan^{-1}\left[\dfrac{(1+e)\tan\alpha}{1-e+2\tan^2\alpha}\right]$.   (I.S.)

9. Two equal smooth billiard balls, whose coefficient of restitution is e, moving with equal velocities in opposite directions, impinge obliquely, the line of centres on impact being inclined at $45°$ to the direction of motion. Prove that the loss of kinetic energy is half what it would have been had the impact been direct. (I.S.)

10. A smooth sphere, moving with velocity u, impinges on an equal smooth sphere at rest, the direction of u just before impact being inclined at an angle α to the line of centres. Find the magnitude and direction of the velocity of each sphere after impact in terms of u, α and the coefficient restitution e. If $\tan^2 \alpha = \frac{8}{27}$, and $e = \frac{2}{3}$, show that the velocity of the first sphere is halved by the impact. (H.S.D.)

11. A smooth sphere of mass m impinges obliquely on a sphere of mass M which is at rest. If after the impact the first sphere is moving in a direction perpendicular to that of its original motion, show that $m < eM$, where e is the coefficient of restitution. Show also that the kinetic energy of the two spheres is reduced by the impact in the ratio $1 : e$. (H.S.D.)

12. A billiard ball is at rest and another equal ball is aimed at the first so that the direction of motion of the centre (when produced geometrically) just touches the first; if the coefficient of restitution is $\frac{4}{5}$, find the directions in which the balls travel after impact, and prove that the amount of kinetic energy transferred to the first ball is about 0·61 of the energy of the other before impact, while the other has about 0·26 of its original energy left. (I.S.)

CHAPTER SIX

PROJECTILES

6.1. We now consider the motion of a particle when projected under gravity in any direction. In doing this we shall assume, as before, that the acceleration due to gravity is constant. We shall also neglect the resistance of the air to the motion. The following terms are used in connection with projectiles:

The Angle of Projection is the angle that the direction in which the particle is projected makes with a horizontal plane through the point of projection. This angle is also called the *angle of elevation*.

The Trajectory is the path described by the particle.

The Range is the distance between the point of projection and the point where the trajectory meets any plane through the point of projection.

The downward acceleration due to the earth's attraction causes the path to be curved, and we shall show later that this curve is always a parabola.

Many important results, however, can be obtained without finding the nature of the path.

6.2. The principle of the method employed is to consider the vertical and horizontal components of the motion separately. Since gravity acts vertically, it has no effect on the velocity of the particle in a horizontal direction.

The horizontal velocity therefore remains constant throughout the motion.

If the particle is projected with velocity u at an elevation α the horizontal and vertical components of the initial velocity are $u \cos \alpha$ and $u \sin \alpha$ respectively.

The horizontal velocity throughout the motion is therefore $u \cos a$, but the vertical velocity is subject to an acceleration g downwards, and therefore at any time t after the instant of projection equals $u \sin \alpha - gt$.

Consequently the horizontal distance gone in time t is $(u \cos \alpha)t$, and the vertical distance is $(u \sin \alpha)t - \frac{1}{2}gt^2$.

From these simple results all the characteristics of the motion can be derived, as we shall now show.

6.3. Suppose the particle is projected from P (Fig. 6.1) with velocity u at an angle α to the horizontal PX through P.

Let A be the highest point of the path, and Q the point where it again meets the horizontal plane through P.

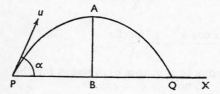

FIG. 6.1

(i) *To find the greatest height attained*

When the particle has reached the highest point A of its path it will have lost all its vertical velocity; the initial vertical velocity is $u \sin \alpha$, and hence we have

$$0 = u^2 \sin^2 \alpha - 2gh$$

$$\therefore \qquad h = \frac{u^2 \sin^2 \alpha}{2g}.$$

(ii) *To find the time taken to reach the greatest height*

Again, as the vertical velocity is zero at the highest point, the time to reach the greatest height is given by

$$0 = u \sin \alpha - gt$$

$$\therefore \qquad t = \frac{u \sin \alpha}{g}.$$

(iii) *To find the time of flight, i.e. the time taken to return to the same horizontal level as* P

Using $\qquad s = ut - \frac{1}{2}gt^2$ and putting $s = 0$ when $t = T$

we get $\qquad 0 = u \sin \alpha \times T - \frac{1}{2}gT^2$

$$\therefore \qquad T = \frac{2u \sin \alpha}{g}.$$

This is twice the time taken to reach the highest point, as we should expect from symmetry.

(iv) *To find the range on the horizontal plane through* P

During the time T the particle has been moving horizontally with uniform velocity $u \cos \alpha$.

$\therefore$ horizontal distance described

$$= u \cos \alpha \times T = \frac{2u^2 \sin \alpha \cos \alpha}{g}.$$

$\therefore$ the range

$$R = \frac{2u^2 \sin \alpha \cos \alpha}{g} = \frac{u^2 \sin 2\alpha}{g}.$$

For a given velocity of projection u, this expression for the range is a maximum when $2\alpha = 90°$, or $\alpha = 45°$.

Hence for a given velocity of projection, *the horizontal range is greatest when the angle of projection is 45°*.

(v) *To find the velocity and direction of motion after a given time*

We know that the horizontal component of the velocity is constant and equal to $u \cos \alpha$.

The vertical component v after a time t is given by

$$v = u \sin \alpha - gt.$$

$\therefore$ if V is the resultant velocity,

$$V^2 = u^2 \cos^2 \alpha + (u \sin \alpha - gt)^2,$$
$$= u^2 - 2ugt \sin \alpha + g^2t^2.$$

If θ is the angle which the direction of motion makes with the horizontal,

$$\tan \theta = \frac{\text{vertical component of velocity}}{\text{horizontal component of velocity}} = \frac{u \sin \alpha - gt}{u \cos \alpha}.$$

θ is positive for those values of t for which $u \sin \alpha - gt$ is positive, and negative when $u \sin \alpha - gt$ is negative, that is, θ is positive if $t < (u \sin \alpha)/g$, the time to reach the highest point, and negative afterwards.

6.4. *For a given velocity of projection there are, in general, two possible angles of projection to obtain a given horizontal range.*

We have seen that the range

$$R = \frac{u^2}{g} \sin 2\alpha.$$

If R and u are given

$$\sin 2\alpha = \frac{gR}{u^2}.$$

Now for a given value of the sine of the angle 2α, there are two values of the angle less than $180°$. If 2θ is one value the other is $180°-2\theta$. Therefore θ and $90°-\theta$ are two possible angles of projection unless $\frac{gR}{u^2} = 1$, when only one value is possible, viz. $90°$ for 2α, or $45°$ for α.

This is the case when the range is a maximum for the given velocity u.

The directions θ and $90°-\theta$ are equally inclined to the horizontal and vertical respectively, so that the direction for maximum range bisects the angle between them.

6.5. EXAMPLE (i)

A particle is projected with a velocity of 196 ms^{-1}, at an elevation of 30°, find: (i) the greatest height attained; (ii) the time of flight and the range on a horizontal plane through the point of projection; (iii) the velocity and direction of motion at a height of 130 m.

The initial horizontal velocity $= 196 \cos 30° = 98\sqrt{3}$ ms^{-1}.
The initial vertical velocity $= 196 \sin 30° = 98$ ms^{-1}.

(i) If h m be the greatest height, then at this height the particle has lost all vertical velocity,

$$\therefore \qquad\qquad 0 = 98^2 - 2gh$$

$$\therefore \qquad\qquad h = \frac{98 \times 98}{2 \times 9.8} = 490.$$

(ii) If t s be the time of flight the vertical height at that time is zero,

$$\therefore \qquad\qquad 0 = 98t - \tfrac{1}{2}gt^2$$

$$\therefore \qquad\qquad t = \frac{98}{4.9} = 20.$$

The horizontal range is the distance travelled horizontally in 20 s with uniform velocity $98\sqrt{3}$ ms^{-1}.

$$= 98\sqrt{3} \times 20 \text{ m}$$

$$= 3395 \text{ m approximately.}$$

(iii) If v ms^{-1} is the vertical velocity at a height of 130 m.

$$v^2 = 98^2 - 2g \times 130$$

$$= 98(98-26) = 98 \times 72$$

$$\therefore \qquad v = 14 \times 6 = 84.$$

The horizontal velocity is $98\sqrt{3}$ ms^{-1}, and if θ is the inclination of the direction of motion to the horizontal.

$$\tan \theta = \frac{84}{98\sqrt{3}} = \frac{42\sqrt{3}}{147}.$$

The resultant velocity V ms^{-1} is given by

$$V^2 = 98^2 \times 3 + 84^2 = 7^2(588 + 144)$$

$$\therefore \qquad V = 7\sqrt{732} = 7 \times 27 \cdot 05$$

$$= 189 \text{ approximately.}$$

EXAMPLE (ii)

A particle is projected with a velocity of 19·6 *m s^{-1}; find the maximum range on a horizontal plane through the point of projection and the two directions of projection to give a range of* 12 *m.*

If the angle of projection is α, the horizontal and vertical components of the initial velocity are 19·6 cos α and 19·6 sin α ms^{-1}.

The time of flight t s is given by

$$0 = 19 \cdot 6 \sin \alpha \times t - \tfrac{1}{2}gt^2$$

$$\therefore \qquad t = \frac{19 \cdot 6 \sin \alpha}{4 \cdot 9} = 44 \sin \alpha.$$

In this time the horizontal range is

$$19 \cdot 6 \cos \alpha \times 4 \sin \alpha$$

$$= 39 \cdot 2 \sin 2\alpha \text{ m.}$$

This is a maximum when $2\alpha = 90°$, or $\alpha = 45°$, and then the value is 39·2 m.

When the range is 12 m we have

$$39 \cdot 2 \sin 2\alpha = 12$$

$$\therefore \qquad \sin 2\alpha = 0 \cdot 306$$

$$\therefore \qquad 2\alpha = 18° \text{ or } 162°$$

$$\therefore \qquad \alpha = 9° \text{ or } 81°.$$

EXAMPLE (iii)

A particle is projected out to sea with a velocity of 49 ms^{-1} from the top of a cliff 98 m high at an angle of 30° with the horizontal: find how far from the bottom of the cliff the particle hits the water.

The initial vertical velocity is 49 sin 30° = 24·5 m s^{-1}.
The initial horizontal velocity is 49 cos 30° = 24·5$\sqrt{3}$ m s^{-1}.
The time t s to reach a point 98 m below the point of projection is given by

$$-98 = 24\cdot5t - 4\cdot9t^2$$

$$\therefore \quad t^2 - 5t - 20 = 0$$

$$\therefore \quad t = \frac{5 \pm \sqrt{(25+80)}}{2} = 7\cdot6.$$

In this time the horizontal distance travelled is

$$7\cdot6 \times 24\sqrt{3} \text{ m} = 316 \text{ m approximately.}$$

EXAMPLE (iv)

A bullet is fired with a velocity whose horizontal and vertical components are u, v: find its position at time t. If the horizontal velocity is 600 ms^{-1}, find the elevation at which it must be fired if it is to hit a mark 2 m above the muzzle at a distance of 500 m.

If x, y are the horizontal and vertical distances from the muzzle after time t,

$$x = ut \tag{i}$$
$$y = vt - \tfrac{1}{2}gt^2. \tag{ii}$$

When $u = 600$ m s^{-1} and $x = 500$ m,

$$t = \frac{x}{u} = \frac{500}{600} = \frac{5}{6}\text{s.}$$

The height at this time has to be 2 m, and substituting $y = 2$, $t = \frac{5}{6}$ in equation (ii),

$$2 = \tfrac{5}{6}v - 4\cdot9(\tfrac{5}{6})^2$$

$$\therefore \quad v = 2\cdot4 + 4\cdot08$$

$$\therefore \quad v = 6\cdot48 \text{ m s}^{-1}.$$

If θ is the angle of elevation initially

$$\tan\theta = \frac{v}{u} = \frac{6\cdot48}{600} = 0\cdot0108$$

$$\therefore \quad \theta = \text{about 37 minutes.}$$

EXAMPLE (v)

If r be the horizontal range of a projectile, and h its greatest height, prove that the initial speed is

$$\left[2g\left(h+\frac{r^2}{16h}\right)\right]^{\frac{1}{2}}.$$

Let u be the initial speed, and α the angle of projection.

The horizontal range

$$r = \frac{2u^2 \sin \alpha \cos \alpha}{g}. \tag{i}$$

The greatest height

$$h = \frac{u^2 \sin^2\alpha}{2g}. \tag{ii}$$

Now the value of u given in the question does not contain α, so that it must be obtained by eliminating α between equations (i) and (ii).

From (ii) we have $\qquad \operatorname{cosec}^2 \alpha = \dfrac{u^2}{2gh}.$

Dividing (i) by (ii), $\qquad 4 \cot \alpha = \dfrac{r}{h} \quad \text{or} \quad \cot \alpha = \dfrac{r}{4h}.$

Now $\qquad\qquad\qquad \operatorname{cosec}^2 \alpha = 1 + \cot^2 \alpha$

$\therefore \qquad\qquad\qquad\quad \dfrac{u^2}{2gh} = 1 + \dfrac{r^2}{16h^2}$

$\therefore \qquad\qquad\qquad\quad u^2 = 2g\left(h+\dfrac{r^2}{16h}\right)$

$\therefore \qquad\qquad\qquad\quad u = \left[2g\left(h+\dfrac{r^2}{16h}\right)\right]^{\frac{1}{2}}.$

EXAMPLE (vi)

A projectile is fired from a point on a cliff to hit a mark 60 m horizontally from the point and 60 m vertically below it. The velocity of projection is that due to falling freely under gravity through 30 m from rest. Show that the two possible directions of projection are at right angles, and that the times of flight are approximately 2·7 and 6·4 s.

The velocity v m s^{-1} acquired in falling 30 m, is given by

$$v^2 = 2g \times 30$$

$\therefore \qquad\qquad\qquad v = \sqrt{(60g)}.$

If α is the angle of elevation at which the projectile is fired,

$$-60 = \sqrt{(60g)} \times \sin\alpha \times t - \tfrac{1}{2}gt^2 \tag{i}$$

Also

$$60 = \sqrt{(60g)} \times \cos\alpha \times t \tag{ii}$$

From (ii) we get

$$t = \sqrt{\left(\frac{60}{g}\right)} \times \sec\alpha$$

Substituting in (i),

$$-60 = 60\tan\alpha - 30\sec^2\alpha.$$
$$= 60\tan\alpha - 30 - 30\tan^2\alpha$$

$$\therefore \qquad \tan\alpha = \frac{2 \pm \sqrt{(4+4)}}{2} = 1 \pm \sqrt{2}.$$

One of these values is negative, and this means that one of the directions is below the horizontal.

The product of the two tangents is

$$(1+\sqrt{2})(1-\sqrt{2}) = -1$$

and this, by a well-known result in geometry, shows that the directions are at right angles.

If
$$\tan\alpha_1 = 1+\sqrt{2}$$

and
$$\tan\alpha_2 = 1-\sqrt{2}$$

$$\therefore \qquad \sec^2\alpha_1 = 1+3+2\sqrt{2}$$
$$= 6\cdot828,$$

$$\therefore \qquad \sec^2\alpha_2 = 1+3-2\sqrt{2}$$
$$= 1\cdot172,$$

$$\therefore \qquad \sec\alpha_1 = 2\cdot61$$

and
$$\sec\alpha_2 = 1\cdot08,$$

$$\therefore \qquad \text{the times are } 2\cdot61\sqrt{\frac{60}{9\cdot8}} = 6\cdot4 \text{ s}$$

and
$$1\cdot08\sqrt{\frac{60}{9\cdot8}} = 2\cdot7 \text{ s, approximately.}$$

EXAMPLE (vii)

A vertical post subtends an angle α at a point A in the same horizontal plane as the foot of the post. Two particles are projected at the same instant from A, in directions making angles θ_1 and θ_2 with the horizontal, so that the former strikes the top of the post at the same moment that the latter strikes the bottom of the post. Prove that

$$\tan\theta_1 - \tan\theta_2 = \tan\alpha.$$

Let u_1, u_2 be the velocities of projection, h the height of the post PQ (Fig. 6.2) and a its horizontal distance from A.

Since the particles describe the same horizontal distance in the same time, their horizontal velocities are equal,

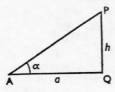

FIG. 6.2

$$\therefore \qquad u_1 \cos \theta_1 = u_2 \cos \theta_2.$$

If t be the time taken to reach the post,

$$t = \frac{a}{u_1 \cos \theta_1} = \frac{a}{u_2 \cos \theta_2}.$$

Also $\qquad h = u_1 \sin \theta_1 \times t - \tfrac{1}{2}gt^2$

and $\qquad 0 = u_2 \sin \theta_2 \times t - \tfrac{1}{2}gt^2$

$\therefore \qquad h = t(u_1 \sin \theta_1 - u_2 \sin \theta_2)$

$$\therefore \qquad \frac{h}{u_1 \cos \theta_1} = t(\tan \theta_1 - \tan \theta_2)$$

$$\therefore \qquad \frac{h}{u_1 \cos \theta_1} = \frac{a}{u_1 \cos \theta_1}(\tan \theta_1 - \tan \theta_2)$$

$\therefore \qquad a \tan \alpha = a(\tan \theta_1 - \tan \theta_2)$ since $h = a \tan \alpha$

$\therefore \qquad \tan \alpha = \tan \theta_1 - \tan \theta_2.$

EXAMPLES 6.1.

1. A particle is projected with a velocity of 30 m s⁻¹ at an elevation of 30°: find (i) the greatest height reached; (ii) the time of flight and the horizontal range; (iii) the velocity and direction of motion at a height of 4 m.

2. Find the greatest range on a horizontal plane when the velocity of projection is (i) 20 m s⁻¹, (ii) 18 m s⁻¹, (iii) 30 m s⁻¹.

3. A man can just throw a stone 60 m: with what velocity does he throw it and how long is it in the air?

4. A projectile is fired horizontally from a point 60 m above a horizontal plane with a velocity of 600 m s⁻¹.

How far will it be horizontally from the point of projection when it reaches the plane?

5. A shot is fired from a gun on the top of a vertical cliff, 160 m high, with a velocity of 180 m s⁻¹, at an elevation of 30°. Find the horizontal distance from the foot of the cliff of the point where the shot strikes the water.

6. Find the velocity and direction of projection of a particle which passes in a horizontal direction just over the top of a wall which is 32 m distant and 12 m high.

7. Find, to the nearest m, the range on a horizontal plane of a rifle bullet fired at an elevation of 3° with a muzzle velocity of 300 m s⁻¹. (I.S.)

8. What is the least velocity of projection required to obtain a horizontal range of 100 m, and what will be the time of flight? (I.A.)

9. Show that a particle starting with a velocity of 30 m s⁻¹ at an angle tan⁻¹ ¾ to the horizon will just clear a wall 9·9 m high at a horizontal distance of 72 m from the point of projection. (I.A.)

10. A body is thrown from the top of a tower 30·4 m high with a velocity of 24 m s⁻¹ at an elevation of 30° above the horizontal: find the horizontal distance from the foot of the tower of the point where it hits the ground. (I.A.)

11. A bullet is fired out to sea in a horizontal direction from a gun situated on the top of a cliff 78·4 m high.

   Calculate the distance out to sea at which the bullet will strike the water, given that the initial velocity of the bullet is 240 m s⁻¹.

   Calculate also the inclination to the horizontal at which the bullet will strike the surface of the water. (H.S.D.)

12. A bullet is fired with an initial velocity of 600 m s⁻¹ in a direction making 25° with the horizontal.

   Calculate how far from the starting-point the bullet will strike the ground again. (H.S.D.)

13. If a particle is projected inside a horizontal tunnel which is 4·8 m high with a velocity of 60 m s⁻¹, find the greatest possible range. (I.S.)

14. A ball is thrown from a height of 0·9 m above the ground to clear a wall, 10·5 m away horizontally, and 4·5 m high.

   Show that the velocity of projection must not be less than that acquired by falling under gravity through 7·35 m, and, when this is the velocity of projection, find how far beyond the wall it will reach the ground. (I.S.)

15. A body is projected at such an angle that the horizontal range is three times the greatest height. Find the angle of projection, and if, with this angle the range is 400 m, find the necessary velocity of projection and the time of flight. (I.A.)

16. A ball is thrown with a velocity whose horizontal component is 12 ms^{-1} from a point 1·3 m above the ground and 6 m away from a vertical wall 4·9 m high in such a way as just to clear the wall. At what time will it reach the ground? (I.E.)

17. A ball is thrown from a point A in a horizontal plane so as just to pass over a wall standing on the same plane, the horizontal component of the ball's velocity being equal to the velocity it would acquire in falling from rest through a distance equal to the horizontal distance of A from the wall. Prove that the ball pitches behind the wall at a distance from it equal to 4 times the height of the wall. (I.E.)

18. Find the least initial velocity which a projectile may have, so that it may clear a wall, 10 m high and 13 m distant, and strike the horizontal plane through the foot of the wall at a distance 7 m beyond the wall, the point of projection being at the same level as the foot of the wall. (H.S.D.)

19. The greatest range of a gun is 25 km: find the muzzle velocity of the shot, and prove that, when the shot has travelled 6·4 km horizontally it has risen about 4·8 km. (H.C.)

20. A bullet is fired from a point O with a velocity whose horizontal and vertical components are u and v respectively: find the direction in which it is moving after a time t. If $u = 30$ ms^{-1}, $v = 90$ ms^{-1}, prove that at two points the direction of the bullet's motion is at right angles to the line joining the bullet to O, and find the positions of these points. (H.C.)

21. A shell is observed to explode at the level of the gun from which it is fired after an interval of 10 s; and the sound of the explosion reaches the gun after a further interval of 3 s. Find the elevation of the gun and the speed with which the shell is fired. (Assume the velocity of sound to be 335 ms^{-1}.) (H.C.)

22. Show that, if R be the maximum horizontal range for a given velocity of projection, a particle can be projected to pass through the point whose horizontal and vertical distances from the point of projection are $\frac{1}{2}R$ and $\frac{1}{4}R$ respectively, provided that the tangent of the angle of projection is either 1 or 3, and that in the second case the range on the horizontal plane is $\frac{3}{5}R$. (I.S.)

23. A shot projected with velocity v can just reach a certain point on the horizontal plane through the point of projection. Show that,

in order to hit a mark h m above the ground at the same point, if the shot is projected at the same elevation, the velocity of projection must be increased to

$$\frac{v^2}{(v^2-gh)^{\frac{1}{2}}}.$$ (I.S.)

24. Prove that the time of flight T and the horizontal range X of a projectile are connected by the equation

$$gT^2 = 2X \tan \alpha,$$

where α is the angle of elevation.

Show that when the maximum horizontal range is 160 km the time of flight is about 3 minutes, and determine the muzzle velocity and the height of the trajectory.   (I.E.)

25. A body is projected so that on its upward path it passes through a point x m horizontally and y m vertically from the point of projection. Show that, if R m is the range on a horizontal plane through the point of projection, the angle of elevation of projection is

$$\tan^{-1}\left(\frac{y}{x}\times\frac{R}{R-x}\right).$$ (I.S.)

26. A particle projected from a point meets the horizontal plane through the point of projection after describing a horizontal distance a, and in the course of its trajectory attains a greatest height b above the point of projection. Find the horizontal and vertical components of the velocity of projection in terms of a and b.

Show that when it has described a horizontal distance x it has attained a height of $4bx(a-x)/a^2$.   (H.C.)

27. If the horizontal range of a particle projected with velocity V is a, show that the greatest height x attained is given by the equation

$$16gx^2-8V^2x+ga^2 = 0.$$

Explain why two values of x are to be expected.   (I.S.)

28. Show that the relative velocity of two bodies moving in any direction under the acceleration of gravity remains constant. A stone is projected horizontally from the top of a tower 54 m high with a velocity of 15 m s⁻¹, and at the same instant another stone is projected in the same vertical plane from the foot of the tower with a velocity of 30 m s⁻¹ at an elevation of 60°. Show that the stones will meet, and find the height above the ground, and the distance from the tower at the instant of meeting. (I.E.)

29. A ball is projected from a point on the ground distant a from the foot of a vertical wall of height b, the velocity of projection being V at an angle α to the horizontal. Find how high above the wall the ball passes it.

    If the ball just clears the wall, prove that the greatest height reached is

$$\frac{1}{4}\frac{a^2 \tan^2 \alpha}{(a \tan \alpha - b)}.$$

                                                                    (N.U.3)

6.6. Range on an inclined plane through the point of projection

Let a particle be projected with velocity u, at an elevation α to the horizontal, from a point P (Fig. 6.3) on a plane of inclina-

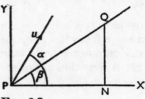

FIG. 6.3

tion β, the direction of projection being in the vertical plane through the line of greatest slope PQ of the inclined plane. Let PQ be the range, and QN the perpendicular on the horizontal plane through P.

    To obtain the time of flight we consider the motion perpendicular to the plane.

    The initial velocity perpendicular to the plane is $u \sin(\alpha - \beta)$ and the acceleration in this direction is $-g \cos \beta$.

    The time of flight T is therefore given by

$$0 = u \sin (\alpha - \beta) \times T - \tfrac{1}{2}g \cos \beta \times T^2$$

$$\therefore \qquad T = \frac{2u \sin (\alpha - \beta)}{g \cos \beta}.$$

The horizontal velocity during this time is constant and equal to $u \cos \alpha$, and the horizontal distance PN described is

$$\frac{2u^2 \sin (\alpha - \beta) \cos \alpha}{g \cos \beta}$$

and PQ $=$ PN sec β.

$$\therefore \qquad \text{range} = \frac{2u^2 \sin(\alpha - \beta) \cos \alpha}{g \cos^2 \beta}. \qquad \text{(i)}$$

6.7. The maximum value of the range for given values of u and β is obtained as follows:

$$R = \frac{2u^2 \sin(\alpha - \beta)\cos\alpha}{g\cos^2\beta} = \frac{u^2}{g\cos^2\beta}[\sin(2\alpha - \beta) - \sin\beta] \qquad \text{(ii)}$$

Now since β and u are given, the quantity outside the bracket

$$\frac{u^2}{g\cos^2\beta}$$

is constant, and the value of the expression in the bracket is a maximum when $\sin(2\alpha - \beta)$ is a maximum, i.e. when

$$2\alpha - \beta = \pi/2.$$

∴ for maximum range

$$\alpha = \frac{\pi}{4} + \frac{\beta}{2}.$$

We see also that when α has this value

$$\alpha - \beta = \frac{\pi}{2} - \alpha$$

or the direction of projection bisects the angle between the plane and the vertical.

The value of the maximum range is

$$\frac{u^2}{g\cos^2\beta}(1 - \sin\beta) = \frac{u^2}{g(1 + \sin\beta)}. \qquad \text{(iii)}$$

6.8. For a given value of the range (other than the maximum value) with a given velocity of projection, we obtain from (ii) a value for $\sin(2\alpha - \beta)$.

Now for a given sine there are two angles less than 180°, so that we get two values for $2\alpha - \beta$; if θ is one value the other is $\pi - \theta$, so that

$$2\alpha - \beta = \theta$$

and

$$\alpha = \frac{\theta}{2} + \frac{\beta}{2}$$

or

$$2\alpha - \beta = \pi - \theta$$

and

$$\alpha = \frac{\pi}{2} + \frac{\beta}{2} - \frac{\theta}{2}.$$

There are thus two angles of projection for a given range. The angle of projection for a maximum is $(\frac{1}{4}\pi+\frac{1}{2}\beta)$.

Also
$$\frac{1}{2}\left(\frac{\theta}{2}+\frac{\beta}{2}+\frac{\pi}{2}+\frac{\beta}{2}-\frac{\theta}{2}\right)=\frac{\pi}{4}+\frac{\beta}{2}.$$

Therefore the two directions of projection for a given range are equally inclined to the direction for maximum range.

6.9. In the preceding paragraphs the direction of projection was expressed as an elevation to the horizontal.

We can also take the elevation *relative to the inclined plane*.

In working problems care must be taken in reading the question to see which of these angles is given.

If θ is the inclination of the direction of projection to the line of greatest slope of the plane the initial velocities perpendicular and parallel to the plane are $u \sin \theta$ and $u \cos \theta$.

The time of flight T is given by

$$0 = u \sin \theta \times T - \tfrac{1}{2}g \cos \beta \times T^2$$

$$\therefore \qquad T = \frac{2u \sin \theta}{g \cos \beta}. \qquad\qquad (iv)$$

The range can be found as before, remembering that the horizontal velocity is now $u \cos (\beta+\theta)$, or by considering the motion *parallel to the plane*.

In time T the distance (R) travelled parallel to the plane is

$$R = u \cos \theta \times T - \tfrac{1}{2}g \sin \beta \times T^2. \qquad\qquad (v)$$

The relations (iv) and (v) are useful in problems where the times of flight for a given range are required. It is easy to eliminate θ from these two equations.

6.10. EXAMPLE (i)

A particle is projected with a velocity of 245 ms⁻¹ at an elevation of 60° to the horizontal from the foot of a plane of inclination 30°. Find the range on the inclined plane and the time of flight.

Let PQ (Fig. 6.4) represent the inclined plane.
The component of velocity perpendicular to the plane is

$$245 \sin 30° = 122 \cdot 5 \text{ m s}^{-1}.$$

The acceleration perpendicular to the plane is

$$g \cos 30° = \frac{\sqrt{3}}{2} g = 4\cdot9\sqrt{3} \text{ m s}^{-2},$$

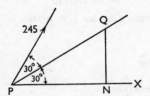

FIG. 6.4

The time of flight t s is given by

$$0 = 122\cdot5t - \tfrac{1}{2} \times 4\cdot9\sqrt{3}t^2$$

$$\therefore \quad t = \frac{122\cdot5}{2\cdot45\sqrt{3}} = \frac{50\sqrt{3}}{3} = 25\cdot5 \text{ nearly.}$$

In 25·5 s the particle travels a horizontal distance

$$25\cdot5 \times 122\cdot5 \text{ m.}$$

The distance up the plane is obtained by multiplying this by

$$\sec 30° \text{ or } \frac{2}{\sqrt{3}}$$

and therefore range on the plane

$$= 25\cdot5 \times 122\cdot5 \times \frac{2}{\sqrt{3}} = 4083 \text{ m.}$$

EXAMPLE (ii)

A particle is projected with a velocity of 20 m s⁻¹ at an angle of 45° to the horizontal. Find its range on a plane inclined at 30° to the horizontal when projected (i) *up,* (ii) *down the plane.*

(i) The component of velocity perpendicular to the plane is

$$20 \sin 15° \text{ m s}^{-1}$$

The acceleration perpendicular to the plane is

$$9\cdot8 \cos 30° = 4\cdot9\sqrt{3} \text{ m s}^{-2}.$$

The time of flight is given by

$$0 = 20 \sin 15° \times t - 2\cdot45\sqrt{3}t^2$$

$$\therefore \quad t = \frac{20 \sin 15°}{2\cdot45\sqrt{3}} = 1\cdot2 \text{ s.}$$

The horizontal velocity is $20/\sqrt{2}$ ms^{-1} and the horizontal distance in time 1·2 s is $12\sqrt{2}$ m.

The range up the plane is obtained by multiplying this by sec 30°.

Therefore range up the plane $= 12\sqrt{2} \times 2/\sqrt{3} = 19\text{·}6$ m.

(ii) The component of velocity perpendicular to the plane is 20 sin 75° ms^{-1}.

The time of flight t s is given by

$$0 = 20 \sin 75° - 2\text{·}45\sqrt{3}\,t$$

$\therefore \qquad t = \dfrac{20 \sin 75°}{2\text{·}45\sqrt{3}} = 4\text{·}6 \text{ nearly.}$

The horizontal velocity is $\dfrac{20}{\sqrt{2}}$ ms^{-1} and the horizontal distance in time 4·6 s is $46\sqrt{2}$ m.

The range down the plane is

$$46\sqrt{2} \times \frac{2}{\sqrt{3}} = 75 \text{ m nearly.}$$

EXAMPLE (iii)

Show that for a given velocity of projection the maximum range down an inclined plane of inclination α *is greater than that up the plane in the ratio* $(1+\sin \alpha)/(1-\sin \alpha)$.

Let u be the given velocity of projection and θ the angle the direction of projection makes with the plane.

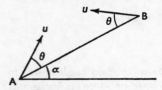

FIG. 6.5

When projected up the plane from A (Fig. 6.5) the time of flight is given by

$$0 = u \sin \theta \times t - \tfrac{1}{2}g \cos \alpha \times t^2$$

$\therefore \qquad t = \dfrac{2u \sin \theta}{g \cos \alpha}.$

The range up the plane is

$$\frac{2u \sin \theta}{g \cos \alpha} \times u \cos (\theta+\alpha) \times \sec \alpha = \frac{2u^2}{g} \times \frac{\sin \theta \cos (\theta+\alpha)}{\cos^2 \alpha}$$

$$= \frac{u^2}{g \cos^2 \alpha}[\sin (2\theta+\alpha) - \sin \alpha].$$

This is a maximum when $\sin(2\theta+\alpha) = 1$, and then

$$\text{range} = \frac{u^2}{g\cos^2\alpha}(1-\sin\alpha).$$

When projected down the plane from B at the same angle to the plane the time of flight has the same value

$$\frac{2u\sin\theta}{g\cos\alpha}.$$

The horizontal velocity is now, however, $u\cos(\theta-\alpha)$, the horizontal distance in time $\dfrac{2u\sin\theta}{g\cos\alpha}$ is $\dfrac{2u^2\sin\theta\cos(\theta-\alpha)}{g\cos\alpha}$, and the range down the plane is

$$\frac{2u^2\sin\theta\cos(\theta-\alpha)}{g\cos^2\alpha} = \frac{u^2}{g\cos^2\alpha}[\sin(2\theta-\alpha)+\sin\alpha].$$

This is a maximum when $\sin(2\theta-\alpha) = 1$, and then

$$\text{range} = \frac{u^2}{g\cos^2\alpha}(1+\sin\alpha).$$

Hence the ratio of the maximum ranges down and up the plane is

$$\frac{1+\sin\alpha}{1-\sin\alpha}.$$

EXAMPLE (iv)

If t_1 and t_2 be the two times of flight on an inclined plane through the point of projection corresponding to any given range short of the greatest, and α the inclination of the plane, prove that

$$t_1{}^2+t_2{}^2+2t_1t_2\sin\alpha$$

is independent of α, the velocity of projection being given.

Let V be the velocity of projection, and θ the inclination of the initial direction to the plane.

The velocity perpendicular to the plane is $V\sin\theta$, and the time of flight t is given by

$$0 = V\sin\theta \times t - \tfrac{1}{2}g\cos\alpha \times t^2. \qquad \textbf{(i)}$$

The velocity parallel to the plane is $V\cos\theta$, the acceleration down the plane is $g\sin\alpha$, and the range in time t is

$$R = V\cos\theta \times t - \tfrac{1}{2}g\sin\alpha \times t^2. \qquad \textbf{(ii)}$$

From (i) and (ii), $V \sin \theta \times t = \frac{1}{2}g \cos \alpha \times t^2$

$$V \cos \theta \times t = R + \frac{1}{2}g \sin \alpha \times t^2.$$

Squaring and adding,

$$V^2 t^2 = R^2 + gR \sin \alpha \times t^2 + \frac{g^2}{4}t^4$$

or

$$\frac{g^2}{4}t^4 + t^2(gR \sin \alpha - V^2) + R^2 = 0.$$

This is a quadratic in t^2, and if $t_1{}^2$, $t_2{}^2$ are its roots,

$$t_1{}^2 + t_2{}^2 = -\frac{4R}{g} \sin \alpha + \frac{4V^2}{g^2}$$

and

$$t_1{}^2 t_2{}^2 = \frac{4R^2}{g^2}$$

∴

$$t_1 t_2 = \frac{2R}{g}$$

∴

$$t_1{}^2 + t_2{}^2 + 2t_1 t_2 \sin \alpha = -\frac{4R}{g} \sin \alpha + \frac{4V^2}{g^2} + \frac{4R}{g} \sin \alpha$$

$$= \frac{4V^2}{g^2} \text{ and is independent of } \alpha.$$

EXAMPLES 6.2

1. A particle is projected with a velocity of 90 m s⁻¹ at an elevation of 60° from the foot of a plane of inclination 30°. The motion being in the vertical plane through a line of greatest slope of the plane, find the range on the plane and the time of flight.

2. A particle is projected with a velocity of 384 m s⁻¹ at an elevation of 75°. Find the range on a plane of inclination 45° when the particle is projected (i) up, (ii) down the plane.

3. A particle is projected from a point on a plane of inclination 30° with a velocity of 400 cm s⁻¹ at right angles to the plane. Find its range on the plane.

4. The greatest range, with a given velocity of projection, on a horizontal plane is 3000 m. Find the greatest ranges up and down a plane inclined at 30° to the horizon.

5. A bullet is fired from the foot of an inclined plane with velocity 600 m s⁻¹ at an elevation of 60°. Find the range if the inclination of the plane is: (i) 30°; (ii) 45°. Find also the maximum ranges which can be obtained on these planes with the given initial velocity.

6. Show that the range up a plane of inclination β through the point of projection of a projectile fired at an elevation α *relative to the plane* is $R \sec \beta (1 - \tan \alpha \tan \beta)$, where R is the range on a horizontal plane, the *relative* elevation α and the velocity of projection being the same.   (I.S.)

7. A heavy particle is projected from a point on an inclined plane, inclined at 2β to the *vertical*, and moves towards the upper part of the plane in the vertical plane through a line of the greatest slope of the inclined plane; the initial velocity of the particle is $u \cos \beta$ and its initial direction of motion is inclined at β to the *vertical*. Prove that the time of flight of the particle is u/g, its range on the plane is $u^2/2g$, the velocity with which it strikes the plane is $u \sin \beta$, and its direction of motion has then turned through a right angle.   (H.C.)

8. A particle is projected with speed u so as to strike at right angles a plane through the point of projection inclined at 30° to the horizon. Show that the range on this inclined plane is $4u^2/7g$.

(I.S.)

9. A particle is projected with velocity V at an elevation α on a line through the point of projection making an angle β with the horizon. Prove that during the flight the direction of motion of the particle turns through an angle whose cotangent is

$$\tfrac{1}{2} \cos \beta \sec \alpha \operatorname{cosec} (\alpha - \beta) - \tan \alpha. \qquad \text{(I.A.)}$$

10. A projectile is to pass through a point whose angular elevations from the point of projection is θ, and at that point to impinge perpendicularly on an inclined plane of slope β to the horizontal. Show that the angle of elevation α at which it must be projected is given by

$$\tan \alpha = \cot \beta + 2 \tan \theta. \qquad \text{(H.C.)}$$

11. If R is the maximum range on an inclined plane through the point of projection of a particle, and T the corresponding time of flight, show that

$$R = \tfrac{1}{2} g T^2. \qquad \text{(H.C.)}$$

12. A shot is fired from a gun in a horizontal direction with a velocity of 300 m s⁻¹. The gun is on the side of a hill of inclination $\tan^{-1} \tfrac{4}{5}$ to the horizontal. Find how far along the hill the shot will strike, and determine its velocity then in magnitude and direction.

(I.C.)

13. A particle is projected with a velocity of 480 ms^{-1}, at an elevation of 30°, from a point on the side of a hill inclined at 30° below the horizontal. Find the range measured along the side of the hill, and the time of flight.   (I.C.)

14. Find the range on an incline α of a shot fired with velocity V from a point on it at an elevation $\alpha+\theta$ so as to move in a vertical plane through a line of greatest slope.

If the shot hits the slope horizontally, show that

$$\tan\theta = \frac{\sin\alpha\cos\alpha}{1+\sin^2\alpha}.$$ (C.W.B.)

6.11. EXAMPLE (i)

A particle is projected with a velocity whose horizontal and vertical components are u, v, so as to pass through a point whose horizontal and vertical distances from the point of projection are h, k. Prove that $2u^2k+gh^2 = 2uvh$.

A particle is projected so as to pass through two points whose horizontal and vertical distances from the point of projection are (36, 11) and (72, 14) m. Find the velocity and direction of projection. (I.S.)

The time taken to describe a horizontal distance h is h/u.

In time h/u the vertical height is k, and hence

$$k = v\frac{h}{u} - \tfrac{1}{2}g\frac{h^2}{u^2}$$

$\therefore$ $2u^2k+gh^2 = 2uvh.$

If $h = 26$, $k = 11$, $2u^2\times 11+9\cdot8\times 36^2 = 2uv\times 36$ (i)

If $h = 72$, $k = 14$, $2u^2\times 14+9\cdot8\times 72^2 = 2uv\times 72$ (ii)

Multiplying (i) by 2, $2u^2\times 22+19\cdot6\times 36^2 = 2uv\times 72$

$\therefore$ $2u^2(22-14)+9\cdot8\times 36^2(2-4) = 0$

$\therefore$ $16u^2 = 19\cdot6\times 36^2$

$\therefore$ $u = 40$ ms^{-1} approximately.

Substituting for u in (i) we get

$$v = 16\cdot8 \text{ ms}^{-1}.$$

The velocity of projection is

$$\surd(u^2+v^2) = \surd(16\cdot8^2+40^2) = 43\cdot4 \text{ ms}^{-1}.$$

The inclination to the horizontal is

$$\tan^{-1}\frac{v}{u} = \tan^{-1}\frac{16\cdot8}{40} = \tan^{-1}0\cdot42.$$

EXAMPLE

A ball thrown from a point P *with velocity* V, *at an inclination* α *to the horizontal, reaches a point* Q *after t s. Find the horizontal and vertical distance of* Q *from* P, *and show that if* PQ *is inclined at* θ *to the horizontal the direction of motion of the ball when at* Q *is inclined to the horizontal at an angle* tan^{-1} (2 *tan* θ—*tan* α). **(I.E.)**

If x, y be the horizontal and vertical distances of Q from P

$$x = V \cos α \times t$$
$$y = V \sin α \times t - \tfrac{1}{2}gt^2.$$

If u, v be the horizontal and vertical components of velocity when at Q

$$u = V \cos α$$
$$v = V \sin α - gt.$$

Now $$\tan θ = \frac{y}{x} = \tan α - \frac{gt}{2V \cos α}.$$

The direction of motion at Q is inclined to the horizontal at

$$\tan^{-1}\frac{v}{u} = \tan^{-1}\left(\tan α - \frac{gt}{V \cos α}\right).$$

But $$\frac{gt}{V \cos α} = 2 \tan α - 2 \tan θ$$

∴ $$\tan^{-1}\frac{v}{u} = \tan^{-1}(\tan α - 2 \tan α + 2 \tan θ)$$

$$= \tan^{-1}(2 \tan θ - \tan α).$$

EXAMPLES 6.3

1. Show that if two particles are simultaneously projected from the same point the direction of the line joining them is unaltered throughout the motion. **(I.A.)**

2. A gun is fired from the top of a cliff of height h, and the shot attains a maximum height of $(h+b)$ above sea-level and strikes the sea at a distance a from the foot of the cliff. Prove that the angle of elevation of the gun is given by the equation

$$a^2 \tan^2 α - 4ab \tan α - 4bh = 0. \qquad \textbf{(I.E.)}$$

3. A projectile, starting from A, passes through B and C. If the horizontal and vertical distances of B from A are a, b respectively, and AC is horizontal and equal to c, find the angle of elevation and the greatest height reached by the projectile. **(Ex.)**

4. A rifle is sighted to hit a mark on a level with the muzzle at an estimated distance of 1200 m. If the muzzle velocity of the bullet is 600 ms⁻¹ find the direction in which the rifle must be pointed.

If the true distance of the mark is 1150 m, find how high above the mark the bullet will pass. (H.S.D.)

5. If, with the same velocity of projection, the range of a projectile is half the greatest range, show that there are two possible angles of projection and find them. Compare the greatest height reached in these two possible paths. (H.S.D.)

6. A particle is projected from a point at a height $3h$ above a horizontal plane, the direction of projection making an angle α with the horizon. Show that, if the greatest height above the point of projection is h, the horizontal distance travelled before striking the plane is $6h \cot \alpha$. (I.S.)

7. Two shells are projected simultaneously from the same point with the same initial velocity so as to move in the same vertical plane, their initial direction of motion making angles α and α' respectively with the horizontal. Prove that the shells move so that the line joining them makes the same constant angle

$$\tfrac{1}{2}(\alpha + \alpha')$$

with the vertical. (I.E.)

8. A projectile is thrown over a double inclined plane from one end of the horizontal base to the other, and just grazes the summit in its flight. Taking the motion to be in a vertical plane through the line of greatest slope, prove that the angle of projection is

$$\tan^{-1}(\tan \alpha + \tan \beta),$$

where α, β are the slopes of the faces. (I.S.)

9. A particle is projected from a point A, and is viewed from a point B of its path, against the vertical through A: show that the particle appears to rise along this vertical at a uniform rate $\tfrac{1}{2}gt_0$, where t_0 is the time taken by the particle to reach B. (H.C.)

10. A ball is projected so as just to clear two walls, the first of height a at distance b from the point of projection, and the second of height b at distance a from the point of projection. Show that the range on a horizontal plane is

$$\frac{a^2 + ab + b^2}{a + b}$$

and that the angle of projection exceeds $\tan^{-1} 3$. (Ex.)

11. Two particles A and B are projected simultaneously in the same vertical plane from the same point with the same speed but in perpendicular directions. Prove that, as long as they are both in motion, the line joining them moves parallel to itself and the distance between them increases at a constant rate. Prove also that, if A reaches the ground first, B has then travelled a horizontal distance equal to 4 times the greatest height of A. (H.S.D.)

12. Two particles are projected simultaneously from the two points A and B (which are not in the same horizontal line) with the same initial velocity V and at the same inclination α to the horizon, so as to move towards each other. Prove that their distance from each other will be a minimum after a time

$$\frac{h}{2V \cos \alpha}$$

where h is the horizontal distance between their points of projection. Prove also that this minimum distance will be k, where k is the initial difference of their vertical heights. (H.S.D.)

13. Two particles are projected simultaneously with the same speed V in the same vertical plane, but at different inclinations θ_1, θ_2. Prove that their velocities are parallel after a time

$$\frac{V}{g} \times \frac{\cos \frac{1}{2}(\theta_1 - \theta_2)}{\sin \frac{1}{2}(\theta_1 + \theta_2)}. \tag{H.S.D.}$$

14. A projectile is aimed at a mark on a horizontal plane through the point of projection and falls 6 m short when its elevation is 30° but overshoots the mark by 9 m when its elevation is 45°. Show that the correct elevation is about 33° 26′. (I.E.)

15. If a man were projected from the earth with velocity V and elevation α and if at the same instant a stone were projected with the same velocity but elevation β, show that the stone would appear to the man to be travelling with constant velocity in a certain fixed direction.

Show further that if $\beta - \alpha = 60°$ the apparent velocity of the stone would be V. (I.E.)

16. If the minimum kinetic energy of a projectile during its flight is $1/n$ of its initial value, prove that the direction of projection makes an angle $\sec^{-1} n^{\frac{1}{2}}$ with the horizontal.

Prove that the curve obtained by plotting the kinetic energy against the time is a parabola. (N.U.3)

17. Show that it is not possible for a body to be projected from a point A so as to pass through another point B unless the speed

of projection is such that if the particle were projected vertically it would rise to a height at least $\frac{1}{2}(AB+BN)$, where BN is the perpendicular from B on the horizontal plane through A.

(N.U.4)

6.12. The path of a projectile (neglecting air resistance) is a parabola

Let u, α be the velocity and angle of projection from P

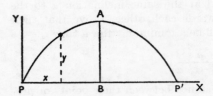

FIG. 6.6

(Fig. 6.6). Taking PX horizontal and PY vertical as co-ordinate axes, we have, after time t,

$$x = u \cos \alpha \times t \tag{i}$$

and
$$y = u \sin \alpha \times t - \tfrac{1}{2}gt^2. \tag{ii}$$

Substituting for t in (ii),

$$y = x \tan \alpha - \frac{gx^2}{2u^2 \cos^2 \alpha}. \tag{iii}$$

This equation represents a parabola with its axis vertical. When $y = 0$, equation (iii) gives

$$x = 0, \text{ and } x = \frac{2u^2 \sin \alpha \cos \alpha}{g}.$$

The first of these values corresponds to P, and the second to P' where PP' is the horizontal range.

6.13. We can obtain the equation of the path in a simpler form by taking the horizontal and vertical through the highest point A (Fig. 6.7) as axes. We know that the horizontal and vertical velocities at A are $u \cos \alpha$ and zero.

Hence in time t from A, if x is measured vertically downwards, and y horizontally,

$$y = u \cos \alpha \times t$$

and

$$x = \tfrac{1}{2}gt^2 = \frac{gy^2}{2u^2 \cos^2 \alpha}$$

$\therefore$

$$y^2 = \frac{2u^2 \cos^2 \alpha}{g} \times x$$

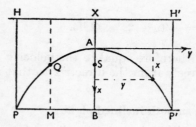

Fig. 6.7

This represents a parabola with vertex at A and axis AB vertical. Its latus rectum is $\dfrac{2u^2 \cos^2 \alpha}{g}$, which depends only on the *horizontal velocity*.

If S is the focus,

$$AS = \frac{u^2 \cos^2 \alpha}{2g}.$$

The directrix HXH′ is horizontal and at a height $\dfrac{u^2 \cos^2 \alpha}{2g}$ above A.

The height of A above P is $\dfrac{u^2 \sin^2 \alpha}{2g}$

$\therefore$ the height of the directrix above P is

$$\frac{u^2 \cos^2 \alpha}{2g} + \frac{u^2 \sin^2 \alpha}{2g} = \frac{u^2}{2g}.$$

This shows that the height of the directrix above the point of projection *depends only on the initial velocity, it is the same for all possible paths with this particular velocity.*

We see also that the height of the directrix above the point of projection is the height to which the particle would rise if projected *vertically* upwards.

The vertical velocity at a point Q is given by

$$v^2 = u^2 \sin^2 \alpha - 2g \times QM,$$

the horizontal velocity is $u \cos \alpha$,

$\therefore$ the resultant velocity at Q is $\sqrt{(u^2 - 2g \times QM)}$.

The velocity acquired by falling to Q from the directrix, a distance of $\dfrac{u^2}{2g} - QM$

is $$\sqrt{\left[2g\left(\frac{u^2}{2g} - QM \right) \right]} = \sqrt{(u^2 - 2g \times QM)}.$$

The velocity at any point is therefore equal to the velocity acquired by an article falling freely from the directrix to that point.

6.14. Motion on the surface of a smooth inclined plane

Suppose a particle is projected with velocity u on the surface of a smooth inclined plane ABCD (Fig. 6.8) of slope β, in a direction inclined at an angle α to the line of greatest slope of the plane.

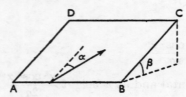

Fig. 6.8

The acceleration due to gravity has components $g \sin \beta$ in the direction of the line of greatest slope of the plane, and $g \cos \beta$ perpendicular to the plane.

The latter is destroyed by the reaction of the plane, so that the particle moves with an acceleration $g \sin \beta$ parallel to the line of greatest slope.

The motion relative to the plane is therefore the same as in 6.3 if we use $g \sin \beta$ for the acceleration instead of g.

EXAMPLE

A particle is projected up an inclined plane (of slope 30°) at an angle of 30° with the line of greatest slope, with initial velocity V. Write down the equations of motion and find the equation of the path on the plane, and the distance of the particle from the starting-point when it again reaches that level.

Taking the horizontal line and the line of greatest slope through the starting-point as axes of x and y, then at time t,

$$x = V \sin 30° \times t \tag{i}$$

and
$$y = V \cos 30° \times t - \tfrac{1}{2}g \sin 30° \times t^2. \tag{ii}$$

These are the equations of motion, and substituting the value of t obtained from (i) in (ii), we get

$$y = x \cot 30° - \frac{g}{4} \times \frac{x^2}{V^2 \sin^2 30°}$$

or
$$y = \sqrt{3}x - \frac{gx^2}{V^2}$$

and this is the equation of the path.

When $y = 0$,
$$\frac{gx^2}{V^2} = \sqrt{3} \times x$$

$$\therefore \qquad x = 0 \text{ or } \frac{\sqrt{3}V^2}{g}.$$

The latter is the distance from the starting-point when the particle again reaches that level.

6.15. Further problems on projectiles

The following examples involve impacts of projected particles.

EXAMPLE (i)

A ball is shot along a smooth horizontal table 1·2 m high, so as to leave it perpendicular to one edge with a speed of 3 ms⁻¹. Show, if the coefficient of restitution for the ball and the floor is $\frac{1}{2}$, that the ball hits the floor, assumed smooth, a second time at a distance of 3 m from the table. When will the ball be at a distance of 4·5 m from the table?

If t s is the time the ball takes to reach the floor, then, since its speed is initially horizontal,

$$1·2 = \tfrac{1}{2} \times 9·8t^2$$

$$\therefore \qquad t^2 = \tfrac{12}{49} \text{ or } t = 0·5 \text{ approximately.}$$

Therefore horizontal distance gone in this time $= 3 \times \frac{1}{2} = 1·5$ m.

Thus the ball hits the floor at a distance of 1·5 m from the table and then rebounds. Its vertical velocity just before it hits the floor is $\tfrac{1}{2}g = 4·9$ ms⁻¹ and its horizontal velocity is, of course, 3 ms⁻¹.

Since the floor is assumed smooth, the ball's horizontal velocity will remain unchanged as a result of the impact, but its vertical velocity will be upwards and equal to $\frac{1}{2}(4 \cdot 9)$ ms^{-1}.

Therefore if R m is the distance gone before the ball hits the floor again, and T s is the time taken, we get

$$R = 13 \times T$$

and

$$0 = 2 \cdot 45T - 4 \cdot 9T^2$$

$\therefore$ $T = \frac{1}{2}$ and $R = 1 \cdot 5.$

Therefore total distance from the table of the ball's second impact with the floor $= (1 \cdot 5 + 1 \cdot 5)$ m $= 3$ m.

As the horizontal velocity of the ball is not altered as a result of the impact with the floor, it remains constant throughout the motion, and hence the ball is at a distance of $4 \cdot 5$ m from the table

after $\dfrac{4 \cdot 5}{3}$ s $= 1 \cdot 5$ s.

EXAMPLE (ii)

A ball is thrown from a point distant a from a smooth vertical wall against the wall, and returns to the point of projection. Prove that the velocity u of projection and the elevation α of projection are connected by the equation

$$u^2 \sin 2\alpha = ag\left(\frac{1+e}{e}\right),$$

where e is the coefficient of restitution between the ball and the wall.

Since the wall is smooth the vertical velocity is unaffected by the impact, i.e. the time of flight is still

$$\frac{2u \sin \alpha}{g}.$$

The ball approaches the wall with horizontal velocity $u \cos \alpha$, and rebounds with horizontal velocity $eu \cos \alpha$.

Hence the times taken to reach the wall and rebound a horizontal distance a are $\dfrac{a}{u \cos \alpha}$ and $\dfrac{a}{eu \cos \alpha}$ respectively.

$\therefore$ $\dfrac{2u \sin \alpha}{g} = \dfrac{a}{u \cos \alpha} + \dfrac{a}{eu \cos \alpha}$

$\therefore$ $\dfrac{2u \sin \alpha}{g} = \dfrac{a(1+e)}{eu \cos \alpha}$

$\therefore$ $u^2 \sin 2\alpha = ag\left(1 + \dfrac{1}{e}\right).$

EXAMPLES 6.4

1. A particle of mass m is projected with velocity v at an angle α to the horizontal, and at the same instant a particle of mass $3m$ is dropped from a height $(v^2 \sin^2 \alpha)/g$, at a horizontal distance of $(v^2 \sin \alpha \cos \alpha)/g$ from the point of projection of the first particle. Show that the particles will collide. If the particles now coalesce, find the position of the point at which the particles strike the ground, and the time which elapses before they reach it. (I.E.)

2. A body slides from rest down a smooth plane of length l and inclination α, and at the bottom impinges on a smooth horizontal plane; show that the range on the horizontal plane after the first rebound is $2el \sin \alpha \sin 2\alpha$, where e is the coefficient of restitution between the body and the horizontal plane. (I.A.)

3. A mass of 300 g moving horizontally at a point A, 18·4 m above the ground with a velocity of 13·2 ms⁻¹, is struck at A by a mass of 30 g moving vertically upwards with a velocity of 165 ms⁻¹, and the two masses unite; find the position of the point at which the combined mass strikes the ground. (I.A.)

4. From a point distant a from a smooth wall a particle, whose initial height above the ground is h, is projected with horizontal velocity u towards the wall. If $a < u \sqrt{\dfrac{2h}{g}}$, show that the particle strikes the ground at a distant point $e\left(u \sqrt{\dfrac{2h}{g}} - a\right)$ from the wall, e being the coefficient of restitution between the wall and the particle. (H.S.C.)

5. A ball is thrown with a speed of 19·6 ms⁻¹ at an angle of elevation of 45°. It strikes a vertical wall 9·8 m away and returns to the point of projection. Find the coefficient of restitution between the ball and the wall. (H.S.C.)

6. An elastic particle is projected with velocity u, at an inclination to the horizontal, from a point on the ground distant a from a smooth vertical wall towards the wall. Prove that, after rebounding from the wall, it can strike the ground again at a point farther from the wall than the point of projection if

$$u^2 > \frac{1+e}{e} ag,$$

where e is the coefficient of restitution.

7. A particle is dropped from a height h on to a smooth and perfectly elastic inclined plane and rebounds. Find how far down the plane is its next point of impact. (H.S.C.)

8. A ball is projected from the ground at an angle α to the horizontal and rebounds from a smooth vertical wall to the point of projection. If the line joining the point of projection to the point of impact makes an angle θ with the horizontal, prove that

$$(1+e) \tan \theta = \tan \alpha,$$

where e is the coefficient of restitution.

9. A particle is projected with a velocity of magnitude V from a point of a plane, inclined to the horizontal at an angle α, in the vertical plane through the line of greatest slope through the point of projection. The direction of projection is up the plane and makes an angle β with the plane. The coefficient of restitution between the plane and the particle is e. Prove that the range of the particle on the plane at the moment of its second impact with the plane is greatest when $\cot 2\beta = (1+e) \tan \alpha$, and that this greatest range is

$$\frac{V^2(1+e) \tan \beta}{g \cos \alpha}$$

where β has the value given by the first equation.   (H.C.)

10. A boy throws a ball with velocity V at an angle α to the horizontal, so that it strikes a smooth vertical wall at a distance a and returns to his hand. If the coefficient of restitution between the ball and the wall is e, show that $V^2 \sin 2\alpha = ga(1+e)/e$.

    Show also that the height of the point of impact on the wall above the point of projection is proportional to $\tan \alpha$.   (L.A.)

11. A ball is projected from a point on smooth level ground. It strikes a vertical wall normally, rebounds and returns to its starting-point after bouncing once on the ground. If the coefficients of restitution between the ball and the wall and between the ball and the ground are equal, prove that each coefficient is $\frac{1}{2}$.   (L.A.)

12. A ball is projected upwards with speed 12 ms^{-1} at an angle $\tan^{-1}$ (4/3) with the horizontal, from a point on the floor of a room. It hits the ceiling (supposed smooth) 3·55 m above the floor, and reaches the floor again 9 m from the point of projection. Find the coefficient of restitution between the ball and the ceiling.   (H.S.C.)

REVISION EXAMPLES B

1. (i) A man whose weight is 70 kg climbs a hill 150 m high in 14 min; what is his average rate of working? (ii) At a certain place the breadth of a river is 90 m, its average depth 3·6 m, and its average velocity 6 kmh^{-1}. What power would it furnish if half its kinetic energy could be transformed into work?

2. Define work and power. An engine working at 450 kW pulls a train of total mass 240 Mg along a level track, the resistances being $\frac{1}{100}$ of the weight of the train. What is the acceleration of the train when its speed is 48 kmh^{-1}? Find also the steady speed at which the engine will pull the train up an incline of 1 in 80 with the same expenditure of power against the same resistances. (H.C.)

3. A car of mass 1000 kg is driven along a horizontal road against a resistance equal to $\frac{1}{25}$ of its weight. Find the greatest speed and the pull of the engine if the engine cannot exert more than 10 kW.

   The car now pulls a trailer of mass 600 kg against an additional resistance of $\frac{1}{20}$ of the weight of the trailer, the engine working at 10 kW. Find the tension in the tow rope at the instant when the speed is 32 kmh^{-1}.

4. A car of mass 1 Mg moves along a horizontal road against a resistance equal to $\frac{1}{30}$ of its weight. Find the greatest speed attainable if the engine cannot exert more than 15 kW.

   Find the pull in the tow-rope if the car (still subject to the resistance) pulls a trailer of mass 600 kg which is resisted by a force equal to $\frac{1}{20}$ of its weight, when the speed is 24 kmh^{-1} and the engine is working at 15 kW. (L.A.)

5. An engine of mass 60 Mg, working at 540 kW, is pulling a train of mass 480 Mg down an incline of sin^{-1} (1/140). Frictional resistances amount to $\frac{1}{100}$ of the total weight of the engine and train. Find the acceleration of the train when its speed is 24 kmh^{-1}. Find also the tension in the coupling between the engine and the first coach at this instant.

6. A locomotive and its train have a combined mass of 500 Mg. Down a slope of 1 in 100 the maximum speed is 96 kmh^{-1}, the maximum speed is 48 kmh^{-1} up the same slope. Assuming that the total resistance to motion varies directly as the speed and that the locomotive works at the same constant power in each case, calculate the magnitude of this power. (L.A.)

7. A motor-car of mass M kg, ascending a slope inclined at an angle α to the horizontal, can just attain a maximum speed of V kmh^{-1}. Descending the same slope, with the engine cut off, it attains a maximum speed of U kmh^{-1}. Assuming that the resistance is proportional to the square of the velocity, find the power which the engine can develop. Give the numerical value when $M = 900$, $V = 60$, $U = 64$, sin $\alpha = 1/21$.   (H.C.)

8. A weight of mass 120 kg is hauled vertically through a height of 30 m starting from rest, by a rope whose tension (T) at different distances (x) from the commencement is given by the following table:

x in m	0	3	6	9	12	15	18	21	24	27	30
$\frac{1}{16} T$ in N	150	179	190	191	185	174	155	125	88	59	50

Find the velocity with which the weight arrives at the end of its rise.

9. A body moving in a straight line is acted upon by a uniform force in that line. Prove that the change of kinetic energy is equal to the work done by the force. A bullet from a horizontal rifle has a range of 400 m on a horizontal plane 2·8 m below the level of the muzzle. When a block of wood, 8 cm thick, is placed in front of the muzzle the range is reduced to 250 m. What thickness of wood would suffice to stop the bullet entirely, supposing the resistance to be uniform and the same in each case?   (I.S.)

10. A particle of mass m is attached by means of two light inextensible strings, each of which passes over a small smooth fixed pulley, to two other particles each of mass $3m$. The pulleys are in the same horizontal line at distance $2a$ apart, and initially the first particle is held at rest midway between them, with the heavier particles hanging freely. If it is now released, show, by considerations of energy or otherwise, that it falls a vertical distance $12a/35$ before coming instantaneously to rest.   (L.A.)

11. A smooth bead of mass m is threaded on a fixed circular wire of diameter $2a$ whose plane is vertical. The bead is attached to the highest point of the wire by an elastic string of natural length l_0 and modulus λ. The bead is held with the string just stretched and is then let go. Prove that the bead will not reach the lowest point if $\lambda a(2a - l_0) > mg(2a + l_0)l_0$.

If l is the greatest length of the string during the motion, prove that the bead will be in equilibrium on the wire with the string stretched to the length $\frac{1}{2}(l + l_0)$.   (C.W.B.)

12. A light string, of length $2l$, supporting at each end a particle of mass m, passes over two fixed smooth pegs which are at a distance $2a$ apart in a horizontal plane, the mid-point of the string being mid-way between the pegs. A particle of mass M is now attached to the mid-point of the string. Show that the particles of mass m begin to rise. Find the potential energy of the three particles when the parts of the string between the pegs make an angle θ with the horizontal. Show that the system comes to instantaneous rest when $\tan \frac{1}{2}\theta = M/2m$, provided that $M < 2m$ and (to ensure that the masses m keep below the pegs) $l(4m^2 - M^2) > a(4m^2 + M^2)$. \hfill (H.C.)

13. A bullet of mass m enters a fixed block of wood with speed u and is brought to rest in a distance c. Find the resistance to penetration, assuming this resistance to be a constant force.

If the bullet, moving with speed u, enters a fixed block of thickness $\frac{3}{4}c$ which offers the same resistance as the first block, find the speed with which the bullet emerges. Find also the time taken to pass through the block. \hfill (L.A.)

14. A long fine inextensible string passes over a smooth peg and carries at its end masses A and B, each 1 kg, which hang in equilibrium. To B is attached a third mass C, also 1 kg, by means of a string 15 cm long. C is held close to B and allowed to fall. Find the velocity with which A starts to move and the height which it ascends during the first half-second of its motion. \hfill (I.E.)

15. A board of mass m rests on a board of mass M which rests on a horizontal table. The table is smooth and the coefficient of friction between the boards is μ. An impulse of magnitude Mu is applied to the lower board. What will be the common velocity of the boards when slipping ceases between them? Show that slipping will occur for a time $Mu/(M+m)\mu g$, and that during this time the fraction $m/(M+m)$ of the kinetic energy will be lost. \hfill (I.S.)

16. Two particles A, B of masses m, $2m$ respectively, connected by an inextensible string of length a, are placed close together on a rough horizontal table. The coefficients of friction between the particles and the table are respectively μ, $\frac{1}{2}\mu$. The particle A is projected along the table with a velocity V which is greater than $\sqrt{(2\mu ga)}$. Find the velocity just after the string becomes tight and show that B will overtake A if $V^2 > 20\mu ga$. \hfill (I.S.)

17. A small sphere, moving with velocity V on a smooth horizontal plane towards a fixed vertical plane in a line at right angles to it,

impinges directly upon an equal sphere at rest at a distance a from the vertical plane. The coefficient of restitution between the spheres and also that between a sphere and the vertical plane is $\frac{1}{2}$. Prove that there are only two impacts between the spheres, the interval between them being $12a/5V$, and that the first sphere has a final velocity of $7V/32$ away from the vertical plane.   (I.S.)

18. A particle of mass m falling vertically strikes a smooth plane fixed at an angle α with the horizontal, where $0 < \alpha \leqslant 45°$. If the particle rebounds horizontally, show that the coefficient of restitution is $\tan^2 \alpha$. Find what fraction of the kinetic energy of the particle is lost at impact. If the particle exerts an impulse I on the plane, find, in terms of I, m and α, the velocities with which it strikes and leaves the plane.   (L.A.)

19. A small smooth sphere of mass m, falling vertically, strikes with speed u the inclined plane face of a smooth wedge, of mass M and angle $\sin^{-1} 3/5$, resting on a smooth inelastic horizontal plane. If e is the coefficient of restitution between the sphere and the wedge, prove that the latter begins to move along the plane with speed

$$12mu(1+e)/(9m+25M).$$ (L.A.)

20. A particle moving in a horizontal plane strikes a vertical wall and rebounds. If the acute angles between the wall and the directions of motion before and after impact are θ, ϕ respectively, prove that $\tan \phi = e \tan \theta$, where e is the coefficient of restitution. Two points P, Q on a smooth horizontal plane are distant 2·4 m and 3·6 m respectively from a vertical wall. The distance between A, B, the feet of the perpendiculars from P, Q to the wall is 6·6 m. A particle is projected from P with a speed of 3·3 m s^{-1} so as to pass through Q after rebounding from the wall. If the coefficient of restitution is $\frac{9}{16}$, find: (i) the distance from A of the point of impact; (ii) the time taken by the particle to go from P to Q.   (I.S.)

21. What is meant by coefficient of restitution? A bucket of mass M is supported by a light string which passes over a smooth fixed pulley and carries at its other end a counterpoise of equal mass. A ball of mass m is dropped vertically so as to strike the bucket with velocity v. Prove that the bucket begins to move with velocity $m(1+e)v/(m+2M)$, where e is the coefficient of restitution. Find also the time which elapses between the first and second impacts of the ball and bucket.   (H.C.)

22. The upper edge of a fixed smooth plane, inclined at 30° to the horizontal, is itself horizontal and smooth, and a light thread

passes over it in a plane perpendicular to it, carrying at one end a particle of mass 30 g hanging freely and attached at the other to a particle of mass 90 g on the plane. Prove that when let go the hanging particle moves upwards with acceleration $\frac{1}{8}g$. Give your argument in full. After the system has moved from rest for $\frac{3}{4}$ s, the hanging particle suddenly picks up another particle of mass 60 g, which is at rest initially; find the new motion, proving that the hanging particle will come to rest momentarily after another $\frac{1}{4}$ s. (C.W.B.)

23. A smooth inclined plane has angle of greatest slope α and vertical height h. A particle of mass m_1 is projected from the lowest point up the line of greatest slope with velocity u and at the same instant a particle of mass m_2 is let slip from rest at the top of the plane so as to collide with the other particle. If the particle of mass m_1 is reduced to instantaneous rest by the collision, prove that e, the coefficient of restitution between the particles, must be less than m_1/m_2, and find u. (H.S.C.)

24. Two smooth spheres, each of radius a but of different masses m_1, m_2, move in opposite directions on a smooth table with velocities v_1, v_2 in parallel lines whose distance apart is $2a \sin \alpha$ and collide. If the coefficient of restitution is e, find the angle between the direction of motion of m_1 after impact and the line of centres at impact. In the special case where $m_1 = m_2$ and $v_1 = v_2$, show that after impact the directions of motion are parallel and make an angle θ with the original direction of motion where

$$\tan \theta = \frac{(1+e) \sin \alpha \cos \alpha}{\sin^2 \alpha - e \cos^2 \alpha}.$$ (H.S.C.)

25. Three spheres A, B, C, of masses m, $2m$, $4m$ respectively, rest on a smooth table with their centres collinear, B lying between A and C, and the coefficient of restitution between A and B being equal to that between B and C. A is projected directly towards B with velocity u, and C moves with velocity $u/4$ after it has been struck by B. Prove that A and B are reduced to rest, and find the coefficient of restitution. (I.S.)

26. A and B are points in a vertical line, B being at a height h above A. A particle is projected vertically upwards from A with velocity $2\sqrt{(gh)}$, and at the same instant a second particle is projected vertically upwards from B with velocity $\sqrt{(gh)}$. Show that the particles collide at a height $3h/2$ above A.

If the particles are of equal mass and the coefficient of restitution between them is $\frac{1}{2}$, find the speed of the first particle when it returns to A. (L.A.)

27. A smooth rod AB of length a is fixed at an angle 30° with the horizontal, its lower end B being at a height a above a horizontal floor. A small ring threaded on the rod is released from rest at A. Find the horizontal distance between B and the point where the ring strikes the floor. (L.A.)

28. A smooth wire in the form of a circle of radius a is fixed with its plane horizontal and two small beads of equal masses are threaded on the wire. One bead is initially at rest and the other is projected along the wire with speed u. If e is the coefficient of restitution between the beads, find the speed of each bead after the second collision and also the time which elapses between the first and second collisions. (L.A.)

29. Shots fired simultaneously from the top and bottom of a vertical cliff, with elevations α and β respectively, strike an object simultaneously at the same point. Show that if a is the horizontal distance of the object from the cliff the height of the cliff is $a(\tan \beta - \tan \alpha)$. (I.S.)

30. A square ABCD of side $2a$ is fixed in position with the corner A on a horizontal table and the diagonal AC vertical. A particle starting from rest at C, slides down the side CB, which is smooth, leaves the square at B, and falls to the table. Prove that it hits the table at a point whose distance from A is $a\sqrt{6}$. (I.S.)

31. A particle P is projected with speed V at an angle α with the horizontal. At time $t = 0$ it is at a point O where its velocity is horizontal. Write down the horizontal and vertical displacements from O after a time t, and show that the path of P is a parabola of latus rectum $(2V^2/g) \cos^2\alpha$. A ball is thrown over three posts of heights h, $h+d$, h at equal distances a apart in the same vertical plane, so as just to clear each post. Show that the ball strikes the ground at a distance $a(1+h/d)^{\frac{1}{2}}$ beyond the middle post. (H.S.C.)

32. A particle is projected with velocity V from a point, so that its range, on a plane through the point and inclined at an angle α to the horizontal, is a maximum. Show that this maximum range is

$$R = V^2/g(1+\sin \alpha).$$

Show that, after two-thirds of the time of flight has elapsed, the vertical distance between the particle and the plane is $2R/9$. (H.S.C.)

33. A particle is projected at an angle of θ to the horizontal from a point on a plane inclined at 45° to the horizontal. Its path is in a vertical plane containing a line of greatest slope. Prove

that the angle at which it meets the plane again is ϕ, where $\tan \phi = (1-\tan \theta)/(3-\tan \theta)$. At what angle must the particle be projected so that it is travelling horizontally at the instant when it meets the plane again?   (H.S.C.)

34. A heavy particle is projected from a point O at an angle of elevation α and describes a parabola under gravity. If co-ordinate axes are taken horizontally and vertically through O, prove that the equation of the parabola is

$$y = x\,(1-x/R)\,\tan\,\alpha$$

where R is the horizontal range.

   If the distance between the two points on the parabola which are at the same height h above the horizontal is $2a$, show that

$$R(R-4h\cot\alpha) = 4a^2.$$ (L.A.)

35. A particle is projected under gravity from a point O with speed u at an acute angle α above the horizontal through O. Prove that the distance of the particle from O first increases and then, if $9\sin^2\alpha > 8$, decreases for a time

$$(u/g)\sqrt{(9\sin^2\alpha - 8)}.$$

   Prove also that, if P is the position of the particle at time t, the tangent to the path at P meets the vertical through O in a point which moves with constant acceleration.   (L.A.)

36. Two heavy particles A and B are projected at the same instant from the same point with equal and opposite velocities of magnitude u in a line which makes an angle a with the horizontal. Find:

   (i) the path of A relative to B;
   (ii) the distance between the particles when their velocities are at right angles.   (L.A.)

37. A smooth plane is inclined at 30° to the horizontal. A small sphere is projected from a point O of the plane with velocity 1·8 ms⁻¹ at right angles to the plane. Immediately after its first impact with the plane the sphere is moving horizontally. Show that the coefficient of restitution between the sphere and the plane is $\frac{2}{3}$.

   Find the distance of the sphere from O when it strikes the plane a second time.   (L.A.)

38. A projectile is fired with initial speed $\sqrt{(2ga)}$ to hit a target at a horizontal distance a from the point of projection and at a vertical distance $\frac{1}{2}a$ above it. Find the two possible angles of

projection and the ratio of the times of flight along the two
paths.   (L.A.)

39. A heavy particle is projected with speed u and elevation α from
a point O. If coordinate axes are taken horizontally and vertically
through O, prove that the equation to the trajectory of the
particle is

$$y = x \tan \alpha - (gx^2 \sec^2 \alpha)/(2u^2).$$

If α_1 and α_2 are the two possible angles of projection for which
the trajectory passes through a given point (x_1, y_1) show, by
writing $\sec \alpha$ in terms of $\tan \alpha$, that

$$\tan (\alpha_1 + \alpha_2) = -x_1/y_1.$$ (L.A.)

40. A particle is projected from ground level in such a way that it
passes through two points at the same height a and a distance b
apart. Find the magnitude and direction of the minimum
velocity of projection.   (L.A.)

CHAPTER SEVEN

MOTION IN A CIRCLE

7.1. In the present chapter we shall consider the motion of a particle moving in a circle with *uniform* speed, and also certain points in connection with the motion of a particle in a vertical circle under gravity.

It is evident that if a particle is describing a circle its velocity is constantly changing in direction, if not in magnitude, and hence it must have an acceleration. If the magnitude of the velocity remains constant its speed is said to be uniform, and we shall show that the acceleration is then directed towards the centre. If the speed is *variable*, however, the acceleration at any instant has a component along the tangent as well as a component towards the centre.

7.2. *If a particle is moving in a circle of radius r with uniform speed v its acceleration is v²/r and is directed towards the centre of the circle.*

Let O (Fig. 7.1) be the centre of the circle, P the position of

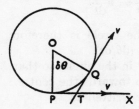

Fig. 7.1

the particle at any instant, and Q its position after a short interval of time δt.

Let the small angle POQ be $\delta\theta$, and the small arc PQ be δs. The velocity at P is v along the tangent PT, and the velocity at Q is v along the tangent TQ, and $\angle QTX = \delta\theta$.

---

* A reader unfamiliar with the subject is recommended to postpone the reading of chapters 7, 8, and 9 until he has read chapters 10, 11, and 12.

Resolving the velocity at Q parallel and perpendicular to PA, the components are

$v \cos \delta\theta$ parallel to PX, and $v \sin \delta\theta$ perpendicular to PX.

The change in velocity parallel to the tangent PX is

$$v \cos \delta\theta - v.$$

Therefore the average acceleration parallel to the tangent PX during the time-interval δt is $(v \cos \delta\theta - v)/\delta t$, and hence the acceleration along the tangent PX is given by the limit of this expression as δt tends to zero, that is,

$$Lt\frac{v(\cos \delta\theta - 1)}{\delta t} = Lt\frac{-2v \sin^2 \dfrac{\delta\theta}{2}}{\delta t}$$

$$= Lt\left\{-v \times \frac{\sin \frac{1}{2}\delta\theta}{\frac{1}{2}\delta\theta} \times \frac{\delta\theta}{\delta t} \times \sin \tfrac{1}{2}\delta\theta\right\} = 0.$$

The change in velocity parallel to the normal PO is $v \sin \delta\theta$, and hence the average acceleration parallel to the normal PO during the time-interval δt is $(v \sin \delta\theta)/\delta t$.

The acceleration at P along PO is therefore

$$Lt\frac{v \sin \delta\theta}{\delta t} = Lt\frac{v \sin \delta\theta}{\delta\theta} \times \frac{\delta\theta}{\delta t} = v\frac{d\theta}{dt}.$$

The acceleration at any point of the circle is therefore directed towards O, and is of magnitude $v(d\theta/dt)$.

Now $d\theta/dt$ is the angular velocity of P in the circle, so that, denoting this by ω, the acceleration is $v\omega$ towards the centre.

Since $v = r\omega$, the acceleration may be written as

$$v^2/r \text{ or } r\omega^2.$$

7.3. If the mass of the particle is m, the force required to produce this acceleration is mv^2/r, or $mr\omega^2$, and it must act continuously towards the centre of the circle.

This force may be produced in various ways, e.g., the particle may be connected to O by an inextensible string, or it may be threaded on a smooth circular wire; in the first case the tension of the string, and in the second case the reaction of the wire, provides the necessary central force.

It must be noticed carefully that although (in the case of a particle swinging round in a circle at the end of a string) the string is in a state of tension, there is no tendency for the particle to move *outwards* along the radius of the circle. If the string breaks the particle will continue to move straight on along the *tangent* to the circle, and its subsequent path will be that of a free projectile.

In the case of a train going round a curve the necessary inward force is provided by the pressure of the outer rail against the flanges of the wheels. In the case of a motor car the force is provided by the friction between the wheels and the ground. In both cases it is possible to make the weight of the train or car provide part or the whole of this inward force by banking up the track so that the outer wheels are above the inner ones. This will be considered later.

EXAMPLE (i)

A mass of 5 kg moves on a smooth horizontal plane with a speed of 8 m s⁻¹, being attached to a fixed point on the plane by a string of length 4 m; find the tension of the string.

Here $v = 8$, $r = 4$.

The acceleration towards the fixed point is $\frac{64}{4} = 16$ m s⁻²,

∴ the tension must be $5 \times 16 = 80$ N.

EXAMPLE (ii)

A particle of mass 3 kg, resting on a smooth table and attached to a fixed point on the table by a rope 1·2 m long, is making 300 rev min⁻¹; find the tension in the rope.

$$300 \text{ rev min}^{-1} = 5 \text{ rev s}^{-1}$$

∴   the angular velocity $= 10\pi$ rad s⁻¹.

The tension is $mr\omega^2 = 3 \times 1\cdot2 \times 10^2\pi^2$ N

$$= 360\pi^2 \text{ N}$$

$$= 3600 \text{ N nearly.}$$

EXAMPLE (iii)

An engine, of mass 80 Mg, is moving in an arc of a circle of radius 240 m, with a speed of 48 km h⁻¹; what force must be exerted by the rails towards the centre of the circle?

$$48 \text{ km h}^{-1} = \tfrac{48}{3600} \times 1000 \text{ m s}^{-1}$$

$$= 40/3 \text{ m s}^{-1}.$$

$\therefore$ the force is

$$\frac{80 \times 1000 \times 40 \times 40}{240 \times 9}\text{N}$$

$$= 0 \cdot 59 \times 10^5 \text{ N}.$$

EXAMPLE (iv)

A particle is tied by an elastic string of length 30 cm to a fixed point on a smooth horizontal table, upon which the particle is describing a circle round the point at a constant speed. If the modulus of elasticity of the string is equal to the weight of the particle and the number of revolutions per minute is 20, show that the extension of the string is nearly 5 cm. (I.S.)

Let m kg be the mass of the particle.

$$20 \text{ r.p.m.} = \tfrac{1}{3} \text{ revs}^{-1}.$$

Therefore the angular velocity is $2\pi/3$ rad s^{-1}.

If x m is the length of the string, the tension ($mr\omega^2$) is

$$mx\frac{4\pi^2}{9}\text{ N}.$$

Now the extension of the string is $(x - 0 \cdot 3)$ m, and since the modulus $\lambda = mg$, the tension T N is given by

$$T = \frac{mg}{0 \cdot 3}(x - 0 \cdot 3)$$

$\therefore$
$$\frac{mg}{0 \cdot 3}(x - 0 \cdot 3) = mx\frac{4\pi^2}{9}$$

$\therefore$
$$x = 0 \cdot 35.$$

The extension is about 5 cm.

EXAMPLES 7.1

1. A particle of mass 2 kg rests on a smooth horizontal plane, and is attached by a string 1·2 m long to a fixed point on the plane. If the particle describes a horizontal circle at 2·4 m s^{-1}, find the tension in the string.

2. A string 60 cm long can just sustain a weight of mass 20 kg without breaking. A mass of 2 kg is attached to one end of the string and revolves uniformly on a smooth table, the other end of the string being fixed to a point on the table; find the greatest number of complete revolutions the mass can make in a minute without breaking the string.

3. An engine, of mass 60 Mg, is moving in an arc of a circle of radius 240 m at 96 km h^{-1}. What force must be exerted by the rails towards the centre of the circle ?

4. A motor car, of mass 2 Mg, is rounding a curve of radius 800 m on a level track at 96 km h^{-1}; what force of friction is necessary between the wheels and the ground ?

5. One end of an elastic string, 60 cm long, is attached to a fixed point on a smooth table, and the other end to a mass of 2 kg resting on the table. If the 2 kg mass were suspended vertically by the string the extension would be 10 cm. The mass is made to describe a circle round the fixed point at 40 rev min^{-1}. Calculate the extension of the string.

6. An elastic string of unstretched length l, fixed at one end, can just support a mass m when hanging vertically, and extended by half its length. The mass and string are now placed on a smooth horizontal table with one end of the string fixed. The string is stretched to double its length and the mass is projected along the table with such velocity that it describes a horizontal circle about the fixed point as centre. Find the time of revolution of the mass. (H.S.D.)

7. Two equal particles are connected by a string passing through a hole in a smooth table, one particle being on the table, the other underneath. How many revolutions per minute would the particle on the table have to perform in a circle of radius 15 cm, in order to keep the other particle at rest. (I.S.)

8. A rough horizontal table can rotate about a vertical axis, and a weight is placed on the table at a distance of 0·6 m from the axis. The table is made to rotate with gradually increasing velocity; if the coefficient of friction between the weight and the table is $\frac{1}{4}$, show that the weight will not move as long as the number of revolutions per minute is less than 19. (H.S.C.)

9. A plane horizontal circular disc is constrained to rotate uniformly about its centre, describing two complete revolutions per second. Show that the greatest distance from the centre of the disc at which a small object can be placed so as to stay on the disc is just over $6·2\mu$ cm, where μ is the coefficient of friction between the object and the disc.

10. The wheels of a bicycle are 75 cm in diameter, the gear-ratio between the crank axle and wheel axle is $2\frac{1}{2}$, and the length of the crank is 20 cm. Find the velocity of the end of the crank and the magnitude and direction of its acceleration when at its highest point, the bicycle travelling at the rate of 9 ms^{-1}. (Q.E.)

7.4. The conical pendulum

If a particle be tied by a string to a fixed point O, and move in a horizontal circle, so that the string describes a cone whose axis is the vertical through O, the string and particle form what is called a conical pendulum.

Let P (Fig. 7.2) represent the particle of mass m, and OP

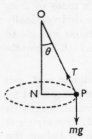

Fig. 7.2

the string of length l, and let ON be the vertical through O. The if PN is perpendicular to ON, N is the centre of the horizontal circle described by P.

Let T be the tension in the string, θ its inclination to the vertical, and ω the angular velocity of the particle about N.

The only forces acting on the particle are the tension of the string and its own weight mg.

It is obvious that P must be below O so that the tension has an upward vertical component to balance the weight mg.

The horizontal component of the tension must provide the central force necessary to keep the particle moving in its circle. The value of this central force is $m\text{PN}\omega^2$ or $ml \sin \theta\omega^2$

$$\therefore \qquad T \sin \theta = ml \sin \theta \times \omega^2 \qquad\qquad \text{(i)}$$

Since there is no vertical acceleration, the vertical component of T must equal the weight mg

$$\therefore \qquad T \cos \theta = mg. \qquad\qquad \text{(ii)}$$

From (i) $\qquad T = ml\omega^2 = 4\pi^2 n^2 ml$

where n is the number of revolutions made by P per second.

Substituting for T in (ii),

$$\cos \theta = \frac{mg}{ml\omega^2} = \frac{g}{l\omega^2}.$$

Now $ON = l \cos \theta$,

$$\therefore \qquad ON = \frac{g}{\omega^2}$$

i.e. the vertical depth of P below O is independent of the length of the string, and varies inversely as the square of the angular velocity.

If we use the speed v of P instead of its angular velocity ω,

$$v = PN \times \omega = l \sin \theta \times \omega.$$

Equation (i) then becomes

$$T \sin \theta = ml \sin \theta \times \frac{v^2}{l^2 \sin^2 \theta} = \frac{mv^2}{l \sin \theta}$$

and, dividing by (ii),

$$\tan \theta = \frac{v^2}{gl \sin \theta}.$$

$$\therefore \qquad v^2 = gl \sin \theta \tan \theta.$$

7.5. Governors of steam-engines

The fact that, when a weight is swung round as a conical pendulum, the depth of the weight below the point of suspension depends only on the angular velocity, is made use of in governors for regulating the supply of steam to an engine which is required to rotate a shaft at a constant rate.

Two light rods are hinged at C (Fig. 7.3) to a vertical shaft

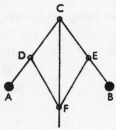

FIG. 7.3

which is rotated by the engine, and at the other ends of these rods are weights A and B. Two other rods DF, EF are hinged to AC and BC and also to a collar F which can slide up and down the shaft.

A lever is attached to F which can open or close a valve

admitting steam to the engine. This is arranged so that when F rises it closes the valve.

When the speed of rotation of the shaft increases, the weights A and B rise and pull F up, thus shutting off some of the steam so that the engine is slowed down. If the speed decreases too much, F is lowered and lets in more steam.

7.6. EXAMPLE (i)

A small body, attached by a string to a fixed point, describes a horizontal circle at the uniform angular speed of 1 rev s⁻¹. Prove that its distance below the fixed point does not depend on the length of the string, and find the tension of the string when the mass of the body is 2 kg, and the length of the string is 35 cm. (H.S.D.)

Let O (Fig. 7.4) be the fixed point, P the body, OP the string inclined at an angle θ to the vertical ON, and PN perpendicular to ON.

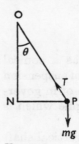

FIG. 7.4

Then, if m is the mass, T the tension of the string, and ω the angular velocity of P,

$$T \sin \theta = m\text{PN} \times \omega^2 = ml \sin \theta \times \omega^2 \qquad \text{(i)}$$

and $$T \cos \theta = mg. \qquad \text{(ii)}$$

From (i) $$T = ml\omega^2 \qquad \text{(iii)}$$

$$\therefore \qquad l \cos \theta = \frac{mg}{m\omega^2} = \frac{g}{\omega^2}.$$

But $l \cos \theta$ is the depth of P below O, which is therefore equal to g/ω^2, and is independent of the length of the string.

When P is making 1 rev s⁻¹, $\omega = 2\pi$, and if $m = 1$ kg, and $l = 0.35$ m, we have, from (iii),

$$T = 0.35 \times 4\pi^2.$$

Taking $\pi^2 = 10$,

$$T = 14 \text{ N.}$$

EXAMPLE (ii)

If the mass of the bob in a conical pendulum is 2 kg, and the length of the string is 60 cm, find the maximum number of revolutions per second of the pendulum when the greatest tension that can with safety be allowed in the string is 400 N.   (I.S.)

Let T N be the tension in the string, ω rad s^{-1} the angular velocity, and θ the inclination of the string to the vertical.

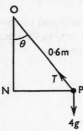

FIG. 7.5

In Fig. 7.5, O is the point of suspension, P the bob, PN the perpendicular on the vertical ON through O.

$$T \sin \theta = 4\mathrm{PN} \times \omega^2 = 4 \times 0.6 \sin \theta \times 4\pi^2 n^2$$

where n is the number of revolutions per second,

$$\therefore \qquad\qquad T = 9.6\pi^2 n^2.$$

The maximum value of the tension is 400 N.

$$\therefore \qquad\qquad \pi^2 n^2 = 400/9.6 = 41.7$$

$$\therefore \qquad\qquad n^2 = 4.17 \text{ taking } \pi^2 = 10.$$

Hence the greatest number of revolutions per second is 2.04.

EXAMPLE (iii)

An elastic thread, whose unstretched length is 50 cm, has a mass of 2·2 kg at one end and makes 60 r.p.m. as a conical pendulum. The string is then 60 cm long; find the tension in the string and find the kinetic energy of the mass and the potential energy due to stretching the thread.   (I.S.)

60 rev min^{-1} = 1 rev s^{-1}, and the angular velocity is 2π rad s^{-1}.

If T N is the tension, and θ the inclination of the string to the vertical,

$$T \sin \theta = 2.2 \times 0.6 \sin \theta \times 4\pi^2$$

$$\therefore \qquad\qquad T = 5.28\pi^2 = 52.8 \text{ nearly.}$$

Also $\qquad\qquad T \cos \theta = 2 \cdot 2g$

$\therefore \qquad\qquad \cos \theta = \dfrac{2 \cdot 2 \times 9 \cdot 8}{52 \cdot 8} = \dfrac{49}{120}$

$\therefore \qquad\qquad \sin \theta = 0 \cdot 91.$

If v ms^{-1} is the speed of the mass,

$$v = 0 \cdot 6 \sin \theta \times \omega = 0 \cdot 6 \times 0 \cdot 91 \times 2\pi = 1 \cdot 09\pi$$

$\therefore$ its kinetic energy $= \frac{1}{2}(2 \cdot 2)(1 \cdot 09\pi)^2 = 1 \cdot 3\pi^2 = 13$ J.

The potential energy due to stretching the thread is equal to the work done in stretching it from its natural length, 50 cm, to 60 cm, i.e. by 0·1 m. The mean of the initial and final tensions is

$$\tfrac{1}{2}T = 26 \cdot 4 \text{ N.}$$

$\therefore$ the work done in stretching is 2·64 J.

The potential energy is therefore 2·64 J.

EXAMPLE (iv)

A mass m at C is freely jointed to two equal light rods CA and CB; the end A of CA is pivoted to a fixed point A, and the end B is freely jointed to a heavy bead of mass m which slides on a smooth vertical bar AB. If the mass C rotates in a horizontal circle with uniform angular velocity ω, prove that the inclination of the rods CA and CB to the vertical is $\cos^{-1}(3g/l\omega^2)$, *where l is the length of either rod.* (I.E.)

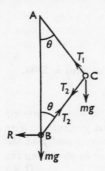

Fig. 7.6

Let T_1, T_2 be the tensions in AC, BC (Fig. 7.6), R the reaction on the mass at B normal to the rod, and θ the angle BAC. Since the weight at B does not move vertically

$$T_2 \cos \theta = mg \qquad\qquad\text{(i)}$$

Also, since the weight at C does not move vertically

$$T_1 \cos \theta = mg + T_2 \cos \theta = 2mg. \tag{ii}$$

Now since the mass at C is describing a horizontal circle of radius $l \sin \theta$ about AB, the two tensions must exert a horizontal force of $ml \sin \theta \omega^2$, towards AB.

$$\therefore \qquad T_1 \sin \theta + T_2 \sin \theta = ml \sin \theta \times \omega^2$$

$$\therefore \qquad\qquad T_1 + T_2 = ml\omega^2.$$

Hence, from (i) and (ii),

$$\frac{2mg}{\cos \theta} + \frac{mg}{\cos \theta} = ml\omega^2$$

$$\therefore \qquad\qquad \cos \theta = 3g/l\omega^2.$$

EXAMPLES 7.2

1. A particle of mass m is describing a circle on a smooth plane at the end of a horizontal string of length a. If the particle makes n complete revolutions a minute, compare the tension of the string with the weight of the particle. A man holds one end of a string, 25 cm long, to the other end of which a weight is attached, and swings the weight round so as to make it describe a horizontal circle at a uniform rate of 80 rev min⁻¹. Show that the inclination of the string to the vertical is very nearly 57°.
(I.S.)

2. A particle moves as a conical pendulum at the end of a string of length 40 cm. If the string is inclined at 60° to the vertical, show that the particle is making approximately 11 revolutions in 10 sec.
(I.A.)

3. A small heavy body is attached by a string 1·2 m long to a fixed point A, and is caused to move with uniform speed in a horizontal circle. If the tension in the string is twice the weight of the body, show that the angular velocity is about 4 rad s⁻¹.
(H.S.D.)

4. An elastic string, of unstretched length 90 cm, has one end attached to a fixed point and the other to a mass of 4 kg which revolves as a conical pendulum, making 40 rev min⁻¹. If the length of the string is then 105 cm, find what the extension will be when the weight hangs at rest.
(I.S.)

5. A mass of 0·5 kg suspended by a cord 1·5 m long, is revolving as a conical pendulum at 80 rev min⁻¹: find the radius of the circle it describes, and the tension of the cord.
(I.A.)

6. Show that in the conical pendulum, the inclination of the string to the vertical being θ, sec $\theta = r\omega^2/g$, where r is the length of the string, and ω the angular velocity. If the string is extensible, so that its tension is equal to $\lambda(r-a)/a$, where r is the stretched and a the natural length, find the cosine of the angle which the string makes with the vertical and show that $ma\omega^2/\lambda$ must be less than unity. (H.S.D.)

7. A particle of mass 1·8 kg is whirled round at the end of a string 50 cm long, so as to describe a horizontal circle, making 60 rev min^{-1}; calculate the tension in the string and prove that the fixed end of the string is a little less than 25 cm above the centre of the circle. (H.C.)

8. A particle suspended by a fine string from a fixed point describes a circle uniformly in a horizontal plane. If it makes 3 complete revolutions every 2 s, show that its vertical depth below the fixed point is 11 cm approximately. (H.C.)

9. A particle, attached to a fixed point by a string 1 m long, describes a horizontal circle. The string can only support a tension equal to 15 times the weight of the particle. Show that the greatest possible number of revolutions per s is just under 2. (H.C.)

10. Two small weights, of mass 60 g and 30 g respectively, are connected by a light inextensible string, 30 cm long, which passes through a smooth fixed ring. The 60-g weight hangs at a distance of 20 cm below the ring, while the 30-g weight describes a horizontal circle. Show that the plane of this circle is 5 cm below the ring, and show also that the 30-g weight makes very nearly 134 rev min^{-1}. (H.C.)

11. Two unequal masses are connected by a string of length l which passes through a fixed smooth ring. The smaller mass moves as a conical pendulum while the other mass hangs vertically. Find the semi-angle of the cone, and the number of revolutions per second when a length a of the string is hanging vertically. (C.S.)

12. A mass $2m$ rests on a smooth horizontal table and is connected to a mass m by a light inextensible string passing through a small ring fixed at a height h above the table. If the mass $2m$ is made to describe a circle of radius $\frac{1}{2}h$ having its centre on the table vertically below the ring, show that the time it takes to describe the circle once is $2\pi(h\sqrt{5}/g)^{\frac{1}{2}}$.

13. A particle is attached by means of two equal strings to two points A and B in the same vertical line, and describes a horizontal circle with uniform angular speed. Prove that, in order

that both strings may remain stretched, the angular speed must exceed $\sqrt{(2g/h)}$, where $h = AB$, and that, if the speed is $2\sqrt{(2g/h)}$, the ratio of the tensions of the strings is 5 : 3. (H.S.D.)

14. A light arm CB, of length a, is freely pivoted at its end C, which is fixed, and carries at B a mass m; the arm is maintained in a horizontal position by a string attached to B and to a point A fixed vertically above C at a distance b from it. Find the magnitude and direction of the stress in CB when CB is revolving about the vertical at the uniform rate of n revs^{-1}. (N.U.3)

15. A particle of mass m moving in a horizontal circle is kept in its path by a string tied to a point at a height h above the centre of the circle. Find the period of rotation.

If $m = 120$ g, $h = 1\cdot2$ cm, and the length of the string is 50 cm, find the tension of the string. (N.U.3)

16. A smooth hemispherical bowl of internal radius a is held with its rim horizontal, and a particle describes in it a horizontal circle of radius c, less than a. Find the period of rotation.

A particle of mass m describes a horizontal circle of radius 24 cm inside a smooth hemispherical bowl of internal radius 25 cm which is held with its rim horizontal. A fine weightless thread tied to the particle passes through a small smooth hole at the bottom of the bowl and supports another particle of mass m which hangs at rest. Show that the speed of the first particle is a little less than 4 m s^{-1}. (N.U.4)

17. A particle of mass m is suspended from a fixed point by an elastic string of natural length a. The tension in the string when stretched a length x is λx. Prove that if the particle describes a horizontal circle steadily with angular velocity ω, the inclination θ of the string to the vertical is given by

$$\omega^2 \cos \theta = \frac{g}{a}\left(1 - \frac{m\omega^2}{\lambda}\right).$$

18. An elastic string of natural length a is found to extend e when a small weight is attached to one end, the other end being fixed. The weight is now made to describe a horizontal circle with angular velocity ω rad s^{-1}; find the extension of the string and the inclination of the string to the vertical.

Show that ω^2 must be less than g/e and greater than $g/(a+e)$.

7.7. The motion of a railway carriage or motor car round a curved track

Let ABCD (Fig. 7.7) represent a section of a railway carriage or car in the vertical plane passing through its centre of mass

G and the centre of the circle which it is describing, A and B being the points where the wheels meet the ground and A on the inside of the curve.

Let v be the speed, r the radius of the circle, and m the mass. The central force $\dfrac{mv^2}{r}$ necessary to cause the circular motion should really be applied at G, the centre of mass, but it can, of course, be applied in practice only at the points of contact with the rails or ground.

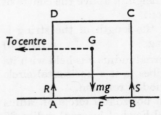

FIG. 7.7

In the case of a railway carriage the flanges of the wheels are on the insides of the rails so that, unless a second (or check) rail is placed on the inside of the curve with the inner flanges between the two rails, all the inward thrust is supplied by the outer rail, the force F shown in the figure.

In either case, if the curve is at all sharp, there is a considerable side-thrust on the rails, and this is usually eliminated or reduced by banking the track as explained below.

A level track has another disadvantage. It is well known that a car rounding a curve at high speeds tends to tilt up on its outer wheels.

The force F (equal to mv^2/r) applied horizontally at B is equivalent to an equal horizontal force at G together with a couple. This couple being clockwise tends to make the carriage rotate in the direction ADCB, that is, to lift the inner wheels off the rail. Effectively this increases the reaction S on the wheels at B and decreases the reaction R on the wheels at A. These two forces and the weight mg must together form a couple, equal and opposite to the other couple, if the carriage does not lift off the rail. In fact, R and S are equivalent to a force mg acting vertically upwards to the right of G (Fig. 7.7) at a distance x

from G, and hence the moment of the counterclockwise couple is mgx.

If h is the height of G above the rails, the moment of the couple tending to produce clockwise rotation is mv^2h/r. Hence in general, $mv^2h/r = mgx$.

If the lateral distance between the rails, i.e. the gauge, is $2a$, and we assume that G is midway between A and B, the greatest value of x is a and this occurs when $R = 0$, i.e. when the inner wheels are on the point of leaving the rail.

Hence the carriage will tilt about B when the speed is such that $\qquad mv^2h/r > mga$ or $v > \sqrt{(gar/h)}$.

7.8. We can obtain this result in another way as follows.

Let R, S be the vertical forces at A and B, and F the resultant horizontal force acting on the outer wheels due to their flanges pressing against the outer rails (Fig. 7.7).

Then as there is no vertical motion

$$R + S - mg = 0 \qquad (1)$$

and as the acceleration inwards is v^2/r we have

$$F = mv^2/r. \qquad (2)$$

Further, as there is no rotation of the carriage about G the sum of the moments of the forces about G must be zero.* Hence

$$Sa - Ra - Fh = 0 \qquad (3)$$

$$\therefore \qquad S = \tfrac{1}{2}m\left(g + \frac{v^2h}{ra}\right) \quad \text{and} \quad R = \tfrac{1}{2}m\left(g - \frac{v^2h}{ra}\right).$$

It is evident that the vertical thrust S on the outer rail is always greater than that on the inner rail, and also that, when $v^2h/ra = g$, $R = 0$, or the vertical thrust on the inner rail vanishes. When this happens the carriage begins to tilt about B.

7.9. Suppose a car or carriage is placed on an inclined track, sloping downwards at an angle θ towards the centre of the curve which is being described, as shown in Fig. 7.8.

We now have the component of the weight, $mg \sin \theta$, acting at G, down the slope.

* The justification of this statement is given later in § 9.26.

The component down the slope of the central acceleration v^2/r is $(v^2/r) \cos \theta$, so that if

$$mg \sin \theta = \frac{mv^2}{r} \cos \theta$$

or
$$\tan \theta = v^2/gr,$$

the component of the weight is sufficient to supply the necessary central force down the slope.

In this case there will be no side-thrust on the track.

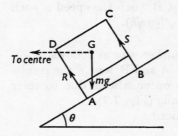

FIG. 7.8

Alternatively, we can write the equations of motion in the form:

$$(R+S) \cos \theta - mg = 0$$

since there is no vertical motion, and

$$(R+S) \sin \theta = mv^2/r$$

since there is a horizontal acceleration of v^2/r. Also taking moments about G, since there is no rotation we get

$$Ra - Sa = 0.$$

These give $R = S$ and $\tan \theta = v^2/gr.$

The value of θ for a given value of r depends on v.

In the case of a railway track the angle is chosen for the average speed at which trains take the curve. At higher speeds than this there is a side-thrust on the outer rail outwards, and at lower speeds there will be an inward thrust on the inner rail, the weight component being greater than is necessary.

In the case of a motor track the banking is graduated, getting steeper towards the outside of the track. As the speed of the car increases it skids or is steered on to the steeper part.

7.10. Motion of a bicyclist riding in a curve

In this case the centre of gravity, if the cycle and rider are upright, is vertically above the line of contact of the wheels with the ground. The weight has therefore no moment about this point and cannot, therefore, counteract the upsetting couple. For this reason the rider has to lean inwards on rounding a corner.

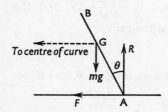

FIG. 7.9

Let AB (Fig. 7.9) represent the bicycle and rider, and G their centre of mass. The friction of the ground F acts inwards at A, and the other forces acting are the weight mg, vertically through G, and the normal reaction of the ground (R) at A.

Since there is no vertical motion

$$R = mg.$$

Since the horizontal acceleration is v^2/r

$$F = mv^2/r$$

and since there is no rotation about G

$$F \times \text{AG} \cos \theta = R \times \text{AG} \sin \theta$$

or $$\tan \theta = F/R.$$

(It might be noted that this relation indicates that the resultant of F and R passes through G.)

Further $$\tan \theta = mv^2/mgr = v^2/gr.$$

This is the same as the angle of banking necessary to prevent any tendency to skid.

7.11. EXAMPLE (i)

A train is running at 72 *km h*$^{-1}$ *on a curve of mean radius* 360 *m, and the distance between the rails is* 1·4 *m. Find how much the outer rail must be raised in order that there may be no side-thrust on the rail.*

(I.S.)

Let m kg be the mass of the train, and θ the angle the plane of the rails makes with the horizontal.

The speed is $72 \times 10^3/3600$ m s^{-1}.

The horizontal inward force required is $\dfrac{m \times 20^2}{360}$ N, and the component of this parallel to the plane of the rails is

$$\frac{m \times 20^2}{360} \cos \theta.$$

The component of the weight in this direction is $mg \sin \theta$, and therefore the required value of θ is given by

$$mg \sin \theta = \frac{m \times 20^2}{360} \cos \theta$$

$$\therefore \qquad \tan \theta = \frac{20^2}{360 \times 9 \cdot 8} \cdot$$

The height to which the outer rail should be raised is 1·41 $\sin \theta$ m. Now as θ is small we may take $\sin \theta = \tan \theta$.

Therefore the height required

$$= 1 \cdot 41 \times \frac{10}{88 \cdot 2} = 0 \cdot 16 \text{ m.}$$

EXAMPLE (ii)

A railway truck of mass 10 *Mg travels round a curve, of* 800 *m radius, at* 24 *km h*$^{-1}$. *The distance between the rails is* 1·5 *m, and the centre of gravity of the truck is* 1·8 *m above the rails. If the rails are at the same level, find the vertical pressure upon each, and the horizontal pressure between the flange and the rail. How much should the outer rail be raised to avoid pressure on the flange?*

(I.E.)

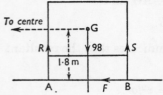

FIG. 7.10

Let A (Fig. 7.10) represent the inner and B the outer point of contact with the rails, and let R and S be the vertical thrusts at A

and B, F the horizontal thrust at B, all measured in 10^3 newton. The weight of the truck is 98×10^3 N.
Hence,

$$R + S = 98$$

and, since the speed is $20/3 \ \mathrm{m\,s^{-1}}$,

$$F = 10 \times (\tfrac{20}{3})^2 / 800 = 5/9$$

Taking moments about G,

$$0 \cdot 75S - 0 \cdot 75R = 1 \cdot 8F$$

$$\therefore \qquad S - R = 2 \cdot 4F$$

$$\therefore \qquad 2S = 98 + 2 \cdot 4F = 98 + 1 \cdot 33 = 99 \cdot 33$$

$$\therefore \qquad S = 49 \cdot 67$$

$$\therefore \qquad R = 48 \cdot 33.$$

If θ is the slope of the track necessary to prevent side-thrust,

$$mg \sin \theta = \frac{mv^2}{r} \cos \theta$$

$$\therefore \qquad \tan \theta = \frac{v^2}{gr} = \frac{400}{9 \times 9 \cdot 8 \times 800} = \frac{1}{176 \cdot 4}.$$

The height to which the outer rail must be raised is

$$1 \cdot 5 \sin \theta \simeq 1 \cdot 5 \tan \theta = 1 \cdot 5 \times \frac{1}{176 \cdot 4} \ \mathrm{m}$$

$$= 0 \cdot 85 \ \mathrm{cm \ nearly.}$$

EXAMPLE (iii)

An aeroplane of mass 1 tonne flies at 150 kmh⁻¹. Find the angle at which it must bank in order to turn without side-slipping in a horizontal circle of 200 m radius, assuming that its design enables it to do this, and that the line of the resultant air pressure lies in the plane of symmetry of the machine.   (Q.E.)

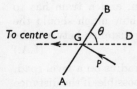

Fɪɢ. 7.11

Let AB (Fig. 7.11) represent the section of the wings, G the centre of gravity, and CGD the horizontal line through G, the centre of the circle described being in the direction of C.

The air pressure may be taken as a force P acting through G perpendicular to AB. Let $\angle BGD = \theta$.

Now P has to support the weight of the plane mg, and also provide the central force mv^2/r along GC.

Here
$$v = \frac{150 \times 10^3}{3600} \text{ m s}^{-1} = 41\tfrac{2}{3} \text{ m s}^{-1},$$

and
$$r = 200 \text{ m}$$

$\therefore$
$$P \cos \theta = mg$$

and
$$P \sin \theta = \frac{m \times 125^2}{9 \times 200}$$

$\therefore$
$$\tan \theta = \frac{125 \times 125}{9 \times 200 \times 9 \cdot 8} = \frac{625}{705 \cdot 6} = 0 \cdot 886$$

$\therefore$
$$\theta = 41° \, 32'.$$

EXAMPLES 7.3

1. The gauge of a railway is 1·41 m, and the line runs along an arc of a circle of radius 800 m. The average speed of the trains on the line is 72 km h^{-1}. What should be the height of the outer above the inner rail? (I.S.)

2. A motor track describes a curve of 75 m radius, and is sloping downwards towards the inside of the curve at an angle $\tan^{-1} \tfrac{1}{5}$. At what speed must a car run along it so that there should be no tendency to side-slip? (I.S.)

3. Explain clearly the advantage of raising the outer rail above the inner on a curved track. Calculate by how much the outer rail should be raised on a circular track of radius r, if b is the breadth between the rails and v is the speed of a train on the track. (I.A.)

4. If the radius of a curved track is 900 m, and a train has to travel round the track at 48 km h^{-1}, by how much should the outer rail be raised above the inner if the distance between the rails is 140 cm? (I.A.)

5. A motor car is rounding a curve of 45 m radius on a level road. Find the maximum speed at which this is possible, if the distance between the wheels is 1·35 m, and the centre of gravity is 0·6 m from the ground and midway between the line of the wheels. Find also the least coefficient of friction between the road and tyres which will prevent side-slip at the maximum speed. (H.S.C.)

6. A motor car is moving round the curve of a track at 120 km h^{-1}, the radius of the curve being 100 m. Calculate the angle which the track makes with the horizon, if the total pressure exerted by the car on the track is normal to the plane of the track. If the mass of the car is 1·5 Mg, calculate the total pressure on the track. (H.S.D.)

7. Assuming that the height of the centre of gravity of a locomotive above the rails is 1·8 m, and the width of the rails is 1·4 m, find the greatest speed at which it could travel on a curve of radius 135 m without toppling over. (I.E.)

8. A train is travelling at 60 km h^{-1} round a curve of radius 180 m. If the width of the rails is 1·5 m, calculate how much the outer rail must be raised above the inner, if lateral pressure on the rails is to be avoided. (H.S.D.)

9. A bicyclist is describing a curve of 15 m radius at a speed of 16 km h^{-1}; find the inclination to the vertical of the plane of the bicycle. What is the least coefficient of friction between the bicycle and the road that the bicycle may not side-slip? [Assume the rider and his machine to be in one plane.] (H.C.)

10. The shape of a cycle track at a corner is that of a circle whose radius is 90 m. Find the angle at which the track should be inclined to the horizontal in order that a rider can take the corner at 48 km h^{-1} without any lateral reaction between his bicycle and the track. If a motor-cyclist can take the corner safely at 96 km h^{-1}, find the least possible value of the coefficient of friction between the track and his tyres. (H.C.)

11. A motor car is rounding a curve of radius 45 m on a level road. What is the maximum speed at which this is possible without overturning when the distance between the wheels is 1·2 m, and the centre of gravity of the car and its load is midway between the wheels and 0·9 m from the ground? (Q.E.)

12. An aeroplane is describing a horizontal circle of 400 m radius at 240 km h^{-1}. Assuming that the air pressure on it acts through its centre of gravity at right angles to the planes, determine the angle at which they must be inclined to the vertical. (H.S.D.)

13. The sleepers of a railway line at a point where the curve of the track has a radius of 60 m have such a slope that a train moving at 48 km h^{-1} exerts no lateral force on the rails. What lateral force would an engine of mass 100 Mg exert on the rails at this point if it were at rest? (I.E.)

14. A car takes a banked corner of a racing track at a speed V, the lateral gradient x being designed to reduce the tendency to

side-slip to zero for a lower speed U. Show that the coefficient of friction necessary to prevent side-slip for the greater speed V must be at least

$$\frac{(V^2 - U^2)\sin\alpha\cos\alpha}{V^2\sin^2\alpha + U^2\cos^2\alpha}.$$ (C.S.)

15. A railway track round a curve of 400 m radius is laid so that there is no lateral pressure on the rails when a train travels round at 64 km h⁻¹. Determine the lateral pressure, in terms of the weight of the train, when the speed is 32 km h⁻¹. [Neglect the length of the train.] (I.C.)

16. A railway truck is loaded so that the pressure on each wheel is 4.9×10^4 N, and the centre of gravity of the loaded truck is 1·8 m above the rails, and the distance from centre to centre of the wheels on an axle is 1·5 m. Find the alteration in the vertical pressure on the rails when the truck is going on the level round a track of 360 m radius at a speed of 24 km h⁻¹.

17. A curve on a railway line is banked up so that the lateral thrust on the inner rail due to a truck moving with speed v_1 is equal to the thrust on the outer rail when the truck is moving with speed v_2 ($v_2 > v_1$). Show that there will be no lateral thrust on either rail when the truck is moving with speed,

$$[\tfrac{1}{2}(v_1{}^2 + v_2{}^2)]^{\frac{1}{2}}.$$ (H.C.)

18. A car travels round a curve on a track of 45 m radius at a speed of 48 km h⁻¹. Show that if there is no side-pressure between the car and the track the track must be banked at an angle of approximately 22°. What would be the component of force on the car across the track, if a car of mass 1 Mg went round this curve at 72 km h⁻¹? (Q.E.)

19. A motor car makes a quick turn on the level round a circle of 9·5 m radius. If the centre of gravity of the car be midway between the wheels and at a height of 0·95 m, and if the wheel gauge is 1·4 m, find the speed at which the car will overturn, assuming that no side-slipping occurs. (Q.E.)

20. In a conical pendulum the speed of the bob is v, and the radius of the circle in which it moves is r, while the string makes an angle α with the vertical. Prove that $v^2 = rg\tan\alpha$.

A cyclist travels on a level track of radius 66 m, and the coefficient of friction between the tyres and the ground is 0·32. Find the greatest speed at which he may travel. (N.U.3)

21. A car travels at v m s^{-1} along a curved track of radius R m. Find the inclination of the track to the horizontal if there is to be no tendency for the car to slip sideways.

Prove that if $v = 9$, $R = 300$ and the inclination of the track is 1 in 100, the total sideways frictional force on the wheels must be about 1·8 per cent of the weight of the car.   (N.U.3)

MOTION IN A VERTICAL CIRCLE

7.12. The complete investigation of the motion of a particle constrained to move on a curve in a vertical plane is beyond the scope of this book. When the curve is smooth we can, however, find the velocity of the particle at any point by means of the principle of energy. The time taken to describe a given length of arc or to acquire a certain velocity cannot be found easily, and in the case of the circle it is impossible to obtain an exact value for it. We shall only consider certain results which can be obtained from a knowledge of the velocity in any position.

When a particle is sliding down a smooth curve we know from the principle of energy that the kinetic energy gained is equal to the potential energy lost, since the reaction of the curve is perpendicular to the direction of motion, and therefore does no work. The same applies to a particle suspended by a string and swinging in a vertical plane about a fixed point.

If m is the mass of the particle, u the initial and v the final velocity, and h the vertical height descended,

$$\tfrac{1}{2}mv^2 - \tfrac{1}{2}mu^2 = mgh$$

$$\therefore \qquad v^2 - u^2 = 2hg, \text{ or } v^2 = u^2 + 2gh.$$

If the particle is moving *up* the curve

$$v^2 = u^2 - 2gh.$$

7.13. In dealing with motion in a vertical circle there are differences in the nature of the problem according to whether the particle is, or is not, able to leave the circle. If a ring is threaded on the circle it cannot leave the curve, but if a particle is suspended by a string this may go slack when it gets above the horizontal position. Similarly, a particle moving down the outside of a vertical circle, or projected up the inside can come away from the curve. In these cases the usual problem is to find where it will leave the curve.

We shall consider first the case of a ring or bead threaded on a smooth circular rod fixed in a vertical plane.

7.14. Motion of a ring threaded on a smooth vertical circular rod

Let C (Fig. 7.12) be the centre of the circular rod, A the lowest point, B the highest point, and a the radius. The rod is held fixed.

Let the mass of the ring be m, and V its velocity of projection from the lowest point.

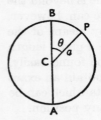

FIG. 7.12

When it reaches a position P, such that $\angle BCP = \theta$, it has risen a vertical distance $a + a \cos \theta$, and its velocity v is given by the equation of energy.

$$\therefore \qquad \tfrac{1}{2}mv^2 = \tfrac{1}{2}mV^2 - mga(1 + \cos \theta).$$

If V is just large enough to take the particle up to B we must have $v = 0$ when $\theta = 0$, and hence

$$0 = V^2 - 4ag.$$
$$V = \sqrt{(4ag)},$$

and with this value of V the ring will just come to rest at B.

In the position P the force along PC required for the circular motion is mv^2/a, and the component of the weight in this direction is $mg \cos \theta$.

If $\qquad mg \cos \theta > mv^2/a$ or $v^2 < ag \cos \theta$.

the weight is more than sufficient to provide the central force, and there is an outward thrust R_1 on the ring given by

$$-R_1 + mg \cos \theta = mv^2/a.$$
$$\therefore \qquad R_1 = m(ag \cos \theta - v^2)/a.$$

If $v^2 > ag \cos \theta$ the weight component is not sufficient to provide the central force, and there is an inward thrust R_2 on the ring given by

$$R_2 + mg \cos \theta = mv^2/a.$$

When P is below the centre the weight component along the radius always acts away from the centre, and there is always an inward thrust on the ring.

The thrust on the circular rod is, of course, equal and opposite to the thrust on the ring.

7.15. Motion of a suspended particle in a vertical circle

Let a particle of mass m be suspended at A (Fig. 7.13) from a point C by a light string of length a.

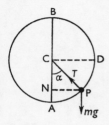

FIG. 7.13 ·

Let the particle be projected at right angles to the string with velocity V. Let v be the velocity at any point P of its path below the level of the centre, and draw PN perpendicular to CA.

Then the particle has risen a vertical distance AN, and

$$AN = a - a \cos \alpha = a(1 - \cos \alpha).$$

Since T does no work, being always perpendicular to the motion of the particle, the equation of energy gives

$$v^2 = V^2 - 2g \times AN$$

$$\therefore \qquad v^2 = V^2 - 2ag(1 - \cos \alpha). \qquad \text{(i)}$$

Now the component of the weight along CP is $mg \cos \alpha$ and acts outwards. A force equal to the tension (T) in the string acts inwards on the particle and is given by

$$T - mg \cos \alpha = mv^2/a.$$

$$\therefore \qquad T = mg \cos \alpha + \frac{mV^2}{a} - 2mg(1 - \cos \alpha)$$

$$= \frac{mV^2}{a} + mg(3 \cos \alpha - 2). \tag{ii}$$

When the particle is at A, $\cos \alpha = 1$, and

$$T = \frac{mV^2}{a} + mg.$$

It is clear that as long as P is below the horizontal radius CD, the weight component acts outwards and the string can never go slack.

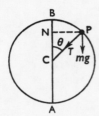

FIG. 7.14

If V is just large enough to take the particle to the level of the centre at D, then from (i)

$$0 = V^2 - 2ag$$

$$\therefore \qquad V = \sqrt{(2ag)}.$$

If V is greater than this value the particle will go above the level of the centre, and in this case it is better to consider the angle made by the string with CB (Fig. 7.14). Let this angle be θ.

The height of P above A is $a + a \cos \theta = a(1 + \cos \theta)$.

Hence, if v is the velocity at P, the equation of energy gives

$$v^2 = V^2 - 2ag(1 + \cos \theta).$$

Now the weight component along the string is $mg \cos \theta$, and acts towards C. The central force necessary to maintain the motion in a circle with velocity v is mv^2/a.

If $mg \cos \theta > mv^2/a$

or $v^2 < ag \cos \theta$

the weight component is greater than the force required owing to the motion, and the string will become slack, the particle leaving the circular path and moving as a free projectile.

It will leave the circle when

$$v^2 = ag \cos \theta.$$

But
$$v^2 = V^2 - 2ag(1 + \cos \theta)$$

$\therefore$
$$V^2 = ag \cos \theta + 2ag(1 + \cos \theta)$$
$$= ag(2 + 3 \cos \theta).$$

This equation gives the value of θ at which the string becomes slack corresponding to a given initial velocity V.

If the string just becomes slack at the highest point, i.e. where $\theta = 0$, we must have

$$V^2 = 5ag$$

or
$$V = \sqrt{(5ag)}.$$

This is the minimum velocity required for the particle to describe a complete circle.

The tension T in the string when the particle is at P is given by

$$T + mg \cos \theta = mv^2/a,$$

$\therefore$
$$T = (mV^2/a) - 2mg(1 + \cos \theta) - mg \cos \theta$$
$$= (mV^2/a) - mg(2 + 3 \cos \theta).$$

The whole of the above argument also applies to the case of a particle projected up the *inside* of a smooth vertical circular hoop. In this case the tension of the string is replaced by the thrust of the hoop.

7.16. Motion on the outside of a smooth vertical circular rod

Let C (Fig. 7.15) be the centre, B the highest and A the lowest

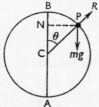

FIG. 7.15

point of the circular rod, and a its radius. The rod is held fixed.

Let a particle of mass m at B be slightly displaced so that it slides down the rod. Let v be its velocity when at a point P such that $\angle\,\text{BCP} = \theta$. Draw PN perpendicular to CB.

The particle has descended a vertical distance

$$\text{BN} = a - a\cos\theta = a(1 - \cos\theta)$$

∴ $$v^2 = 2ag(1 - \cos\theta).$$

Let R be the thrust of the rod on the particle, then, since the component of the weight along the radius is $mg\cos\theta$, the resultant force acting on the particle in the direction PC is

$$mg\cos\theta - R.$$

But since the particle is moving in a circle about C with velocity v, the central force towards C must be mv^2/a.

∴ $$mv^2/a = mg\cos\theta - R$$
∴ $$R = mg\cos\theta - mv^2/a$$
$$= mg\cos\theta - 2mg(1 - \cos\theta)$$
$$= mg(3\cos\theta - 2).$$

If $3\cos\theta > 2$ there is a thrust between the rod and the particle.

If $3\cos\theta < 2$ the thrust R becomes negative, which means that the particle has left the rod.

The thrust R becomes zero, and the particles leaves the rod when

$$3\cos\theta = 2$$

or $$\cos\theta = \tfrac{2}{3}.$$

The particle then moves as a free projectile, its initial velocity v being given by

$$v^2 = 2ag(1 - \tfrac{2}{3}) = \tfrac{2}{3}ag$$

or $$v = \sqrt{(2ag/3)}.$$

Its initial direction of motion is inclined downwards at an angle $\cos^{-1}\tfrac{2}{3}$ to the horizontal.

7.17. EXAMPLE (i)

A particle of mass m is suspended from a fixed point by a string of length l. It is projected horizontally with a velocity of $2\sqrt{(lg)}$. Find the height of the particle above the point of suspension when the string becomes slack. *Find also the tension in the string when the particle is at a depth ½l below the point of suspension.*

Let C (Fig. 7.16) be the point of suspension, and A the lowest point from which the particle is projected.

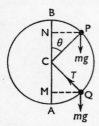

Fig. 7.16

If CP is the position of the string when it becomes slack, and $\angle BCP = \theta$, then if v is the velocity of the particle at P,

$$v^2 = 4lg - 2lg(1 + \cos\theta)$$
$$= 2lg(1 - \cos\theta).$$

Now since the string becomes slack in this position,

$$mv^2/l = mg\cos\theta$$

or

$$v^2 = lg\cos\theta$$

$$\therefore \quad lg\cos\theta = 2lg(1 - \cos\theta)$$

$$\therefore \quad \cos\theta = \tfrac{2}{3}.$$

Therefore the height above C is $l\cos\theta$ or $\tfrac{2}{3}l$.

In the position Q where $CM = AM = \tfrac{1}{2}l$, $\angle ACQ = 60°$, and the velocity v is given by

$$v^2 = 4lg - 2g \times \frac{l}{2} = 3lg.$$

The tension T in the string is given by

$$T - mg\cos 60° = mv^2/l$$

$$\therefore \quad T = \tfrac{1}{2}mg + 3mg = \tfrac{7}{2}mg.$$

EXAMPLE (ii)

Show that the velocity with which a particle hanging from a fixed point by a string of length a must be started so as to describe a complete vertical circle must not be less than $\sqrt{(5ag)}$. The particle is started with a velocity $2\sqrt{(ag)}$, and when the string is horizontal is held at such a point that the particle just completes the circle. Where must the point be situated on the string?   (I.E.)

The result in the first part of the question was obtained in the general discussion in 7.15. We can, however, obtain it without considering the intermediate inclined positions of the string.

Let A (Fig. 7.17) be the lowest and B the highest points of the circle whose centre is C the point of suspension.

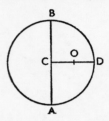

Fɪɢ. 7.17

Let V be the velocity at A, and v that at B, then

$$v^2 = V^2 - 4ag.$$

Now if the particle is to describe the complete circle, the string must be just taut when the particle reaches B,

∴ mv^2/a must not be less than mg

or $v^2 \nless ag$

∴ $V^2 - 4ag \nless ag$

∴ $V^2 \nless 5ag.$

If $V = 2\sqrt{(ag)}$, the velocity v when the particle is level with the centre at D is given by

$$v^2 = 4ag - 2ag = 2ag.$$

If the string is now held at a point O distant x from D, and the particle is just to complete the vertical circle about O as centre, the string must be just taut when the particle is vertically over O, i.e. at a height x above O. Now at this height its velocity u is given by

$$u^2 = v^2 - 2gx$$
$$= 2ag - 2gx$$

and as the string is just taut,

$$mu^2/x = mg$$

or $u^2 = gx$

∴ $gx = 2ag - 2gx$

∴ $3gx = 2ag$

∴ $x = \tfrac{2}{3}a.$

EXAMPLE (iii)

A particle is hanging from a fixed point by a light cord 90 cm long, and is started moving with an initial horizontal speed such that the cord slackens when the particle is 1·5 m above its lowest point. Find how much higher it will rise.

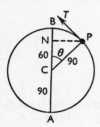

FIG. 7.18

Let C (Fig. 7.18) be the point of suspension, A the lowest point of the vertical circle with C as centre.

The cord slackens in the position CP where $\cos \theta = \frac{2}{3}$.

Now if v ms^{-1} is the velocity at P, then, since the cord slackens,

$$mv^2/0{\cdot}9 = mg \cos \theta$$

$$\therefore \qquad v^2 = 0{\cdot}9g \cos \theta = 0{\cdot}6g$$

$$\therefore \qquad v = \sqrt{(0{\cdot}6g)} = \sqrt{5{\cdot}88} = 2{\cdot}42.$$

The particle now moves as a free projectile, its initial velocity being 2·42 ms^{-1} along the tangent PT, and inclined to the horizontal at an angle $\cos^{-1} \frac{2}{3}$.

The vertical component of its velocity is

$$2{\cdot}42 \sin \theta = \frac{2{\cdot}42}{3}\sqrt{5} \text{ ms}^{-1}.$$

If h m is the height it rises,

$$0 = \frac{5{\cdot}88}{9} \times 5 - 2 \times 9{\cdot}8h$$

$$\therefore \qquad h = \tfrac{1}{6}.$$

EXAMPLE (iv)

A particle attached to a fixed point O by an inelastic string of length r is let fall from a point in the horizontal through O at a distance r cos θ from O. Show that the velocity of the particle, when it is vertically below O, is $\sqrt{[2gr(1-\sin^3 \theta)]}$. (H.S.D.)

Let OA (Fig. 7.19) be horizontal and equal to r, OB vertical and equal to r, and let P be the point in OA from which the particle is let fall.

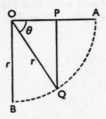

FIG. 7.19

Then, since $OP = r \cos \theta$, the particle reaches the circle through A and B whose centre is O, at a point Q such that $\angle POQ = \theta$.

At this point the particle has fallen a vertical distance PQ, which is equal to $r \sin \theta$, and hence its velocity u is given by

$$u^2 = 2gr \sin \theta.$$

Now when the string becomes taut all velocity in the direction of the string is destroyed, and the particle begins to move along the arc QB with a velocity equal to the component of u perpendicular to OQ, i.e. $u \cos \theta$.

Hence, if v is the velocity in the circle at Q after the jerk,

$$v^2 = 2gr \sin \theta \cos^2 \theta.$$

When the particle reaches B it has descended a further vertical distance $r - r \sin \theta = r(1 - \sin \theta)$, and its velocity V is given by

$$V^2 = v^2 + 2gr(1 - \sin \theta)$$
$$= 2gr \sin \theta \cos^2 \theta + 2gr(1 - \sin \theta)$$
$$= 2gr(\sin \theta - \sin^3 \theta + 1 - \sin \theta)$$
$$= 2gr(1 - \sin^3 \theta).$$
$$\therefore \qquad V = \sqrt{[2gr(1 - \sin^3 \theta)]}.$$

EXAMPLE (v)

A bead slides on a smooth fixed circular wire of radius a in a vertical plane, AB being the vertical diameter. The bead is projected with speed V from the highest point A and impinges upon and coalesces with another bead of equal mass at B. If the combined mass just reaches A, show that $V^2 = 12ga$.   (H.S.C.)

If v_1 is the velocity with which the projected bead reaches B, then by the equation of energy

$$\tfrac{1}{2}mv_1^2 = \tfrac{1}{2}mV^2 + 2mga$$

$$\therefore \qquad v_1^2 = V^2 + 4ga. \qquad\qquad \text{(i)}$$

Let v_2 be the velocity with which the combined mass $2m$ begins to move. Since momentum is conserved, we get

$$2mv_2 = mv_1$$

$$\therefore \qquad v_2 = \tfrac{1}{2}v_1. \qquad\qquad \text{(ii)}$$

The combined mass will just reach A if

$$\tfrac{1}{2}(2m)v_2^2 = 2mg(2a)$$

that is, if $\qquad\qquad v_2^2 = 4ga$

that is, if $\qquad\qquad v_1^2 = 16ga$ from equation (ii),

that is, if $\qquad\qquad V^2 = 12ga$ from equation (i).

EXAMPLES 7.4

1. A mass of 60 g is attached by a string 1·2 m long to a fixed point, and is describing a circle in a vertical plane round that point. Find the least velocity at the lowest point in order that the mass may make complete revolutions. Find also the tension of the string in this case when the mass is 60 cm below the horizontal diameter of the circle.   (I.S.)

2. A heavy particle is free to move in a vertical circle of radius l; the particle is projected with velocity u from the lowest point A of the circle, and just reaches a point B; show by applying the principle of energy that $u = \sqrt{(g/l)} \times$ AB.   (I.S.)

3. A mass of 1 g, hanging by a string 1 m long, is swinging as a pendulum through an arc of total magnitude 1 rad. Find the central acceleration and the tension of the string when the mass is passing through its lowest point.   (I.S.)

4. A weight, attached to an inextensible string, is whirled in a vertical circle of 60 cm radius. If the greatest and least tensions of the string are in the ratio of 11 : 1, calculate the least velocity of the weight (approximately).   (I.A.)

5. A mass of 200 g is attached by a light string 90 cm long to a fixed point. The string is held taut and horizontally, and the mass is allowed to fall. Find the speed of the mass when the string makes an angle θ with the horizontal. Find also the tension of the

string when it is vertical, and when it makes an angle of 30° with the vertical.

On passing through the lowest point the mass catches up a ring of mass 100 g at rest and carries it on. How high will the two masses rise?

6. A mass of 1 kg is whirled round in a vertical plane with a constant speed of 6 m s⁻¹ at the end of an elastic cord. The natural length of the cord is 1·8 m, and it extends 0·1 m when subject to a tension of 10 N. Find the length of the cord at the top and bottom of the path of the mass.

7. A heavy particle at the end of a tight 1·2 m string, the other end of which is fixed, is let fall from a horizontal position of the string; when the string is vertical it encounters an obstruction at its middle point so that the particle continues in a circle of 0·6 m radius. Find how high the particle will go before the string becomes slack.   (H.S.C.)

8. A motor car, of mass 1 Mg, runs under a bridge at 48 km h⁻¹, the roadway being in the form of an arc of a circle of radius 19 m. Find the reaction between the car and the road at the lowest point of the arc.   (H.S.C.)

9. The roadway of a bridge over a canal is in the form of a circular arc of radius 15 m. What is the greatest speed at which a motor cycle can cross the bridge without leaving the ground at the highest point?   (I.S.)

10. A particle, of mass m, oscillates through 180° on the inside of a smooth circular hoop of radius a fixed in a vertical plane. If v is the speed at any point, prove that the pressure on the hoop at that point is $3mv^2/2a$.   (H.C.)

11. A stone of mass 450 g is whirled round in a horizontal circle at the end of a string 0·9 m long, whose other end is fixed. If the string can only stand a tension of 35 N, what is the greatest velocity which the stone can have and how many revolutions does it make per second in this case?

If the stone is whirled round in a vertical circle what is the greatest velocity that the stone can have at the highest point of its path in order that it may describe the complete circle without the string breaking?   (I.E.)

12. A rope 6 m long has one end A attached to a fixed point and at the other end B carries a small mass of 45 kg. The rope is held taut and horizontally and the mass allowed to fall. Calculate the tension when the rope is vertical. In the vertical position the rope catches against a peg 3·6 m below A, so that the mass

begins a new path of radius 2·4 m. Show that the tension in the rope is thereby doubled and find whether or no the mass will describe a complete circle about the peg as centre. (Q.E.)

13. A smooth circular tube is held fixed in a vertical plane. A particle of mass m, which can slide inside the tube, is slightly displaced from rest at the highest point of the tube. Find the pressure between the particle and the tube when it is at an angular distance θ from the highest point of the tube. Also find the vertical component of the acceleration of the particle when $\theta = 120°$.

(C.S.)

14. A particle slides, from rest at a depth $\frac{1}{2}r$ below the highest point, down the outside of a smooth sphere of radius r; prove that it leaves the sphere at a height $\frac{1}{3}r$ above the centre. Show further that when the particle is at a distance $r\sqrt{2}$ from the vertical diameter of the sphere it is at a depth $4r$ below the centre of the sphere.

(C.S.)

15. A string with equal heavy particles at the ends lies over a smooth fixed pulley. In the position of equilibrium each particle is level with the centre of the pulley. One particle is slightly displaced downwards, so that the system moves under gravity. Find the pressure exerted by the second particle on the pulley as it passes the highest point, and prove that it leaves the pulley when it has traversed an arc of about $108\frac{1}{2}°$. (H.S.C.)

16. Two particles m and m' begin simultaneously to slide down a smooth circular tube whose plane is vertical, starting from the extremities of a horizontal diameter, so that they collide at the lowest point. Show that the vertical heights to which they rise after impact are in the ratio.

$$[(2e+1)m'-m]^2:[(2e+1)m-m']^2,$$

where e is the coefficient of restitution between the masses.

(I.A.)

17. A heavy particle is tied to one end of an inelastic string 1·8 m long, the other end of which is attached to a fixed point O. The particle is held, with the string tight, at a point 0·9 m above O and then let fall; find the velocity of the particle immediately after the string again becomes tight, and the height above O to which it subsequently rises.

18. A heavy particle is suspended as a simple pendulum by a string of length a. When in its lowest position it is projected horizontally with a velocity equal to that which it would acquire by falling freely through a height h. Show that, if the string becomes

slack during the subsequent motion, it does so when the particle
is at a vertical height $\frac{2}{3}(h-a)$ above the fixed end of the string.

19. A particle, suspended from a fixed point by a string of length a, is
projected horizontally so as to describe part of a circle in a vertical plane; show that if the parabolic path of the particle after
the string becomes slack passes through the original point of
projection, the velocity of projection is $(\frac{7}{2}ga)^{\frac{1}{2}}$. Show that in the
subsequent motion the particle oscillates between two points at
vertical height $\frac{1}{18}a$ above its original position.   (H.C.)

20. A particle is attached by a string 0·6 m long to a point O, and it is
projected horizontally with a velocity of 3·6 m s⁻¹ from a point
0·6 m vertically above O. Prove that the string will remain
tight while the particle describes complete vertical circles. But if
the string will not stand a tension of more than 5 times the weight
of the particle, prove that it will break and find the vertical
distance below O of the particle when the string breaks.

CHAPTER EIGHT

SIMPLE HARMONIC MOTION

8.1. We now proceed to the consideration of a very important type of oscillatory motion. If a weight hanging from a spiral spring is disturbed vertically from its equilibrium position it oscillates to and fro about this position. In this case, as in many others, it is found that the weight has an acceleration which is always directed towards the equilibrium position and varies in magnitude approximately directly as the distance of the particle from this position.

8.2. This kind of motion is very common in nature, and since it is the kind which produces all musical notes it is called *Simple Harmonic Motion* (abbreviated to S.H.M.), which may be defined as follows:

When a particle moves so that its acceleration along its path is directed towards a fixed point in that path, and varies directly as its distance from this fixed point, the particle is said to move with simple harmonic motion.

Let x be the displacement from a fixed point O in the path, and $\omega^2 x$ the magnitude of the acceleration towards O at this distance, where ω is some constant, then, since the acceleration is in the opposite direction to that in which x increases, we have

acceleration in the direction of x increasing $= -\omega^2 x$.   (i)

This is the fundamental equation representing a simple harmonic motion, and may be written

$$d^2 x/dt^2 = -\omega^2 x \qquad \text{(ii)}$$

where t denotes the time when the particle is at distance x from O.

8.3. We shall consider first the case when the motion takes place in a straight line, but it may be pointed out at once that any motion which can be represented by an equation such as (ii), where x is a displacement from a fixed position, is simple harmonic. For example, x may be the distance of a point P on a curve measured along the curve from a fixed point on the curve; then P will move along the curve with simple harmonic motion.

Again, x may be the angle made by a line fixed in a body, which is moving about a fixed axis through O, with some line through O fixed in space. The body will then move about the axis through O with simple harmonic motion.

Mathematically, the solution of equation (ii), i.e. the value of x in terms of t, has a certain form, and when x represents a displacement of any kind from a fixed position the equation represents the same kind of motion whether x is a straight, curved, or angular displacement.

It can be verified that the general solution of equation (ii) is

$$x = a \cos (\omega t + \alpha)$$

where a and α are arbitrary constants.

We shall proceed to derive this solution in the special case of motion in a straight line by means of a simple but very useful geometrical representation.

8.4. Simple harmonic motion in a straight line

Simple harmonic motion in a straight line can be given a direct geometrical representation. Consider a particle P moving in a circle of radius a with uniform angular velocity ω about the centre O.

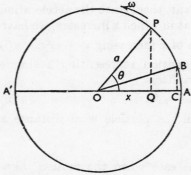

FIG. 8.1

Suppose AOA' (Fig. 8.1) is any diameter of the circle, and that another particle Q is moving along AOA' in such a manner that PQ is always perpendicular to the diameter AOA'.

Then as P describes the circle, Q oscillates to and fro along the diameter. We can show that the motion of Q is simple harmonic.

For the acceleration of P is $a\omega^2$ in the direction PO. But the acceleration of Q must equal the component of the acceleration of P in the direction QO.

$\therefore$ the acceleration of Q $= a\omega^2 \cos\theta$ towards O, where $\theta =$ angle POQ.

If OQ $= x$, then $\cos\theta = x/a$ and acceleration of Q towards O $= \omega^2 x$. *Hence the motion of Q along AOA′ is simple harmonic.*

Other characteristics of the motion of Q can now be found. If the velocity of Q is denoted by v we have

$v =$ component of the velocity of P parallel to A′A

$\quad = -a\omega \sin\theta$

$\therefore \quad v = \pm\omega\sqrt{(a^2 - x^2)}$

the two signs corresponding to the two directions of motion of Q along AOA′.

Further, the displacement of Q from the centre O at any time t is given by

$$x = a\cos\theta.$$

But $\theta = \omega t$, if t is measured from the instant when P and Q were at A, and hence

$$x = a\cos\omega t.$$

If, however, P is initially at the point B where the angle BOA $= \alpha$, so that Q is initially at C, then $\theta = \omega t + \alpha$, and

$$x = a\cos(\omega t + \alpha).$$

This is the general form of the displacement x and can clearly be written in the form

$$x = a_1\cos\omega t + a_2\sin\omega t$$

where a_1 and a_2 are constants expressible in terms of a and α.

Further, the period T of a complete oscillation, that is, the time taken for Q to move from A to A′ and back to A, is the same as that taken by P to describe the circle once. Thus

$$T = 2\pi/\omega.$$

Also, the time t taken for Q to move from A to a point distant x from O is the time taken by the other particle to move along the circle from A to P, that is, θ/ω, where θ is the angle AOP. The time taken for Q to move any distance along its path can therefore be found.

8.5. **We collect together the fundamental formulae of simple harmonic motion. They are:**

Acceleration	$\mathrm{d}^2x/\mathrm{d}t^2 = -\omega^2 x$	**(1)**
Velocity	$v = \pm\omega\sqrt{(a^2-x^2)}$	**(2)**
Displacement	$x = a\cos(\omega t+\alpha)$	**(3)**
Period of a complete oscillation $T = 2\pi/\omega$		**(4)**

It should be noted that equations (2) and (3) can be derived from equation (1) by using the methods of the calculus. The reader is referred to § 8.8 of *Intermediate Mechanics*, Vol. I, Dynamics, by D. Humphrey.

Equation (4) follows directly from (3).

8.6. O is known as the *centre* of the motion.

The maximum value of the displacement is a, and this is called the *amplitude* of the motion.

If x is written in the form $a\cos(\omega t+\alpha)$ the quantity α is known as the *Epoch*. Also the *Phase** of the motion is defined as the time that has elapsed since the particle was at its maximum distance a, in the positive direction.

Taking $\qquad x = a\cos(\omega t+\alpha)$,

then $x = a$ at time t_0 given by

$$\omega t_0+\alpha = 0$$

$\therefore$ the phase at time t is $t-t_0 = t+\alpha/\omega = (\omega t+\alpha)/\omega$.

For two simple harmonic motions of the same period given by

$$x = a_1\cos(\omega t+\alpha_1)$$
$$x = a_2\cos(\omega t+\alpha_2)$$

the difference in phase is $(\alpha_1-\alpha_2)/\omega$.

* Phase is defined differently by other writers; cf. Lamb, *Dynamics*.

If $\alpha_1 = \alpha_2$ the motions are in the same phase. If $\alpha_1 - \alpha_2 = \pi$ they are said to be in opposite phases.

8.7. EXAMPLE (i)

If the period of a simple harmonic motion is 8 s, and the particle oscillates through a distance of 1·2 m on each side of the central position, find the maximum velocity, and also the velocity when the particle is 0·6 m from the central position.

Since the period
$$T = \frac{2\pi}{\omega}$$

we have
$$\omega = \frac{2\pi}{T} = \frac{2\pi}{8} = \frac{\pi}{4}.$$

The amplitude
$$a = 1\cdot2 \text{ m}.$$

The velocity at displacement x is
$$v = \omega\sqrt{(a^2 - x^2)}.$$

The maximum velocity is when $x = 0$, and then
$$v = \omega a = (\pi/4) \times 1\cdot2 = 0\cdot94 \text{ m s}^{-1}.$$

When $x = 0\cdot6$ m,
$$v = (\pi/4)\sqrt{(1\cdot44 - 0\cdot36)} = (\pi/4)\sqrt{1\cdot08} = 0\cdot82 \text{ m s}^{-1}.$$

EXAMPLE (ii)

If the acceleration of a particle moving in a straight line with simple harmonic motion is $\omega^2 x$ when the displacement from the central position is x, prove that the velocity v of the particle is given by
$$v^2 = \omega^2(a^2 - x^2),$$
where a is the amplitude.

If the displacement, velocity and acceleration at a particular instant of a particle describing simple harmonic motion are respectively 7·5 cm, 7·5 cm s^{-1} and 7·5 cm s^{-2}, find the greatest velocity of the particle and the period of the motion. (I.S.)

The first part has been proved in 8.4 above.

Since when $x = 0\cdot075$ m, the acceleration $= 0\cdot075$ m s^{-2},
$$0\cdot075 = \omega^2 \times 0\cdot075$$

$\therefore$
$$\omega = 1.$$

Also since the velocity, $v = 0 \cdot 075$ m s^{-1} when $x = 0 \cdot 075$ m.

$$(0 \cdot 075)^2 = \omega^2 \{a^2 - (0 \cdot 075^2)^2\}.$$

$\therefore$ $\qquad\qquad\qquad a^2 = 2(0 \cdot 075)^2$ since $\omega = 1.$

$\therefore$ $\qquad\qquad\qquad a = 0 \cdot 075 \sqrt{2}$ m.

$\therefore$ $\qquad$ Greatest velocity $= \omega a$ when $x = 0$

$$= 0 \cdot 075 \sqrt{2} \text{ m s}^{-1} = 0 \cdot 106 \text{ m s}^{-1}.$$

Also the period of the motion

$$= 2\pi/\omega = 2\pi \text{ s}.$$

EXAMPLE (iii)

If the displacement of a moving point at any time be given by an equation of the form

$$x = a \cos \omega t + b \sin \omega t,$$

show that the motion is a simple harmonic motion.

If $a = 3, b = 4, \omega = 2$, determine the period, amplitude, maximum velocity and maximum acceleration of the motion.   (I.S.)

We have to show that the acceleration varies directly as the displacement.

Now $\qquad\qquad x = a \cos \omega t + b \sin \omega t$

$$= c \cos (\omega t + \alpha) \qquad\qquad\qquad\text{(i)}$$

where $a = c \cos \alpha$ and $b = -c \sin \alpha$, that is,

$$c = \sqrt{(a^2 + b^2)} \text{ and } \tan \alpha = -b/a.$$

We can verify directly that

$$\mathrm{d}^2x/\mathrm{d}t^2 = -\omega^2 x$$

or we can give a geometrical representation of x as in 8.4, and deduce that the acceleration at any distance x is $-\omega^2 x$.

It follows that the motion is simple harmonic.

From (i) the period $= 2\pi/\omega = \pi$ if $\omega = 2$. Further from (i) the maximum value of x is clearly c.

$\therefore$ $\qquad\qquad\qquad$ amplitude $= c$

$$= \sqrt{(3^2 + 4^2)} = 5.$$

The velocity at any time is given by

$$\mathrm{d}x/\mathrm{d}t = -c\omega \sin (\omega t + \alpha),$$

so that the maximum velocity is $c\omega = 10.$

Further, the maximum acceleration is when x is a maximum, i.e. when $x = 5$.

$\therefore$ maximum acceleration $= 5\omega^2 = 20$.

EXAMPLE (iv)

At the ends of three successive seconds the distances of a point moving with S.H.M. from its mean position, measured in the same direction, are 1, 5, and 5. Show that the period of the complete oscillation is

$$\frac{2\pi}{\cos^{-1}\frac{3}{5}}\, s. \qquad \text{(H.S.C.)}$$

Using $x = a \sin \omega t$, and putting $x = 1$ when $t = T$, $x = 5$ when $t = T+1$ and $x = 5$ when $t = T+2$, we have

$$1 = a \sin \omega T,$$

$$5 = a \sin (\omega T+\omega) \ = a \sin \omega T \cos \omega +a \cos \omega T \sin \omega.$$

$$5 = a \sin (\omega T+2\omega) = a \sin \omega T \cos 2\omega +a \cos \omega T \sin 2\omega.$$

Substituting for $a \sin \omega T$ in the last two equations,

$$\cos \omega +a \cos \omega T \sin \omega = 5 \qquad \text{(i)}$$

$$\cos 2\omega +a \cos \omega T \sin 2\omega = 5 \qquad \text{(ii)}$$

$\therefore \qquad \sin 2\omega \cos \omega +a \cos \omega T \sin \omega \sin 2\omega = 5 \sin 2\omega$

and $\qquad \sin \omega \cos 2\omega +a \cos \omega T \sin 2\omega \sin \omega = 5 \sin \omega$

$\therefore \qquad \sin 2\omega \cos \omega - \cos 2\omega \sin \omega = 5 \sin 2\omega - 5 \sin \omega$

$\therefore \qquad \sin \omega = 5 \sin 2\omega - 5 \sin \omega$

$\therefore \qquad 6 \sin \omega = 10 \sin \omega \cos \omega.$

This gives $\sin \omega = 0$, or $\cos \omega = \frac{3}{5}$.

If $\sin \omega = 0$, ω must be zero or a multiple of π, and these values do not satisfy equations (i) and (ii), so that they may be rejected.

The other value gives $\omega = \cos^{-1} \frac{3}{5}$, and hence the period is $2\pi/\omega = 2\pi/\cos^{-1} \frac{3}{5}$ sec.

An alternative method is as follows:

Suppose the point is moving along the line A'OA about the centre O (Fig. 8.2). Let $OA = a$.

At some instant it is at B where $OB = 1$, at the next instant at C where $OC = 5$ and at the next instant it is again at C, having been to A and back again.

The corresponding particle moving in the circle with uniform angular velocity ω will be at P, Q, R respectively at these instants, and hence the angles POQ and QOR must each equal ω.

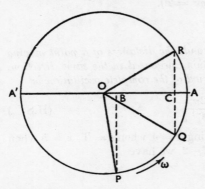

FIG. 8.2

From the figure, QOA $\angle = \angle$ AOR $= \frac{1}{2}\omega$.

Thus, $OB = 1 = a \cos 3\omega/2$ (i)

and $OC = 5 = a \cos \omega/2$ (ii)

$\therefore$ $5 \cos 3\omega/2 = \cos \omega/2.$

$\therefore$ $5(4 \cos^3 \frac{1}{2}\omega - 3 \cos \frac{1}{2}\omega) = \cos \frac{1}{2}\omega.$

$\therefore$ $20 \cos^3 \frac{1}{2}\omega = 16 \cos \frac{1}{2}\omega.$

$\therefore$ $\cos \frac{1}{2}\omega = 0$ or $\cos^2 \frac{1}{2}\omega = \frac{16}{20} = \frac{4}{5}.$

But $\cos \frac{1}{2}\omega = 0$ does not satisfy equation (ii) and must be rejected, so that the only solution is given by

$$\cos^2 \frac{1}{2}\omega = \frac{4}{5},$$

or $\cos \omega = 2 \cos^2 \frac{1}{2}\omega - 1 = \frac{3}{5}.$

$\therefore$ The period $= 2\pi/\omega = 2\pi/\cos^{-1}(\frac{3}{5}).$

EXAMPLE (v)

A particle performs S.H.M. along a straight line between the points A and B. If P is a point in AB such that AP : PB = 1 : 3, show that the time taken from A to P is half the time taken from P to B.

Show that the kinetic energy of the particle at P is three-quarters of its maximum kinetic energy.   (I.S.)

Suppose O is the centre of the motion, and $OA = OB = a$. Draw a circle with centre O and radius a (Fig. 8.3). Draw CP perpendicular to AB.

Since $\qquad AP : PB = 1 : 3$, $AP = \frac{1}{2}a$ and $PB = \frac{3}{2}a$.

$\therefore \qquad \cos \angle COP = OP/OC = \frac{1}{2}$ and hence $\angle COP = 60°$.

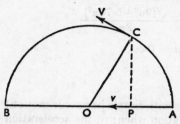

FIG. 8.3

Therefore arc $AC = \frac{1}{2}$ arc CB, and hence a particle describing the circle with uniform speed will cover the arc AC in half the time it covers the arc CB.

Therefore corresponding particle moving along the diameter with S.H.M. will move from A to P in half the time it takes from P to B.

Now $\qquad v =$ speed of the particle at $P = V \sin 60°$,

where $\qquad V =$ speed of the particle moving in the circle.

$\therefore$ Kinetic energy of the particle at $P = \frac{1}{2}mv^2 = \frac{1}{2}mV^2 \sin^2 60°$

$$= \frac{3}{4}(\frac{1}{2}mV^2)$$

$$= \frac{3}{4} \text{ (maximum K.E. of the particle).}$$

EXAMPLE (vi)

A particle is moving with S.H.M. in a straight line and takes 3 s to perform a complete oscillation. Its farthest distance from the centre of force is 1·2 m. Find its maximum acceleration and maximum velocity. If, when at its farthest point, it receives a blow which drives it in with an initial velocity of u m s^{-1}, find its new amplitude. What value of u will make the amplitude 1·5 m instead of 1·2 m? $\qquad$ (H.S.C.)

Since the period is 3 s, $2\pi/\omega = 3$.

$\therefore \qquad\qquad\qquad\qquad\qquad \omega = 2\pi/3$.

$\therefore$ Maximum acceleration $\qquad = (2\pi/3)^2 \times 1·2 \text{ m s}^{-2}$.

$\qquad\qquad\qquad\qquad\qquad\qquad = 4·8\pi^2/9 \text{ m s}^{-2}$.

Also, maximum velocity $\qquad = (2\pi/3) \, 1·2 \text{ m s}^{-1}$.

$\qquad\qquad\qquad\qquad\qquad\qquad = 0·8\pi \text{ m s}^{-1}$.

Let the new amplitude $\qquad\qquad = A$ m.

Then, since the new velocity is u m s^{-1} when $x = 1 \cdot 2$ m, we have

$$u^2 = \omega^2(A^2 - 1 \cdot 2^2).$$

$$\therefore \qquad u^2 = \frac{4\pi^2}{9}(A^2 - 1 \cdot 2^2).$$

$$\therefore \qquad A^2 = \frac{9u^2}{4\pi^2} + 1 \cdot 44 \text{ or } A = \frac{\sqrt{(9u^2 + 5 \cdot 76\pi^2)}}{2\pi}.$$

If $A = 1 \cdot 5$, then $u^2 = 0 \cdot 36\pi^2$ or $u = 0 \cdot 6\pi$.

EXAMPLES 8.1

1. A particle moves in a straight line with simple harmonic motion; find the time of a complete oscillation when: (i) the acceleration at a distance of $1 \cdot 2$ m is $2 \cdot 4$ ms^{-2}; (ii) the acceleration at a distance of 20 cm is $3 \cdot 2$ ms^{-2}.

2. The amplitude of a particle moving with S.H.M. is $1 \cdot 5$ m, the acceleration at a distance of $0 \cdot 6$ m from the mean position is $1 \cdot 2$ ms^{-2}, find the velocity when the particle is in its mean position, and also when it is $1 \cdot 2$ m from this position.

3. A particle, moving with S.H.M., has a velocity of $1 \cdot 8$ ms^{-1} when passing through its mean position, and the acceleration at $0 \cdot 6$ m from the mean position is $2 \cdot 4$ ms^{-2}. Find the amplitude and the period of the oscillation.

4. A point, moving with S.H.M., has velocities of $1 \cdot 2$ ms^{-1} and $0 \cdot 9$ ms^{-1} when at distances of $0 \cdot 9$ m and $1 \cdot 2$ m from its central position. Find the period and the maximum acceleration.

5. A particle is moving with S.H.M. of period π s, and the maximum velocity is $2 \cdot 4$ ms^{-1}. Find the amplitude and the velocity at a distance of $0 \cdot 9$ m from the central position.

6. If a particle is making simple harmonic oscillations, the period being 2 s, and the amplitude being $0 \cdot 9$ m, find the maximum velocity and the maximum acceleration.   (H.S.D.)

7. A particle starts from rest, and moves with S.H.M. with a period of $2T$. Show that it describes $\frac{1}{4}$ of the distance before it next comes to instantaneous rest in $\frac{1}{3}$ of the time T, and attains half of its maximum velocity in $\frac{1}{6}$ of the time T.   (I.S.)

8. A particle moving with S.H.M. passes through two points A and B, 56 cm apart, with the same velocity, having occupied 2 s in passing from A to B; after another 2 s it returns to B. Find the period and amplitude of the oscillation.   (I.A.)

9. A particle performs 150 complete simple harmonic oscillations per minute, and its greatest acceleration is 3 ms^{-2}; find its greatest velocity and the distance between the extreme positions.

(I.S.)

10. A point is moving in a straight line with S.H.M. about a fixed point O of the line. The point has a velocity v_1 when its displacement from O is x_1, and a velocity v_2 when its distance from O is x_2. Show that the period of the motion is

$$2\pi\sqrt{\left(\frac{x_1{}^2 - x_2{}^2}{v_2{}^2 - v_1{}^2}\right)}.$$

(I.S.)

11. The velocity of a particle moving in a straight line is given by the equation

$$v = k\sqrt{(a^2 - x^2)},$$

where k and a are constants, and x is the distance of the particle from a fixed point in the line; prove that the motion is simple harmonic, and find the amplitude and the periodic time of the motion.

(I.E.)

12. A particle is performing a simple harmonic motion of period T about a centre O, and it passes through a point P with velocity v in the direction OP; prove that the time which elapses before its return to P is

$$\frac{T}{\pi}\tan^{-1}\frac{vT}{2\pi\text{OP}}.$$

(I.S.)

13. If the speeds of a point moving with S.H.M at distances x_1 and x_2 from the centre of motion be v_1 and v_2, find the periodic time, the amplitude and the maximum speed and maximum acceleration. Calculate the numerical values if $x_1 = 0.6$ m, $x_2 = 0.9$ m, $v_1 = 1.5$ ms^{-1}, $v_2 = 1.2$ ms^{-1}.

(I.E.)

14. Prove that, in S.H.M., if f is the acceleration and v the velocity at any moment and T is the periodic time, then $f^2T^2 + 4\pi^2v^2$ is constant, and find the numerical value of this constant for a motion whose periodic time is 2 s and in which the amplitude is 0.7 m.

(H.S.D.)

15. A body, moving in a straight line OAB with S.H.M., has zero velocity when at the points A and B whose distances from O are a and b respectively, and has velocity v when halfway between them. Show that the complete period is $\pi(b-a)/v$.

(H.S.D.)

16. A point P describes a circle of radius a and centre O, with uniform angular velocity ω; show that a point Q which describes a diameter AOB of the circle, so that PQ is always perpendicular to AOB, has an acceleration which is proportional to OQ.

If Q_1, Q_2 are points bisecting OA, OB, find the time the point Q takes to travel from Q_1 to Q_2, and the velocity of the point Q at Q_2 and at Q_1.   (I.S.)

17. In a particular S.H.M. the number of complete oscillations is 45 per minute. The velocity at a point 2·5 cm away from the mean position is 30 cms^{-1}. Calculate the greatest distance reached measured from the mean position. If A and B are two points distant 2·5 cm and 5 cm from the centre of motion respectively, find the time occupied in going from A to B. (Q.E.)

18. A point moving with S.H.M. is making 3 complete oscillations per second. The extent of the motion on either side of the mean position is 5 cm. Calculate the maximum velocity and maximum acceleration. Find also the velocity and acceleration when the point is 2·5 cm distant from the centre.   (Q.E.)

19. Show that in S.H.M. the mean velocity (during motion from one end of the path to the other) with respect to the distance is $\pi/4 \times$ the maximum velocity, and with respect to the time is $2/\pi \times$ the maximum velocity.   (Q.E.)

20. A particle is moving with S.H.M., and while making an excursion from one position of rest to the other, its distances from the mid-point of its path at three consecutive seconds are observed to be x_1, x_2, x_3; prove that the time of a complete oscillation is

$$2\pi/\cos^{-1}\left(\frac{x_1+x_3}{2x_2}\right).$$ (I.C.)

21. A particle moving with acceleration $-\mu x$ has coordinates x_1 and x_2 and velocities v_1 and v_2 at any two moments. At the moment midway in time between them its coordinate and velocity are $\bar{x}$ and $\bar{v}$; show that

$$(x_1-x_2)/(v_2-v_1) = \bar{v}/\mu\bar{x}$$

and that

$$(x_1+x_2)/(v_1+v_2) = \bar{x}/\bar{v}.$$ (H.C.)

22. If a be the amplitude and n the number of complete oscillations per second in S.H.M., find the velocity in any position in terms of: (i) the distance from the centre, and (ii) the time that has elapsed since the moving particle was at rest. Show that the time

that elapses as the particle moves from the position of maximum velocity to the position in which the velocity is half the maximum is $1/6n$ s.   (I.S.)

23. A circle of radius a rolls with uniform angular speed on the inside of a fixed circle of radius $2a$. Prove that any point on the circumference of the moving circle describes a straight line with S.H.M.   (I.E.)

24. A piston of mass 10 kg has a stroke of 1·2 m. Using the line of motion as the axis of x, make graphs to show the value of the velocity and of the accelerating force at any point of the stroke, assuming the motion to be S.H.M.   (I.E.)

25. A point P moves in a straight line through a fixed point O in such a manner that its acceleration at each instant is towards O and equal to μOP; prove that the velocity is $\sqrt{\{\mu(OA^2 - OP^2)\}}$, where A is one of the points where P comes to rest.

    If Q is the point on OA such that $2OQ^2 = OA^2$, show that the time from O to Q is the same as the time from Q to A.   (I.S.)

26. A heavy smoked glass plate is dropped past the end of a vibrating tuning-fork, making n complete simple harmonic oscillations per second, and by means of a light style attached to the fork a rippling trace is obtained on the plate. The vertical length of a certain 10 consecutive ripples is found to be l cm, and of the next 10 is found to be l' cm. Deduce that the value of g is

$$(l' - l)n^2/100 \text{ cm s}^{-2}. \qquad \text{(I.A.)}$$

27. A particle performs 150 complete simple harmonic oscillations a minute and its greatest acceleration is 3 ms^{-2}; find: (i) its greatest velocity; (ii) its mean velocity during the motion from one extreme position to the other.   (Q.E.)

28. A point is moving in a straight line with S.H.M. Its velocity has the values 0·9 ms^{-1} and 0·6 ms^{-1} when its distances from the mean position are 0·3 m and 0·6 m respectively. Find the length of its path and the period of its motion. Find also, correct to the third significant figure, what fraction of the period is occupied in passing between the specified points.   (Q.E.)

29. A particle describing S.H.M. does 100 complete vibrations per minute, and its velocity in passing through its mean position is 4·5 ms^{-1}. What is the length of its path? What is its velocity (i) when it is half-way between its mean position and an extremity of its path; (ii) at a time after leaving its mean position equal to half the time required to reach an extremity of its path?   (Q.E.)

8.8 Force necessary to produce simple harmonic motion

Since the force F required to produce an acceleration a in a mass m is measured by ma, it follows that (if m is constant) F must obey the same law as a. Hence, in the case of simple harmonic motion, the force must be always directed towards the central or equilibrium position, and its magnitude must be directly proportional to the displacement from that position.

The force tending to restore an elastic body to its natural shape or size is generally of this nature, e.g. the force exerted by a spiral spring when extended or compressed.

8.9. The simplest case is that of a particle on a smooth horizontal plane attached by a spring to a fixed point in the plane, the particle being displaced in the direction of the length of the spring.

Let A (Fig. 8.4) be the fixed point, AB the natural length of the spring (l), and λ the modulus of elasticity of the spring.

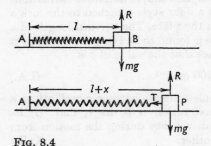

FIG. 8.4

If a particle of mass m is attached to the end B, then B is the equilibrium position, and if the particle is displaced along the line AB and released it will oscillate about B, as we shall now show.

If P is any displaced position of the particle where BP $= x$, the tension, acting towards B, if Hooke's law holds, is $\lambda x/l$, and this is the only force acting on m which tends to produce motion along the line AB.

$$\therefore \qquad m\frac{\mathrm{d}^2x}{\mathrm{d}t^2} = -\frac{\lambda}{l}x.$$

$$\therefore \qquad \text{Acceleration in the direction AB} = \frac{\mathrm{d}^2x}{\mathrm{d}t^2} = -\frac{\lambda}{ml}x.$$

The motion is therefore simple harmonic about B as centre, and the constant ω^2 in the standard form of the equation is replaced by λ/ml.

The period of oscillation is therefore

$$2\pi\sqrt{(ml/\lambda)}.$$

It is evident that the constant ω, and therefore the period of the motion, depends only on the material and length of the spring and the mass of the particle, and not on the amplitude of the oscillation. If the particle is pulled out to a point C(BC = a) and then let go, it will move through B to a point C' at an equal distance on the other side of B and then back again to C and so on. The amplitude is equal to the distance from the equilibrium position to that at which the particle is released from rest.

8.9. Particle suspended by a spiral spring

Suppose that a particle of mass m is suspended from a fixed point (Fig. 8.5) by a spring of natural length l and modulus

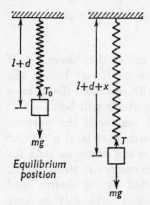

$l+d$ T_0

mg

Equilibrium position

$l+d+x$ T

mg

Moving position

FIG. 8.5

λ. When the particle is hanging in equilibrium it will extend the spring an amount d where

$$mg = (\lambda/l)d.$$

If the particle is displaced vertically and released it will oscillate in a vertical line, and we can show that the motion is simple harmonic about the equilibrium position as centre.

For if at time t the particle has a displacement x downwards from the equilibrium positions, so that the total length of the spring is $l+d+x$, we have:

Tension of the spring, $\qquad T = \dfrac{\lambda}{l}\,(d+x).$

The resultant force acting upwards is

$$T-mg = \frac{\lambda}{l}\,(d+x)-mg.$$

But $\qquad\qquad\qquad\qquad mg = \dfrac{\lambda}{l}\,d$

∴ the restoring force is $\lambda x/l$, and is therefore proportional to the displacement from the equilibrium position.

Hence the particle moves with S.H.M. about this position as centre. Also, the acceleration vertically downwards is

$$\frac{\mathrm{d}^2x}{\mathrm{d}t^2} = -\frac{\lambda}{ml}\,x,$$

and hence the period of one complete oscillation will be

$$2\pi\sqrt{(ml/\lambda)}.$$

The amplitude will depend on the initial displacement. If the particle is pulled down a distance $a<(l+d)$ below the equilibrium position and released it will rise this distance a above and then descend again; the amplitude will be a.

In the case of a spring it does not matter if the particle rises so high that the spring is compressed, that is, if $a>d$, for the law for compression of the spring is the same as that for extension, and the motion will be simple harmonic throughout.

If, however, the particle is suspended by an elastic cord instead of a spring the working above will hold only as long as the string is stretched. If the particle rises so high that the string is no longer stretched the motion will be simply free vertical motion under gravity. This will happen if the particle is pulled down a distance a greater than the statical extension d.

8.10. EXAMPLE (i)

A spiral spring is found to extend 2·5 cm for each additional kg of loading. It is hung up carrying a mass of 2 kg, and put in vibration. Find the period. (I.E.)

Let AB (Fig. 8.6) represent the natural length, l m, of the spring. The mass of 2 kg will extend it 5 cm = 0·05 m, so that in equilibrium the mass will hang at O where OB = 5 cm.

If λ be the modulus of elasticity

$$g = \frac{\lambda}{l} \times 0 \cdot 025$$

$\therefore$ $\lambda / l = 40g.$ Fig. 8.6

If P represent any displaced position of the mass, and OP = x m the tension T N in this position is given by

$$T = \frac{\lambda}{l}(0 \cdot 05 + x)$$

$$= 40g(0 \cdot 05 + x).$$

The restoring force is

$$T - 2g = 2g + 40gx - 2g$$

$$= 40gx$$

$\therefore$ the acceleration is

$$\frac{40g}{2}x = 20gx$$

$\therefore$ the period is

$$\frac{2\pi}{\sqrt{(20g)}} = \frac{2\pi}{\sqrt{196}} = \frac{\pi}{7}\text{s}.$$

EXAMPLE (ii)

A light elastic string is stretched by e_0 when a certain weight is suspended by it. Prove that, if the weight is displaced in a vertical line any distance not greater than e_0, and set free, it will return to the initial position in time $2\pi \sqrt{(e_0/g)}$. (I.E.)

Let m be the mass attached, λ the modulus, and l the natural length of the string. Since the weight mg stretches it a distance e_0,

$$mg = \frac{\lambda}{l}e_0$$

$\therefore$ $\dfrac{\lambda}{l} = \dfrac{mg}{e_0}.$

For a further extension x, the tension is

$$\frac{\lambda}{l}(e_0+x) = mg + \frac{mg}{e_0}x,$$

and the restoring force is therefore $\dfrac{mg}{e_0}x$.

Therefore the acceleration is $\dfrac{g}{e_0}x$, and the motion is S.H.M.

The time taken to return to the initial position from which the weight is released is a complete period and is therefore $2\pi\sqrt{(e_0/g)}$.

Note. It is stipulated in the question that the displacement is not greater than e_0, the statical extension, so that the motion is simple harmonic throughout.

EXAMPLE (iii)

A particle of mass m on a smooth table is attached to two points A *and* B *of the table by means of two exactly similar stretched elastic strings. Prove that if the particle is displaced in the direction of the line* AB, *through such a distance that neither string goes slack, and is then released, it will perform simple harmonic oscillations.* (I.E.)

Let l_0 be the natural length of each string, λ its modulus, and l the stretched length.

The equilibrium position of the particle is at C (Fig. 8.7), the mid-point of AB, and AC = CB = l.

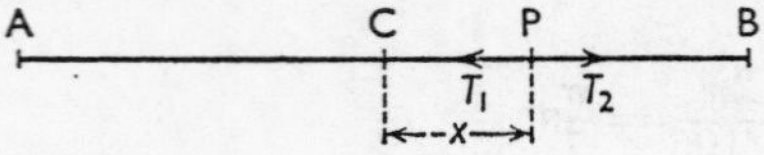

FIG. 8.7

Suppose the particle in a displaced position P, towards B, where CP = x.

The tension in AP is

$$T_1 = \frac{\lambda}{l_0}(l-l_0+x)$$

and the tension in PB is

$$T_2 = \frac{\lambda}{l_0}(l-l_0-x).$$

Therefore the resultant force tending to bring the particle back to C is

$$T_1-T_2 = 2\frac{\lambda}{l_0}x.$$

Therefore the restoring force is proportional to the displacement from C, and hence the motion is simple harmonic about C as centre.

The acceleration is
$$\frac{2\lambda}{ml_0}\, x$$

and the period is
$$2\pi\sqrt{\left(\frac{ml_0}{2\lambda}\right)}.$$

Note. If the particle is displaced so far that one string goes slack, then for the part of the motion when both strings are tight the acceleration is as above, but for the part of the motion when one string is slack the acceleration is $(\lambda/ml_0)x$.

The complete motion is then made up of two simple harmonic motions of different periods, the whole of the motion of period $2\pi\sqrt{(ml_0/2\lambda)}$ being described, but only a portion of the other.

EXAMPLE (iv)

An elastic thread is fixed at one end to a point O in a smooth horizontal table. It passes through a fixed ring C, where OC is the unstretched length of the thread, and is attached to a small mass m which can slide on a fixed smooth horizontal wire. It is held at a point A on this wire and then released. Show that it will perform simple harmonic oscillations and construct the other extremity of the path.   (I.S.)

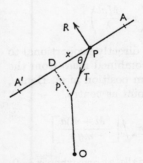

Let D (Fig. 8.8) be the point where the perpendicular from C meets the wire. Then D is the equilibrium position of m.

If P is any displaced position of m the extension of the string is CP, and if l is the natural length and λ the modulus of the string the tension T is given by

$$T = \lambda CP/l.$$

FIG. 8.8

The only other force acting on m is the normal reaction R between it and the smooth wire.

If $DP = x$, and $\angle DPC = \theta$, the component of T along the wire is
$$T \cos \theta = (\lambda CP/l) \cos \theta = \lambda x/l.$$

The force tending to move m towards D is therefore proportional to the displacement from D, and the motion is S.H.M. about D. The other extremity of the path will be at A' on the other side of D, where DA' = DA.

EXAMPLE (v)

A mass m is suspended from a spring causing an extension a. If a mass M is added to m, find the periodic time of the ensuing motion and the amplitude of the oscillation.   (C.S.)

If the natural length of the spring is l and the modulus λ we have

$$mg = \lambda a/l.$$

In the ensuing motion, when M is added, let the total extension at time t be $(a+x)$. Then the acceleration downwards, d^2x/dt^2, is given by

$$(M+m)\frac{d^2x}{dt^2} = (M+m)g - \lambda \times \frac{a+x}{l}$$

$$= Mg - \lambda\frac{x}{l} \text{ since } mg = \frac{\lambda a}{l}$$

$$= -\frac{\lambda}{l}\left(x - \frac{Mgl}{\lambda}\right).$$

$$\therefore \quad \frac{d^2x}{dt^2} = -\frac{\lambda}{l(M+m)} \times \left(x - \frac{Mgl}{\lambda}\right).$$

Therefore the acceleration downwards is directly proportional to $x - (Mgl/\lambda)$, that is, to the distance of the combined mass from the point a distance Mgl/λ below the equilibrium position of m. Hence, the motion is simple harmonic about this point as centre.

$$\therefore \quad \text{The period} = 2\pi\sqrt{\left[\frac{l(M+m)}{\lambda}\right]} = 2\pi\sqrt{\left[\frac{(M+m)a}{mg}\right]}.$$

Moreover, since the combined mass is initially at rest when $x = 0$, the amplitude equals Mgl/λ, that is, Ma/m.

This latter result can also be found using the equation of energy.

For if the amplitude $= b$, the combined mass must descend a distance $2b$ before it comes to instantaneous rest. Hence the potential energy lost in descending a distance $2b$ must equal the gain in the energy of the spring due to the increased extension.

$$\therefore \quad (M+m)g \times 2b = \text{mean tension} \times \text{extension}$$

$$= \tfrac{1}{2} \times (\lambda/l) \times \{(a+2b)+a\} \times 2b.$$

$$\therefore \quad (M+m)g = \frac{\lambda(a+b)}{l}$$

$$= \frac{mg(a+b)}{a}$$

$$\therefore \quad a(M+m) = m(a+b).$$

$$\therefore \quad b = Ma/m.$$

EXAMPLES 8.2

1. A spiral spring supports a carrier of mass 1 kg, and when a 5-kg weight is placed on the carrier the spring extends 5 cm. The carrier with its load is then pulled down another 7·5 cm and let go. How high does it rise, and what is the period of its oscillation?
(I.S.)

2. A spring loaded with a certain weight is extended 2 cm when in equilibrium. Find the time of oscillation if the load is pulled vertically downwards through a further distance of 1 cm and then let go. Find also the velocity and acceleration when the weight is at a distance of 0·5 cm below its equilibrium position. (I.S.)

3. A body of mass 5 kg is suspended by a spring and makes three complete vertical oscillations per second. Find how far the spring would be stretched by a load of 4 kg hanging at rest. (I.S.)

4. A particle of mass 500 g is acted upon by a variable force which makes it move with S.H.M. The maximum speed attained is 1·5 ms^{-1} and the complete period is 2 s. Find: (i) the amplitude of the motion, and (ii) the maximum rate at which the applied force does work. (I.S.)

5. A mass is suspended from a fixed point by a spiral spring and set in vertical oscillation. Show that the period of an oscillation is $2\pi\sqrt{(l/g)}$, where l is the extension of the spring produced by the weight of the attached mass. (I.S.)

6. An elastic string of natural length $2a$ can just support a certain weight when it is stretched till its whole length is $3a$. One end of the string is now attached to a point in a smooth horizontal table, and the same weight is attached to the other end and can move on the table. Prove that, if the weight is pulled out to any distance and then let go, the string will become slack again after a time $\tfrac{1}{2}\pi\sqrt{(a/g)}$. (I.S.)

7. If a particle describes a harmonic oscillation of amplitude a in complete period T, prove that it will be at a distance x from the centre, from which it started, in a time $\theta T/2\pi$, and be moving with a speed $2\pi \dfrac{\sqrt{(a^2-x^2)}}{T}$, where $a \sin \theta = x$.

An elastic thread is stretched between two points on a smooth horizontal table. A particle of given mass is fastened to the mid-point, and after being drawn towards one of the points, the string remaining taut, is set free. Show that it will describe its oscillations in a period independent of the original extent of displacement. (I.S.)

8. A particle is attached to the mid-point of an elastic string which is stretched between two points A and B on a smooth table 2·7 m apart, and displaced a distance of 2·5 cm in the direction of the string. If the initial tension of the string is twice the weight of the particle, find the periodic time and the maximum velocity attained by the particle.

9. A spiral spring 0·6 m long is hung up at one end. Its length would be doubled by a steady pull of 30 N. A weight of mass 1·5 kg is hung to the lower end, and let go. Find how far it falls before first coming to rest and the time of a complete oscillation.
(H.S.C.)

10. If two unequal weights are hanging together at one end of an elastic string whose other end is fixed, and one of them falls off, show that the other will perform simple harmonic oscillations or not according as the one which falls off is the lighter or the heavier of the two. (H.S.C.)

11. A mass of 500 g suspended by a spring extends it 2·5 cm when in equilibrium. If a mass of 1·5 kg be attached to the spring and released from rest with the spring extended 12·5 cm, find the number of oscillations per minute and the maximum velocity in the course of an oscillation. (I.C.)

12. A weight of mass 5 kg is suspended from a spring, causing an extension of 25 cm. If the weight is pulled down a further distance of 2·5 cm and then released, find the periodic time of the motion, the velocity when the weight is 1·25 cm above the lowest point, and the tension in the spring at the top of the path.
(Q.E.)

13. A light spiral spring is carrying a weight of mass 6 kg; it extends 5 cm when an extra weight of mass 1·5 kg is placed on it. The extra weight is removed suddenly. Find the period of oscillation of the 6-kg weight, the tension in the spring, and the velocity of the weight when it is 2·5 cm above its lowest point. (Q.E.)

14. A light helical spring hangs vertically and carries a load of 5 kg; it extends 5 cm per extra kg of load. It is extended 5 cm and released. Draw graphs for the kinetic and potential energies at different phrases of the subsequent motion.   (Q.E.)

15. A certain spring has attached to it a mass of 25 in certain unknown units; on increasing the load by 6 of these units it extends 2·5 cm. What is the time of oscillation under the original load? What will be the velocity and acceleration when it is midway between its lowest and mean positions if it is loaded as at first, pulled down 5 cm and let go?   (Q.E.)

16. A scale pan of mass 500 g is attached to a light spiral spring and causes it to extend 5 cm. A 1-kg weight is then placed in the pan and released. Find to what depth the pan will fall, the tension of the spring when the pan is at its lowest point, and the period of the oscillation.   (Q.E.)

17. A mass of 2·5 kg hangs at rest on a light spring, extending it 5 cm. Another mass of 1·5 kg is attached to the first without moving it, and the two together are then released. Find the amplitude, period, and maximum velocity of the resulting motion.   (Q.E.)

18. A weight of mass 5 kg is suspended by means of an elastic string which is extended 5 cm when the weight is hanging at rest. If the upper end is suddenly jerked upwards a distance of 2·5 cm, and then held fixed, find the greatest velocity attained by the weight and the period of the oscillation set up.   (Q.E.)

19. A spring of length 25 cm, whose stiffness is such that a weight of mass 1 kg would double its length, hangs vertically from a fixed point and has attached to its lower end a scale pan of mass 100 g. Show that if the pan is pulled downwards from its equilibrium position and then released it will execute simple harmonic oscillations and find their period. Show also that if the total amplitude of the oscillations exceeds 5 cm a small particle in the scale pan will not remain in contact with it during the whole oscillation, but will repeatedly rebound from it.   (H.S.D.)

20. A particle is attached to the mid-point of an elastic string stretched between two points A and B on a smooth horizontal table. If the particle be displaced through a small distance perpendicular to AB, and then released, show that its subsequent motion is approximately a simple harmonic one. (The displacement is so small that the tension of the string is supposed to be constant.) If AB = 2·7 m the tension of the string is twice the

weight of the particle, and the original displacement is 1·2 cm, find the periodic time, and the maximum velocity attained by the particle.   (Ex.)

21. A particle P of mass m is attached to the mid-point of an elastic string AB, whose unstretched length is $2a$ and whose modulus of elasticity is equal to the weight of the particle. A and B are attached to fixed points on a smooth horizontal table at a distance $3a$ apart. AP is initially equal to $2a$, PB is equal to a. Prove that when P is let go it will perform simple harmonic oscillations whose period is $2\pi\sqrt{(a/2g)}$, and will oscillate through a distance a.   (H.S.C.)

22. A mass m hangs from a fixed point by means of a light spring, which obeys Hooke's law. The mass is given a small vertical displacement, and n is the number of oscillations per second in the resulting harmonic motion. If l is the length of the spring when the system is in equilibrium, find the natural length of the spring, and show that, when the spring is extended to double its natural length, the tension is $m(4\pi^2n^2l-g)$.   (C.S.)

23. A fine elastic string OAB, whose modulus of elasticity is λ and unstretched length a, has one end fixed at O, and passes over a smooth pulley fixed at A, where $OA = a$. A particle of mass m hangs in equilibrium at B. Show that if a horizontal impulse I is applied to the particle it will move in a horizontal line with S.H.M. of amplitude $I(a/\lambda m)^{\frac{1}{2}}$.   (H.C.)

24. A spiral spring supports a carrier of mass 500 g, and when a weight of mass 2·5 kg is placed on the carrier the spring extends 5 cm. The carrier with its load is pulled down a further distance of 5 cm and is then let go. How far does it rise, and what is the greatest velocity it attains?   (Q.E.)

15. Given that the amplitude of a S.H.M. is a, and the greatest speed is V, find the period of an oscillation and the acceleration at distance b from the centre of the oscillation.

A body lies on a horizontal platform which describes a S.H.M. vertically of amplitude 5 cm and complete period 1 s. Compare the greatest and least pressures of the body on the platform.   (N.U.3)

8.11. The simple pendulum

This consists of a heavy particle or bob attached to a fixed point by a weightless string and swinging in a vertical plane. It is thus a case of motion in a vertical circle, but we shall now consider more fully the details of the motion when the displacement of the string from the vertical is very small.

Let O (Fig. 8.9) be the point of suspension, OA the vertical position of the string, l the length of the string, and m the mass of the particle.

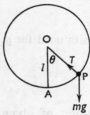

FIG. 8.9

If P is any displaced position of the particle, where the angle AOP $(= \theta)$ is small, the force tending to bring m back to A along the circle is $mg \sin \theta$.

∴ the acceleration of P along the circle towards A

$$= g \sin \theta = g\theta \text{ approximately,}$$

if θ is measured in radians and is small.

In this case the acceleration of P along the circle towards A

$$= (g/l)s$$

where s is the length of the arc AP.

The acceleration along the circle is therefore directly proportional to the displacement along the circle measured from A, the equilibrium position.

The motion is therefore approximately simply harmonic about A as centre, and the period of a complete oscillation is

$$2\pi\sqrt{(l/g)}.$$

It must be remembered that this is only a good approximation when the angle of swing is so small that $\sin \theta$ is very nearly equal to θ. By the use of tables, the reader can verify that, when $\theta = 10°$, $(\sin \theta)/\theta$ differs from unity by about $\frac{1}{2}$ per cent.

8.12. The seconds pendulum

The period $2\pi\sqrt{(l/g)}$ is the time for a complete oscillation to and fro.

A seconds pendulum is one which vibrates from rest to rest (i.e. makes *half a complete oscillation*) in 1 second.

The period of a seconds pendulum is therefore 2 s.

If l is the length of the seconds pendulum,

$$1 = \pi\sqrt{l/g}$$

$\therefore$
$$l = g/\pi^2.$$

The unit of length for l will depend on the units used for g. Taking $g = 981$ cm s^{-2} and $\pi = \frac{22}{7}$,

$$l = 99\cdot3 \text{ cm}.$$

8.13. Since the time of oscillation of a pendulum of given length depends on the value of g, this time will vary in different places, and will also vary with the height above or below the earth's surface.

If the whole pendulum is subject to some other acceleration, such as that due to being in a lift moving with uniform acceleration, or in a train going round a curve, the apparent value of g is altered and so is the time of oscillation.

If T s is the period of oscillation of any pendulum, and n the number of oscillations per second, $n = 1/T$.

A seconds pendulum should beat 86 400 times a day, and the time for a half oscillation is $\frac{86\ 400}{86\ 400}$ s.

If the pendulum gains x seconds a day the time of a half oscillation is

$$\frac{86\ 400}{86\ 400 + x} \text{ s.}$$

If it loses x seconds a day the time is $\dfrac{86\ 400}{86\ 400 - x}$ s.

These expressions are useful in problems where the number of seconds lost or gained by a seconds pendulum is required.

The following examples illustrate variations in period due to different causes.

EXAMPLE (i)

If a seconds pendulum be lengthened by $\frac{1}{100}$th of its length, how many seconds will it lose in a day?

If l is the length of the seconds pendulum the new length is $\frac{101}{100}l$. If x is the number of seconds lost in the day,

$$\frac{86\,400}{86\,400} = \pi\sqrt{\frac{l}{g}}$$

and

$$\frac{86\,400}{86\,400-x} = \pi\sqrt{\left(\frac{101}{100}\frac{l}{g}\right)}$$

$$\therefore \qquad \frac{86\,400-x}{86\,400} = \sqrt{\frac{100}{101}}.$$

Instead of working out $\sqrt{\frac{100}{101}}$, by taking the square root or using logarithms, it is better to write it $(\frac{101}{100})^{-\frac{1}{2}}$ or $(1+\frac{1}{100})^{-\frac{1}{2}}$, and expand by the Binomial Theorem.

We have

$$\left(1+\frac{1}{100}\right)^{-\frac{1}{2}} = 1 - \frac{1}{200} \text{ approximately}$$

$$\therefore \qquad \frac{86\,400-x}{86\,400} = 1 - \frac{1}{200}$$

$$\therefore \qquad \frac{x}{86\,400} = \frac{1}{200}$$

$$\therefore \qquad x = 432, \text{ approximately.}$$

EXAMPLE (ii)

A seconds pendulum gains 10 s a day in one place and loses 10 s a day in another; compare the values of g in the two places.

Let l be the length of the seconds pendulum, g_1 and g_2 the values of g at the two places, then

$$\frac{86\,400}{86\,410} = \pi\sqrt{\frac{l}{g_1}}$$

and

$$\frac{86\,400}{86\,390} = \pi\sqrt{\frac{l}{g_2}}$$

$$\therefore \qquad \sqrt{\frac{g_1}{g_2}} = \frac{86\,410}{86\,390} = 1 + \frac{2}{8639}$$

$$\therefore \qquad \frac{g_1}{g_2} = \left(1+\frac{2}{8639}\right)^2 = 1 + \frac{4}{8639} \text{ approximately}$$

$$= \frac{8643}{8639} = 1 \cdot 000\,5.$$

EXAMPLE (iii)

A seconds pendulum is in a lift which is ascending with a uniform acceleration of $0 \cdot 3 \ ms^{-2}$. Show that it will gain at the rate of a little over 55 s per hour.

The upwards acceleration of the lift increases the effective value of g by $0 \cdot 3 \ ms^{-2}$.

Hence if x is the number of seconds gained per hour

$$\frac{3600}{3600} = \pi \sqrt{\frac{l}{9.8}}$$

and

$$\frac{3600}{3600+x} = \pi \sqrt{\frac{l}{10.1}}$$

$\therefore \quad 1 + \dfrac{x}{3600} = \sqrt{\dfrac{10 \cdot 1}{9 \cdot 8}} = \left(1 + \dfrac{3}{98}\right)^{\frac{1}{2}} = 1 + \dfrac{3}{196}$ approximately.

$\therefore \qquad\qquad \dfrac{x}{3600} = \dfrac{3}{196}$

$\therefore \qquad\qquad\qquad x = 55 \cdot 1.$

Therefore the pendulum gains a little over 55 s per hour.

EXAMPLE (iv)

A seconds pendulum at the bottom of a mine, $0 \cdot 8 \ km$ deep, loses 10 s a day; at the top of a mountain $0 \cdot 8 \ km$ high show that it will lose about $15 \cdot 4 \ s$ a day, assuming that the radius of the earth is 6400 km.

[Inside the earth the weight of a body varies directly as its distance from the centre; outside the earth the weight varies inversely as the square of its distance from the centre.] (I.S.)

Let g_1, g, g_2 be the values of the acceleration due to gravity at the bottom of the mine, at the surface, and at the top of the mountain respectively.

Then $\qquad \dfrac{g_1}{g} = \dfrac{6400 - 0 \cdot 8}{6400} \quad$ and $\quad \dfrac{g_2}{g} = \dfrac{6400^2}{(6400 + 0 \cdot 8)^2}$

$\therefore \qquad\qquad \dfrac{g_2}{g_1} = \dfrac{6400^3}{(6400 \cdot 8)^2 (6400 - 0 \cdot 8)}$

$$= \frac{1}{\left(1 + \dfrac{1}{8000}\right)^2 \left(1 - \dfrac{1}{8000}\right)}$$

$$= \left(1 + \frac{1}{8000}\right)^{-2} \left(1 - \frac{1}{8000}\right)^{-1}.$$

Also $\dfrac{86\,400}{86\,390} = \pi\sqrt{\dfrac{l}{g_1}}$ and $\dfrac{86\,400}{86\,400-x} = \pi\sqrt{\dfrac{l}{g_2}}$

if the pendulum loses x s a day at the top of the mountain.

$$\therefore \quad \frac{86\,400-x}{86\,390} = \sqrt{\frac{g_2}{g_1}} = \left(1+\frac{1}{8000}\right)^{-1}\left(1-\frac{1}{8000}\right)^{-\frac14}$$

$$= \left(1-\frac{1}{8000}\right)\left(1+\frac{1}{16\,000}\right)$$

$$= 1-\frac{1}{16\,000}\ \text{approximately};$$

$$\therefore \quad 86\,400-x = 86\,390-\frac{8639}{1600} = 86\,390-5\cdot4$$

$$\therefore \quad x = 10+5\cdot4 = 15\cdot4.$$

EXAMPLES 8.3

1. A pendulum beats seconds accurately at a place where the acceleration of gravity is $9\cdot8$ ms^{-2}. If taken to a place where the value of this acceleration is $9\cdot86$ ms^{-2}, will it gain or lose, and how many seconds in 24 hours? (I.S.)

2. Calculate the length of a seconds pendulum at a place where g is 981 cms^{-2}. If a pendulum clock loses 9 minutes per week, find in millimetres what change is required in the length of the pendulum in order that the clock may keep correct time. (I.S.)

3. Show that an incorrect seconds pendulum of a clock which loses x s a day must be shortened by $x/432$ per cent of its length in order to keep correct time. (H.S.C.)

4. A seconds pendulum is correct at a place where the value of g is $9\cdot8$ ms^{-2}. How many seconds a day will it gain or lose if taken to a place where the value of g is $9\cdot9$ ms^{-2}?

5. A seconds pendulum is correct at a place where $g = 9\cdot85$ ms^{-2}. By what percentage of its length must it be altered in order to keep correct time at a place where $g = 9\cdot8$ ms^{-2}?

6. A seconds pendulum is carried down with a lift at a uniform acceleration of $0\cdot6$ ms^{-2}. At the rate of how many seconds an hour will it lose?

7. A pendulum clock gains 20 s each day. Calculate the required alteration in the length of the pendulum.

   At what height above the earth's surface would the clock with the uncorrected pendulum give correct time? (The earth's radius is 6400 km, and the force of gravity varies inversely as the square of the distance from the earth's centre.)   (H.S.D.)

8. A pendulum, which at the surface of the earth gains 10 s a day, loses 10 s a day when taken down a mine; compare the acceleration due to gravity at the top and bottom of the mine and find its depth.

9. Prove that if a pendulum swings from rest to rest n times per second, then $g = n^2\pi^2 l$, where l is the length of the pendulum.

   In old French measure the length of the seconds pendulum (for which $n = 1$) at Paris is 3·06 French ft; calculate the value of g in these units.   (I.A.)

10. A simple pendulum making small oscillations is allowed to swing from a position in which it makes $\alpha°$ with the vertical. If v is the maximum speed, show that the complete period is $360v/g\alpha$.   (H.S.C.)

11. A pendulum bob of mass 500 g is hung from the roof of a railway carriage by a 90 cm string. The carriage is moving at 72 km h^{-1} round a curve of radius 0·8 km. Find the distance of the bob from the vertical through the point of support and the tension in the string. Find also the approximate time of a small oscillation while the train is moving round the curve.   (I.E.)

CHAPTER NINE

DYNAMICS OF A RIGID BODY

9.1. A *rigid body* has been defined earlier as one whose shape and size are invariable, so that the distance between any two points of it is always the same.

Such a body is said to be moving in two dimensions when all points in the body move in parallel planes, e.g. a cube swinging about one of its edges, or sliding on a horizontal plane with the same face always in contact with the plane.

We shall consider first the case where some line in the body is fixed and the body rotates about this line as axis.

9.2. Kinetic energy of a body rotating about a fixed axis

Let the Fig. 9.1 represent a section of the body which is rotating with angular velocity ω about an axis through O perpendicular to the plane of the paper.

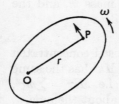

FIG. 9.1

Consider a particle of the body of mass m at P, where $OP = r$. The velocity of P is $r\omega$, and the kinetic energy of the particle m is therefore $\frac{1}{2}mr^2\omega^2$.

The kinetic energy of the whole body is the sum of the kinetic energies of all its particles, i.e. $\sum \frac{1}{2}mr^2\omega^2$, the $\sum$ denoting summation over the whole of the body, both in the plane shown in the figure and for all parallel planes, the value of r for each particle being its perpendicular distance from the axis of rotation.

Now ω is the same for all the particles.

$$\therefore \qquad \sum \tfrac{1}{2}mr^2\omega^2 = \tfrac{1}{2}\omega^2 \sum mr^2.$$

The quantity $\sum mr^2$ is of great importance, and occurs in all problems involving the rotation of a rigid body. It is called the *Moment of Inertia* of the body about the axis from which r is measured and is usually denoted by I.

The moment of inertia of a body about any axis is thus obtained by multiplying the mass of each particle of the body by the square of its distance from that axis, and adding the results for all the particles of the body.

If the body consists of a finite number of particles the value of $\sum mr^2$ is obtained by ordinary addition. In the case of a rigid body, where the number of particles is infinitely great, the summation is effected by integration.

If a body is rotating with angular velocity ω about a fixed axis, and its moment of inertia about the axis is I, the kinetic energy of the body is

$$\tfrac{1}{2}I\omega^2.$$

This expression corresponds to the value $\tfrac{1}{2}mv^2$ for a particle, the moment of inertia I taking the place of the mass m, and the angular velocity ω replacing the linear velocity v.

9.3. If the whole mass M of a body be supposed concentrated at a point distant k from the axis such that Mk^2 has the same value as the moment of inertia about that axis, i.e. $Mk^2 = \sum mr^2$, the length k is called the *Radius of Gyration* about the axis.

The form Mk^2 is the one in which moments of inertia are usually expressed. For a given body, M is the same for all axes, but the value of k differs for different axes. If M is in kilogrammes and k in metres the moment of inertia is in kilogramme-metre squared or kg m^2 units.

9.4. Moment of inertia of a thin uniform rod about an axis through its centre perpendicular to its length

Let AB (Fig. 9.2) be the rod, $2a$ its length, O its middle point, and m the mass per unit length.

The mass of an element of length dx at P is $m\,dx$, and if

$OP = x$, the moment of inertia of the element about YY′ is mx^2dx.

To obtain the moment of inertia of the whole rod we have to

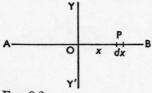

FIG. 9.2

sum this expression for the whole length of the rod, i.e. we have to evaluate the integral

$$\int_{-a}^{+a} mx^2dx.$$

Now, m is constant, and $\int x^2dx = \frac{1}{3}x^3$.

$$\therefore \qquad \int_{-a}^{+a} mx^2dx = m\left[\frac{x^3}{3}\right]_{-a}^{a} = \frac{2}{3}ma^3.$$

Also, if M is the mass of the rod, $M = 2am$.

Therefore the moment of inertia about YY′ $= \dfrac{Ma^2}{3}$.

If the axis is perpendicular to the rod through one end the expression mx^2dx has to be integrated from 0 to $2a$, where x is now measured from the end of the rod.

We get $\qquad \displaystyle\int_{0}^{2a} mx^2dx = m\left[\frac{x^3}{3}\right]_{0}^{2a} = m\frac{8a^3}{3} = M\frac{4a^2}{3}.$

This is the moment of inertia of the rod about a perpendicular axis *through one end*.

The moment of inertia of the rod about an axis *parallel* to its length at a distance p away is Mp^2, since every particle of the rod is at a distance p from the axis.

9.5. Moment of inertia of a uniform rectangular lamina about an axis through its centre parallel to one of the sides

Let ABCD (Fig. 9.3) be the rectangle, AB $= 2a$, BC $= 2b$, and G the centre.

To obtain the moment of inertia about XX′, parallel to AB, we divide the rectangle into elementary strips, as PQ, parallel to XX′.

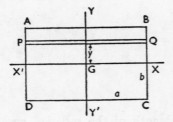

Fɪɢ. 9.3

Suppose PQ is at distance y from XX′ and the strip is of width δy.

Therefore the mass of the strip $= M\dfrac{\delta y}{2b}$

where M is the mass of the whole rectangle, provided the rectangle is uniform.

Therefore the moment of inertia of the strip about XX′ is

$$M \times \frac{\delta y}{2b} \times y^2,$$

since the strip is parallel to XX′.

Therefore the moment of inertia of the rectangle about XX′

$$= \int_{-b}^{b} \frac{M}{2b} y^2 dy = \frac{M}{2b}\left[\frac{y^3}{3}\right]_{-b}^{b} = \tfrac{1}{3}Mb^2.$$

Similarly the moment of inertia about YY′ parallel to BC is

$$\tfrac{1}{3}Ma^2.$$

9.6. Moment of inertia of a circular ring about an axis through its centre perpendicular to the plane of the ring

Let the radius of the ring be a. Since each particle of the ring is at the same distance a from the axis

$$\sum mr^2 = \sum ma^2 = a^2 \sum m$$
$$= Ma^2$$

where M is the mass of the ring.

9.7. Moment of inertia of a uniform circular disc about an axis through its centre perpendicular to the plane of the disc

Let O (Fig. 9.4) be the centre of the disc, a its radius, and m the mass per unit area which will be assumed constant.

Divide the disc into concentric rings of breadth dx.

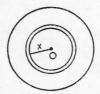

FIG. 9.4

The mass of a ring of radius x is $2\pi mx\,dx$, and its moment of inertia about the axis through the centre perpendicular to its plane is $2\pi mx^3\,dx$.

The moment of inertia of the whole disc is obtained by integrating this expression between the limits 0 and a.

$$\text{Now} \quad \int_0^a 2\pi mx^3\,dx = 2\pi m\left[\frac{x^4}{4}\right]_0^a = \frac{2\pi ma^4}{4} = \frac{\pi ma^4}{2}$$

and if M is the mass of the disc,

$$\pi ma^2 = M.$$

Therefore the moment of inertia of the disc about its axis is $\frac{1}{2}Ma^2$.

The moment of inertia of a uniform cylinder about its axis is of the same form, i.e. if M is the mass of the cylinder and a its radius, the moment of inertia is $M(a^2/2)$. For if we divide the cylinder into slices perpendicular to the axis the moment of inertia of each slice is equal to its mass multiplied by $\frac{1}{2}a^2$. The moment of inertia of the whole cylinder, which is equal to the sum of the moments of inertia of the slices, is therefore equal to the total mass multiplied by $\frac{1}{2}a^2$.

9.8. Moment of inertia of a solid sphere about a diameter

Let O (Fig. 9.5) be the centre of the sphere, a its radius, m the mass per unit volume, and AB any diameter.

Divide the sphere into circular slices of thickness dx perpendicular to AB.

For a slice PQ, distant x from O, the volume is $\pi(a^2-x^2)dx$, and the moment of inertia about AB is

$$\tfrac{1}{2}\pi m(a^2-x^2)^2dx.$$

The moment of inertia of the whole sphere is the integral of this, between the limits $-a$ and $+a$, but, as the value of the

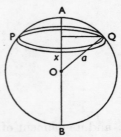

FIG. 9.5

integral is evidently the same for the upper and lower halves of the sphere, this is the same as twice the integral from 0 to a.

$$2\frac{\pi m}{2}\int_0^a (a^2-x^2)^2dx = \pi m\int_0^a (a^4-2a^2x^2+x^4)dx$$

$$= \pi m\left[a^4x-\tfrac{2}{3}a^2x^3+\tfrac{1}{5}x^5 \right]_0^a$$

$$= \pi m\tfrac{8}{15}a^5.$$

Now if M is the mass of the sphere, $M = \tfrac{4}{3}\pi a^3m$, if m is constant.

Therefore the moment of inertia about a diameter $= \tfrac{2}{5}Ma^2$.

9.9. We shall now prove two theorems which are very useful for calculating the moments of inertia of a body about other axes when we know the moments of inertia about certain standard axes. In this way a large amount of integration is avoided.

9.10. Theorem of parallel axes

If the moment of inertia of a body, of mass M, about an axis through its centre of mass is I, the moment of inertia about a parallel axis at a distance d from the first axis is $I+Md^2$.

Let the Fig. 9.6 represent a section of the body through its centre of mass G, and let the moment of inertia about an axis through G perpendicular to the plane of the paper be I. We require the moment of inertia about a parallel axis through O where $GO = d$.

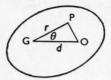

FIG. 9.6

Let P be any particle of the body of mass m, $GP = r$, and $\angle OGP = \theta$.

The moment of inertia about the axis through O is

$$\sum m \times OP^2 = \sum m(r^2 + d^2 - 2dr \cos \theta)$$
$$= \sum mr^2 + \sum md^2 - 2d \sum mr \cos \theta.$$

Now $\sum mr^2 = I$, $\sum md^2 = Md^2$, and $\sum mr \cos \theta = 0$.

The last result follows from the formula for finding the centre of mass of a body.* The distance of the centre of mass from a plane through G perpendicular to GO is $\sum mr \cos \theta / \sum m$, and, as G is the centre of mass, this must be zero, so that $\sum mr \cos \theta = 0$.

Hence the moment of inertia about the parallel axis through O is $I + Md^2$.

For example, the moment of inertia of a thin rod, of length $2a$, about a perpendicular axis through its centre is $\frac{1}{3}Ma^2$.

Hence the moment of inertia about a perpendicular axis through one end is

$$\tfrac{1}{3}Ma^2 + Ma^2 = M\frac{4a^2}{3}.$$

This is the result arrived at by integration in 9.4.

9.11. Perpendicular Axes Theorem

If the moments of inertia of a lamina about two perpendicular axes in its plane which meet at O are A and B the moment of inertia about an axis through O perpendicular to the plane of the lamina is A+B.

* See paragraph 16.6 later.

Let OX, OY (Fig. 9.7) be the two perpendicular axes in the plane of the lamina, and OZ an axis perpendicular to the lamina.

If m is the mass of a particle of the lamina at P, where OP $= r$, the moment of inertia of the lamina about OZ is $\sum mr^2$.

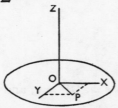

FIG. 9.7

But if x, y are the coordinates of P referred to OX, OY as axes,

$$r^2 = x^2 + y^2$$

$$\therefore \qquad \sum mr^2 = \sum mx^2 + \sum my^2.$$

Now $\sum mx^2$ is the moment of inertia about OY $(= \text{B})$, and $\sum my^2$ is the moment of inertia about OX $(= \text{A})$; therefore the moment of inertia about OZ $= \text{A} + \text{B}$.

9.12. In 9.5 we proved that the moments of inertia of a rectangular lamina of sides $2a$, $2b$ about the axes through its centre parallel to the sides $2b$, $2a$ are $\frac{1}{3}Ma^2$ and $\frac{1}{3}Mb^2$ respectively.

From the theorem of the last paragraph the moment of inertia about an axis through the centre of the rectangle perpendicular to its plane is

$$M\frac{a^2}{3} + M\frac{b^2}{3} = M\frac{a^2+b^2}{3}.$$

From the theorem of parallel axes the moment of inertia about one of the sides of length $2a$ is

$$M\frac{b^2}{3} + Mb^2 = M\frac{4}{3}b^2.$$

In 9.7 we proved that the moment of inertia of a circular disc about an axis through its centre perpendicular to its plane is $\frac{1}{2}Ma^2$. Now by the theorem of the last paragraph this is equal to the sum of the moments of inertia about two perpendicular diameters. But the moment of inertia is the same about all diameters, hence the moment of inertia about a diameter is half that about the perpendicular axis through the centre.

Therefore the moment of inertia about a diameter $= \frac{1}{4}Ma^2$.

From the theorem of parallel axes we see that the moment of inertia about a tangent line is

$$M\frac{a^2}{4} + Ma^2 = M\frac{5a^2}{4}.$$

9.13. Moment of inertia of a rectangular prism about an axis through its centre perpendicular to a pair of faces

Let the length of the sides by $2a$, $2b$, $2c$, and the axes Ox, Oy, Oz perpendicular to the faces as shown in Fig. 9.8, O being the centre of the prism.

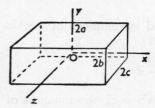

FIG. 9.8

To find the moment of inertia about Ox we divide the prism into slices perpendicular to this axis. The edges of each of these rectangular slices are $2b$ and $2c$, and the moment of inertia of each slice about Ox is the product of its mass and $(b^2+c^2)/3$.

Hence the moment of inertia of the whole prism is

$$M\frac{b^2+c^2}{3}.$$

Similarly for the axis Oz perpendicular to the faces whose edges are $2a$ and $2b$, the moment of inertia is

$$M\frac{a^2+b^2}{3}.$$

If the prism is a cube of edge $2a$, then $b = c = a$, and the moment of inertia about any of the three axes through the centre perpendicular to a pair of faces is

$$M\frac{2a^2}{3}.$$

9.14. Moment of inertia of a solid circular cylinder about a diameter of an end face

Let AB (Fig. 9.9) be a diameter of an end face, a the radius and l the length of the cylinder, m the mass per unit volume.

Divide the cylinder into circular slices, as PQ, of thickness dx perpendicular to the axis.

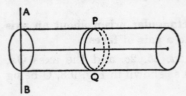

FIG. 9.9

The mass of a slice is $\pi m a^2 dx$, and its moment of inertia about *its own diameter parallel* to AB *is*

$$\pi m a^2 dx \frac{a^2}{4} \text{ or } \frac{\pi m a^4}{4} dx.$$

If the distance of the slice from AB is x, the moment of inertia about AB (by the Theorem of Parallel Axes) is

$$\tfrac{1}{4}\pi m a^4 dx + (\pi m a^2 dx)x^2.$$

Hence the moment of inertia of the whole cylinder about AB is obtained by integrating this expression from $x = 0$ to $x = l$.

Now, $$\int_0^l \tfrac{1}{4} m a^4 dx + \int_0^l \pi m a^2 x^2 dx$$
$$= \tfrac{1}{4}\pi m a^4 l + \tfrac{1}{3}\pi m a^2 l^3.$$

The volume of the cylinder is $\pi a^2 l$, and its mass is $M = \pi m a^2 l$, if m is constant.

Hence the moment of inertia about AB is

$$M \frac{a^2}{4} + M \frac{l^2}{3} = M\left(\frac{a^2}{4} + \frac{l^2}{3}\right).$$

The moment of inertia about an axis through the centre of gravity perpendicular to the axis of the cylinder, i.e. parallel to AB, is

$$M\left(\frac{a^2}{4} + \frac{l^2}{3}\right) - M\frac{l^2}{4} = M\left(\frac{a^2}{4} + \frac{l^2}{12}\right).$$

EXAMPLES 9.1

1. Find the moment of inertia of a circular ring, of mass M and radius a, about an axis through a point of the ring perpendicular to its plane.

2. Prove that the moment of inertia of a uniform rod of length $2a$ about an axis intersecting the rod at right angles at a distance b from its centre is $M(\frac{1}{3}a^2+b^2)$, where M is the mass of the rod.
   (H.C.)

3. Find the moment of inertia of a square lamina, of mass M and side $2a$, about an axis through one corner perpendicular to the plane of the lamina.

4. Find the moment of inertia of a rectangular lamina, of mass M and sides $2a$, $2b$, about an axis through one corner perpendicular to the plane of the lamina.

5. Find the moment of inertia of a circular ring, of mass M and radius a, about a diameter.

6. Prove that the radii of gyration of (i) a circular disc of radius a, (ii) a circular ring of radius a, about a tangent line are respectively $(\sqrt{5}/2)a$ and $(\sqrt{6}/2)a$.

7. Show that the moment of inertia of a square lamina, of mass M and side $2a$, about any line through its centre in the plane of the lamina is $\frac{1}{3}Ma^2$.

8. Three equal uniform rods of length l and mass M are rigidly jointed to form an equilateral triangle. Find the moment of inertia of the rods about an axis through one vertex perpendicular to the plane of the triangle.

9. Show that the moment of inertia of a cube, of mass M and edge $2a$, about one of its edges is $\frac{8}{3}Ma^2$.

10. Prove that the moment of inertia of a solid cone about its axis is $\frac{3}{10}Ma^2$, where M is the mass of the cone and a the radius of the base.

11. In a uniform circular plate, of $1\cdot5$ m diameter, is punched a hole of $0\cdot3$ m diameter, the centre of the hole being 45 cm from the centre of the plate. Find the moment of inertia of the plate: (i) about the diameter which passes through the centre of the hole; (ii) about the diameter which is perpendicular to this.   (I.E.)

12. Three rectangular areas, $0\cdot6$ m by 4 cm, $0\cdot9$ m by 4 cm, and $0\cdot3$ m by 4 cm, are fitted together to form an I figure, the longest and shortest areas forming the cross-pieces. Find the moment of inertia of the figure about the outer edge of the shortest area.
    (I.E.)

13. Find the moment of inertia of a thin uniform rod about an axis through its centre inclined at an angle θ to the rod.

14. Find the moment of inertia of a lamina in the form of a parallelogram about an axis through its centre parallel to one of the sides.

15. Find the moment of inertia of a uniform triangular lamina about: (i) an axis through a vertex parallel to the opposite side, and (ii) a parallel axis through its centre of mass.

16. Show that the moment of inertia of a rectangular lamina, of mass M and sides $2a$ and $2b$, about a diagonal is

$$2Ma^2b^2/3(a^2+b^2).$$

17. Find the moment of inertia of a thin hollow sphere about a diameter.

18. Assuming that the moment of inertia of a uniform solid sphere about a diameter is $\frac{2}{5}Mr^2$, deduce the moment of inertia of a uniform solid hemisphere about a diameter of its plane face.

19. Find the moment of inertia of a uniform semi-circular lamina about: (i) its straight edge, and (ii) about its axis of symmetry.

20. Show that the moment of inertia of a hollow sphere, whose external and internal radii are a and b, about a diameter is

$$\frac{2M}{5} \times \frac{a^5-b^5}{a^3-b^3},$$

where M is the mass of the sphere.

21. A solid flywheel of 45 cm diameter and 10 cm thick is keyed on to the end of a shaft of 10 cm diameter whose whole length is 70 cm.
    Find the moment of inertia of the wheel and shaft about a diameter of the outer face of the flywheel.

22. Show that the moment of inertia of a hollow circular cylinder, whose length is h, and external and internal radii R and r, about an axis through its centre at right angles to its length, is

$$\tfrac{1}{4}M(R^2+r^2+\tfrac{1}{3}h^2). \tag{Q.E.}$$

23. A sledge hammer consists of an iron rectangular block 15 cm $\times$ 5 cm $\times$ 5 cm. A central circular hole of 2·5 cm diameter is bored through it at right angles to one of its longer faces and a light shaft, 0·9 m long, of wood is fitted into it. Find the moment of inertia of the hammer about a line drawn through the mid-point of the far end of the shaft normal to the axis of the shaft and parallel to the small face of the block. (Take the density of iron as 7200 kg m^{-3}.) (C.S.)

24. Find the moment of inertia of a thin hemispherical bowl: (i) about the radius through the centre of gravity; (ii) about a perpendicular line through the centre of gravity.

25. Show that the moment of inertia of a paraboloid of revolution about its axis is $\frac{1}{3}M \times$ the square of the radius of its base.

9.15. Motion of a rigid body about a fixed axis

Equation of Energy. A number of results in connection with the motion of a rigid body about a fixed axis can be deduced from the principle of energy. We have seen that if the moment of inertia of a body about the fixed axis is I and ω is its angular velocity its kinetic energy is $\frac{1}{2}I\omega^2$. Hence if the body is released from rest in any position we can find its angular velocity in any other position by equating $\frac{1}{2}I\omega^2$ to the loss of potential energy, provided there is no friction. This loss is equal to the product of the weight of the body and the distance the centre of gravity has descended.

Again, if a weight is connected to a fine string wound round a flywheel which is suspended so that it can rotate on a horizontal axis, and the weight is allowed to run down, the sum of the kinetic energies of the flywheel and the weight in any position must be equal to the loss of potential energy of the weight (assuming that there is no loss of energy due to friction).

This method is illustrated in the following examples:

EXAMPLE (i)
A uniform rod, of length 2a, can turn freely about one end; if it be let fall from a horizontal position, find its angular velocity when it first becomes vertical.

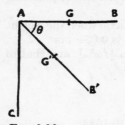

Fig. 9.10

Let M be the mass of the rod, AB (Fig. 9.10) its initial position, A being the fixed end and G the centre of gravity.

Its moment of inertia about the axis at A is $\frac{4}{3}Ma^2$.

When it has descended to the position AG'B', where $\angle BAB' = \theta$, the centre of gravity has descended a vertical distance $a \sin \theta$, and the loss of potential energy is $Mga \sin \theta$.

The angular velocity is $d\theta/dt$, and the kinetic energy is $\frac{1}{2} \times \frac{2}{3} Ma^2 (d\theta/dt)^2$.

Hence the angular velocity is given by

$$\tfrac{2}{3} Ma^2 \left(\frac{d\theta}{dt} \right)^2 = Mga \sin \theta$$

$$\therefore \qquad \left(\frac{d\theta}{dt} \right)^2 = \frac{3g}{2a} \sin \theta.$$

When the rod is in the vertical position AC, the angle $\theta = \pi/2$, and the angular velocity $= \sqrt{\left(\dfrac{3g}{2a} \right)}$.

EXAMPLE (ii)

The mass of a solid flywheel is 450 kg, its diameter is 0·6 m, the axle is of diameter 10 cm and mass 50 kg. The wheel and axle are set in motion by means of a string wound round the axle and carrying a mass of 10 kg. Find the kinetic energy of the wheel and axle when the weight reaches the floor 3 m below the starting-point.

The moment of inertia of the wheel $= 450 \times \frac{1}{2} (0·3)^2$ kg m².

The moment of inertia of the axle $= 50 \times \frac{1}{2} (0·05)^2$ kg m².

The total moment of inertia

$$I = 20·25 + 0·0625$$
$$= 20·3125 \text{ kg m}^2.$$

When the 10 kg weight has descended 3 m, the loss of potential energy is $30g$ J.

If ω is the angular velocity of the wheel and axle when the weight reaches the ground, the velocity of the weight is $0·05\omega$ ms⁻¹.

The kinetic energy of the wheel and axle is $\frac{1}{2} I \omega^2$ J, and that of the weight is $\frac{1}{2} \times 10 \times (0·05\omega)^2$ J.

Hence by the principle of energy

$$10·1563 \, \omega^2 + 0·0125\omega^2 = 30g$$
$$\therefore \qquad\qquad \omega^2 = 30 \times 9·8/10·1688$$
$$\therefore \qquad\qquad \omega^2 = 294/10·1688.$$

The kinetic energy of the wheel and axle is

$$10·156 \, \omega^2 = 294 \text{ J approximately.}$$

9.16. Determination of the moment of inertia of a flywheel

The method of the last example can be modified to determine the moment of inertia of a flywheel.

The axle of the wheel is mounted horizontally on ball bearings to reduce friction. There is usually a small peg on the axle over which a loop in one end of the string, to which the weight is attached, is placed. This peg is also useful in counting the number of revolutions made by the wheel in any time. The height h of the position from which the weight is to be released is measured carefully, and the number of revolutions made by the wheel while the weight is descending is obtained by placing the weight on the ground and counting the number of turns of the wheel required to wind it up to its starting-point, say n_1. The length of the string is adjusted so that the loop comes off the peg as the weight reaches the ground.

The weight is released from rest and the number of revolutions made by the wheel after the weight strikes the ground is measured, and also the time taken for the wheel to come to rest; let these be n_2 and t.

The friction in the bearings and the rate of retardation of the wheel may be assumed constant, so that the average angular velocity taken over the whole time required to come to rest will be *half* the initial angular velocity ω.

The average angular velocity $= 2\pi n_2/t$.

$$\therefore \qquad \omega = 4\pi n_2/t.$$

The velocity v of the weight on reaching the ground is given by $v = wr$, where r is the radius of the axle of the flywheel.

If m is the mass of the weight and I the moment of inertia of the flywheel their kinetic energies when the weight reaches the ground are $\frac{1}{2}mv^2$ and $\frac{1}{2}I\omega^2$.

The loss of potential energy is mgh.

Now some work has been done against friction. Let w be the amount done in *one* revolution, then in n_1 revolutions the work is n_1w, and this is the amount done while the weight is descending.

$$\therefore \qquad mgh = \tfrac{1}{2}mv^2 + \tfrac{1}{2}I\omega^2 + n_1w.$$

But the kinetic energy of the wheel, $\frac{1}{2}I\omega^2$, is destroyed by the friction in n_2 revolutions.

$$\therefore \qquad\qquad n_2 w = \tfrac{1}{2}I\omega^2$$

$$\therefore \qquad\qquad w = \tfrac{1}{2}I\omega^2/n_2$$

$$\therefore \qquad\qquad mgh = \tfrac{1}{2}mv^2 + \tfrac{1}{2}I\omega^2(1 + n_1/n_2).$$

All the quantities in this equation, except I, are known, and therefore I can be calculated.

If m is in grammes, r and h measured in centimetres, then I will be obtained in $\mathrm{g\,cm^2}$ units.

EXAMPLES 9.2

1. A heavy circular disc, of mass 10 kg and radius 30 cm, is capable of rotation about its centre in a vertical plane. A mass of 5 kg is attached to the rim at the highest point, and the whole slightly displaced. Find the angular velocity when the mass of 5 kg is at the lowest point. (I.E.)

2. A wheel has a cord of length 3 m coiled round its axle; the cord is pulled with a constant force of 100 N, and when the cord leaves the axle the wheel is rotating 5 times per second. Calculate the moment of inertia of the wheel and axle. (I.E.)

3. A straight uniform rod 1·2 m long, mass 10 kg, can turn freely in a vertical plane about a horizontal axis through the rod at a distance of 0·3 m from one end. The rod is held in a horizontal position and then let go. Find the velocity of the lower end when the rod is vertical, and the kinetic energy of the rod. (Q.E.)

4. A circular hoop of small section and 0·9 m radius has a mass of 5 kg and has a weight of mass 2·5 kg attached to a point on the rim. It is pivoted about a horizontal axis, perpendicular to the plane of the hoop, on the rim exactly opposite the weight. If it be turned until the weight is at the highest point and then let go, find the angular velocity with which the weight passes its lowest point. (Q.E.)

5. A uniform circular disc of mass 50 kg has a radius of 0·6 m; it is pivoted about a horizontal axis through its centre perpendicular to its plane, and a weight of mass 50 kg is fixed to a point on the disc 45 cm from the axis. The whole is held with that point of attachment level with the axis, and is then let go. What will be the maximum velocity of the rim of the disc in the subsequent motion? (Q.E.)

6. The power of a machine is 4 kW; a shearing operation has to be performed every 10 s which absorbs 0·8 of the whole energy supplied during that time. If the number of revolutions may vary only between 100 and 130 per minute, find the least moment of inertia of the flywheel. (I.E.)

7. Three equal uniform rods, each of length l and mass m, form the sides of an equilateral triangle ABC. Find the moment of inertia of the frame about the axis through A perpendicular to the plane of the triangle. (Assume that the moment of inertia of each rod about an axis through its mid-point perpendicular to the rod is $\frac{1}{12}ml^2$.) The triangular frame is attached to a smooth hinge at A which it can rotate in a vertical plane. The frame is held with AB horizontal, and C below AB, and then let go from rest. Find the maximum angular velocity of the triangle in the subsequent motion. (I.E.)

8. A torpedo is driven by expending the energy stored in a flywheel initially rotating at 10 000 rev min^{-1}. If the mass of the flywheel is 100 kg and it is regarded as a uniform circular disc of diameter 0·6 m, show that it will be rotating at half the initial rate after about 685 m run at 48 km h^{-1}, assuming that the average power necessary for this speed is 36 kW. (I.E.)

9. Find the radius of gyration of a thin uniform circular hoop, of radius a and mass m, about a fixed horizontal axis perpendicular to the plane of the hoop and passing through a point O on the hoop.

If, when the diameter OA of this hoop is horizontal, the point A is moving downwards with velocity V, find the angular velocity of the hoop when A is vertically below O, assuming that the hoop can move freely about the horizontal axis through O. Show also that the hoop will make complete revolutions about the horizontal axis through O if $V > 2\sqrt{(ga)}$. (I.E.)

10. A uniform wire in the form of a circle of radius a swings in a vertical plane about a point A in the circumference. It starts from rest with the diameter AB horizontal. Find its angular velocity when AB is vertical.

11. A flywheel, 0·6 m in diameter and of mass 10 kg, is keyed on to a shaft of 15 cm diameter, which can turn freely in smooth horizontal bearings; a long fine string is attached to and wrapped round the axle and carries at its other end a mass of 8 kg. The wheel is turned until it acquires a speed of 480 rev min^{-1}, and is then left running. Prove that it will come to rest after about 33

more revolutions. [Neglect the masses of the axle and string, and assume the mass of the wheel to be concentrated in and uniformly distributed round its rim.] (H.C.)

12. Calculate the energy of a disc of 0·9 m diameter and 0·3 cm thick, of material weighing 900 kg m^{-3}, rotating about an axis through its centre at right angles to its plane and making 2000 revmin^{-1}. (Q.E.)

13. A uniform straight rod 1·8 m long swings in a vertical plane about one end; if V is the velocity of the free end of the rod in its lowest position, find the least value of V consistent with the rod making a complete revolution.

Compare this with the case of a weight hung by a cord of the same length as the rod, and making a complete revolution in a circle. (Q.E.)

14. A circular disc of uniform thickness, of radius a and mass M, is rotating with angular velocity ω about a fixed axis at right angles to its plane, at a distance b from its centre; find its kinetic energy.

15. A flywheel, of mass 45 kg and diameter 1·2 m, is fixed to the end of a light horizontal axle of 0·3 m diameter. A long light cord wound round and fastened to this axle carries at its free end a particle of mass 9 kg. The flywheel is turning at the rate of 2 revs^{-1} in the direction to wind up the particle, when it is suddenly left to itself. How many revolutions will the wheel make before coming to instantaneous rest? (N.U.3)

16. One end of a light elastic string, of natural length 0·9 m, is attached to a fixed point and the other end to a point in the circumference of the axle of a wheel, so that the string being just unstretched is tangential to the axle. The radius of the axle is 5 cm, the mass of the wheel and axle is 1·4 kg, its radius of gyration is 15 cm, and the modulus of elasticity of the string is 50 N.

The wheel is turned through three complete revolutions winding the string which slips freely on the axle, and the system is then released from rest. Find in radians per second (rads^{-1}) the angular speed of the wheel at the instant when the string becomes again unstretched. (I.E.)

9.17. Angular momentum of a rigid body

Consider again a body rotating about a fixed axis with angular velocity ω. Fig. 9.11 represents a section of the body perpendicular to the axis, which passes through O.

A particle of mass m at P, where $OP = r$, has linear momentum $m\omega r$ perpendicular to OP. The moment of this momentum about the axis through O equals $(m\omega r)r$, and is known as the *angular momentum* of the particle about O.

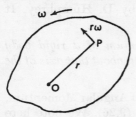

Fig. 9.11

The *angular momentum* of the whole body has a magnitude $\sum m\omega r^2$, where the summation extends over the whole body.

Now as ω is the same for all the particles comprising the body, we get

$$\sum m\omega r^2 = \omega\sum mr^2 = I\omega,$$

where I is the moment of inertia of the body about the axis of rotation.

Thus, the angular momentum of a rigid body rotating with angular velocity ω about a fixed axis is $I\omega$, where I is the moment of inertia of the body about the axis.

This expression $I\omega$ corresponds to the expression mv for the linear momentum of a particle, I taking the place of the mass m, and the angular velocity ω replacing the linear velocity v, as in the case of kinetic energy (cf. 9.2).

9.18. Motion of a rigid body about a fixed axis

Principle of angular momentum

We have shown earlier that the basic postulate in the Newtonian dynamics of a particle, known as Newton's Second Law of Motion, asserts that the rate of change of linear momentum of a particle is directly proportional to the external force acting on the particle.

In fact, with a suitable choice of the units of force, it follows that the rate of change of linear momentum of a particle equals the force acting on the particle. This can be extended to apply to a rigid body, but in addition a corresponding postulate has to be made involving the rotational motion of a rigid body.

This may be introduced in various forms. One such postulate is due to D'Alembert, and for this the reader is referred to *Intermediate Mechanics*, Vol. I (§ 229), by D. Humphrey. It leads to the following result:

The rate of change of angular momentum of a rigid body rotating about a fixed axis equals the moment about that axis of the external forces acting on the body.

We shall refer to this as the Principle of Angular Momentum, and we shall give its general form later (9.26). We note here that we can avoid introducing such assumptions as D'Alembert had to make by accepting this Principle, once and for all, as the further postulate necessary in dealing with the rotational motion of a rigid body. This we propose to do. It is justified, like other assumptions in science, in that it leads to results in agreement with observation.

A special form of the principle is that the angular momentum of a rigid body rotating about a *fixed* axis remains constant, if the sum of the moments of the external forces about that axis is zero.

In general, if L is the moment of the forces acting on the rigid body about the fixed axis of rotation we can write

$$\text{Rate of change of } I\omega = L.$$

$$\therefore \qquad I \times \text{rate of change of } \omega = L.$$

$$\therefore \qquad I \times \text{angular acceleration} = L.$$

or $$I\frac{\mathrm{d}\omega}{\mathrm{d}t} = L. \qquad\qquad \text{(i)}$$

If θ is the angle of rotation of the body at time t, $\omega = \mathrm{d}\theta/\mathrm{d}t$ so that $\mathrm{d}\omega/\mathrm{d}t = \mathrm{d}^2\theta/\mathrm{d}t^2$. Hence

$$\frac{\mathrm{d}^2\theta}{\mathrm{d}t^2} = \frac{L}{I} = \frac{\text{moment of forces about axis of rotation}}{\text{moment of inertia about axis of rotation}}.$$

We might compare this equation with the equation of linear momentum of a particle of mass m, subject to a force F, moving in direction of the axis of x, namely

$$m\frac{\mathrm{d}^2x}{\mathrm{d}t^2} = F \text{ or } \frac{\mathrm{d}^2x}{\mathrm{d}t^2} = \frac{F}{m}.$$

We note that just as the mass m is a measure of the 'inertia' of the particle to motion in a straight line, I seems to be a measure of the 'inertia' of the rigid body to rotational motion, whence its name.

Equation (i), when integrated, will give the value of $d\theta/dt$ and θ at any time. The constant introduced at each integration is determined from the initial values of $d\theta/dt$ and θ.

We shall now consider a special case, the motion of a rigid body about a fixed *horizontal* axis under the action of gravity. Such a body is often called a Compound Pendulum.

9.19. The compound pendulum

Take the vertical plane through the axis of rotation as the plane of reference, and the plane through the axis and the centre of gravity of the body as the plane fixed in the body. If the angle between these planes at times t is θ the angular velocity of the body is $d\theta/dt$.

Figure 9.12 represents a section perpendicular to the axis of rotation through the centre of gravity G, cutting the axis in O.

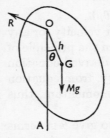

FIG. 9.12

OA is the vertical through O.

Let R denote the reaction acting on the body at the axis.

Let $\angle AOG = \theta$, $OG = h$, and let the moment of inertia about the axis through G, parallel to the axis of rotation, be Mk^2.

The moment of inertia about the axis of rotation is therefore $M(k^2+h^2)$. In the position shown, the moment of all the forces acting on the body about the axis through O is $Mgh \sin \theta$.

$$\therefore \qquad \frac{d^2\theta}{dt^2} = -\frac{Mgh \sin \theta}{M(k^2+h^2)}$$

$$\text{or} \qquad \frac{d^2\theta}{dt^2} = -\frac{gh}{k^2+h^2} \sin \theta. \tag{i}$$

If θ is small we have, $\sin \theta = \theta$ approximately, and the equation becomes

$$\frac{d^2\theta}{dt^2} = -\frac{gh}{k^2+h^2}\,\theta. \qquad (ii)$$

This represents a simple harmonic motion of period T where

$$T = 2\pi \sqrt{\left(\frac{k^2+h^2}{hg}\right)}.$$

In the case of a simple pendulum, of length l, the period is $2\pi\sqrt{(l/g)}$; hence $(k^2+h^2)/h$ corresponds to l, and a simple pendulum of length $(k^2+h^2)/h$ would have the same period of oscillation as the compound pendulum. The expression $(k^2+h^2)/h$ is therefore called the **length of the equivalent simple pendulum.**

Equation (i) can be integrated once, and the result is

$$\left(\frac{d\theta}{dt}\right)^2 = \frac{2gh}{k^2+h^2}\cos\theta + C \qquad (iii)$$

where C is determined by the initial value of $d\theta/dt$.

Equation (iii) gives the value of the angular velocity for any value of θ, but this is obtained more easily from the principle of energy, as explained in 9.15. In fact, we have derived equation (iii), which is essentially the equation of energy, from equation (i), which expresses the principle of angular momentum, thus verifying that the two are equivalent.

Equation (iii) cannot be integrated again to give θ in terms of t without introducing what are called Elliptic Functions.

The study of these is a branch of advanced mathematics, and we can only deal here with the connection between θ and the time when θ is small, i.e. we must use equation (ii).

This equation gives

$$\theta = A\cos(\omega t + B)$$

where $\omega = \sqrt{\left(\dfrac{gh}{k^2+h^2}\right)}$, and A, B are constants depending on the initial values of $d\theta/dt$ and θ.

9.20. Centre of oscillation

The point O where the plane through the centre of gravity perpendicular to the axis of rotation cuts this axis is called the *centre of suspension.*

If l is the length of the equivalent simple pendulum, then, as in the last paragraph,

$$l = \frac{k^2 + h^2}{h}.$$

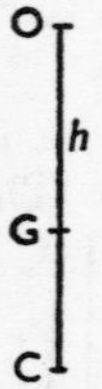

Produce OG (Fig. 9.13) to C, so that OC $= l$. Then C is called the *centre of oscillation*. If the whole mass were collected at the centre of oscillation and suspended by a thread from the centre of suspension O its angular motion and time of oscillation would be the same as that of the body under the same initial conditions.

FIG. 9.13

If the body is suspended from C, then since CG $= l-h$, the length of the simple equivalent pendulum l' is now given by

$$l' = \frac{k^2 + (l-h)^2}{l-h}.$$

But

$$k^2 = lh - h^2$$

$\therefore \qquad l' = \frac{lh - h^2 + l^2 - 2lh + h^2}{l-h} = \frac{l(l-h)}{l-h} = l$

$\therefore \qquad\qquad\qquad l' = l.$

Hence the period of oscillation about C is the same as that about O, and if we can find two points, on a line through the centre of gravity and on opposite sides of it, about which the periods of oscillation are equal, the distance between these points is the length of the equivalent simple pendulum.

This is made use of in Kater's pendulum, which consists of a bar with two knife-edges on opposite sides of its centre of gravity and a movable mass which slides on the bar. The position of the mass is adjusted so that the times of oscillation about the two knife-edges are equal. The distance between the knife-edges then gives l, and

$$T = 2\pi\sqrt{(l/g)}.$$

T and l being known, we can calculate g.

This is a very accurate method of determining g.

9.21. Minimum time of oscillation of a compound pendulum

We have seen that the period T is given by

$$T = 2\pi \sqrt{\left(\frac{k^2 + h^2}{hg}\right)}.$$

The graph of T^2 against h has the form given in Fig. 9.14.

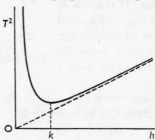

FIG. 9.14

Now, T will be a minimum when $(k^2 + h^2)/h$ or $h + k^2/h$ is a minimum. This is the case when

$$\frac{\mathrm{d}}{\mathrm{d}h}\left(h + \frac{k^2}{h}\right) = 0$$

or

$$1 - (k^2/h^2) = 0$$

i.e. when

$$h = k.$$

In this case $l = 2k$.

The period is therefore a minimum when the distance between the axis of suspension and the centre of gravity is equal to the radius of gyration about the axis through the centre of gravity parallel to the axis of suspension.

This only gives the minimum value for axes drawn in a given direction. To get the absolute minimum we should have to find the direction of the axis through the centre of gravity for which the radius of gyration is least.

9.22. EXAMPLE (i)

A heavy uniform rod AB of length 2l and mass M has a mass m attached to it at B. The whole oscillates freely about a horizontal axis through A. Prove that the time of a small oscillation is

$$4\pi \sqrt{\left[\frac{(M + 3m)l}{3(M + 2m)g}\right]}. \qquad \text{(I.E.)}$$

Let AB (Fig. 9.15) represent the rod, G its centre of gravity. The moment of inertia of the rod about the axis through A is $\frac{4}{3}Ml^2$, and that of the mass m is $4ml^2$.

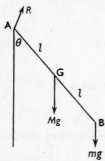

FIG. 9.15

The moment of inertia of the rod and mass is therefore

$$4\left(\frac{M+3m}{3}\right)l^2.$$

The moment of the restoring force about A when the angular displacement from the vertical is θ is

$$Mgl\sin\theta + 2mgl\sin\theta = (M+2m)gl\sin\theta.$$

Hence $\dfrac{\mathrm{d}^2\theta}{\mathrm{d}t^2} = -\dfrac{(M+2m)gl}{\frac{4}{3}(M+3m)l^2}\sin\theta$

$$= -\frac{3(M+2m)g}{4(M+3m)l}\theta \quad \text{if } \theta \text{ is small.}$$

The period of oscillation is therefore $2\pi\sqrt{\left[\dfrac{(4M+3m)l}{3(M+2m)g}\right]}$.

EXAMPLE (ii)

A cylindrical rod 60 cm long and 5 cm in radius is free to swing about a horizontal axis at right angles to its geometrical axis and intersecting it. Find the position of the axis of suspension if the length of the equivalent simple pendulum is a minimum.   (I.E.)

If k is the radius of gyration about an axis through the centre of gravity parallel to the axis of suspension, h the distance of the centre of gravity from the axis of suspension, and L the length of the equivalent simple pendulum,

$$L = \frac{k^2+h^2}{h}$$

and L is a minimum when $h = k$ (9.21).

Now we found (9.14) that the moment of inertia of a solid cylinder about an axis through its centre of gravity perpendicular to the axis of the cylinder is

$$M\left(\frac{a^2}{4} + \frac{l^2}{12}\right)$$

where a is the radius and l the length of the cylinder.

Here $a = 0.005$ m, $l = 0.6$ m,

$$\therefore \quad\quad k^2 = \left(\frac{a^2}{4} + \frac{l^2}{12}\right) = \frac{0.005^2}{4} + \frac{0.6^2}{12} = 0.0306$$

$$\therefore \quad\quad k = 0.173.$$

Hence the axis of suspension for the minimum period of oscillation must be 17·3 cm from the centre of gravity.

9.23. Motion of a flywheel acted on by a couple

If Mk^2 is the moment of inertia of the flywheel about its axis, and L is the moment of the couple,

$$\frac{d^2\theta}{dt^2} = \pm \frac{L}{Mk^2}$$

according as L tends to increase or diminish the angular velocity.

It may be noted that if the moment L of the couple is constant, $d^2\theta/dt^2$ is constant, from which $d\theta/dt$ and θ can easily be found.

For if $$\frac{d^2\theta}{dt^2} = \gamma, \text{ a constant}$$

then $$\frac{d\theta}{dt} = \gamma t + A.$$

Denoting $d\theta/dt$ by ω and its value at time $t = 0$ by ω_0, we get

$$\frac{d\theta}{dt} = \omega = \omega_0 + \gamma t \tag{1}$$

Further, $$\theta = \omega_0 t + \tfrac{1}{2}\gamma t^2 \tag{2}$$

if $\theta = 0$ at time $t = 0$.

Eliminating t from equations (1) and (2) we get

$$\omega^2 = \omega_0{}^2 + 2\gamma\theta. \tag{3}$$

The equations (1), (2), and (3) for constant angular acceleration correspond exactly to the fundamental equations of uniformly accelerated motion of a particle, namely,

$$v = u + at, \quad s = ut + \tfrac{1}{2}at^2, \quad v^2 = u^2 + 2as.$$

EXAMPLE (i)

A flywheel of mass 1 Mg and radius of gyration 1 m is rotating once every second. What is its kinetic energy and how long will it take to come to rest under a frictional torque round the axis of 60 N m?

The moment of inertia is 1000 kg m², and the angular velocity is 2π rad s⁻¹.

The kinetic energy is

$$\tfrac{1}{2} \times 1000 \times 4\pi^2 \text{ J} = 2000\pi^2 \text{ J}.$$

The equation of motion is

$$1000 \frac{\mathrm{d}^2\theta}{\mathrm{d}t^2} = -60$$

$$\therefore \qquad \frac{\mathrm{d}^2\theta}{\mathrm{d}t^2} = -0.06$$

$$\therefore \qquad \frac{\mathrm{d}\theta}{\mathrm{d}t} = -0.06\,t + C;$$

and

$$\frac{\mathrm{d}\theta}{\mathrm{d}t} = 2\pi \text{ when } t = 0$$

$$\therefore \qquad C = 2\pi$$

$$\therefore \qquad \frac{\mathrm{d}\theta}{\mathrm{d}t} = 2\pi - 0.06t.$$

Hence, $\dfrac{\mathrm{d}\theta}{\mathrm{d}t}$ is zero when

$$0.06t = 2\pi$$

or

$$t = \frac{100\pi}{3} = 104.7 \text{ s.}$$

EXAMPLE (ii)

The moment of inertia of a pulley of 16 cm diameter is 0.008 kg m² units. A long cord with a weight of mass 500 g suspended from its end is wound round the pulley. Through what angle will the pulley turn in 2 s from the instant when the weight is released? What will then be the combined kinetic energy of the pulley and weight? (Q.E.)

Let θ be the angle turned through by the pulley, x m the distance descended by the 500 g mass in time t.

Then $x = 0{\cdot}08\theta$, $\dot{x} = 0{\cdot}08\dot{\theta}$, $\ddot{x} = 0{\cdot}08\ddot{\theta}$, where $\dot{x}$ denotes dx/dt.
Let T N be the tension in the string.
The equations of motion for the pulley and the mass are

$$0{\cdot}008\ddot{\theta} = 0{\cdot}08T \qquad\qquad \text{(i)}$$

and

$$0{\cdot}5\ddot{x} = 0{\cdot}5g - T \qquad\qquad \text{(ii)}$$

Since $\ddot{x} = 0{\cdot}08\ddot{\theta}$, if the cord does not slip over the pulley, the second equation gives

$$0{\cdot}04\ddot{\theta} = 0{\cdot}5g - T$$

$$\therefore \qquad 0{\cdot}04\ddot{\theta} = 0{\cdot}5g - 0{\cdot}1\ddot{\theta}$$

$$\therefore \qquad 0{\cdot}14\ddot{\theta} = 0{\cdot}5g$$

$$\therefore \qquad 0{\cdot}14\dot{\theta} = 0{\cdot}5gt$$

the constant of integration being zero, since $\dot{\theta} = 0$ when $t = 0$;

$$\therefore \qquad 0{\cdot}14\theta = 0{\cdot}25gt^2$$

the constant of integration being zero, since $\theta = 0$ when $t = 0$.
Hence, when $t = 2$,

$$\theta = \frac{9{\cdot}8}{0{\cdot}14} = 70 \text{ rad.}$$

Also $\dot{\theta} = 70$ when $t = 2$, and the combined kinetic energy is
$$\tfrac{1}{2}(0{\cdot}008)\dot{\theta}^2 + \tfrac{1}{2}(0{\cdot}5)(0{\cdot}08\dot{\theta})^2 = 0{\cdot}0056\dot{\theta}^2$$

$$= 0{\cdot}0056 \times 70^2 \text{ J} = 27{\cdot}44 \text{ J.}$$

This problem can also be solved by using the principle of energy.
If $\dot{\theta}$ and $\dot{x}$ are the velocities of the pulley and mass when the latter has descended a distance x the kinetic energy of the two is

$$0{\cdot}004\dot{\theta}^2 + 0{\cdot}25\dot{x}^2 = 0{\cdot}875\dot{x}^2.$$

But the loss of potential energy is $0{\cdot}5\,gx$.

$$\therefore \qquad 0{\cdot}875\dot{x}^2 = 0{\cdot}5gx.$$

The acceleration, a, is obtained by differentiating with respect to t. We get

$$\therefore \qquad 0{\cdot}875(2\dot{x}\ddot{x}) = 0{\cdot}5g\dot{x}$$

$$\therefore \qquad a = \ddot{x} = g/3{\cdot}5.$$

The acceleration of the falling weight is therefore constant.
The distance moved by the mass in 2 s is therefore

$$\tfrac{1}{2} \times \frac{g}{3{\cdot}5} \times 4 = \frac{19{\cdot}6}{3{\cdot}5} \text{ m} = 5{\cdot}6 \text{ m.}$$

The angle turned through by the pulley is therefore

$$\frac{5 \cdot 6}{0 \cdot 08} = 70 \text{ rad.}$$

Also, when $t = 2$, the velocity of the mass is $2g/3 \cdot 5 = \dfrac{19 \cdot 6}{3 \cdot 5}$
$= 5 \cdot 6 \text{ ms}^{-1}$.

The total kinetic energy is therefore

$$0 \cdot 875 \dot{x}^2 = 0 \cdot 875 (5 \cdot 6)^2 \text{ J} = 27 \cdot 44 \text{ J.}$$

EXAMPLE (iii)

*A string passes round the rim of a wheel of radius a fixed with its axis
horizontal and carries masses m_1 and m_2 at its ends. Assuming that
friction at the axis of the wheel is negligible, show that, if $m_2 > m_1$,
the acceleration of the masses is*

$$\frac{(m_2 - m_1)g}{m_2 + m_1 + I/a^2},$$

where I is the moment of inertia of the wheel about its axis.

Let the tensions in the two parts of the string be T_1 and T_2.
T_2 is not equal to T_1, unless the rim of the wheel is smooth, in which
case the string will slip over the wheel and the wheel will not rotate.
The forces acting on the masses and the wheel are as shown (Fig.
9.16).

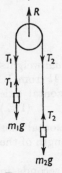

FIG. 9.16

If m_2 is descending at time t with acceleration f, m_1 is ascending
with acceleration f. Also if ω is the angular velocity of the wheel at
this instant the equations of motion are:

For m_1: $\qquad\qquad m_1 f = T_1 - m_1 g.$ $\qquad\qquad$ (i)

For m_2: $\qquad\qquad m_2 f = m_2 g - T_2.$ $\qquad\qquad$ (ii)

For the wheel: $\qquad\quad I \dfrac{d\omega}{dt} = (T_2 - T_1)a.$ $\qquad\qquad$ (iii)

As there are four unknown quantities T_1, T_2, f and ω, an additional equation is necessary, and this is provided by the condition that the string does not slip over the wheel. The linear velocity of any element of the string in contact with the wheel is $a\omega$, and the linear acceleration is therefore $a(\mathrm{d}\omega/\mathrm{d}t)$. Hence for no slipping

$$a\frac{\mathrm{d}\omega}{\mathrm{d}t} = f. \tag{iv}$$

Thus equation (iii) can be written

$$\frac{I}{a^2} \times f = T_2 - T_1.$$

Substituting for T_2 and T_1 from equations (i) and (ii) we get

$$\left(\frac{I}{a^2} + m_2 + m_1\right)f = (m_2 - m_1)g$$

which shows that the acceleration of the masses is constant.

It might be noted that this result can be used with Attwood's Machine (cf. 3.18–19). It shows that to correct for the rotation of the wheel I/a^2 must be added to $(m_2 + m_1)$ in the expression for the acceleration of the moving masses, or alternatively, $I/2a^2$ must be added to both m_2 and m_1.

EXAMPLES 9.3

1. A rod AB of length l and negligible weight has two equal weights w attached to the end B and to a point M distant $\frac{1}{3}l$ from B. Find the period of small oscillations about a horizontal axis through A.   (I.E.)

2. A uniform bar of length $2a$ oscillates about a horizontal axis distant c from the centre of the bar; prove that the length of the simple equivalent pendulum is $c + \frac{1}{3}a^2/c$.

   Assuming that a simple pendulum 1 m long beats seconds (in swinging from rest to rest), prove that the least period of complete oscillation for a bar 1 m long is about 1·5 s, and that the horizontal axis is then placed about 29 cm above the centre.
                                                                        (Q.E.)

3. Calculate the period of small oscillations of a uniform rod, 1·8 m long, about a horizontal axis through one end, when a particle of weight equal to that of the rod is attached to its mid-point.   (H.C.)

4. A trap door, 1·2 m square and of uniform thickness, is hanging vertically by its hinges. If the door is set swinging through a small angle, find the periodic time, neglecting the friction of the hinges. (Q.E.)

5. A uniform circular disc of radius a has a particle of mass equal to that of the disc fixed to a point of its circumference. The disc can turn freely about a fixed horizontal axis through its centre at right angles to its plane. Assuming that the radius of gyration of the disc about this axis is $a/\sqrt{2}$, show that the length of the simple equivalent pendulum for small oscillations of the system about its position of stable equilibrium is $3a/2$. (H.C.)

6. A wheel has a diameter of 0·6 m and a mass of 25 kg which may be regarded as distributed uniformly round the rim. Calculate the energy stored in the wheel when it is making 600 revmin^{-1}. If the wheel is to be stopped in 50 s by a brake pressing on the rim, calculate the pressure required, assuming that the coefficient of friction is 0·1 between the brake-block and the rim. (H.C.)

7. A flywheel of mass 100 kg is rotating about its axis at 150 revmin^{-1}, and it is acted on by a constant frictional couple, so that after 10 s it is rotating at 100 revmin^{-1}. Find how many more revolutions it will make before it is brought to rest. If the value of the couple is 50 Nm, find the radius of gyration of the wheel. (N.U.3)

8. A wheel spins about a fixed axle, and a constant frictional couple is exerted on it by the bearings. If the wheel is set spinning at 200 revmin^{-1} and comes to rest in $1\frac{1}{2}$ min, find how many revolutions it makes in this time.

   If the moment of inertia of the wheel about the axle is 270 kgm^2, find the moment of the frictional couple. (N.U.3)

9. A solid flywheel of diameter 0·6 m, bored for shaft and of mass 450 kg, is keyed on to a horizontal shaft of diameter 10 cm and of mass 50 kg. What is the kinetic energy of the flywheel and shaft at 1200 revmin^{-1}? What uniform retarding couple would reduce the flywheel to rest in 2 min, and through what angle would it turn in this time? (Q.E.)

10. Two equal circular wheels, each of mass 100 kg, and radius 48 cm, are rotating freely in the same horizontal plane about their centres.

    A connecting rod of mass 40 kg is pin-jointed to the rim of each, and is always parallel to the line of centres of the wheels. Show that the angular velocity of the wheels is constant in the absence of friction, and find the kinetic energy of the whole system if each wheel makes 50 rev min^{-1} and its mass is concentrated in its rim.

If the system is reduced to rest in 60 revolutions by the action of equal retarding torques on each wheel, find the torques, assuming that they are constant. (Q.E.)

11. A uniform circular cylinder of mass M can rotate freely about its axis, which is fixed in a horizontal position; a light inextensible string is coiled round the cylinder and carries at its free end a particle of mass m. If the system is allowed to move, show that the particle will descend with uniform acceleration.

$$\frac{2mg}{M+2m}$$ (B.Sc.)

12. The mass of a flywheel is 50 kg and a mass of 5 kg hangs by a string wrapped round the axle, which is horizontal and has a radius of 5 cm. If the mass of 5 kg falls through 6 m from rest in 16 s, show that the radius of gyration of the flywheel is a little over 22 cm. (B.Sc.)

13. A bucket of mass m hangs at the end of a light rope which is coiled round a wheel of mass M. If the wheel can rotate freely about its axis, which is horizontal, and if its entire mass is supposed concentrated in its rim, find the speed of the bucket when it has fallen a distance x from rest. (I.S.)

14. A mass of 5 kg hangs at the end of a light cord which is wrapped many times round the circumference of a pulley of 0·9 m diameter. The pulley is mounted upon a horizontal axis, about which it is free to turn. On starting from rest the mass is found to descend 4·8 m in 5 s. Show that if there is no friction at the bearing the moment of inertia of the pulley is about 25 kg m² units. (Q.E.)

15. A flywheel of 1 kg mass and radius of gyration 15 cm is set revolving with an angular velocity of 20 rev s^{-1}, and is reduced to rest in 3 min by the action of a constant frictional couple at the bearings of the axis. Find the magnitude of this couple. If a string passes without slipping over the rim of the wheel, which is 20 cm in radius, and carries at both ends masses, one of which is 30 g, find the mass of the other so that when the wheel is set in motion this mass may descend with constant velocity. (I.E.)

16. A weight of mass 2·5 kg is attached to a string which is wrapped round the rim of a flywheel of radius 30 cm and mass 150 kg and in descending causes the flywheel to rotate. After descending 5·4 m in 6 s from rest, the weight is suddenly detached and the flywheel

thereafter makes 50 revolutions before coming to rest. If the frictional forces remain constant throughout and are equivalent to a tangential force of F N at the rim, calculate the magnitude of F and the radius of gyration of the flywheel. (I.E.)

17. A uniform solid cylinder of mass 28 kg and diameter 0·3 m can rotate about its axis, which is horizontal. One end of a string is attached to the cylinder around which it is wrapped and the other end to a mass of 2 kg hanging freely. If the system is started from the rest and a frictional couple of 1·5Nm acts on the cylinder, find the distance the 2-kg mass will descend in 3 s.
(I.E.)

18. A pulley of mass 20 g, radius 10 cm, and radius of gyration 6 cm rotates about a horizontal axis through its centre. The pulley carries a light inextensible string, sufficiently rough not to slip on the pulley, and masses of 40 g and 50 g are attached to the ends of the string. If friction at the axis of the pulley can be neglected, find the acceleration of the masses when motion takes place.

Find also the least frictional couple acting on the pulley that will prevent motion. (I.E.)

19. Prove that the kinetic energy of a body rotating about a fixed axis with angular velocity ω is $\frac{1}{2}I\omega^2$, where I is the moment of inertia of the body about the axis.

Masses of 2 and 3 g are attached to a light string which passes over a pulley of mass 5 g and radius 4 cm. If the system starts from rest, obtain the energy equation when the heavier mass has fallen x cm. If the acceleration of the system be $g/10$, determine the radius of gyration of the pulley. (I.E.)

20. Two weights of mass 1 and 1·2 kg respectively are connected by a thin light string hanging over a heavy pulley of diameter 20 cm and moment of inertia 2×10^{-2} SI units. No slipping occurs between the string and the pulley, and it is observed that the heavier weight descends 2 m from rest in 4 s.

Find the value of the constant friction torque exerted on the pulley by its bearings during motion. (Q.E.)

21. Explain what is meant by the principle of angular momentum. A uniform straight tube, of mass M and length $2a$, free to rotate about its mid-point, with closed ends, contains a quantity of powder of total mass m uniformly distributed along its length. It is set in rotation in a horizontal plane with angular velocity ω, and the powder slips along to the ends of the tube and remains there. Show that when all the powder is collected at the ends the angular velocity is reduced to $(M+m)\omega/(M+3m)$. (B.Sc.)

9.24. General motion of a rigid body in two dimensions

We have so far confined our considerations to the motion of
a rigid body about a *fixed* axis. We now proceed to the more
general case of motion in two dimensions with no point of the
body fixed.

It can be shown that a rigid body can be brought from any
one position to any other position by first moving some chosen
point of it (say its centre of mass) to its new position without
rotation, and then rotating the body about the point.

The first part of this displacement is known as a translation;
every particle of the rigid body moves the same distance in the
same direction. In the second part of the displacement every
particle describes an arc of a circle about the chosen point.

For example, the rectangle ABCD (Fig. 9.17) can be moved
to some other position A'B'C'D' by first moving ABCD without
rotation to the position A"B"C"D" and then rotating A"B"C"D"
about G' into the position A'B'C'D'. In the motion of translation every particle of the rectangle moves a distance equal
and parallel to GG'.

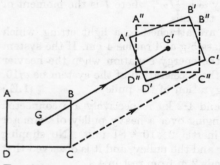

Fig. 9.17

It follows that if the body is moving in a continuous
manner its motion at any instant may be considered as compounded of a velocity of translation equal to that of some point
of the body, e.g. the centre of mass, and an angular velocity
about an axis through the chosen point.

In fact, it can be shown that

I. The kinetic energy of a rigid body at any instant is equal to
   the kinetic energy of the whole mass assumed concentrated

at the centre of mass G, and moving with the velocity of G, together with the kinetic energy of the rotational motion about G,

and

II. The angular momentum of a rigid body at any instant about any axis is equal to the angular momentum, about that axis, of the whole mass assumed concentrated at the centre of mass G and moving with the velocity of G, together with the angular momentum, about a parallel axis through G, of the rotational motion about G.

9.25. Let M be the mass of the body, V the velocity of its centre of mass, ω the angular velocity about some axis through its centre of mass and Mk^2 the moment of inertia about that axis.

Therefore the kinetic energy of the rigid body

$$= \tfrac{1}{2}MV^2 + \tfrac{1}{2}Mk^2\omega^2.$$

Also, the angular momentum of the rigid body about the axis through some point O parallel to the axis of rotation $= MVp + Mk^2\omega$, where p is the length of the perpendicular OA from O on the direction of motion of the centre of mass. (Care must be taken with the signs of the two parts of the angular momentum. In Fig. 9.18 they are both positive.)

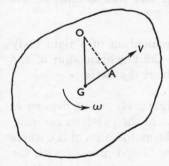

Fig. 9.18

For example, if a circular disc of radius a and mass m rolls along a rough horizontal plane with angular velocity ω, the velocity of the centre of mass $= \omega a$.

Therefore kinetic energy of translational motion $= \tfrac{1}{2}m(\omega a)^2$.

But, kinetic energy of rotational motion about a horizontal axis through the centre of mass $G = \frac{1}{2}I\omega^2$ where $I = \frac{1}{2}ma^2$.

Therefore total kinetic energy $= \frac{3}{4}m\omega^2a^2$.

We note that this can be written as $\frac{1}{2}I'\omega^2$, where $I' = \frac{3}{2}ma^2$, that is, I' is the moment of inertia of the disc about the parallel axis through A, the point of the circumference in contact with the plane. This point A, as we have seen previously, is instantaneously at rest.

Also the angular momentum of the disc about the horizontal axis through $G = I\omega = \frac{1}{2}ma^2\omega$.

But, about the parallel axis through A the angular momentum of the disc $= (m\omega a)a + I\omega = \frac{3}{2}ma^2\omega = I'\omega$.

9.26. The equations of two-dimensional motion of a rigid body

Two basic postulates have to be made relating the motion of translation and the motion of rotation of the rigid body to the forces producing the motion.

They are the *Principles of Linear and Angular Momentum*, which may be stated:

I. The rate of change of linear momentum of a rigid body in any direction equals the sum of the components of the external forces in that direction.

II. The rate of change of angular momentum of a rigid body about any *fixed* axis is equal to the algebraic sum of the moments of the external forces about that axis.

Now the linear momentum of a rigid body, being defined as the vector sum of the linear momenta of the particles comprising the body, can be shown to equal the momentum of the whole mass concentrated at the mass-centre G and moving with the velocity of G. Thus the principle of linear momentum leads to:

(a) *The motion of the centre of mass of a rigid body, acted on by any forces, is the same as if the whole mass were collected at the centre of mass, and all the forces were applied at that point parallel to their former directions.*

If M is the mass of the body and V the velocity of the centre of mass of the body at time t, we have

$M(\mathrm{d}V/\mathrm{d}t)$ = sum of the components of all the forces in the direction of V.   (i)

Similarly, because of the relation II of 9.24, the principle of angular momentum leads to:

(*b*) *The rate of change of angular momentum of the body about the axis through the instantaneous position of the centre of mass perpendicular to the plane of motion is equal to the algebraic sum of the moments of the external forces about the axis.*

In other words, the rotational motion of the body at any instant is the same as if the centre of mass were fixed and the same forces acted on the body.

If I is the moment of inertia of the body about the axis of rotation through the instantaneous position of G, and ω is the angular velocity about this axis at time t, we have

$$I\frac{\mathrm{d}\omega}{\mathrm{d}t} = \text{Moment of all the forces about this axis} \qquad \text{(ii)}$$

Equations (i) and (ii), together with any geometrical conditions, suffice to solve the problem of the motion of a rigid body in two dimensions when subject to any set of forces.

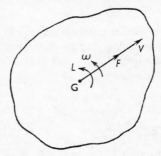

FIG. 9.19

The results (*a*) and (*b*) on which equations (i) and (ii) are based can perhaps be appreciated if it is remembered that any set of coplanar forces acting on a rigid body are equivalent to a force F acting through the centre of mass G, together with a couple of moment L. This force F equals the vector-sum of all the forces acting on the body, and may be pictured as responsible for the motion of translation of the body, while the couple, whose moment L equals the moment of all the forces about an axis through G, produces the rotational motion about this axis. V is in the direction of F and ω in the direction of L, as shown in Fig. 9 19.

9.27. EXAMPLE (i)

A wheel with a diameter of 0·9 m, and a mass of 32 kg, which may be regarded as distributed uniformly round the rim, is rolling along a horizontal road at a speed of 18 kmh⁻¹. Calculate the energy stored in the wheel.

If it comes to a hill rising 1 in 5 along the road, how far will it go before it stops? (In a rolling motion no work is done against friction.)
(H.C.)

The moment of inertia of the wheel about its axis of rotation is

$$32(0·45)^2 \, \text{kg} \, \text{m}^2.$$

Since the centre is moving at $18\,000/3600$ ms⁻¹, the angular velocity is $5 \div 0·45 = \frac{100}{9}$ rads⁻¹.

The kinetic energy due to rotation $= \dfrac{1}{2} \times 32(0·45)^2 \times \dfrac{100^2}{9^2}$ J.

The kinetic energy due to translation $= \frac{1}{2} \times 32 \times 25$ J.

The total kinetic energy $= 400 + 400 = 800$ J.

The wheel will run up the hill until the gain of potential energy is equal to the kinetic energy on the level (assuming that no change in speed occurs when it begins to mount the hill).

Hence, if x m is the vertical height it rises,

$$32 \times 9·8 x = 800$$

$$\therefore \qquad\qquad x = \frac{800}{32 \times 9·8} = 2·55.$$

The distance it goes up the slope is 12·75 m.

EXAMPLE (ii)

A uniform solid sphere of mass M and radius a rolls down an inclined plane, rough enough to prevent sliding; find the motion.

Let α be the inclination of the plane, O (Fig. 9.20) the point of contact when the sphere was initially at rest, C the centre of the sphere, A the point on the sphere which was originally in contact with O, and N the point of contact at time t.

Take O as origin, ON as axis of x, CA as the line fixed in the body, and the normal to the plane as the line fixed in space for measuring the angular velocity, and let $\angle ACN = \theta$.

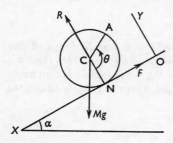

Fig. 9.20

The external forces acting on the sphere are the friction F up the plane, the reaction R perpendicular to the plane, and the weight of the sphere vertically downwards.

Considering the motion of the centre of mass parallel and perpendicular to the plane,

$$M\ddot{x} = Mg \sin \alpha - F \tag{i}$$

and

$$M\ddot{y} = R - Mg \cos \alpha. \tag{ii}$$

Taking moments about the centre of mass C,

$$Mk^2\ddot{\theta} = Fa \tag{iii}$$

Now since the sphere remains in contact with the plane

$$\ddot{y} = 0$$

$\therefore$

$$R = Mg \cos \alpha.$$

Since there is no slipping,

$$x = a\theta$$

$\therefore$

$$\ddot{x} = a\ddot{\theta}. \tag{iv}$$

Also $k^2 = \frac{2}{5}a^2$, and from (iii) and (iv) we get

$$F = \frac{2}{5}Ma\ddot{\theta} = \frac{2}{5}M\ddot{x}$$

$\therefore$ from (i)

$$\frac{7}{5}M\ddot{x} = Mg \sin \alpha$$

$\therefore$

$$\ddot{x} = \frac{5}{7}g \sin \alpha.$$

From (i) $F = \frac{2}{7}Mg \sin \alpha$

and $R = Mg \cos \alpha$

$\therefore$ $F/R = \frac{2}{7}\tan \alpha.$

The coefficient of friction necessary to prevent sliding is therefore not less than $\frac{2}{7}\tan \alpha$.

EXAMPLE (iii)

A thin uniform rod of length 2a, attached to a smooth hinge at one end O, is allowed to fall from a horizontal position; show that the horizontal strain on the hinge is greatest when the rod is inclined at an angle of 45° to the vertical, and that the vertical strain is then $\frac{11}{8}$ times the weight of the rod.

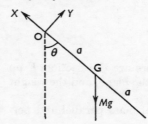

FIG. 9.21

Let G (Fig. 9.21) be the centre of gravity of the rod.

Let M be the mass of the rod, and θ the inclination of the rod to the vertical at time t. Let X and Y be the components along and perpendicular to the rod of the reaction acting on it at O.

The velocity of G is $a(d\theta/dt)$ perpendicular to the rod, so that its acceleration is $a(d^2\theta/dt^2)$ perpendicular to the rod and $a(d\theta/dt)^2$ towards O (since G is moving in a circle of radius a with variable angular velocity $d\theta/dt$).

Therefore the equations of motion of G are

$$Ma \frac{d^2\theta}{dt^2} = Y - Mg \sin \theta \qquad \text{(i}(a)\text{)}$$

and

$$Ma \left(\frac{d\theta}{dt}\right)^2 = X - Mg \cos \theta \qquad \text{(i}(b)\text{)}$$

and taking moments about an axis through G parallel to the axis of rotation through O we have

$$I \frac{d^2\theta}{dt^2} = -Ya \qquad \text{(ii)}$$

where $I = \frac{1}{3}Ma^2$.

From (i(a)) and (ii) we get

$$Ma^2\ddot{\theta} = \tfrac{1}{3}Ma^2\ddot{\theta} - Mga\sin\theta$$

$$\therefore \qquad \tfrac{4}{3}Ma^2\ddot{\theta} = -Mga\sin\theta \qquad\qquad \text{(iii)}$$

which we note is the equation of angular momentum about the fixed axis through O, as applied earlier in 9.19, and could be written down directly.

Therefore from (ii) and (iii) or from (i(a)) and (iii)

$$Y = -\tfrac{1}{3}Ma\ddot{\theta} = \tfrac{1}{4}Mg\sin\theta.$$

Integrating (iii), or using the equation of energy, we get

$$\left(\frac{\mathrm{d}\theta}{\mathrm{d}t}\right)^2 = \frac{3g}{2a}\cos\theta + C.$$

Since $\mathrm{d}\theta/\mathrm{d}t = 0$ when $\theta = \tfrac{1}{2}\pi$, C must be zero.
Therefore from (i(b)),

$$X = \tfrac{3}{2}Mg\cos\theta + Mg\cos\theta = \tfrac{5}{2}Mg\cos\theta.$$

The horizontal pressure at O

$$X\sin\theta - Y\cos\theta = \tfrac{5}{2}Mg\sin\theta\cos\theta - \tfrac{1}{4}Mg\sin\theta\cos\theta$$

$$= \tfrac{9}{4}Mg\sin\theta\cos\theta$$

$$= \tfrac{9}{8}Mg\sin 2\theta,$$

which is obviously a maximum when $2\theta = 90°$, i.e. $\theta = 45°$.

The vertical pressure at O is

$$X\cos\theta + Y\sin\theta = \tfrac{5}{2}Mg\cos^2\theta + \tfrac{1}{4}Mg\sin^2\theta$$

and when $\theta = 45°$ this becomes

$$\tfrac{5}{4}Mg + \tfrac{1}{8}Mg = \tfrac{11}{8}Mg.$$

EXAMPLE (iv)

The shank of a cotton reel, of mass m, is a cylinder of radius a and the moment of inertia of the reel about its axis is mk^2. The free end of the cotton is held, and the reel falls, unwinding the cotton, the axis of the reel remaining in a fixed horizontal direction. Show that the acceleration is $ga^2/(a^2+k^2)$, and find the tension of the cotton.

Show also that the upward acceleration that must be given to the free end of the cotton to keep the centre of gravity of the reel at rest is ga^2/k^2.

(B.Sc.)

In Fig. 9.22, the end of the cotton is held at O. Let T be the tension in the cotton and ω the angular velocity of the reel at time t.

If the axis of the reel is at a distance y below O at time t, the acceleration of the centre of gravity is d^2y/dt^2, and the equations of motion are

$$m\,\frac{d^2y}{dt^2} = mg - T \tag{i}$$

and

$$mk^2\,\frac{d\omega}{dt} = Ta. \tag{ii}$$

But the acceleration of the point A of the cotton as it leaves the reel is $d^2y/dt^2 - a(d\omega/dt)$ and is obviously zero. Hence

$$\frac{d^2y}{dt^2} = a\,\frac{d\omega}{dt}. \tag{iii}$$

Fig. 9.22

From (i) and (ii)

$$m\left(a\,\frac{d^2y}{dt^2} + k^2\,\frac{d\omega}{dt}\right) = mga$$

$$\therefore \qquad \frac{d^2y}{dt^2}\left(a + \frac{k^2}{a}\right) = ga$$

$$\therefore \qquad \frac{d^2y}{dt^2} = \frac{ga^2}{a^2 + k^2}.$$

Hence

$$T = m\left(g - \frac{d^2y}{dt^2}\right) = \frac{mgk^2}{a^2 + k^2}.$$

If O is given an upward acceleration f, let T_1 be the new tension in the string and ω_1 the angular velocity of the reel at time t.

Since the centre of gravity of the reel is at rest,

$$T_1 - mg = 0$$

and since the reel is rotating with angular acceleration $d\omega_1/dt$

$$mk^2\,\frac{d\omega_1}{dt} = T_1 \times a.$$

$$\therefore \qquad k^2\,\frac{d\omega_1}{dt} = ga.$$

But the acceleration of the point A of the cotton is now $a(d\omega_1/dt)$ and also equals f. Hence

$$a\,\frac{d\omega_1}{dt} = f$$

$$\therefore \qquad f = \frac{ga^2}{k^2}.$$

EXAMPLES 9.4

1. Show that the acceleration of a uniform circular disc, rolling down a plane of inclination α which is rough enough to prevent sliding, is $\frac{2}{3}g \sin \alpha$.

2. Show that the acceleration of a thin uniform circular ring, rolling down a plane of inclination α which is rough enough to prevent sliding, is $\frac{1}{2}g \sin \alpha$. Show also that the least coefficient of friction necessary to prevent sliding is $\frac{1}{2} \tan \alpha$.

3. One end of a thread, which is wound on to a reel, is fixed, and the reel falls in a vertical line, its axis being horizontal and the unwound part of the thread vertical. If the reel is a solid cylinder of radius a and mass M, show that the acceleration of the centre of the reel is $\frac{2}{3}g$ and that the tension of the thread is $\frac{1}{3}Mg$.

4. A girder is being pushed horizontally on three rollers at a speed 200 m h^{-1}, the diameter of each roller being 15 cm; find the speed of their forward motion if there is no slipping. If the girder has a mass of 1 Mg, and each roller 100 kg, find the kinetic energy of the system. (I.E.)

5. The total mass of a railway truck was 2 Mg. It had two pairs of wheels, each pair having a mass of 240 kg with the attached axle. The radius of gyration of each wheel was 25 cm, and the distance from the centre of the axle to the rail was 36 cm. Calculate the kinetic energy of the truck when travelling at 18 ms^{-1}. If it can be brought to rest by the brakes in 80 s, without slipping of the wheels on the rails, find the retarding force, supposed constant, exerted by the rails. (I.E.)

6. Prove that the moment of inertia of a uniform cylindrical tube of mass M, about its axis, is equal to $\frac{1}{2}M(a^2+b^2)$, where a and b are the internal and external radii of the tube.

   The tube starts from rest and rolls, with its axis horizontal, down an inclined plane of inclination α. Show that T, the time occupied in travelling a distance l along the plane, is given by

$$l\left(3+\frac{a^2}{b^2}\right) = gT^2 \sin \alpha.$$

7. A circular cylinder of radius r has its centre of mass in its axis, and has a radius of gyration k about this axis. Prove that, when it rolls down a plane of inclination α, the acceleration is

$$\frac{r^2 g \sin a}{r^2 + k^2}.$$

(N.U.3)

8. Prove that if the rotational velocity of a rigid body is zero the sum of the moments of the forces acting on it about its centre of mass must be zero, even if the body has an acceleration of translation.

The centre of gravity of a table is 1·2 m above a smooth horizontal floor and midway between the front and back pair of legs, which are 1·5 m apart. The table, which has a mass of M kg, is being accelerated by a force $\frac{1}{4}Mg$ N, acting horizontally 0·9 m above the floor in a direction from the middle of the back to the middle of the front pair of legs. Find the upward thrust of the floor on each pair of legs. (N.U.3)

9. A fine circular hoop of weight W is free to move about a fixed horizontal tangent. It falls over from the position in which it is vertical so that its centre describes a circle in a vertical plane perpendicular to the tangent. Show that, in the positions when the hoop is vertical, the stress on the support is $\frac{11}{3}W$ or W. (H.C.)

10. A uniform rod of weight W, free to turn about a fixed smooth pivot at one end, is held horizontally and released. Prove that when in the subsequent motion the rod makes an angle θ with the vertical the pressure on the pivot is $\frac{1}{4}W\sqrt{(1+99\cos^2\theta)}$.

11. A uniform solid circular cylinder makes complete revolutions under gravity about a horizontal generator. Show that the supports must be able to bear at least 11/3 times the weight of the cylinder. (C.S.)

12. A uniform circular lamina of weight W can turn in a vertical plane about an axis at right angles to its plane through a point in its circumference. If it starts from rest from the position in which the diameter through this point is horizontal, prove that the horizontal and vertical components of the pressure on the axis, when this diameter makes an angle θ with the horizontal, are
$$W\sin 2\theta \text{ and } \tfrac{1}{3}W(4-3\cos 2\theta). \quad \text{(B.Sc.)}$$

13. A uniform lamina, in the form of a square ABCD of side $2a$, oscillates in its own plane about a horizontal axis through A perpendicular to its plane. In the extreme position a side of the square is directed vertically downwards. Show that the greatest velocity of the corner C is $[6ga(\sqrt{2}-1)]^{\frac{1}{4}}$. Prove that the stress on the axis, when AC is vertical, is very nearly 1·44 times the weight of the lamina. (B.Sc.)

14. A uniform cube swings about one of its edges, which is horizontal, and in the highest position, the centroid is level with the axis of

rotation. Find the stress on the axis in any position, and show that it varies between $\frac{1}{4}W$ and $\frac{5}{2}W$, where W is the weight of the cube. (The moment of inertia of a cube, of mass M and edge $2a$, about an axis through its centroid parallel to an edge is $\frac{2}{3}Ma^2$.)

(B.Sc.)

15. A uniform cube is free to turn about one edge which is horizontal. Show that the length of the equivalent simple pendulum is $\frac{2}{3}a$, where a is the length of a diagonal of one of the faces. Also show that if the cube starts from rest in its highest position the vertical component of pressure on the fixed edge vanishes when the cube has turned through an angle $\cos^{-1}(\frac{1}{3})$.

(S.)

16. A cylinder, of radius a, mass M, and moment of inertia Mk^2 about its axis, turns freely about a light axle which is supported by and slides along two smooth horizontal bars perpendicular to its length. A light string is wrapped round the cylinder and the free end passes horizontally over a smooth fixed pulley and supports a mass m. Show that, when the system moves freely, the tension of the string is

$$Mmk^2g/\{(M+m)k^2+ma^2\}.$$

(B.Sc.)

REVISION EXAMPLES C

1. A particle is projected with speed u from the lowest point of a fixed smooth hollow sphere of radius a so as to slide on the inner surface. Prove that, if $5ga > u^2 > 2ga$, the particle leaves the sphere at a height $(u^2+ga)/3g$ above the starting-point.

   If $u = \sqrt{(7ga/2)}$, show that the particle leaves the sphere and strikes it at the starting-point.

(L.A.)

2. A particle is slightly displaced from rest at the highest point of a fixed smooth sphere of radius a. After leaving the surface of the sphere the particle moves freely under gravity. Find the magnitude and direction of the velocity with which the particle strikes a fixed horizontal plane touching the sphere at its lowest point.

(L.A.)

3. A small mass m is attached by a fine light inextensible string of length a to a fixed point O. When at rest vertically below O the mass is projected horizontally with speed u, where $u^2 = kga$. Obtain the expression for the tension in the string when it is inclined at an angle θ to the downward vertical and deduce the minimum value of k if the mass is to describe a complete circle in a vertical plane.

If k exceeds this minimum value, show that the difference in the greatest and least tensions in the string is the same whatever value k may then have.   (L.A.)

4. A particle of mass m is attached to a point O by a string of length l. The particle is held at a point C, at a distance $l\sqrt{3}/2$ from O and on the same level, and then dropped. Show that the impulse in the string when it tightens is $\frac{1}{2}m\sqrt{(gl)}$, and that immediately afterwards the tension in the string is $5mg/4$.   (I.S.)

5. A car is travelling round a circular track of radius r with speed u. Show that if there is no side-thrust on the wheels the track must be banked at an angle $\tan^{-1}(u^2/gr)$ with the horizontal. If the car now travels round the banked track at a speed $v(>u)$, show that the side-thrust on the wheels is $\dfrac{W(v^2-u^2)}{(u^4+g^2r^2)^{\frac{1}{2}}}$, where W is the weight of the car.   (I.E.)

6. A is a fixed point at height h above a perfectly inelastic smooth horizontal plane. A light inextensible string of length l $(>h)$ has one end attached to A and the other to a heavy particle. The particle is held at the level of A, with the string taut, and released from rest. Show that when the particle is next instantaneously at rest its height above the plane is h^5/l^4.   (L.A.)

7. A light rod of length 0·6 m, freely hinged at the upper end, hangs vertically and has a particle of mass 500 g attached to the lower end. If the particle is projected horizontally with velocity 4·8 $\mathrm{m\,s^{-1}}$, show that the rod will not quite reach the position in which the particle is vertically above the hinge. Find the tension in the rod when it is horizontal, and the angle which the rod makes with the vertical when there is no stress in it.   (I.S.)

8. Find the period of revolution of a conical pendulum. The ends of a light string of length $2a$ are attached to two points A and B in the same vertical line; A is above B and AB $= 2c$. The string passes through a small smooth ring of mass m. Show that, if the ring revolves in a horizontal circle at the level of B, its velocity v is given by $v^2 = (a^2-c^2)g/c$.   (C.W.B.)

9. A light inextensible string passes through a small smooth ring A which is fixed with its plane horizontal. One end B of the string supports a particle of mass M hanging at rest, and to the other end C is fastened a particle of mass m. If C is describing a horizontal circle of radius a at a depth b below A, find the ratio $M : m$ and the angular velocity of the plane BAC.

If B is distant d below A and the string AC is suddenly cut, find the horizontal and vertical distances between B and C at a subsequent time t.   (L.A.)

10. A particle describes a circle of radius r with uniform angular velocity ω. Find the magnitude and direction of its acceleration.

Five light rods, each of length a, are freely jointed together at their ends to form a frame in the shape of a rhombus OACB stiffened by the diagonal AB. Particles of masses m_1, m_2, m_3 are attached at A, B, C respectively. The frame is rotated with uniform angular velocity ω in a horizontal plane about a fixed vertical axis through O. Find the forces in the rods, distinguishing between tensions and thrusts.   (L.A.)

11. A particle is constrained to move in a smooth vertical circular tube of radius a, of which A is the lowest point and AB and CD the vertical and horizontal diameters. It is projected downwards from C with speed u and the pressure on it from the tube shifts from the outside to the inside of the tube as the particle passes the mid-point of arc BD. Determine u and with what speed the particle reaches B. If the part of the tube between B and C has no outer surface, at what point will the particle leave the tube?
(H.S.C.)

12. Define simple harmonic motion and prove from your definition that if the speed of a particle describing such a motion is v when the distance of the particle from the mean position is x, then

$$v^2 T^2 = 4\pi^2(a^2 - x^2),$$

where a is the amplitude and T the period. If the velocity is trebled when the distance from the mean position is $2a/3$, the period remaining unaltered, find the new amplitude.   (I.S.)

13. Define simple harmonic motion.

A particle moving in simple harmonic motion makes consecutive passages through a certain point of its path, with a speed of 0.9 ms^{-1}, at alternate intervals of 2 and 6 s. Find the period, amplitude, and maximum speed of the motion.

In what ratio does the point divide the distance between the positions of instantaneous rest?   (L.A.)

14. A weight rests on a platform which moves horizontally to and fro with simple harmonic motion of amplitude 0.6 m, making twenty complete oscillations per minute. If the weight remains at rest relative to the platform throughout the motion, show that the coefficient of friction must be not less than 0.274 approximately.
(I.S.)

15. (i) If a particle describes simple harmonic motion, show that the ratio of the average speed with which it describes the complete path in one direction to its maximum speed is approximately 0.64. (ii) A particle describing simple harmonic motion

keeps passing and repassing through the same point with speed V at intervals of time $t_1, t_2, t_1, t_2, \ldots$ Prove that the maximum speed of the particle is

$$V \sec \left\{ \frac{(\pi t_1 - t_2)}{2(t_1 + t_2)} \right\}. \tag{I.S.}$$

16. Show that in the small oscillations of a simple pendulum the bob moves in simple harmonic motion, and find the time period. A heavy particle at C is attached by a light string to a fixed point A; the mid-point of the string rests (when hanging vertically) against a horizontal edge at B the mid-point of AC and the particle is set swinging as a pendulum in a plane perpendicular to this edge so that for part of its motion it swings about A, and for part about B. Compare the times taken and the angular amplitudes (which are small) in the two parts of the motion.

(H.S.C.)

17. One end of a light elastic string is fixed, and to the other is attached a particle of mass m which hangs freely under gravity. Show that, if the particle is given a small vertical displacement from the position of equilibrium, it performs simple harmonic oscillations of period $2\pi \sqrt{(am/\lambda)}$, where a is the natural length and λ the modulus of the string.

The particle is now attached to the string at its middle point and the ends of the string are fixed to two points in a vertical line. In the position of equilibrium both parts of the string are in tension. Show that, if the particle is given a small vertical displacement, it performs simple harmonic oscillations of period $\pi \sqrt{(am/\lambda)}$. (L.A.)

18. A particle P of mass m moves along a straight line AB under the action of two forces, one $2\mu m \mathrm{AP}$ towards the point A and the other $\mu m \mathrm{BP}$ towards the point B. If μ is a constant, prove that the motion of P is simple harmonic with period $2\pi/\sqrt{(3\mu)}$.

If $AB = 2a$ and the particle is instantaneously at rest at the mid-point of AB, find the distance from A of the point at which it is next instantaneously at rest. (L.A.)

19. An elastic string, of natural length a and modulus λ, is fastened at one end to a fixed point A on a smooth horizontal table, and a particle of mass m is attached to the other end of the string. If the particle is pulled along the table to a distance $2a$ from A and then released, prove that it will move in simple harmonic motion until the tension of the string vanishes. Show that the string will be of length a after a time $\frac{1}{2}\pi \sqrt{(ma/\lambda)}$ and that the particle will reach A after a time

$$(\tfrac{1}{2}\pi + 1)\sqrt{(ma/\lambda)}. \tag{C.W.B.}$$

20. Find the work done against the tension in a light elastic string of natural length l and modulus of elasticity λ in extending it by a length x. One end of such an elastic string of natural length l and modulus mg is attached to a fixed point O, the other to a particle of mass m which is projected vertically upward from O with kinetic energy $\frac{1}{2}(n^2+2)mgl$. Show that the particle begins to descend after a time

$$\{(n^2+2)^{\frac{1}{2}}-n+\tan^{-1}n\}(l/g)^{\frac{1}{2}}.$$ (H.S.C.)

21. A uniform circular disc has mass m and radius a. Prove that its moment of inertia about the axis through its centre perpendicular to its plane is $\frac{1}{2}ma^2$.

If $m = 50$ kg, $a = 1\cdot2$ m, and the disc rotates freely about the axis at an angular speed of 50 rev min^{-1}, calculate its kinetic energy. (L.A.)

22. Find the moment of inertia of a uniform thin circular disc, of mass M and radius a, about the axis through its centre perpendicular to its plane.

A particle of mass m is fastened to the highest point of a circular disc, of mass M and radius a, which is free to rotate about a horizontal axis through its centre perpendicular to its plane. If the system is slightly disturbed from rest, find the angular velocity of the disc: (i) when the particle is at the level of the axis; (ii) when it is vertically below the axis. (L.A.)

23. Prove that the moment of inertia of a uniform solid sphere, of mass M and radius a, about a diameter is $2Ma^2/5$. Deduce that the radius of gyration of a uniform solid hemisphere, of radius a, about *any* axis through the centre of its plane face is $a\sqrt{(2/5)}$.

Two identical uniform solid hemispheres are such that one can rotate freely about its axis of symmetry, which is fixed, and the other can rotate freely about a fixed axis which coincides with a tangent to the circular rim of its plane face. Find the ratio of their angular velocities when their kinetic energies are equal. (L.A.)

24. Prove that, for a compound pendulum performing small oscillations in a vertical plane about a horizontal axis to which it is freely pivoted, the periodic time is

$$2\pi\sqrt{\{(k^2+h^2)/gh\}},$$

where k is the radius of gyration about a parallel axis through the centre of gravity and h the distance of the pivot axis from the centre of gravity.

A non-uniform rod AB of length a is made to oscillate as a compound pendulum, first, about a horizontal axis through A, and secondly, about one through B. If the lengths of the equivalent simple pendulums are $3a/4$ and $2a/3$ respectively, find the ratio AG : GB, where G is the centre of gravity of the rod.

Also show that $k^2 = 5a^2/49$. (L.A.)

25. A uniform circular plate has radius a and mass M. Show that its moment of inertia about an axis through its centre and perpendicular to its plane is $\frac{1}{2}Ma^2$.

Particles each of mass m are fixed at four points which are on the circumference of the plate which are the vertices of a square. The system can turn freely in a vertical plane about any fixed point on the circumference. Find the period of small oscillation.

(L.A.)

26. A rigid body is free to turn about a fixed axis. Prove that the length of the equivalent simple pendulum is K^2/h, where K is the radius of gyration of the body about the axis and h the distance of its centroid from the axis. Find the period of a small oscillation of the body. A thin uniform rod, of mass m and length $2a$, is free to turn about the end O. A particle of mass $4m/3$ can be attached at any point of the rod. Prove that the length of the equivalent simple pendulum is least when the point of attachment is at a distance $a/2$ from O. (H.C.)

27. Write down equations sufficient to determine the angular acceleration of a heavy rigid body turning about a fixed horizontal axis and the reactions of the axis on the body. A uniform circular disc swings in its own plane about a fixed point on its circumference. Show that, if the diameter through the fixed point swings through two right angles, the horizontal component of the reaction on the fixed point is greatest when the diameter through that point is inclined at 45° to the horizontal. (H.C.)

28. A uniform rod OA, of length $2a$, hinged to a smooth horizontal axis through O, is held with its centre of mass G at a height z_0 above the level of O and is then released from rest. In the subsequent motion, when G is at a horizontal distance x from O and a height z above the level of O, show that the angular velocity and the angular acceleration of the rod are respectively

$$\left\{\frac{3g}{2a^2}(z_0-z)\right\} \text{ and } \frac{3gx}{4a^2}.$$

Show that the reaction at O first becomes vertical when $z = \frac{2}{3}z_0$.

(H.S.C.)

29. A trolley consists of a plank of mass m rigidly and symmetrically mounted on four equal wheels, each of which is a uniform solid circular disc of mass M. The trolley is placed on a plane of inclination α to the horizontal with the axles of the wheels horizontal. Find the acceleration of the trolley down the plane, it being assumed that the motion is one of pure rolling. If a uniform solid sphere and the trolley both start from rest level with each other, find the ratio of the mass of the plank to that of the wheels if the sphere and the trolley arrive at the foot of the plane at the same time. (C.W.B.)

30. A uniform flywheel of radius 15 cm can turn freely about its axis, which is fixed and horizontal. A light string passing over the flywheel ca rries at its ends masses of 1·5 and 1 kg respectively. The system is released from rest in a position in which the parts of the the string not in contact with the flywheel are vertical and each mass is found to move through 2·7 m in 3 s. Assuming that the string does not slip, calculate the moment of inertia of the flywheel about its axis and also the tensions in the vertical parts of the string. (L.A.)

CHAPTER TEN

STATICS OF A PARTICLE

10.1. We now consider that part of mechanics, known as statics, which deals with solids at rest under the influence of forces. Again we shall assume to start with that the dimensions of the solid body may be neglected. We shall, as earlier, refer to such a body as a *particle* and represent it by a point.

10.2. Force

In Chapter Three we defined *force* as any cause which alters or tends to alter a body's state of rest or of uniform motion in a straight line. Force accelerates a body, and only if there is no resultant force acting on the body will it continue at rest, relative to some assigned system of reference, or continue to move with uniform velocity. In statics we are concerned to examine the relations that must exist between the forces acting on a body when the resultant force is zero.

10.3. To specify completely a force which acts on a particle, we require: (i) its magnitude, and (ii) its direction in space.

In the case of a rigid body the point of application of the force must *also* be specified.

The magnitude of a force can be measured by its effect. In dynamics this is usually done by the motion it will produce in a given body in a given time, or more strictly, by the acceleration it will produce in the body at any instant. Thus the unit of force, *the newton* (N), is defined as the force which, acting on a mass of 1 kg, produces an acceleration of 1 m s^{-2}.

We can also measure a force by the weight it will just support. In this case the value will depend on the force of gravity at the place where the force is measured.

Such a unit of force has a different value at different places on the earth's surface, because of the variation in the gravitational force.

However, in Statics we are usually concerned only with the *relative* values of forces at the same place. We can therefore conveniently use any unit of force, for the ratios of forces all expressed in terms of any chosen unit will not vary from place to place.

10.4. Vectors

We can represent a given force completely by means of a straight line AB. For one extremity A can represent the point of application, the direction of the line in space can represent the direction of the force, and the length of the line can be made to represent the magnitude of the force to some convenient scale.

Any quantity which, like a force, possesses both magnitude and direction is called a *Vector*.

Other examples of vectors which occur in dynamics are velocity, momentum, and acceleration, and they can all be represented completely by straight lines.

When a force is represented by a line AB the direction of the force is indicated by the order of the letters, i.e. AB represents a force acting from A to B, and BA represents a force acting from B to A. These are denoted by the vectors **AB** and **BA**, and we note that **AB** = −**BA**.

The fundamental law satisfied by all vectors is the *law of vector addition*. This states that the sum of any two vector quantities of the same kind represented by **AB** and **BC** is a vector represented by **AC**.

If **AB** and **BC** are given, **AC** can be found by drawing the triangle ABC.

10.5. Basis of statics

To build up the science of Mechanics we start with some laws or postulates based on, or supported by, experiment or observation.

Now Statics is really a particular case of Dynamics in which the bodies are at rest relative to some system of reference. If we choose the laws relating to the action of forces on bodies by considering the more general case of bodies in motion (Dynamics) they will hold for the particular case of when the bodies are at rest (Statics).

It is, of course, possible to base the science of Statics on laws which are independent of the idea of motion. Historically, in fact, Statics was developed before Dynamics. For the latter we had to wait until the seventeenth century, the foundations being laid by Galileo and Newton, whereas Statics goes back at least to the early Greeks, some two thousand years earlier. Although Aristotle (384–322 B.C.) made some contribution to mechanics, it was Archimedes of Syracuse (287–212 B.C.) who developed the principle of the lever and effectively constituted a science of Statics (cf. 11.17).

Now we can take as our starting-point in Statics the fundamental theorem known as the *Parallelogram of Forces*. This merely states that the law of vector addition is true for forces, but it can be deduced from the fundamental laws of Dynamics, known as *Newton's Laws of Motion*, as has been explained in Chapter Three (see 3.12). Thus Statics and Dynamics comprise one science based on one set of fundamental postulates.

10.6. The parallelogram of forces

If two forces, acting on a particle at O, *be represented in magnitude and direction by the two straight lines* OA, OB *drawn from* O *they are equivalent to a single force which is represented in magnitude and direction by the diagonal* OC *of the parallelogram* OACB.

This is the fundamental theorem of Statics, and it can be verified by experiment. As for any other scientific law, this is its basic justification. **OC** is the vector sum of **OA** and **OB**, so that the theorem simply states that forces are added (or compounded) like vectors.

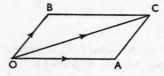

FIG. 10.1

The single force represented by OC is known as the *resultant* of the two forces represented by OA and OB. Conversely, the forces represented by OA and OB are known as the *components* of the force represented by OC.

In the simple case when the two forces are in the same direction their resultant is clearly equal to their sum, and when they act in opposite directions their resultant is equal to their difference and acts in the direction of the greater.

The resultant is zero only if the two forces are equal in magnitude and act in opposite directions.

The magnitude and direction of the resultant of any two forces acting at O can be found by drawing a parallelogram OACB on an appropriate scale, or by calculation, as is now explained.

10.7. Let two forces P and Q acting at O be represented by OA and OB (Fig. 10.2). Their resultant, R, is represented by the diagonal OC of the parallelogram OACB.

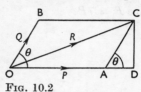

Fɪɢ. 10.2

Let θ be the angle between the directions of P and Q, i.e. angle AOB $= \theta$. Draw CD perpendicular to OA, produced if necessary.

Then

$$OC^2 = OD^2 + DC^2$$
$$= (OA + AD)^2 + DC^2$$
$$= (OA + AC \cos \theta)^2 + (AC \sin \theta)^2.$$

$\therefore \qquad R^2 = (P + Q \cos \theta)^2 + (Q \sin \theta)^2$
$$= P^2 + Q^2 (\cos^2 \theta + \sin^2 \theta) + 2PQ \cos \theta$$
$$= P^2 + Q^2 + 2PQ \cos \theta.$$

Therefore $\quad R = +\sqrt{(P^2 + Q^2 + 2PQ \cos \theta)}$.

To find the direction of OC we have

$$\tan COD = \frac{CD}{OD} = \frac{AC \sin \theta}{OA + AC \cos \theta} = \frac{Q \sin \theta}{P + Q \cos \theta}.$$

If the forces are at right angles, $\theta = 90°$, so that

$$R = \sqrt{(P^2 + Q^2)}, \text{ and } \tan COA = Q/P.$$

If the forces are equal, say each equal to P, then

$R = \sqrt{[P^2(1 + 1 + 2 \cos \theta)]} = P\sqrt{[2(1 + \cos \theta)]}$
$$= P\sqrt{(\cos^2 \tfrac{1}{2}\theta)} = 2P \cos \tfrac{1}{2}\theta.$$

Also $\qquad \tan COA = \dfrac{P \sin \theta}{P + P \cos \theta} = \dfrac{2 \sin \tfrac{1}{2}\theta \cos \tfrac{1}{2}\theta}{2 \cos^2 \tfrac{1}{2}\theta} = \tan \tfrac{1}{2}\theta.$

Hence in this case the resultant bisects the angle between the forces. This can also be deduced from the fact that when the forces are equal the parallelogram is a rhombus.

10.8. EXAMPLE (i)

If the resultant of forces $3P$, $5P$ is equal to $7P$, find the angle between the forces.

If θ is the angle between the forces $3P$ and $5P$, and R is the resultant,

$$R^2 = 9P^2 + 25P^2 + 30P^2 \cos \theta$$

$\therefore$ $34P^2 + 30P^2 \cos \theta = 49P^2$, since $R = 7P$

$\therefore$ $30P^2 \cos \theta = 15P^2$

$\therefore$ $\cos \theta = \frac{1}{2}$

$\therefore$ $\theta = 60°.$

EXAMPLE (ii)

If two forces P and Q act at such an angle that $R = P$, show that if P is doubled the new resultant is at right angles to Q.

Let OA, OB (Fig. 10.3) represent P and Q. Then the diagonal OC of the parallelogram OACB, which represents R, is equal to OA.

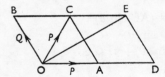

FIG. 10.3

Produce OA to D, making AD = OA, then OD represents $2P$, and the resultant of Q and $2P$ is represented by the diagonal OE of the parallelogram ODEB.

Now   BC = OA = P

and   CE = AD = P.

$\therefore$ CB = CE = CO.

Therefore BE is the diameter of a semicircle with centre C passing through O,

$\therefore$ $\angle$BOE is a right angle.

Or $\angle$CEO = $\angle$COE, since CE = CO,

and $\angle$CBO = $\angle$COB, since CB = CO,

$\therefore$ $\angle$CEO + $\angle$CBO = $\angle$BOE,

$\therefore$ $\angle$BOE is a right angle.

10.9. Smooth bodies

There is, of course, no such thing as a perfectly smooth body. In practice, when one body is pressing against another there is always some force acting along their common surface tending to prevent the slipping of one over the other. This is known as *friction*.

With highly polished surfaces this force may be very small, and in many problems the bodies are supposed to be perfectly smooth. In such cases the only force between the bodies is perpendicular to their common surface. This is called the *normal reaction*.

The *direction* of the normal reaction acting on any smooth body, where it is in contact with another body or surface, is always perpendicular to the direction in which the body is capable of moving.

When a rod is resting against a smooth plane the reaction is normal to the plane.

When a rod is resting against a smooth peg the reaction is perpendicular to the rod.

When the end of a rod is resting against the curved surface of a smooth sphere or against a smooth circular arc the reaction is normal to the sphere or circle, and therefore passes through its centre.

These cases should be noted particularly, as they occur frequently.

10.10. Tension of a string

When a string is used to suspend a weight or move a body the string is in a state of tension.

If we consider a string of negligible weight supporting a weight W vertically the tension in the string is approximately the same throughout its length and may be taken equal to W. If, however, the string is heavy the tension in the string varies from point to point; the tension at any point A, if the string is at rest, equals W plus the weight of the string below A. If the weight of the string is to be neglected we shall refer to it as a *light* string.

If a string supporting a weight is passed over a small, smooth pulley as at A (Fig. 10.4) it is found that the force required to keep the weight in position is unaltered, and it makes no difference whether the string is held in the position AB, AC, or AD. This is *not* true if the pulley is rough.

We note that the tension in a *light* string passing round a smooth peg or pulley is the same throughout its length.

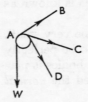

Fig. 10.4

We shall usually assume that the string is inextensible, but we shall consider a few problems in which the string is elastic and satisfies Hooke's law. In the latter case the tension varies with the extension of the string (see 4.19).

10.11. EXAMPLE

Two equal weights of mass 10 kg are attached to the ends of a thin string which passes over three smooth pegs in a wall arranged in the form of an equilateral triangle with one side horizontal. Find the thrust on each peg.

Let A, B, C (Fig. 10.5) be the positions of the pegs.

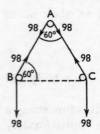

Fig. 10.5

Since the pegs are smooth, the tension is the same throughout the string and equal to 10 g N = 98 N.

The thrust on A is the resultant of the two tensions of 98 N inclined at an angle of 60°. If R N is the magnitude of this resultant,

$$R^2 = 98^2 + 98^2 + 2 \times 98^2 \cos 60° = 3 \times 98^2$$

∴　　　　　$R = 98\sqrt{3} = 170.$

The thrust on B or C is the resultant of the two tensions of 98 N inclined at an angle of 150°. If S N is the magnitude of this resultant,

$$S^2 = 98^2 + 98^2 + 2 \times 98^2 \cos 150°$$
$$= 98^2(2 - \sqrt{3}) = 98^2 \times 0.268$$
$$\therefore \qquad S = 98 \times 0.518 = 50.8.$$

Since the component forces in each case are equal, the directions of the thrusts bisect the angles between the portions of the string on each side of the peg.

10.12. Resolution of a force

A force may be resolved into two components in an infinite number of ways; for an infinite number of parallelograms can be constructed on a given line as diagonal.

In practice, the directions of the components are known, and the most important case is when these directions are at right angles to each other.

Let OC (Fig. 10.6) represent a given force F, and suppose we wish to resolve it into two components, one along OX, and the other along a perpendicular direction OY.

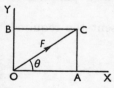

FIG. 10.6

Draw CA perpendicular to OX and CB perpendicular to OY.

Then OA and OB represent the components of F along OX and OY respectively.

If the angle COX $= \theta$ we have

$$OA = F \cos \theta \quad \text{and} \quad OB = F \sin \theta.$$

Hence a force F is equivalent to a force $F \cos \theta$ along a line making an angle θ with its own direction together with a force $F \sin \theta$ perpendicular to the direction of the first component.

When a force is resolved in this manner into two forces whose directions are at right angles these forces are sometimes called the *Resolved Parts* or *Resolutes* of the given force in these two directions.

The resolved part of a force F in a direction making an angle θ with it is $F \cos \theta$.

The expression 'horizontal component' of a force, which is often used, must be taken to mean the resolved part in the horizontal direction, i.e. it is understood that the other component is vertical.

Generally, we shall use the term component (and not the term resolved part), it being understood, unless the contrary is indicated, that we are concerned with resolving the force (or the vector) into two perpendicular components.

10.13. If we do require the components of a force F in directions making angles α and β with it they can be found as follows:

Let OC (Fig. 10.7) represent F. Draw OA and OB, making

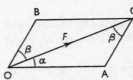

Fig. 10.7

angles of α and β with OC, and through C draw parallels to complete the parallelogram OACB.

Then OA and OB, or OA and AC represent the required components.

Hence, from the triangle OAC

$$\frac{OA}{\sin \beta} = \frac{AC}{\sin \alpha} = \frac{OC}{\sin (\alpha + \beta)}$$

$$\therefore \qquad OA = \frac{F \sin \beta}{\sin (\alpha + \beta)}.$$

Similarly, $$\qquad OB = \frac{F \sin \alpha}{\sin (\alpha + \beta)}.$$

EXAMPLES 10.1

1. In the following cases P and Q denote two forces, θ the angle between them, and R is their resultant:

    (i) If $P = 9$, $Q = 12$, $\theta = 90°$,   find R.

    (ii) If $R = 13$, $Q = 5$, $\theta = 90°$,   find P.

    (iii) If $Q = 7$, $Q = 8$, $\theta = 60°$,   find R.

    (iv) If $P = 10$, $Q = 10$, $\theta = 120°$,   find R.

    (v) If $P = 12$, $Q = 5$, $R = 11$,   find θ.

    (vi) If $P = 3$, $Q = 5$, $\theta = \sin^{-1} \frac{3}{5}$,   find R.

2. Show that the resultant of two forces each equal to P, and inclined at any angle of 120°, is also equal to P.

3. Find the angle between two equal forces P when their resultant is: (i) equal to P; (ii) equal to $P\sqrt{3}$.

4. The resultant of two forces P and Q is equal to P in magnitude, and that of two forces $2P$, Q (acting in the same directions as before) is also equal to P. Find the magnitude of Q, and prove that the direction of Q makes an angle of 150° with that of P.

(H.C.)

5. The sum of two forces is 24 N, and their resultant, which is at right angles to the smaller of the two forces, is 12 N. Find the magnitudes of the two forces, and the angle between them.

6. Two equal weights of mass 10 kg are attached to the ends of a light string which passes over three smooth pegs in a wall arranged in the form of an isosceles triangle, with the base horizontal and with a vertical angle of 120°. Find the pressure on each peg.

7. Two equal weights of mass 5 kg are attached to the ends of a light string which passes over two smooth pegs in a wall, one of which is higher than the other, and such that the line joining them makes an angle of 30° with the horizontal. Find the pressure on each peg.

8. At what angle must two forces of 5 and 12 N be inclined if they are balanced by a force of 15 N?

9. A, B are two fixed points on the circumference of a circle ABC. P is a point which moves on the arc ACB. Forces of constant magnitude act along PA and PB. Prove that the line of action of their resultant passes through a fixed point.

10. The resultant of two forces P and $2P$, acting at a point, is perpendicular to P. Find the angle between P and $2P$.

11. The resultant of forces of 3 N and 5 N is at right angles to the smaller force. Find the magnitude of their resultant and the angle between the forces.

12. Forces of 4 N and 6 N act at an angle of 60°. Find their resultant graphically, and check by calculation.

13. Find graphically the resultant of forces of 5 N and 6 N, inclined at an angle of 40°.

14. The resultant of two forces is 8 N, and its direction is inclined at 60° to one of the forces whose magnitude is 4 N. Find graphically the magnitude and direction of the other force.

15. When two equal forces are inclined at an angle 2α their resultant is twice as great as when they are inclined at an angle 2β. Show that $\cos \alpha = 2 \cos \beta$.

16. A force of 25 N is inclined at $\theta°$ to the horizontal. If the vertical component is 15 N, find the horizontal component and the value of θ.

17. Resolve a force of 10 N into two perpendicular components such that: (i) the components are equal, and (ii) one component equals 3 times the other.

18. A force P N is resolved into two components each of magnitude $2P$ N; find their directions.

19. One component of a force of 12 N is 4 N at an angle of 30°. Find the magnitude and direction of the other component.

20. In pulling a garden roller of mass 60 kg across a horizontal lawn a man exerts a force of 500 N at an angle of 45° with the ground. Find: (i) the forward pull exerted on the roller, and (ii) the vertical reaction between the roller and the lawn.

21. A body of mass 25 kg is supported by two strings, one inclined at 60° and the other at 20° to the vertical. Calculate the tension in each string, and check by means of a graphical construction.

10.14. Particle subject to forces

In dynamics, we have shown that if a particle is subject to *one* force F, the particle will move in the direction of F with an acceleration a given by $F = ma$, where m is the mass of the particle. Again, if the particle is subject to *two* forces P and Q the particle will move in the direction of the resultant of P and Q. This resultant is zero only if P and Q are equal in magnitude and opposite in direction. In this case the particle will remain at rest (or if in motion, continue to move with uniform velocity). For example, if a weight W is suspended from a fixed point by a string it rests in equilibrium under the action of two forces viz. its weight W acting vertically downwards and a force T vertically upwards due to the string equal to the tension in the string. In this case $T = W$.

10.15. Three forces acting on a particle

Let P, Q, R (Fig. 10.8) be three forces acting on a particle at O.

If two of these, say P and Q, be represented by OA and OB their resultant is represented by the diagonal OC of the parallelogram OACB.

Hence if R can be represented in magnitude and direction by CO it will balance the resultant of P and Q, and the three forces P, Q, R will be in equilibrium.

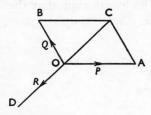

FIG. 10.8

Hence if the three forces P, Q, R can be represented in magnitude and direction by OA, AC, and CO they will be in equilibrium.

(It should be noticed that AC represents Q in magnitude and direction but not in line of action.)

This result is known as the **Triangle of Forces**, which is usually stated as follows:

If three forces, acting at a point, can be represented in magnitude and direction by the sides of a triangle taken in order the forces will be in equilibrium.

The converse of this is also true:

If three forces acting at a point are in equilibrium they can be represented in magnitude and direction by the three sides of a triangle taken in order.

This can be verified experimentally.

10.16. *Graphical method*

The converse of the triangle of forces enables us to obtain simple graphical solutions of problems on the equilibrium of three forces.

Suppose we know that three forces P, Q, R acting at a point O in given directions OX, OY, OZ (Fig. 10.9) are in equilibrium.

Then if we know the magnitude of *one* of the three forces, say
P, we can obtain the magnitudes of the other two as follows:

Since the forces are in equilibrium, we know that they can
be represented in magnitude and direction by the sides of a
triangle taken in order.

Draw AB parallel to OX and make its length represent the
magnitude of *P* to some convenient scale.

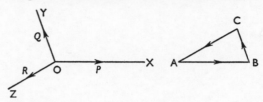

FIG. 10.9

From A draw AC parallel to OZ, and from B draw BC
parallel to OY. Since AB represents *P*, the other two sides of
the triangle ABC must represent *Q* and *R*. BC represents *Q*, and
CA represents *R*, on the same scale that AB represents *P*. The
order of the letters represents in each case the direction of the
force, and this order is obtained by continuing round the
triangle in the same direction.

10.17. In Fig. 10.9 we saw that CA represents the force *R* which
is in equilibrium with the resultant of *P* and *Q*. Hence AC must
represent the resultant of *P* and *Q* in magnitude and direction.
We may therefore obtain the magnitude and direction of the
resultant of *P* and *Q* from the triangle ABC without using the
parallelogram.

*If two forces acting at some point are represented in magnitude
and direction by the sides* AB, BC *of a triangle* ABC *the third side*
AC *will represent their resultant in magnitude and direction.*

In vector notation **AC** is the vector sum of **AB** and **BC**, that
is,

$$\mathbf{AC} = \mathbf{AB} + \mathbf{BC}$$

or $$\mathbf{AB} + \mathbf{BC} + \mathbf{CA} = 0.$$

It must be clearly understood that AC does not represent
the *position* of the resultant which will act at the point where
the forces represented by AB and BC act.

If AB and BC are actually the lines of action of the forces their resultant will act at B, but it will be equal and parallel to AC.

10.18. The converse of the triangle of forces can also be put in a trigonometrical form, usually called *Lami's Theorem*.

If three forces acting at a point are in equilibrium each is proportional to the sine of the angle between the other two.

Let P, Q, R (Fig. 10.10) be the three forces acting at O.

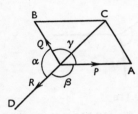

FIG. 10.10

Let OA represent P, and OB represent Q, then CO represents R in magnitude and direction.

Let α, β, γ be the angles between Q and R, R and P, P and Q respectively.

In the triangle OAC we have

$$\angle ACO = \angle BOC = 180° - \alpha, \qquad \therefore \sin ACO = \sin \alpha.$$
$$\angle COA = 180° - \beta, \qquad \therefore \sin COA = \sin \beta.$$
$$\angle CAO = 180° - \gamma, \qquad \therefore \sin OAC = \sin \gamma.$$

Also
$$\frac{OA}{\sin ACO} = \frac{AC}{\sin COA} = \frac{CO}{\sin OAC}$$

$$\therefore \qquad \frac{P}{\sin \alpha} = \frac{Q}{\sin \beta} = \frac{R}{\sin \gamma}.$$

10.19. EXAMPLE (i)

Forces equal to $7P$, $8P$ and $5P$ acting on a particle are in equilibrium; find by drawing and by calculation the angle between the forces $8P$ and $5P$.

Since the forces are in equilibrium, they can be represented by the sides of a triangle taken in order. As in Fig. 10.11A, we draw the triangle ABC with AB = 7 units, BC = 8 units and CA = 5 units. The forces must therefore be parallel to the sides of this triangle.

By measurement $\angle ACB = 60°$. By calculation, if $\angle ACB = \theta$ we have

$$7^2 = 8^2 + 5^2 - 2 \times 8 \times 5 \times \cos \theta$$
$$\therefore \quad 49 = 64 + 25 - 80 \cos \theta$$
$$\therefore \quad \cos \theta = 40/80 = \tfrac{1}{2}$$
$$\therefore \quad \theta = 60°.$$

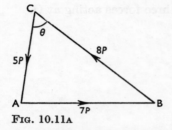

FIG. 10.11A

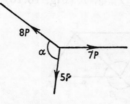

FIG. 10.11B

The forces must be directed as shown in Fig. 10.11B, where the vectors representing the forces have been drawn parallel to the corresponding sides of the triangle ABC.

The angle between the forces $8P$ and $5P$ is $180° - \theta = 120°$.

EXAMPLE (ii)

A weight of mass 5 kg hangs from a fixed point O by a light inextensible string. It is pulled aside by a horizontal force P N and rests in equilibrium with the string inclined at an angle of 30° to the vertical. Find P.

In Fig. 10.12 A is the equilibrium position of the weight.

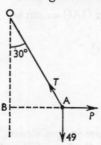

FIG. 10.12

The weight is acted upon by three forces: (i) its weight 49 N; (ii) the horizontal force P N; and (iii) a force T N equal to the tension in the string.

If AB is drawn horizontally the sides of the triangle OAB are parallel to the three forces, and therefore represent them on a certain scale.

$$\therefore \qquad \frac{T}{AO} = \frac{P}{BA} = \frac{49}{OB}$$

$$\therefore \qquad P = 49\,\frac{BA}{OB} = 49 \tan 30° = 49/\sqrt{3} = 28\cdot3.$$

10.20. Another method which may be used to solve many problems associated with a particle in equilibrium under the action of three forces depends upon the following theorem.

If two forces act on a particle the sum of their components in any given direction is equal to the component of the resultant of the two forces in that direction.

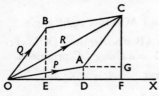

Fig. 10.13

Let OA and OB represent the two forces P and Q and OC their resultant R, so that OACB is a parallelogram (Fig. 10.13).

Let OX be the given direction.

Draw AD, BE, CF perpendicular to OX, and AG perpendicular to CF.

The triangles OBE, ACG have their sides OB and AC equal, and their sides are parallel, so that they are equal in all respects,

$$\therefore \qquad OE = AG = DF$$

$$\therefore \qquad OF = OD+DF = OD+OE.$$

But OD, OE, OF represent the components of P, Q, R in the direction of OX, and hence the theorem follows.

This theorem may obviously be extended to any number of forces.

It follows that if three or more forces acting on a particle are in equilibrium the algebraic sum of the components of the forces in *any* direction must be zero.

It can be shown, conversely, that if the algebraic sums of the components of the forces in *any two* directions are zero, then the forces must be in equilibrium (see 10.26).

EXAMPLE (i)

A particle of mass 50 kg is suspended by two strings 3 m and 4 m attached to two points at the same level, whose distance apart is 5 m. Find the tensions in the strings.

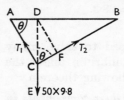

FIG. 10.14

Let AC, BC (Fig. 10.14) be the two strings, and let T_1, T_2 N be the tensions in the strings.

AC = 3 m, BC = 4 m, AB = 5 m, and ACB is a right angle.

Let CD be perpendicular to AB; since AB is horizontal, DC is vertical, and the weight of the particle at C acts along DC produced.

Let $\angle$DCB = θ, then $\angle$BAC = θ, and

$$\cos \theta = \tfrac{3}{5}, \sin \theta = \tfrac{4}{5}.$$

Method (*a*): Resolving horizontally, the component towards the left must equal that towards the right,

$$\therefore \qquad\qquad T_1 \cos \theta = T_2 \sin \theta. \qquad\qquad \text{(i)}$$

Resolving vertically, the sum of the upward components must equal the downward one, and hence

$$T_1 \sin \theta + T_2 \cos \theta = 50 \times 9\text{·}8 = 490. \qquad \text{(ii)}$$

From (i) $\tfrac{3}{5}T_1 = \tfrac{4}{5}T_2$ or $T_2 = \tfrac{3}{4}T_1$

and from (ii) $\tfrac{4}{5}T_1 + \tfrac{3}{5} \times \tfrac{3}{4}T_1 = 490$

$$\therefore \qquad\qquad \tfrac{25}{20}T_1 = 490$$

$$\therefore \qquad\qquad T_1 = 392 \text{ and } T_2 = 294.$$

Otherwise, resolving along AC and CB we have immediately

$$T_1 = 490 \sin \theta = 392$$

and $$T_2 = 490 \cos \theta = 294.$$

Method (*b*): Produce DC to E, then by Lami's Theorem,

$$\frac{T_1}{\sin \text{BCE}} = \frac{T_2}{\sin \text{ACE}} = \frac{50}{\sin \text{ACB}}.$$

But sin BCE = sin θ, sin ACE = sin $(90-\theta)$ = cos θ, and $\angle$ACB = 90°.

Hence
$$\frac{T_1}{\frac{4}{5}} = \frac{T_2}{\frac{3}{5}} = \frac{490}{1}$$

$\therefore$ $\qquad\qquad T_1 = 392$ and $T_2 = 294$.

Method (c): If the figure be drawn to scale, and DF be drawn parallel to AC, the sides of the triangle DCF are parallel respectively to the weight 490, the tension T_2, and the tension T_1.

Hence CF and FD represent T_2 and T_1 to the same scale that DC represents 490. But CF/CD $= \cos\theta = \frac{3}{5}$. Hence $T_2 = 294$.

EXAMPLE (ii)

A particle of mass 5 kg is placed on a smooth plane inclined to the horizontal at an angle of 30°. Find the magnitude of the force (a) acting parallel to the plane, (b) acting horizontally, required to keep the particle in equilibrium.

Let AB (Fig. 10.15) be the surface of the plane, AC horizontal, P the particle.

Since the plane is smooth, it cannot exert any force parallel to its surface tending to prevent the particle sliding down. There is only a normal reaction equal to: (a) R_1 N, and (b) R_2 N.

(a) the force F_1 acting parallel to the plane (Fig. 10.15A) neces-sary to prevent the particle sliding down is evidently 49 sin 30° = 24·5 N, acting upwards. The component of the weight perpendicular to AB is balanced by the reaction R_1 of the plane.

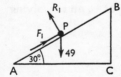

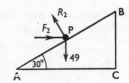

Fig. 10.15A   Fig. 10.15B

(b) If a force F_2 acts horizontally as shown (Fig. 10.15B), its component F_2 sin 30 perpendicular to AB merely presses the particle against the plane. Its component $F_2 \cos 30°$ parallel to the plane must therefore be sufficient to balance the component of the weight, 24·5 N, acting down the plane.

$\therefore$ $\qquad\qquad F_2 \cos 30° = 24\!\cdot\!5$

$\therefore$ $\qquad\qquad F_2 = \frac{49}{\sqrt{3}} = \frac{49}{3}\sqrt{3}\ \text{N}.$

We note that $R_2 = F_2 \sin 30° + 49 \cos 30° = 98\sqrt{3}/3$.

EXAMPLE (iii)

A string ABCD is suspended from two points A and D at the same level. A weight of 10 N is hung from a string knotted to ABCD at B, and a weight w N from a string knotted to ABCD at C. If AB and CD make angles of 45° and 60° respectively with the horizontal, and if BC is horizontal, find the tension in the string BC and the weight w.

Let the tensions in the strings AB, BC, CD be T_1, T_2, T_3 N respectively (Fig. 10.16).

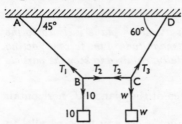

FIG. 10.16

Considering the three forces acting at B, and resolving horizontally and vertically, we get

$$T_1 \cos 45° = T_2$$

and
$$T_1 \sin 45° = 10.$$

Hence,
$$T_1 = 10\sqrt{2} \text{ and } T_2 = 10.$$

Similarly, considering the three forces acting at C, and resolving horizontally and vertically, we get

$$T_3 \cos 60° = T_2$$

and
$$T_3 \sin 60° = w.$$

Hence,
$$T_3 = 2T_2 = 20 \text{ and } w = 10\sqrt{3}.$$

Alternatively, we can construct a triangle of forces for the forces acting at B by drawing BM perpendicular to AD. It follows immediately that $T_1 = 10\sqrt{2}$ and $T_2 = 10$. Similarly, if we draw CN perpendicular to AD the triangle CND will serve as a triangle of forces for the forces acting at C.

EXAMPLES 10.2

1. A weight of mass 20 kg is suspended by two light strings of lengths 6 m and 8 m from two points at the same level and 10 m apart. Find the tensions in the strings.

2. A mass of 90 kg is suspended by two light strings of lengths 9 m and 12 m from two points at the same level and 15 m apart. Find the tensions in the strings.

3. A weight of 26 kg is suspended by two light strings of lengths 5 m and 12 m from two points at the same level, and 13 m apart. Find the tension in the strings.

4. A smooth, weightless pulley carries a weight of mass 15 kg, and can slide freely up and down a smooth vertical groove. It is held up by a string passing round the pulley so that the two parts of the string make angles of 30° and 60° with the horizontal; show that the tension in the string is slightly under 108 N.   (H.C.)

5. Two strings of lengths 1·5 m and 1·8 m are fastened to a particle of mass 10 kg, their other ends being fastened to points at the same level 2·4 m apart. Find the tension in each string.   (I.A.)

6. A weight of mass 5 kg is suspended by two strings of length 7 cm and 24 cm attached to two points in the same horizontal line at a distance 25 cm apart. Find the tensions of the strings.   (I.S.)

7. A particle of mass 10 kg is placed on a smooth plane of inclination 60°. What force applied (i) parallel to the surface of the plane, (ii) horizontally, will keep the particle at rest?

8. A small body of mass 10 kg is suspended from two points A, B, 12 m apart, and in the same horizontal line, by strings of lengths 7 m and 10 m attached to the same point in the body. Find the tension in each string.   (I.S.)

9. A particle of mass 6 kg, resting on a smooth inclined plane of slope 30°, is connected by a light string passing over a smooth pulley at the top of the plane to a weight of mass M kg hanging vertically. Find the value of M so that the weights may be in equilibrium and find also the pressure on the pulley when this condition is satisfied.

10. A 10-kg mass C is hung up by two cords AC, BC of respective lengths 2 m and 3 m, the ends A, B of the cords being attached to pegs 4 m apart on the same level. Find the tensions in the cords.

11. Three forces, P, Q, R, meet at a point, and the resultants of Q and R, of R and P, and of P and Q are each known in magnitude and direction. Show how to determine each of the forces, P, Q, R.   (I.S.)

12. Find (i) the horizontal force, and (ii) the force up the plane required to support particles of the following masses on planes of the inclinations given:

 (i) 10 kg on an incline of length 10 m and height 6 m.

 (ii) 45 kg on an incline of length 25 m and height 20 m.

 (iii) 5 Mg on an incline of 30°.

13. A body of mass 10 kg rests on a smooth plane inclined at 30° to the horizontal. Find the least value of the force required to keep it in equilibrium and the resultant reaction of the plane.

14. A particle of mass 5 kg is supported by means of two strings attached to it. If the direction of one string be at 60° to the horizontal, find the direction of the other in order that its tension may be as small as possible, and the values of the tensions in the two strings in this case.

15. A weightless wire is stretched between two points A and B on the same level 1·2 m apart. A mass of 5 kg is hung at the mid-point of the wire, and causes it to drop 5 cm below the line AB. Find the tension of the wire.

16. Three strings are attached to a light particle P which is in equilibrium. Two of them pass over pulleys and then hang vertically, carrying weights, while the third supports a weight of mass M kg. The inclinations of the upper strings are respectively 30° and 45° to the upward vertical through P. An additional weight of mass 10 kg is now attached to W. Find what additional weights must be added to the other two strings to ensure that P shall remain in equilibrium in the same position.

 (N.U. 3 and 4)

17. Two strings, 40 cm and 30 cm long, are tied to a mass of 6 kg and have their other ends fastened to two nails, 50 cm apart in a horizontal line. By drawing or otherwise, find the tension in the longer string.

 The nails are now replaced by smooth pulleys, over which the strings are passed with mass of 4·5 kg and 6 kg tied respectively to their free ends and hanging freely. In the new position of equilibrium find, by drawing or otherwise, the angles which the sloping portions of the strings make with the vertical.

18. A weight of mass 10 kg hangs from a fixed point O by a light inextensible string. It is pulled aside by a force P N which always acts perpendicular to the string. Find P, if in the equilibrium position the string makes an angle of (i) 45°, (ii) 30° with the vertical.

19. A string, which breaks at a tension of 100 N, hangs freely from a fixed point, and has a weight of mass 6 kg attached to it at B. A horizontal pull P now acts at B and drags it sideways. In the position of equilibrium when P is 25 N, find the tension in the string and the slope of the string to the vertical.

   In the position when the string is about to break, find the magnitude of the horizontal pull P and the slope of the string.

20. The figure (Fig. 10.17) represents a weight W attached to two strings which pass over two smooth pegs at the same level and support weights P, Q at their free ends. Prove that, in the position of equilibrium,

$$\sin \theta = (W^2 + P^2 - Q^2)/2WP.$$

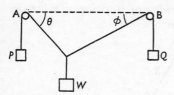

FIG. 10.17

21. A light string ABCD is supported at A and D, which are points in the same horizontal plane. At B hangs a weight of mass 10 kg and at C a weight of mass M kg. The string AB is at 45° to the vertical, DC is at 30° to the vertical and BC slopes upward at 45° to the horizontal. Find the tensions in AB, BC and CD, and the value of M.

22. ABCD is a light string attached to two fixed points A and D, has two equal weights attached at B and C and rests with the portions AB and CD inclined at 30° and 60° respectively to the vertical. Prove that the tension in the portion BC is equal to either weight, and that BC is inclined at 60° to the vertical.

23. A and D are points in a horizontal line 48 cm apart; the ends of a light cord 66 cm long are attached to A and D; B is a point in the cord 25 cm from A and C a point in the cord 29 cm from D. A mass of 14 g is suspended from B. Find the mass of Q which must be suspended from C, so that the portion BC of the cord shall be horizontal.

24. Weights of 2, 4, and 3 kg are attached to points B, C and D of a string of which the ends A and E are attached to fixed supports. If each of the portions of the string BC and CD makes an angle of 25° with the horizontal, prove that AB and DE make angles of approximately 43° and 49° 23′ with the horizontal.   (Q.E.)

10.22. Particle subject to more than three forces

If a particle is acted upon by several forces we can show that
the forces are in general equivalent to a single force, the resultant of the forces. The particle will be in equilibrium if the
resultant of the forces is zero.

Two important problems arise; firstly, how can the resultant
of any number of forces be found, and secondly, what are the
relations between the forces when they are in equilibrium?

10.23 The polygon of forces

*If any number of forces, acting on a particle, can be represented
in magnitude and direction by the sides of a polygon taken in
order, the forces will be in equilibrium.*

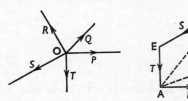

FIG. 10.18

Let the sides AB, BC, CD, DE, EA of the polygon ABCDE
(Fig. 10.18) represent the forces acting on a particle at a point O.

The resultant of forces represented by AB and BC is represented in magnitude and direction by AC.

The resultant of forces represented by AC and CD is represented in magnitude and direction by AD, and similarly the
resultant of forces represented by AD and DE is represented in
magnitude and direction by AE. Hence the resultant of P, Q,
R, S is equal and opposite to T and, since all the forces act at
a point, this resultant and T balance and the system of forces
is in equilibrium.

This method of proof will evidently apply whatever the
number of forces.

It is also clear that the forces need not be in one plane.

Resultant of any number of forces

10.24. If we have a number of forces acting on a particle at O,
as in the last paragraph, and we draw a polygon with its sides

proportional and parallel to these forces (always drawing the next side from the point where the previous side ended), then if the polygon closes we know that the system is in equilibrium, but if it does *not* close the resultant of the forces is represented by the straight line necessary to close the figure, the direction of this resultant being opposite to that in which the figure has been drawn, that is, from the first vertex to the last vertex.

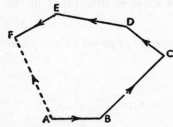

FIG. 10.19

Thus, if we obtained a figure ABCDEF, as in Fig. 10.19, the resultant of the five forces is a force acting at O, represented in magnitude and direction by AF.

In vector notation,

$$\mathbf{AB+BC+CD+DE+EF = AF}.$$

The vectors representing the forces can be drawn in *any* order, that is, the resultant is independent of the sequence in which the forces are added. In Fig. 10.19A the force-polygon

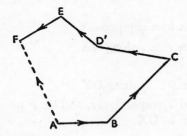

FIG. 10.19A

differs from that in Fig. 10.19, the order of the third and fourth forces having been interchanged, but AF is the same in each case.

This method of obtaining the resultant of a number of

forces graphically is obviously very convenient and much easier than applying the parallelogram of forces to pairs of the forces in turn.

It is often used, as will be seen later, when the forces are acting on a rigid body.

However, it is more accurate and often quicker to calculate the resultant of a number of forces by resolving the forces in two perpendicular directions in the manner illustrated in the following paragraph.

10.25. *To find the resultant of any number of forces in one plane acting on a particle.*

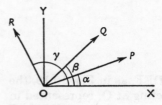

FIG. 10.20

Let the forces, P, Q, R, etc., act upon a particle at O (Fig. 10.20). Through O draw any two axes OX, OY, at right angles to each other. We assume all the forces act in the XOY plane.

Let the forces, P, Q, R . . . make angles α, β, γ . . . with OX. The components of P in the directions OX and OY are $P \cos \alpha$ and $P \sin \alpha$ respectively; similarly the components of Q are $Q \cos \beta$ and $Q \sin \beta$, and so on.

Hence the forces are equivalent to a component

$$P \cos \alpha + Q \cos \beta + R \cos \gamma \text{ . . . along OX,}$$

and a component

$$P \sin \alpha + Q \sin \beta + R \sin \gamma \text{ . . . along OY.}$$

Let these components be X and Y respectively, and let F be their resultant and θ its inclination to OX.

Then $$F \cos \theta = X$$
and $$F \sin \theta = Y$$
$\therefore$ $$F^2 = X^2 + Y^2$$
and $$\tan \theta = \frac{Y}{X}.$$

EXAMPLE (i)

A particle is acted on by forces of 1, 2, 3, and 4 N, the angles between them being 60°, 30°, and 60° respectively. Find the magnitude and direction of the resultant.

It is convenient to take as the axis of x the line of action of one of the forces.

Let O (Fig. 10.21) be the position of the particle, and OX the line of action of the 1 N force. The 3 N force then acts along OY.

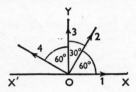

FIG. 10.21

The component of the resultant along OX is

$$1+2 \cos 60 - 4 \cos 30 = 1+1-2\sqrt{3}$$
$$= 2 - 3{\cdot}464 = -1{\cdot}464,$$

i.e. a force of 1·464 N in the direction OX′.

The component of the resultant along OY is

$$2 \cos 30 + 3 + 4 \cos 60 = \sqrt{3} + 3 + 2 = \sqrt{3} + 5 = 6{\cdot}732.$$

The resultant is

$$\sqrt{[(1{\cdot}464)^2 + (6{\cdot}732)^2]} = 6{\cdot}9 \text{ N.}$$

If θ is the angle made by this resultant with OX,

$$\tan \theta = -\frac{6{\cdot}732}{1{\cdot}464} = -4{\cdot}597$$

∴ $$\theta = 102° \ 16' \text{ about.}$$

This problem may also be solved graphically as follows. As in Fig. 10.21A, draw AB, BC, CD, DE parallel to the given forces and of magnitudes 1, 2, 3, 4 respectively.

Then **AE** represents the resultant of the forces in magnitude and direction.

By measurement, AE = 6·9 and angle EAB = 102°. If these

quantities are calculated, using Fig. 10.21A, the equivalence of the two methods is obvious.

It is instructive to draw the sides of the force-polygon ABCDE in a different order.

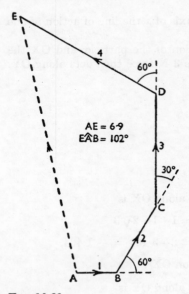

$AE = 6.9$
$E\hat{A}B = 102°$

FIG. 10.21A

EXAMPLE (ii)

Three forces of magnitude 15P, 10P, 5P act on a particle in directions which make 120° with one another. Find their resultant.

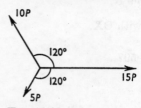

FIG. 10.22

Method (i)

Sum of the components of the forces parallel to the force 15P

$$= 15P - 10P \cos 60° - 5P \cos 60°$$
$$= 15P/2.$$

Also, sum of the components of the forces perpendicular to the force $15P$

$$= 10P \sin 60° - 5P \sin 60° = 5\sqrt{3}P/2.$$

Hence, the resultant $R = \frac{1}{2}P\sqrt{[15^2 + (5\sqrt{3})^2]} = 5\sqrt{3}P$ at an angle $\theta = \tan^{-1}(5\sqrt{3}/15) = 30°$ with the force $15P$.

Method (ii)

We note that forces $5P$, $5P$, $5P$ in the directions indicated are in equilibrium, since they can be represented in magnitude and direction by the sides of an equilateral triangle.

Hence, the three given forces are equivalent to forces $10P$ and $5P$ inclined at an angle of $120°$, of which the resultant R is given by

$$R^2 = (10P)^2 + (5P)^2 + 2 \times 10P \times 5P \times \cos 120°$$
$$= 100P^2 + 25P^2 - 50P^2 = 75P^2$$

$$\therefore \qquad R = 5\sqrt{3}P.$$

The angle θ the resultant makes with the direction of the force $15P$ is given by

$$\tan \theta = \frac{5 \sin 60°}{10 - 5 \cos 60°} = \frac{5\sqrt{3}}{15} = \frac{1}{\sqrt{3}}$$

so that $\qquad\qquad \theta = 30°.$

Method (iii)

Draw a vector-polygon ABCD (Fig. 10.23), where **AB**, **BC**, **CD** represents the forces $15P$, $10P$, $5P$ respectively.

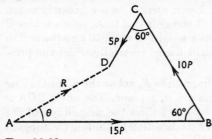

Fig. 10.23

Then **AD** represents the resultant of the three forces.

By measurement, or by calculation, $AD = 8.7P$ and angle $DAB = 30°$.

EXAMPLES 10.3

1. Forces of 4, 3, 2, and 1 N act as a point A in directions AB, AC, AD, and AE, where $\angle BAC = 30°$; $\angle CAD = 30°$, $\angle DAE = 90°$. Find the magnitude of their resultant, and the

inclination of its direction to AB. Verify by drawing a vector-diagram.

2. A particle is acted on by forces of 2 and 4 N at right angles, and also by a force of $4\sqrt{2}$N, whose direction bisects the angle between the other two. Find the resultant force on the particle.

3. Three forces of 5, 10, and 13 N act in one plane at a point, the angle between any two of their directions being 120°. Find the magnitude and direction of their resultant.

4. ABCD is a square, and forces of 2, 4, and 5 N act at A in the directions AB, AC, AD respectively. Find the magnitude of their resultant.

5. Find the magnitude and direction of the resultant of the following forces acting at a point: 20 N east, 42 N north-west, 60 N 30° south of west, 15 N south.   (H.C.)

6. ABCDEF is a regular hexagon. Forces of 2, $4\sqrt{3}$, 8, $2\sqrt{3}$, and 4 N act at A in the directions AB, AC, AD, AE and AF respectively. Find the magnitude of their resultant and the inclination of its direction to AB. Verify by drawing a vector-diagram.

7. Four horizontal wires are attached to a telephone post and exert the following tensions on it: 80 N north, 120 N east, 160 N south-west, and 200 N south-east. Calculate the resultant pull on the post and find its direction.   (H.C.)

8. Four smooth pegs, A, B, C, D are fixed in the same vertical plane so that they form the four lower corners of a regular hexagon with the side BC horizontal. A string is tied to A, passes under B and C, over D and A, and has a weight of mass 10 kg attached to the free end so that the weight hangs vertically. Find the pressures on the four pegs.

9. Three forces, each of equal magnitude F, act at the point O along the lines OA, OB, OC, which are in a plane. The angle BOA is +45°, and the angle BOC is −90°. Find the magnitude of the resultant force, and determine its direction by finding the tangent of the angle it makes with OB.

10. Three forces act upon a point in directions north-west, north-east, and south, the forces being respectively of the value 100, 200, 300 N. Find and state accurately the direction and value of the resultant equivalent single force of these three forces.

11. The sides BC, CA, AB of a triangle are 7, 5, and 3 cm respectively. Find graphically, or otherwise, the magnitude and the inclination to BC of the resultant of the following forces *acting at a point*: 5 N in direction BC, 9 N in direction AC, and 3 N in direction AB.   (I.A.)

12. Forces of 2, 3, and 4 N act at a point in directions parallel to the sides AB, AC, BC respectively of an equilateral triangle. Find their resultant.

13. Forces of 5, 4, 12, and 4 N act at a point A along AB, AC, AD, AE respectively. $\angle BAC = 30°$, $\angle BAD = 90°$, $\angle BAE = 150°$. Find the magnitude of the resultant and the angle its line of action makes with AB.

14. ABC is an equilateral triangle, and G the point of intersection of its medians. Forces of 8, 8, and 16 N act at G along GB, GC, GA respectively. Find the magnitude and direction of their resultant.

15. Forces of 11, 20, and 5 N act along the lines OA, OB, OC respectively, where tan AOB = cot AOC = $\frac{3}{4}$, and OB lies between OA and OC. Find the resulting force in the direction OA, and also the magnitude of the total resultant.

16. Four forces, 10, 9, 4, and 1 N, act at a point O in directions north, east, south, and west respectively. Find the magnitude of their resultant, and its inclination to the north.

    Find also the magnitude and direction of the new resultant if a force of $\sqrt{8}$ N be added at O in a north-west direction.

17. The following coplanar forces act at a point, the unit of force being 1 N, and the directions being reckoned counterclockwise from a given line OX:

    2 at 0°, 3 at 30°, 3 at 150°, 2 at 240°, 4 at 270°.

    Find the magnitude and direction of their resultant: (i) graphically by the polygon of forces; (ii) by calculating its components parallel and perpendicular to OX.

18. ABCD is a square of side 30 cm. Forces of 4, 2, and 2 N act along the sides DA, AB and BC respectively. Show that the resultant of the forces along AB and BC cuts DA produced at E such that AE = 30 cm, and hence find the magnitude, direction and line of action of the resultant of the three forces.

19. Forces of 1, 2, and 3 N act along the sides AB, BC and CA of an equilateral triangle of side 5 cm. Find by drawing where the resultant of the forces along AB and BC cuts AC produced, and hence find the magnitude and direction of the resultant of the three forces and where its line of action cuts BC produced.

20. If k is a constant and ABC is a triangle with sides of length a, b, c, find: (i) the resultant of a force ka along BC and a force kc along AB; (ii) the resultant of a force ka along BC and a force kc along BA. Give the magnitude and line of action in each case.

Prove that a force $2ka$ along BC and a force kc along BA are equivalent to a force $3k$BD along BD, where D is a point on CA such that AD = 2DC.

10.26. *Conditions of equilibrium of any number of forces acting on a particle.*

If we resolve the forces in any two directions at right angles and the sums of the components in these directions be X and Y, the resultant F is given by

$$F^2 = X^2 + Y^2.$$

But if the forces are in equilibrium F must be zero.

Now the sum of the squares of two real quantities cannot be zero, unless each quantity is separately zero,

$$\therefore \qquad\qquad X = 0 \text{ and } Y = 0.$$

Hence, *if any number of forces acting on a particle are in equilibrium the algebraic sums of their components in any two directions at right angles must separately vanish.*

Conversely, *if the sums of their components in two directions at right angles are both zero the forces are in equilibrium.*

For then both X and Y are zero, and therefore F is zero.

10.27. In problems where forces acting at a point are in equilibrium the result of the last paragraph gives us the most general method of obtaining a solution by calculation.

To apply this result we resolve the given forces in two directions at right angles (usually horizontally and vertically) and equate the sum of the components in each of these directions to zero.

The graphical methods involving the triangle and polygon of forces can be used for any number of forces, but they usually take longer and are less accurate than calculation.

A vector method is often very convenient.

EXAMPLE (i)

A string is tied to two points at the same level, and a smooth ring of weight W which can slide freely along the string is pulled by a horizontal force P. If in the position of equilibrium the portions of the string are inclined at angles 60° and 30° to the vertical, find the value of P and the tension in the string.

Let A, B (Fig. 10.24) be the points to which the string is tied, C the position of the ring, and CD perpendicular to AB, so that $\angle ACD = 60°$ and $\angle BCD = 30°$. Since the ring is smooth, the tension T is the same throughout the string.

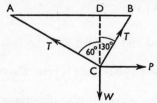

FIG. 10.24

Resolving vertically,

$$T \cos 30° + T \cos 60° = W$$

$$\therefore \quad \left(\frac{\sqrt{3}}{2} + \frac{1}{2}\right) T = W$$

$$\therefore \quad T = \frac{2W}{\sqrt{3}+1} = W(\sqrt{3}-1).$$

Resolving horizontally,

$$P + T \sin 30° = T \sin 60°$$

$$\therefore \quad P = \frac{\sqrt{3}}{2} T - \tfrac{1}{2}T = \frac{T}{2} (\sqrt{3}-1)$$

$$\therefore \quad P = \frac{W}{2} (\sqrt{3}-1)^2 = W(2-\sqrt{3}).$$

EXAMPLE (ii)

ABCD *is a parallelogram and* P *is any point. Prove that the system of forces represented by* PA, BP, PC, DP *is in equilibrium.*

In Fig. 10.25 it is clear that the resultant of the forces represented by BP, PA is represented in magnitude and direction by BA. This resultant acts, of course, at P.

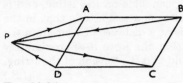

FIG. 10.25

The resultant of the forces represented by DP, PC is represented in magnitude and direction by DC, and acts at P.

Now AB is equal and parallel to DC, so that the resultants are equal in magnitude, and as they act at the same point P they are in the same straight line. Since their directions are opposite, they will balance and the system is in equilibrium.

Vectorially, we can write:

The vector-sum of the forces

$$= (\mathbf{BP} + \mathbf{PA}) + (\mathbf{DP} + \mathbf{PC})$$
$$= \mathbf{BA} + \mathbf{DC}$$

which is zero, since AB and DC are equal and parallel and the two vectors are oppositely directed.

Since the forces act at a point and their vector-sum is zero, they are in equilibrium.

In this case resolving the forces in two perpendicular directions would not be a good method to apply.

EXAMPLES 10.4

1. Two forces, 9 and 10 N, act at a point and are inclined to each other at an angle whose tangent is $\frac{4}{3}$.

   Two other forces P and Q are introduced at the point so that the four forces are in equilibrium; Q acts in a direction opposite to that of the force of 9 N, and P is perpendicular to Q. Find their magnitudes.

2. E is the mid-point of the side CD of a square ABCD. Forces 16, 20, P, Q N act along AB, AD, EA, CA in the directions indicated by the order of the letters. Find P and Q, if the forces are in equilibrium.

3. A string of length 0·6 m is attached to two points A and B at the same level and at a distance of 0·3 m apart. A ring of weight 50 N, slung on to the string, is acted on by a horizontal force P which holds it in equilibrium vertically below B. Find the tension in the string and the magnitude of P. (N.U. 3 and 4)

4. A string of length 31 cm has its ends tied to two points in a horizontal line at a distance 25 cm apart. A small ring from which is suspended a weight of mass 90 g can slide on the string, and is acted on by a horizontal force of such a magnitude that in the position of equilibrium the ring is at a distance of 7 cm from the nearer end of the string. Show that the force is approximately equal to a weight of mass 50 g, and find the tension of the string.
   (I.S.)

5. ABCD is a square. Forces of 2, $3\sqrt{2}$, and 9 N act at A in the directions AB, AC, and AD respectively. Find the additional force at A that will balance these forces.

6. Forces of 3, $\sqrt{3}$, 5, $2\sqrt{3}$, 6 N respectively act at a vertex of a regular hexagon towards the other five vertices. Find the

additional force that must be applied at the vertex to maintain these forces in equilibrium.

7. Five forces acting at a point are in equilibrium. Four of them have magnitudes 1, 2, 3, 4 N respectively and make angles of 0°, 60°, 120°, 210° with a given straight line. Find the magnitude and direction of the other force, and verify by means of a drawing.

8. ABCDEF is a regular hexagon. Show that forces represented by **AB**, **AC**, 2**DA**, **AE**, and **AF** are in equilibrium.

9. ABCD is a square, and BEC is an equilateral triangle lying in the same plane with E outside ABCD. If the forces represented by p**AB**, q**AD**, **AC**, and **EA** are in equilibrium, find p and q.

10. If D, E, F are the mid-points of the sides BC, CA, AB of the triangle ABC, show that three forces acting at a point represented by AD, BE, CF are in equilibrium.

Friction

10.28. When one body slides on another it is found, by experience, that a force tending to resist motion comes into play. This force is called the force of friction.

If we place a block of wood A (Fig. 10.26), of known weight, on a table and attach to it a piece of string passing over a pulley and carrying a light scale pan at the other end we can find the laws which govern the action of the force of friction.

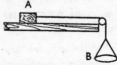

FIG. 10.26

On placing a small weight on the pan B no motion is produced in A. The friction between A and the table must then be equal to the weight of the pan B and the added weight. It is found that we can go on gradually increasing the weight on B until at a certain point A begins to move. This shows that only a limited amount of friction can be called into play.

As the force tending to move A increases from zero, so the force of friction increases from zero at the same rate until a certain maximum or limiting value is reached, and then motion takes place. The total weight of B is then equal to the force of friction. If we now place a weight on A so as to increase the reaction between A and the table, and repeat the experiment, we find that more weight has to be added to B before motion takes place, i.e. the maximum friction has increased. If we repeat the experiment with different weights on A we get a series of values for the maximum friction, which obviously depends on the reaction between A and the table. On dividing the total weight of B by the total weight of A in each case, we find that the number obtained is very nearly constant.

Similar experiments can be performed using blocks of different materials. The results of such experiments are embodied in the following:

Laws of Friction

1. *The direction of the friction is opposite to the direction in which the body tends to move.*

2. *The magnitude of the friction is, up to a certain point, exactly equal to the force tending to produce motion.*

3. *Only a certain amount of friction can be called into play. The maximum amount is called limiting friction.*

4. *The magnitude of the limiting friction (for given surfaces) bears a constant ratio μ to the normal reaction between the surfaces. This ratio μ depends on the nature of the surfaces, and is called the Coefficient of (Statical) Friction.*

5. *The amount of friction is independent of the areas and shape of the surfaces in contact provided the normal reaction is unaltered.*

6. *When motion takes place the friction still opposes the motion. It is independent of the velocity and proportional to the normal pressure, but is slightly less than the limiting friction.*

It must be clearly understood that these laws are experimental and, with the exception of the first three, are subject to limitations. Thus, for very great pressures the surfaces where they are in contact may be crushed and Law 4 will no longer hold.

Law 4 tells us that if F is the limiting friction (i.e. the force of friction when motion is just about to take place), R the normal reaction, and μ the coefficient of statical friction, then

$$F/R = \mu \text{ or } F = \mu R.$$

Great care must be taken not to assume that the friction *always* equals μR. It only has this value when motion is about to take place; otherwise it may have any value *from zero up to μR*.

10.29. Angle of friction

If the normal reaction R and the force of friction F be compounded into a single force (Fig. 10.27) this force is called the

FIG. 10.27

Resultant or Total Reaction, and it makes an angle $\tan^{-1} F/R$ with the normal.

As F increases from zero the angle made by this resultant with the normal increases until the friction F reaches its maximum value μR. In this case the tangent of the angle between the resultant and the normal is $\mu R/R$ or μ. When the friction is limiting the angle made by the resultant reaction with the normal is called the *Angle of Friction*, and is denoted by λ. We see that $\tan \lambda = \mu$.

The resultant reaction can make any angle with the normal up to this value, but cannot be inclined at a greater angle. Whatever direction along the surface the body tends to move, the limiting position of the corresponding resultant reaction will lie on a cone whose semivertical angle is λ or $\tan^{-1}\mu$.

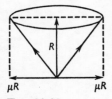

FIG. 10.28

This cone is called the *Cone of Friction* (Fig. 10.28). The resultant reaction must always lie within or on the surface of this cone, and in the latter case the equilibrium is limiting.

10.30. Equilibrium of a particle on a rough inclined plane

Suppose a particle of weight W be placed on a rough plane whose inclination to the horizontal is gradually increased (Fig. 10.29). At any inclination α the component of the weight down

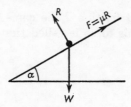

Fig. 10.29

the plane is $W \sin \alpha$. The normal reaction between the particle and the plane is $W \cos \alpha$. The limiting or minimum friction is $\mu W \cos \alpha$. Hence when $W \sin \alpha = \mu W \cos \alpha$, or $\tan \alpha = \mu$, motion is just about to take place.

The particle will therefore begin to slide down under its own weight when the angle of inclination is such that $\tan \alpha = \mu$, i.e. when the inclination of the plane is equal to the angle of friction.

10.31. Particle on rough horizontal plane acted on by an external force

If the force is horizontal (as in Fig. 10.30) and equal to P, then for motion to take place P must be greater than μR. But $R = W$, since there is no vertical motion, and hence P must be greater than μW.

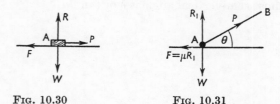

Fig. 10.30   Fig. 10.31

If the force P is inclined upwards, along AB, as in Fig. 10.31, at an angle θ, it will have an upward vertical component, and this reduces the pressure between the particle and the plane.

The normal reaction R_1 is now $W - P \sin \theta$, and the corresponding limiting friction is $\mu(W - P \sin \theta)$. When the motion is just about to take place we must therefore have

$$P \cos \theta = \mu(W - P \sin \theta).$$

$\therefore \qquad P(\cos \theta + \mu \sin \theta) = \mu W$

$\therefore \qquad P\left(\cos \theta + \dfrac{\sin \lambda}{\cos \lambda} \sin \theta\right) = \dfrac{\sin \lambda}{\cos \lambda} W$

where $\lambda =$ angle of friction;

$\therefore \qquad P\dfrac{\cos \theta \cos \lambda + \sin \theta \sin \lambda}{\cos \lambda} = \dfrac{\sin \lambda}{\cos \lambda} W$

$\therefore \qquad P \cos (\theta - \lambda) = W \sin \lambda$

$\therefore \qquad P = W\dfrac{\sin \lambda}{\cos (\theta - \lambda)}.$

The value of P will be a minimum when $\cos (\theta - \lambda)$ is a maximum, i.e. when $\theta = \lambda$, and then $P = W \sin \lambda$.

If P is inclined *downwards* along CA, as in Fig. 10.32, it has

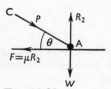

FIG. 10.32

a downward vertical component which increases the normal reaction and hence increases the friction. To move the particle with the least possible force the force should therefore be applied in an upward direction at an angle to the horizontal equal to the angle of friction.

When P is applied downwards (Fig. 10.32) the friction is

$$\mu(W + P \sin \theta)$$

and for the motion to take place, we must have

$$P \cos \theta > \mu(W + P \sin \theta)$$

$\therefore \qquad P\left(\cos \theta - \dfrac{\sin \lambda \sin \theta}{\cos \lambda}\right) > \dfrac{W \sin \lambda}{\cos \lambda}$

$\therefore \qquad P > \dfrac{W \sin \lambda}{\cos (\theta + \lambda)}.$

Now if $(\theta+\lambda)$ is nearly $90°$ the denominator of the right-hand side is very small. For motion to take place P must be very large. If $(\theta+\lambda)$ becomes equal to $90°$ the particle will not move, however large P may be.

Also if $(\theta+\lambda)$ is greater than $90°$ its cosine is negative, and it is impossible for P to move the particle. The negative value means that P must act in the opposite direction, i.e. along AC.

EXAMPLE

A particle of mass 30 kg resting on a rough horizontal plane is just on the point of motion when acted on by horizontal forces of 24 N and 32 N at right angles to each other. Find the coefficient of friction between the particle and the plane, and the direction in which the friction acts.

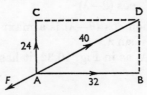

FIG. 10.33

In problems of this kind we must find the *resultant* force tending to move the particle; the particle tends to move in the direction of this resultant and the friction acts in the opposite direction.

Let AB, AC (Fig. 10.33) be the directions of the forces, A the particle. The resultant of the forces is

$$\sqrt{(24^2+32^2)} = 40 \text{ N},$$

and it acts along AD, making an angle $\cos^{-1}\frac{4}{5}$ with the 32 N. The friction acts in the direction DA. Since limiting friction $= \mu R$, where R is the normal reaction on the particle,

$$40 = 30 \times 9 \cdot 8\mu, \text{ or } \mu = \frac{4}{29 \cdot 4} = 0 \cdot 14.$$

10.32. Particle on rough inclined plane acted on by an external force

I. *When the inclination of the plane is less than the angle of friction*

In this case the friction is enough to prevent the particle sliding down under its own weight.

To find the force P, applied in a vertical plane through the line of greatest slope, required to move the particle up or down the plane, we proceed as follows.

(a) If P acts upwards at an angle θ to the plane, as in Fig. 10.34, the normal reaction R_1 equals $W \cos \alpha - P \sin \theta$.

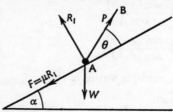

FIG. 10.34

Hence the limiting friction is $\mu(W \cos \alpha - P \sin \theta)$ and acts down the plane. The component of the weight down the plane is $W \sin \alpha$. When the particle is on the point of moving up the plane we have therefore

$$P \cos \theta = W \sin \alpha + \mu(W \cos \alpha - P \sin \theta),$$

$$\therefore \quad P\left(\cos \theta + \frac{\sin \lambda}{\cos \lambda} \sin \theta\right) = W\left(\sin \alpha + \frac{\sin \lambda \cos \alpha}{\cos \lambda}\right)$$

$$\therefore \quad P\frac{\cos (\theta - \lambda)}{\cos \lambda} = W\frac{\sin (\alpha + \lambda)}{\cos \lambda}$$

$$\therefore \quad P = W\frac{\sin (\alpha + \lambda)}{\cos (\theta - \lambda)}.$$

This is a minimum when $\theta = \lambda$, and then $P = W \sin (\alpha + \lambda)$. If $\theta = 0$, i.e. if P acts parallel to the plane,

$$P = W\frac{\sin (\alpha + \lambda)}{\cos \lambda}.$$

(b) If P acts downwards at an angle θ to the plane, along AC (Fig. 10.35), the limiting friction is again $\mu(W \cos \alpha - P \sin \theta)$,

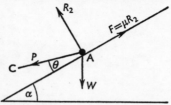

FIG. 10.35

but it now acts up the plane, as the particle is on the point of motion down the plane.

$$\therefore \qquad P \cos \theta + W \sin \alpha = \mu(W \cos \alpha - P \sin \theta)$$

$$\therefore \qquad P\left(\cos \theta + \frac{\sin \lambda \sin \theta}{\cos \lambda}\right) = W\left(\frac{\sin \lambda \cos \alpha}{\cos \lambda} - \sin \alpha\right)$$

$$\therefore \qquad P \frac{\cos (\theta - \lambda)}{\cos \lambda} = W \frac{\sin (\lambda - \alpha)}{\cos \lambda}$$

$$\therefore \qquad P = W \frac{\sin (\lambda - \alpha)}{\cos (\theta - \lambda)}.$$

P is again a minimum when $\theta = \lambda$, and its value is then

$$W \sin (\lambda - \alpha).$$

II. *When the inclination of the plane is greater than the angle of friction*

In this case the particle will slide down unless supported by external force. We have now to consider: (i) the force required to *move* the particle *up* the plane; (ii) the force required to *support* it.

(i) This is exactly the same as in I (i). The force acting parallel to the plane is, putting $\theta = 0$,

$$W \frac{\sin (\alpha + \lambda)}{\cos \lambda}.$$

If acting upwards at an angle θ,

$$P = W \frac{\sin (\alpha + \lambda)}{\cos (\theta - \lambda)}.$$

P is a minimum when $\theta = \lambda$, and then its value is $W \sin (\alpha + \lambda)$.

(ii) If P acts upwards at an angle θ (Fig. 10.36), then, as

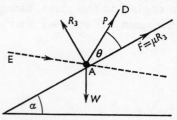

Fig. 10.36

above, the normal reaction R_3 is $W \cos \alpha - P \sin \theta$, and the limiting friction is

$$\mu(W \cos \alpha - P \sin \theta).$$

The friction now acts *up* the plane as the particle is on the point of moving *down*.

$$\therefore \qquad P \cos \theta + \mu(W \cos \alpha - P \sin \theta) = W \sin \alpha,$$

$$\therefore \qquad P\left(\cos \theta - \frac{\sin \lambda \sin \theta}{\cos \lambda}\right) = W\left(\sin \alpha - \frac{\sin \lambda \cos \alpha}{\cos \lambda}\right),$$

$$\therefore \qquad P\frac{\cos (\theta + \lambda)}{\cos \lambda} = W\frac{\sin (\alpha - \lambda)}{\cos \lambda},$$

$$\therefore \qquad P = W\frac{\sin (\alpha - \lambda)}{\cos (\theta + \lambda)}. \tag{i}$$

P will be a minimum when $\theta = -\lambda$, i.e. when P acts along EA. This can also be shown as follows.

If P acts along EA it has a component perpendicular to the plane which increases the normal reaction; the limiting friction becomes $\mu(W \cos \alpha + P \sin \theta)$ and acts *up* the plane.

$$\therefore \qquad P \cos \theta + \mu(W \cos \alpha + P \sin \theta) = W \sin \alpha$$

$$\therefore \qquad P\left(\cos \theta + \frac{\sin \lambda \sin \theta}{\cos \lambda}\right) = W\left(\sin \alpha - \frac{\sin \lambda \cos \alpha}{\cos \lambda}\right)$$

$$\therefore \qquad P\frac{\cos (\theta - \lambda)}{\cos \lambda} = W\frac{\sin (\alpha - \lambda)}{\cos \lambda}$$

$$\therefore \qquad P = W\frac{\sin (\alpha - \lambda)}{\cos (\theta - \lambda)}. \tag{ii}$$

This is a minimum when $\theta = \lambda$, and then $P = W \sin (\alpha - \lambda)$.

EXAMPLES 10.5

1. A body of mass 20 kg is resting on a rough horizontal plane, the coefficient of friction being 0·5; find the least force which, acting (i) horizontally, (ii) at an angle of 30° with the horizontal, would move the body.

2. A body of mass 40 kg is resting on a rough horizontal plane and can just be moved by a force of 98 N acting horizontally; find the coefficient of friction.

3. Find the least force required to move a mass of 20 kg along a rough horizontal plane when the coefficient of friction is 0·25.

4. A small wooden block of weight W is pushed along a rough floor by a force acting at the centre of its upper face and inclined at an angle θ to the vertical. Prove that the block will not move if θ is less than the angle of friction. Prove that, if θ is greater than the angle of friction λ the least force which will move the block is

$$W \sin \lambda \ \text{cosec} \ (\theta - \lambda).$$

5. The length of an inclined plane is 5 m, and the height is 3 m; a force of 49 N acting parallel to the plane will just prevent a mass of 10 kg from sliding down. Find the coefficient of friction.

6. A body of mass 10 kg rests in limiting equilibrium on a rough plane whose slope is 30°; the plane is raised until its slope is 60°. Find the force parallel to the plane required to support the body.

7. A body of mass 20 kg is placed on a rough inclined plane whose slope is $\sin^{-1} \frac{3}{5}$; if the coefficient of friction between the plane and the body is 0·2, find the least force acting parallel to the plane required: (i) to prevent the body sliding down; (ii) to pull it up the plane.

8. A weight of mass 40 kg is on the point of sliding down a rough inclined plane when supported by a force of 196 N acting parallel to the plane, and is on the point of moving up the plane when acted on by a force of 294 N parallel to the plane. Find the coefficient of friction.

9. A weight of mass 610 kg is placed on a rough inclined plane of slope $\tan^{-1} \frac{11}{60}$ and coefficient of friction $\frac{1}{6}$, and is attached to a rope whose direction makes an angle $\tan^{-1} \frac{5}{12}$ with the upper surface of the plane. Find, to the nearest integer, the extreme values of the tension of the rope consistent with equilibrium.

10. Find the least force which will move a mass of 80 kg up a rough plane inclined to the horizontal at 30° when the coefficient of friction is 0·75. (I.S.)

11. If the least force which will move a weight up a plane of inclination α is twice the least force which will just prevent the weight slipping down the plane, show that the coefficient of friction between the weight and the plane is $\frac{1}{3} \tan \alpha$.

12. The least force which will move a weight up an inclined plane is P. Show that the least force, acting parallel to the plane, which will move the weight upwards is

$$P\sqrt{(1 + \mu^2)},$$

where μ is the coefficient of friction. (I.S.)

13. A plane is inclined at 20° to the horizontal, and a mass of 100 kg is to be dragged up, the coefficient of friction being 0·25. Find the direction and magnitude of the least force required.

                                                         (H.S.C.)

14. Two inclined planes have a common vertex, and a string passing over a smooth pulley at the vertex is attached to two equal weights, one on each plane. If one plane is smooth and the other rough, find the relation between the angles of inclination of the two planes when the weight on the smooth plane is on the point of moving down.

15. Particles of mass 2 kg and 1 kg are placed on the equally rough slopes of a double inclined plane, whose angles of inclination are respectively 60° and 30°, and are connected by a light string passing over a small smooth pulley at the common vertex of the planes; if the heavier particle is on the point of slipping downwards, show that the coefficient of friction is $5\sqrt{3}-8$.

16. A weight of mass 20 kg is placed on a rough plane inclined at 22° to the horizontal. It is found that the least force which, acting downwards, along the slope of the plane, will cause it to move is 24 N. Find: (i) the coefficient of friction, and (ii) the least force which, acting along the slope of the plane, will just cause the weight to move upwards.   (I.S.)

17. A weight W is dragged up a line of greatest slope of a rough plane of inclination α by a force P inclined at an angle β above the plane. If the coefficient of friction is μ, find the value of P which will just drag W. Find the work done by this force P in dragging W up a length l of the plane. If $W = 50$ N, $\alpha = 15°$, $\beta = 30°$, $\mu = 0·20$, $l = 30$ m, calculate the work done.   (I.E.)

18. A body of weight W can be just supported on a rough inclined plane by a horizontal force P; it can also be just supported by a force Q acting up the plane. Find the cosine of the angle of friction in terms of P, Q, and W only.   (I.S.)

19. A particle of weight W is placed on a rough inclined plane, the inclination of which exceeds the angle of friction. The least horizontal force required to prevent motion down the plane is W, the least horizontal force required to produce motion up the plane is $W\sqrt{3}$. Find the inclination of the plane and the angle of friction. Find also the magnitude and direction of the least force that can maintain the particle in equilibrium.   (I.S.)

20. Two equal weights attached by a light string rest on the surface of a rough sphere of radius R, one of the weights being at the

highest point of the sphere. Find the greatest possible length of the string if the angle of friction is equal to α, and the friction of the string can be neglected.   (Ex.)

21. A block of wood, mass 2 kg, rests on a horizontal plank 1·8 m long. It is found that when the end of the plank is raised 0·6 m the block will just slide; find the coefficient of friction. If the vertical height of the end is increased to 0·9 m, find the least force perpendicular to the plank which will maintain equilibrium. (H.C.)

22. A plane is inclined to the horizontal at an angle of 30°; on it is a load of mass 20 kg. Find the force parallel to the plane which will prevent the load slipping down. If the plane is rough, the coefficient of friction being $\frac{1}{4}$, find the least force parallel to the plane which will just drag the load up the plane.   (H.C.)

23. The force P acting along a rough inclined plane is just sufficient to maintain a body on the plane, the angle of friction λ being less than α, the angle of the plane. Prove that the least force, acting along the plane, sufficient to drag the body up the plane is

$$P \frac{\sin(\alpha+\lambda)}{\sin(\alpha-\lambda)}. \qquad \text{(I.E.)}$$

24. A body of weight W rests on a rough plane of inclination α. Show that the least magnitude of a force that will move it up the plane is $W \sin(\alpha+\lambda)$, where λ is the angle of friction. If the direction of the force be kept constant, show that if $\alpha > \lambda$ the magnitude of the force may be reduced to $W \sin(\alpha-\lambda) \sec 2\lambda$ before the body moves down the plane.   (C.W.B.)

CHAPTER ELEVEN

STATICS OF A RIGID BODY— PARALLEL FORCES—MOMENTS— COUPLES

11.1. In the previous chapter we have considered the action of forces on a particle. We shall now begin to consider the action of forces on a rigid body. In these cases it is evident that we may have to find the resultant of two forces which are parallel and not in the same straight line. Since such forces do not meet in a point, we cannot obtain their resultant by direct application of the parallelogram of forces. The rules for obtaining the resultant of parallel forces are, however, obtained from the parallelogram law as explained in the next two paragraphs.

Two parallel forces are said to be *like* when they act in the same direction; when they act in opposite parallel directions they are said to be *unlike*.

11.2. To find the resultant of two like parallel forces acting on a rigid body

Let P and Q be the forces acting at points A and B (Fig. 11.1) of the body, and let them be represented by the lines AC and BD.

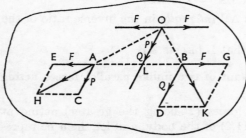

FIG. 11.1

At A and B introduce two equal and opposite forces, F, acting in the line AB, represented by AE and BG. The introduction of these forces will not disturb the action of P and Q, since, the body being rigid, the force F at A may be supposed transferred to B, where it would balance the other force F. Complete the parallelograms AEHC and BGKD, and produce the diagonals HA, KB to meet at O. Draw OL parallel to AC or BD to meet AB in L.

The forces P and F at A have a resultant represented by AH which may be supposed to act at O. Similarly, Q and F at B have a resultant represented by BK which may also be supposed to act at O.

These forces may now be resolved at O into their components P along OL, F parallel to AE, and Q along OL, F parallel to BG. The two forces F are in equilibrium.

Hence the original forces P and Q are equivalent to a force $(P+Q)$ acting along OL, i.e. parallel to the original directions of P and Q, and acting at L in AB.

To find the position of the point L.

The triangles OLA, ACH are similar by construction.

$$\therefore \qquad \frac{OL}{LA} = \frac{AC}{CH} = \frac{P}{F}$$

$$\therefore \qquad P \times LA = F \times OL. \tag{i}$$

The triangles OLB, BDK are similar.

$$\therefore \qquad \frac{OL}{LB} = \frac{BD}{DK} = \frac{Q}{F}$$

$$\therefore \qquad Q \times LB = F \times OL. \tag{ii}$$

Hence from (i) and (ii)

$$P \times LA = Q \times LB,$$

i.e. the point L divides AB *internally* in the inverse ratio of the forces.

We note if $P = Q$ that L bisects AB.

11.3. To find the resultant of two unlike parallel forces acting on a rigid body

Let P and Q be the forces (P being the greater) acting at points A and B (Fig. 11.2) of the body, and let them be represented by AC and BD.

At A and B introduce two equal and opposite forces, F, acting in the line AB and represented by AE and BG.

Since the body is rigid, these forces will be in equilibrium, and will not disturb the action of P and Q.

Complete the parallelograms AEHC, BGKD, and produce the diagonals AH, KB to meet at O. (The diagonals will always meet unless they are parallel, which is the case when P and Q are equal.)

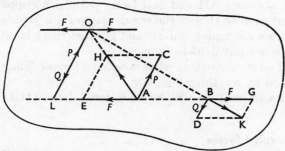

FIG. 11.2

Draw OL parallel to CA and BD to meet BA produced in L. The forces P and F at A have a resultant represented by AH which may be supposed to act at O. Similarly, Q and F at B have a resultant represented by BK which may also be supposed to act at O.

These forces may now be resolved at O into their components, P along LO, F parallel to AE, and Q along OL, F parallel to BG.

The two forces F are in equilibrium.

Hence the original forces P and Q are equivalent to a force $(P-Q)$ acting along LO, i.e. parallel to P in the same direction as P, and acting through L in BA produced.

To find the position of the point L.

The triangles OLA, HEA are similar.

$$\therefore \qquad \frac{OL}{LA} = \frac{HE}{EA} = \frac{P}{F}$$

$$\therefore \qquad P \times LA = F \times OL.$$

The triangles OLB, BDK are similar.

$$\therefore \qquad \frac{OL}{LB} = \frac{BD}{DK} = \frac{Q}{F}.$$

$$\therefore \qquad Q \times LB = F \times OL.$$

$$\therefore \qquad P \times LA = Q \times LB,$$

i.e. L divides the line AB *externally* in the inverse ratio of the forces.

11.4. *Case of failure*

In the figure of the preceding paragraph, if $P = Q$, the triangles AEH, BGK are equal in all respects. In this case $\angle$HAE $=$ $\angle$GBK, so that the lines AH and KB being parallel will not meet at any point such as O, and the construction fails. Hence when the two forces are equal, unlike, and parallel there is no single force which is equivalent to them.

Such a pair of forces constitute what is called a *Couple*. They cannot be replaced by anything simpler.

The properties of couples will be considered later (11.14 and 12.16).

11.5. Centre of parallel forces

Let a system of like parallel forces W_1, W_2, W_3, . . . act at the points A_1, A_2, A_3, . . . (Fig. 11.3).

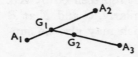

Fig. 11.3

The resultant of the forces W_1, W_2 acting at A_1 and A_2 is equal to $W_1 + W_2$, and always passes through a point G_1 in A_1A_2 (such that $W_1 \times A_1G_1 = W_2 \times G_1A_2$), whatever the direction of the two forces. Similarly, the resultant of like parallel forces $W_1 + W_2$ at G_1 and W_3 at A_3 is equal to $W_1 + W_2 + W_3$, and always passes through a fixed point G_2 in G_1A_3, such that

$$(W_1 + W_2)G_1G_2 = W_3 \times G_2A_3.$$

Hence, provided all the forces are like and parallel, their resultant is equal to the sum of the forces and always passes through a point whose position is fixed relative to A_1, A_2, etc. Its position does not depend on the common direction of the parallel forces.

This point is called the *Centre of the Parallel Forces*, and it is evident that the above argument holds whether the forces are all in one plane or not.

11.6. A very important application of the theorem of the preceding paragraph occurs in connection with the weight of a

body. Every particle of matter is attracted towards the centre of the earth. This force of attraction is proportional to the mass of the particle, and is called its weight (see 3.10).

A body may be considered as made up of a very large number of particles, and if the size of the body is small compared with that of the earth the forces on all the particles of it will be very nearly parallel.

For bodies of ordinary size we shall consider them as being parallel.

Hence the points A_1, A_2, etc. in Fig. 11.3 may be taken to represent the particles of the body, and as the weights of these particles form a system of parallel forces, their resultant (which is equal to the weight of the body) always passes through some point G, whose position relative to the body is fixed and does not depend on the orientation of the body. This point is called the *Centre of Gravity* or *Centre of Mass* of the body.

The position of the centre of gravity of bodies of various shapes will be considered in Chapter 16. It will be seen that this point need not be a point in the body, but often is.

For some simple bodies the position is easy to determine, e.g. a uniform thin rod, a rectangle or parallelogram, a triangle. As these cases occur in a large number of problems, we shall consider them now.

11.7. Centre of gravity of a thin uniform rod

Since the rod is uniform, equal lengths of it, however small, have the same weight.

Let AB (Fig. 11.4) represent the rod, and let G be its mid-point.

A   P   G   Q   B

FIG. 11.4

Take any point P between G and A, and a point Q between G and B, such that PG = GQ.

The centre of gravity of equal particles of the rod at P and Q is evidently at G, since the resultant of equal like parallel forces at P and Q passes through G.

Also for every particle such as P between G and A there is an equal particle at an equal distance from G, lying between G and B.

The centre of gravity of each of these pairs of particles is at G, and hence the centre of gravity of the whole rod is at G.

It will be noticed that the direction in which the parallel forces (the weights of the particles) act makes no difference; i.e. the resultant of the weights of all the particles passes through G in whatever position the rod is placed.

11.8. Centre of gravity of a thin plate or lamina in the shape of a parallelogram

Let ABCD (Fig. 11.5) be the parallelogram. Suppose it is divided into a very large number of very narrow strips, such as PQ, parallel to AD.

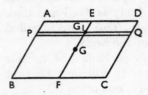

FIG. 11.5

Each of these strips may be considered as a thin uniform rod, and its centre of gravity will be at its mid-point G_1.

Hence the centre of gravity of the whole figure will lie on the line joining the mid-points of the strips, i.e. the line EF joining the mid-points of AD and BC. Similarly, by supposing the figure divided into strips parallel to AB, we see that the centre of gravity must lie on the line joining the mid-points of AB and DC.

The centre of gravity is therefore at G, where these lines intersect. G is also, of course, the point of intersection of the diagonals of the parallelogram.

11.9. Centre of gravity of a thin triangular plate or lamina

Let ABC (Fig. 11.6) be the triangular lamina.

Suppose it is divided into a very large number of narrow strips, such as B_1C_1 parallel to BC.

The centre of gravity of each strip is at its mid-point. Hence the centre of gravity of the whole triangle lies in the line joining the mid-points of the strips, i.e. in the median AD.

Similarly, by supposing the strips taken parallel to AC, we

see that the centre of gravity lies in the median BE. The centre of gravity is therefore at G, the point of intersection of the medians.

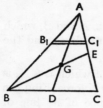

Fig. 11.6

We know from Geometry that this point is $\frac{1}{3}$ of the way up each median, i.e. DG = $\frac{1}{3}$DA.

11.10. *The centre of gravity of any uniform triangular lamina is the same as that of three equal particles placed at the vertices of the triangle.*

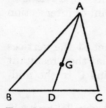

Fig. 11.7

Let ABC (Fig. 11.7) be the lamina. The resultant of like parallel forces, each equal to W acting at B and C, is a parallel force $2W$, acting through D, the mid-point of BC. The resultant of like parallel forces $2W$ at D and W at A is a force $3W$ acting at G in AD, where AG = 2GD. Hence G, which is the centre of gravity of three equal particles placed at A, B, and C, lies in AD and GD = $\frac{1}{3}$AD, i.e. it is the same point as the centre of gravity of the lamina.

EXAMPLES 11.1

1. Like parallel forces of 40 and 70 N act at points A and B, which are 22 cm apart. Find the magnitude of their resultant and the point in which it cuts AB. Find also the magnitude of the resultant and the point where it cuts AB produced if the forces are unlike.

2. Like parallel forces of 9 and 12 N act at points A and B which are 42 cm apart. Find the magnitude of their resultant and the point in which it cuts AB. Find also the magnitude and position of the resultant when the forces are unlike.

3. Unlike parallel forces of 12 and 8 N act at points A and B, which are 12 cm apart. Find the magnitude of the resultant and the point where it cuts AB produced.

4. The resultant of two like parallel forces, one of which is 8 N, is 20 N, and acts at a distance of 6 cm from the 8 N force. Find the magnitude of the other force and the distance of its line of action from the 8 N force.

5. Find the magnitude of two like parallel forces, acting at a distance of 4 m apart, which are equivalent to a force of 100 N acting at a distance of 1 m from one of the forces.

6. Four equal like parallel forces act at the corners of a square; show that their resultant passes through the centre of the square.

7. Three equal like parallel forces act at the vertices of a triangle; show that their resultant passes through the point of intersection of the medians of the triangle.

8. Like parallel forces of magnitudes P, P, $2P$ act at the vertices A, B, C respectively of a triangle ABC. Show that their resultant passes through the mid-point of the line joining C to the mid-point of AB.

9. P and Q are like parallel forces. If Q is moved parallel to itself, through a distance x, prove that the resultant of P and Q moves through a distance $Qx/(P+Q)$.

10. Three equal like parallel forces act at the mid-points of the sides of a triangle; show that their resultant passes through the point of intersection of the medians of the triangle.

11. Like parallel forces of magnitude 4, 2, 4 units act at the corners A, B, C respectively of a square ABCD. What is the magnitude of the parallel force that must be applied at D in order that the resultant of the four forces should pass through the centre of the square?

     If the like parallel force applied at D has a magnitude of 5 units, find the position of the line of action of the resultant.

12. Like parallel forces of magnitude 2, 5, 3 N act at the corners A, B, C, respectively, of a triangle ABC, where AB = 4 cm, BC = 3 cm, CA = 5 cm. Find the position of the line of action of the resultant.

11.11. Moment of a force

A system of forces acting on a rigid body may tend to rotate the body.

If a single force acts on a rigid body, of which one point is fixed, then, unless the line of action of the force passes through the fixed point the body will tend to turn about that point.* This introduces the idea of the *turning effect* or *moment* of a force which is usually defined as follows:

The moment of a force about a given point is the product of the force and the perpendicular drawn from the given point to the line of action of the force.

Fɪɢ. 11.8

Thus the moment of a force P, whose line of action is as shown in Fig. 11.8, about a point O, is $P \times ON$, where ON is the perpendicular drawn from O to the line of action of P.

It is clear that if the line of action of P passes through O its moment about that point is zero.

If O is a fixed point in a body, whose section by a plane containing O and the line of action of P is shown in the figure, the product $P \times ON$ is a measure of the tendency of P to turn the body about O. The turning power is increased if *either*: (1) P is increased; *or* (2) its distance from O is increased.

The moment of a force about a given point may be positive or negative, according to the direction in which the force tends to turn the body about the point.

In the figure the force P tends to turn the body in a direction opposite to that in which the hands of a clock move. In such cases the moment is said to be *positive*. If the force tends to turn the body in a clockwise direction its moment is said to be *negative*.

* Strictly, other forces come into play at the point where the body is fixed.

When a number of forces are acting on a body the *algebraic sum of their moments* is obtained by giving the value of the moment of each force its proper sign and adding them together.

The moment of a force has both magnitude and direction, and is therefore a vector quantity.

The unit of the moment of a force is the unit of force multiplied by the unit of length, e.g. newton-metre, written Nm.

11.12. Graphical representation of a moment

If the length AB marked off on the line of action of the force P (Fig. 11.9) represents the magnitude of P, then the moment of P about O is represented by $AB \times ON$.

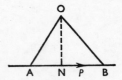

FIG. 11.9

But the area of the triangle AOB is $\frac{1}{2}AB \times ON$; hence twice the area of the triangle AOB represents the moment of P about O. We shall now use this graphical method of representation to prove the fundamental theorem on the moments of coplanar forces.

11.13. The algebraic sum of the moments of two forces about any point in their plane is equal to the moment of their resultant about that point. (Varignon's Theorem)

There are two cases to be considered.

(i) *Let the forces meet in a point.*

Let the forces be P and Q, acting at A, as shown in Figs. 11.10A and B, and let O be any point in their plane.

Draw OC parallel to direction of P to meet the line of action of Q in C. Take the length AC to represent the magnitude of Q, and on the same scale let AB represent P. Complete the parallelogram ABCD, and join OA, OB.

AD represents the resultant R of P and Q.

In either figure,

the moment of P about O is represented by 2 $\triangle$AOB,

"   " Q "   O   "   "   2 $\triangle$AOC,

"   " R "   O   "   "   2 $\triangle$AOD.

Also $\triangle$AOB = $\triangle$ADB, same base and parallels.

              = $\triangle$ADC.

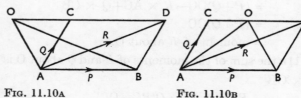

FIG. 11.10A   FIG. 11.10B

In Fig. 11.10A the moments are both positive, and their algebraic sum is represented by

$$2 \triangle AOB + 2 \triangle AOC = 2 \triangle ADC + 2 \triangle AOC$$

$$= 2 \triangle OAD = \text{moment of } R.$$

In Fig. 11.10B the moments are in opposite directions, that of P being positive and Q negative; their algebraic sum is represented by

$$2 \triangle AOB - 2 \triangle AOC = 2 \triangle ADC - 2 \triangle AOC$$

$$= 2 \triangle OAD$$

$$= \text{moment of } R.$$

(ii) *Let the forces be parallel.*

Let P and Q be two parallel forces acting as in Figs. 11.11A and 11.11B and O any point in their plane.

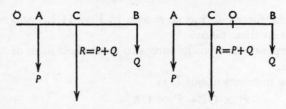

FIG. 11.11A   FIG. 11.11B

Draw OAB perpendicular to the forces to meet their lines of action in A and B.

The resultant R (equal to $P+Q$) is parallel to P and Q, and acts through a point C in AB, such that

$$P \times AC = Q \times CB.$$

In Fig. 11.11A the sum of the moments of P and Q about O is

$P \times OA + Q \times OB$

$$\begin{aligned} &= P(OC-AC)+Q(OC+CB) \\ &= (P+Q)OC - P \times AC + Q \times CB \\ &= (P+Q)OC \\ &= \text{moment of } R \text{ about O.} \end{aligned}$$

In Fig. 11.11B the sum of the moments of P and Q about O is

$P \times OA - Q \times OB$

$$\begin{aligned} &= P(OC+AC)-Q(BC-OC) \\ &= (P+Q)OC + P \times AC - Q \times BC \\ &= (P+Q)OC \\ &= \text{moment of } R \text{ about O.} \end{aligned}$$

11.14. *If the forces form a couple* there is no single resultant and the theorem does not apply.

In this case it is easy to show that the sum of the moments of the forces forming the couple is the same about any point in the plane of the forces.

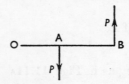

Fig. 11.12

Let P, P be the forces acting as shown in Fig. 11.12, and let O be any point in their plane.

Draw OAB perpendicular to the forces to meet their lines of action in A and B.

The sum of the moment about O is

$$\begin{aligned} &P \times OB - P \times OA \\ &= P(OB-OA) \\ &= P \times AB \end{aligned}$$

and this is independent of the position of O.

The product $P \times$ AB, where P is the magnitude of either of the forces of the couple, and AB is the perpendicular distance between the forces, is called the *Moment of the Couple*.

It should be noticed that the moment of a couple is equal to the moment of either of the forces of the couple about any point in the line of action of the other, and may be positive or negative, depending on the sense of rotation of the couple.

11.15. It is evident that the theorem of paragraph 11.13 may be extended to any number of forces which have a single resultant. For the theorem holds for any two of the forces not forming a couple; it also holds for the resultant of these two and any other of the forces not forming a couple with it, and so on successively until all the forces have been included. The resultant of all the forces but one cannot form a couple with the last remaining force, since we are assuming that the system has a single resultant.

We thus arrive at the general *Principle of Moments*, which may be stated as follows:

If any number of coplanar forces acting on a rigid body have a resultant, the algebraic sum of their moments about any point in their plane is equal to the moment of their resultant about that point.

11.16. If a system of coplanar forces is in equilibrium their resultant is zero, and its moment about any point must therefore be zero.

Hence, *when a system of coplanar forces is in equilibrium the algebraic sum of their moments about any point in their plane is zero.*

The converse of this is not necessarily true. For since the moment of a force about any point in its own line of action is zero, the sum of the moments of a system of coplanar forces about any point in the line of action of their resultant is zero. Hence, the fact that the sum of their moments about *one* point is zero does not necessarily mean that they are in equilibrium, for the point might be on the line of action of their resultant.

EXAMPLES 11.2

1. An equilateral triangle ABC is 8 cm high, it has forces of 2, 4, and 8 N acting along the sides AB, BC, CA respectively. Find the moment of this system of forces about each angular point. (C.E.)

2. Four forces, 3, 4, 5, and 6 N respectively, act in a clockwise direction along the sides of a square, each side of which is 20 cm. long. Find the value of the moments of these forces, about: (i) the centre of the square, and (ii) the point of intersection of the forces 3 and 6 N. State clearly the units of the answers.   (C.E.)

3. Forces of 4, 5, and 6 N act along the sides BC, CA, AB of an equilateral triangle ABC of side 2 m in the directions indicated by the order of the letters. Find the sum of their moments about the point of intersection of the medians of the triangle.

4. Four forces of 2, 4, 2, and 4 N act along the sides AB, CB, DC, DA respectively of a square ABCD of side 3 m. Find the sum of their moments: (i) about A, and (ii) about the centre of the square.

5. A, B, C, D are four points in order in a horizontal line at equal distances of 1 m apart. A force of 2 N acts at B perpendicular to AD and downwards; a force of 4 N acts at C upwards in a direction making an angle of 30° with CD; and a force of 1 N acts upwards at D perpendicular to AD. Find the sum of their moments: (i) about A; (ii) about C.

6. Forces of 1, 2, 3, 4, 5, and 6 N act along the sides of a regular hexagon AB, BC, CD, DE, EF, FA respectively. If the side of the hexagon is 2 cm, find the sum of the moments of the forces: (i) about the centre of the hexagon; (ii) about A.

11.17. The *principle of moments* is of extreme importance, and it will be used continually throughout the remainder of the book. In the present chapter we shall illustrate its use in dealing with some simple cases where a rigid rod, resting on supports, or pivoted about some point, is acted on by forces in addition to its own weight.

Instead of equating the algebraic sum of the moments to zero, it is often convenient to equate the sum of those acting in one direction round the point to the sum of those acting in the opposite direction.

It might be noted here that the Principle of Moments and the results established earlier in this chapter can be *verified experimentally* by applying known forces to a rigid body, such as a bar, and making appropriate measurements. As was suggested in 10.5, the Principle of Moments can be used as the basis of statics and the whole science developed from this starting-point.

EXAMPLE (i)

A uniform rod AB, *of length* 12 *m, and of mass* 50 *kg, rests on two supports, one at* A *and the other* 2 *m from* B. *Masses of* 4, 5, *and* 10 *kg are attached at points* 2 *m,* 4 *m, and* 8 *m respectively from* A. *Find the thrusts on the supports.*

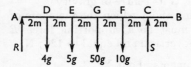

FIG. 11.13

Let C (Fig. 11.13) be the position of the other support, G the centre of gravity of the rod, and D, E, F, the points where the masses are attached. Let R, S N be the reactions at A and B.

The weight of the rod is 50g N and acts at G. The weights acting at D, E, F are 4g, 5g, 10g respectively.

Taking moments about A,

$$10S = 4g \times 2 + 5g \times 4 + 50g \times 6 + 10g \times 8$$
$$= (8 + 20 + 300 + 80) \text{ g}$$
$$= 408g$$
$$\therefore \quad S = 40 \cdot 8g = 399 \cdot 8.$$

Taking moments about C,

$$10R = 10 \text{ g} \times 2 + 50 \text{ g} \times 4 + 5 \text{ g} \times 6 + 4 \text{ g} \times 8$$
$$= (20 + 200 + 30 + 32) \text{ g}$$
$$= 282g$$
$$R = 28 \cdot 2g = 276 \cdot 4.$$

Since we know that the sum of R and S must equal the sum of all the weights (including that of the rod), we might have obtained R by subtracting S from this total (69g). In practice it is better, however, to find each reaction separately, and the fact that their sum must equal that of the weights provides a check on the working; otherwise a mistake in calculating the first will cause both results to be wrong.

EXAMPLE (ii)

*A uniform beam is 12 m long and has a mass of 50 kg and masses of
30 kg and 40 kg are suspended from its ends; at what point must the
beam be supported so that it may rest horizontally?*

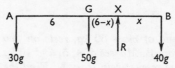

FIG. 11.14

Let AB (Fig. 11.14) be the beam, G its centre of gravity.

The required point X is the point about which the moments of
the three weights balance. There must be a supporting force R
acting on the beam at X. R must be vertical and equal to $120g$ N.

Let BX $= x$ m, then, taking moments about X,

$$40x = 50(6-x)+30(12-x)$$
$$= 300-50x+360-30x$$
$$120x = 660$$
$$\therefore \qquad x = 5\tfrac{1}{2}.$$

We can also obtain this position of X by taking moments of *all*
the forces about one end of the rod.

Hence, taking moments about B,

$$Rx = 50g \times 6+30g \times 12$$
$$= (300+360)\ g$$
$$\therefore \qquad 120x = 660$$
$$\therefore \qquad x = 5\tfrac{1}{2}.$$

EXAMPLE (iii)

*A uniform rod AB, 3·6 m long and of mass 25 kg, is pivoted at a
point 0·9 m from A. A mass of 100 kg is suspended from A. What force
applied at B, in a direction perpendicular to the rod, will keep it in
equilibrium with A below B and AB inclined at 60° to the horizontal?*

Let G (Fig. 11.15) be the mid-point of the rod, C the position of
the pivot. Let R N equal the reaction acting on the rod at the pivot.

The rod will be in equilibrium when the sum of the moments
about C of the weight acting vertically through G and the force
P N acting at B perpendicular to AB, is equal to the moment of
the 980 N force about C.

To obtain the moments of the force about C, we must find the *perpendicular* distances of their lines of action from C.

The perpendicular distance of the line of the 980 N is 0·9 cos 60° = 0·45m, and this is also the distance of the line of the 245 N force.

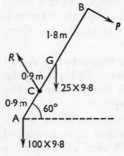

Fig. 11.15

The perpendicular distance of the line of P from C is 2·7 m.

$$\therefore \qquad 2{\cdot}7P + 245 \times 0{\cdot}45 = 980 \times 0{\cdot}45$$
$$\therefore \qquad\qquad 2{\cdot}7P = 735 \times 0{\cdot}45.$$
$$\therefore \qquad\qquad\qquad P = 122{\cdot}5$$

EXAMPLES 11.3

1. A uniform rod, 1·8 m long and of mass 10 kg, rests horizontally on supports at its ends; if a weight of mass 3 kg is attached at a point 1·2 m from one end, find the pressures on the supports.

2. A uniform beam AB, 10 m long and of mass 40 kg, rests on two supports, one at A and the other 2 m from B. If a weight of mass 20 kg is attached to the beam at a point 6 m from A, find the pressures on the supports.

3. Two men carry a load of 100 kg which hangs from a light pole of length 2·4 m, each end of which rests on a shoulder of one of the men. The point from which the load is hung is 0·6 m nearer to one man than the other. What is the pressure on each shoulder?

4. A uniform beam 3 m long, with a weight of mass 25 kg hanging from one end balances in a horizontal position about a point 0·9 m from this end. Find the mass of the beam.

5. Masses of 1 kg, 2 kg, 3 kg, 4 kg, and 5 kg are suspended from a uniform rod AB 1·8 m long, of mass 3 kg and supported at its ends, at distances of 0·3 m, 0·6 m, 0·9 m, 1·2 m, and 1·5 m from A. Find the pressures on the supports.

6. Mass of 1 kg, 2 kg, 3 kg, 4 kg are suspended from a uniform rod of length 1·5 m and mass 3 kg, at distances of 0·3 m, 0·6 m, 0·9 m, 1·2 m from one end. Find the position of the point about which the rod will balance.

7. Find the magnitude and line of action of the resultant of parallel forces 3, 6, 8 in one direction and 12 in the opposite direction, acting at points A, B, C, D respectively in a straight line, where AB = 1 m, BC = 3 m, CD = 5 m.

8. A beam AB, 3 m long and of mass 6 kg, is supported at A and at another point. A load of 1 kg is suspended at B, loads of 5 kg and 4 kg at points 1 m and 2 m from B. If the pressure on the support at A is 40 N, where is the other support?

9. A heavy uniform beam, of length 3·6 m and mass 30 kg is suspended in a horizontal position by two vertical strings, each of which can just sustain a tension of 196 N. Within what distance from the centre can a weight of mass 7·5 kg be suspended without breaking either string?

10. A uniform bar AB, of mass 3 kg and length 75 cm, rests on two supports C and D, distant 10 and 60 cm from A. At points E and F, distant 20 and 50 cm from A respectively are suspended masses of 7 and 2 kg. Find the reactions at C and D, and the moment about the mid-point of the rod of all the forces acting on the bar to the right of that point.

11. A uniform rod, of length 1·8 m and mass 1 kg, rests in a horizontal position with its ends on two supports, each of which will bear the weight of a mass of 6 kg and no more. Find on what part of the rod a weight of mass 8·5 kg can be placed without breaking either support. (I.S.)

12. Prove that if a passenger of weight W advances a distance a along the top of a motor bus, a weight Wa/b is transferred from the back springs to the front springs, where b is the distance between the axles. (I.E.)

13. A uniform bar, 0·6 m long and of mass 17 kg, is suspended by two vertical strings. One is attached at a point 7·5 cm from one end, and can just support the weight of a mass of 9 kg without breaking; the other is attached 10 cm from the other end, and can just support a mass of 10 kg. A weight of mass 1·7 kg is now attached to the rod; find the limits of the positions in which it can be attached without breaking either string. (I.S.)

14. Coplanar forces of 10, 3, 7 units act vertically upwards at distances (measured positive to the right) of 5, −9, 2 m respectively from a fixed point O in their plane. A force of 20 units acts

vertically downwards through O. Find the resultant. If the force through O be increased to 30 units, find the resultant.

15. A rod AB, of length $(a+b)$ and weight W, has its centre of gravity at distance a from A. It rests on two parallel knife-edges at distance c apart in the same horizontal plane, so that equal portions of the rod project beyond each knife-edge. Prove that the pressures on the knife-edges are respectively

$$(a-b+c)W/2c \text{ and } (b-a+c)W/2c. \qquad \text{(I.E.)}$$

16. A heavy uniform rod, of mass 10 kg and length 1·2 m, is supported in a symmetrical position by two props 0·9 m apart. A mass of 2 kg is now suspended from one end of the rod. Calculate the pressures on the two props. (H.S.D.)

17. A light horizontal rod, 30 cm long, is supported by two vertical props, each 7·5 cm from an end of the rod, and is loaded with 16 kg at each end. What weights hung from the ends will produce in one prop a pressure double and in the other prop a pressure half of that produced by the 16 kg load? (H.C.)

18. Four metres of a plank, 12 m long and of mass 100 kg, project over the side of a quay. What mass must be placed on the end of the plank so that a man of mass 75 kg may be able to walk to the other end without the plank tipping over? (H.C.)

19. A horizontal beam ABCD rests on two supports at B and C, where AB = BC = CD. It is found that the beam will just tilt when a mass of p kg is hung from A or when a mass of q kg is hung from D. Find the mass of the beam, and prove that its centre of gravity divides AD in the ratio $2p+q : p+2q$. (H.C.)

20. A uniform beam AB is 1·8 m long and has a mass of 24 kg. It rests on two vertical supports at C and D, CD being a distance of 0·9 m and the pressure on the support at C and is double that on the support at D. Find the lengths of AC and DB, assuming that A is nearer to C than D.

21. A uniform beam rests in a horizontal position supported at a point distant 0·6 m from one end and carrying a mass of 10 kg suspended from this end. The pressure on the support is 300 N. Determine the mass and length of the beam.

22. A stiff heavy rod ABGCD, whose mass is 12 kg and whose centre of gravity is at G, is suspended by vertical strings attached to B and C, each of which could just support the weight of the rod. AB = 5 cm; BG = 7·5 cm; GC = 10 cm; CD = 7·5 cm. Find the tensions in the strings when masses of M_1 kg, M_2 kg are suspended from A and D respectively, and find the values of M_1 and M_2 when both strings are on the point of breaking. (I.S.)

23. A uniform beam, 3·6 m long and of mass 25 kg, rests on two supports at equal distances from the ends. Find the maximum value of this distance so that a man of mass 77 kg may stand anywhere on the beam without tilting it.

24. A uniform plane lamina in the form of a regular hexagon ABCDEF is free to rotate in its own plane, which is vertical, about its centre O. Masses of 1, 2, 3, 4, 5, and 6 kg are attached to the vertices A, B, C, D, E, F respectively. Find the inclination of AD to the vertical for which the system is in equilibrium.

(N.U. 3 and 4)

25. A light horizontal rod, 6 m long, is loaded with three 10-kg masses at points respectively 0·9, 2·1, and 4·5 m from one end, and it is subject to an upward thrust equal to 49 N at the mid-point. Find the resultant of these parallel forces acting on the rod, and if the rod is supported at its two ends deduce the pressures on the supports.   (C.W.B.)

11.18. The lever

A lever consists essentially of a rigid bar which can turn about a fixed point called the *fulcrum*.

As mentioned earlier (10.5), the principle of the lever was known to Archimedes (287–212 B.C.), and until the sixteenth century, when the Parallelogram of Forces was discovered, it was the fundamental principle of Statics.

This principle is simply the principle of moments, i.e. when the lever is in equilibrium the algebraic sum of the moments about the fulcrum of the forces acting on it is zero.

We shall now consider some practical forms of lever.

11.19. The balance

This consists essentially of a rigid beam as in Fig. 11.16, where the extremities of the dotted line AB represent the points where the scale pans are attached.

The fulcrum is usually a knife-edge made of agate fixed through the beam and resting on an agate plate at O.

The scale pans hang from agate plates which rest on agate knife-edges at the points A and B.

The beam is constructed so that its centre of gravity G is below the line AB, and the fulcrum O is placed very close to AB in such a manner that, when the beam is horizontal, G and H (the mid-point of AB) are vertically below O. This ensures that when the beam is horizontal the weights of the scale pans and their contents act at equal distances from the fulcrum.

This is expressed by saying that the arms of the balance are equal, a most important condition.

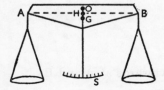

FIG. 11.16

A pointer, rigidly attached to the beam and at right angles to AB, moves over a fixed scale S, and shows whether the beam is horizontal.

The weights of the scale pans and their attachments must be equal. We shall now show that, when these conditions are satisfied, the beam can rest only in a horizontal position when equal weights are placed in the pans, and that it can rest inclined at a definite angle to the horizontal when the weights are unequal.

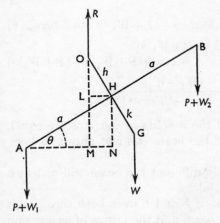

FIG. 11.17

The points A, B, O, H, and G are represented in Fig. 11.17, where the beam AB is inclined at an angle θ to the horizontal.

Let $P =$ the weight of each scale pan

$W =$ the weight of the beam

W_1, $W_2 =$ the weights placed in the pans

$a =$ the length of each arm (i.e. AH = BH = a)

$h =$ OH

$k =$ HG.

The beam is acted on by forces

$P+W_1$, $P+W_2$ vertically downwards at A and B,

W vertically downwards at G,

and the vertical upward reaction R at O.

In the figure the angle LOH = θ, AN = $a \cos \theta$,

LH = $h \sin \theta$ and the distance of G from the vertical through H is $k \sin \theta$.

The distance of $(P+W_1)$ from O is AM = $a \cos \theta - h \sin \theta$.

,,   ,, $(P+W_2)$,, O $= a \cos \theta + h \sin \theta$.

,,   ,, W ,, O $= h \sin \theta + k \sin \theta$.

Taking moments about O, we get

$$(P+W_1)(a \cos \theta - h \sin \theta)$$
$$= W(h+k) \sin \theta + (P+W_2)(a \cos \theta + h \sin \theta)$$
$$\therefore \sin \theta [W(h+k)+(P+W_2)h+(P+W_1)h]$$
$$= \cos \theta [(P+W_1)a-(P+W_2)a]$$
$$\therefore \qquad \tan \theta = \frac{(W_1-W_2)a}{(W_1+W_2+2P)h+W(h+k)}$$

This result shows that if the weights in the pans are equal, i.e. $W_1 = W_2$, θ is zero, and the beam can rest only in a horizontal position.

If the weights are slightly different the beam will rest at a definite angle to the horizontal.

It should be noticed that if h and k were both zero, i.e. if the centre of gravity of the beam and the centre of suspension coincided in the line AB, the beam could rest in any position when equal weights were placed in the pans and could rest only in a vertical position if the weights were different.

11.20. The requisites of a good balance are that it must be

(i) *true*, (ii) *sensitive*, (iii) *stable*, (iv) *rigid*.

(i) The balance will be true if the arms are equal, the weights of the scale pans are equal, and if the centre of gravity of the beam, the mid-point of the beam, and the fulcrum are in a straight line perpendicular to the beam.

(ii) In a sensitive balance the beam must, for a very small difference between the weights in the scale pans, be inclined at an appreciable angle to the horizontal. Using the result obtained in the last paragraph, the ratio $\dfrac{\tan \theta}{W_1 - W_2}$ may be taken as a measure of the sensitivity, which is therefore equal to

$$\frac{a}{(W_1 + W_2 + 2P)h + W(h+k)}.$$

This expression shows that the sensitiveness diminishes as the weights increase.

If, however, $h = 0$, i.e. if all the knife-edges are in the same plane, the sensitivity becomes a/Wk and is independent of the weights in the pans.

This condition is usually aimed at, but the slight bending of the beam prevents its being attained exactly.

For given weights the sensitivity increases with a, i.e. with the length of the arms; it also increases as W decreases, so that it is an advantage to have a long light beam. Too light a beam might mean loss of rigidity, and in better balances the beam is usually of an open girder type.

Diminishing k also increases the sensitivity.

(iii) Stability affects the time taken for the balance to come to rest at its position of equilibrium, and is really a dynamical question. Actually the condition is best satisfied when the moment of the forces about O is greatest, i.e. if W_1 is the weight in each pan, when $[2(P+W_1)h + W(h+k)] \sin \theta$ is greatest.

This is the case for a given value of θ when h and k are greatest.

Since the balance is most sensitive when h and k are small, and most stable when they are large, it is clear that great sensitivity and quickness in weighing cannot be attained together.

11.21. If a balance is not true and the cause is only that the scale pans differ in weight the error can be adjusted by putting paper or sand in the lighter pan or by means of a small screw working in the end of the beam near the points where the pans are attached.

If the arms of the balance are unequal no adjustment of this kind will make it true.

Whatever the cause of inaccuracy, however, the correct weight of a body can be obtained as follows:

Place the body in one pan and balance it by placing sand in the other pan.

Remove the body and put weights in the pan until they balance the sand.

These weights must be equal to the weight of the body.

This is sometimes called *Borda's method*.

11.22. *Double weighing*

Let the lengths of the arms be a_1 and a_2, and the weights of the pans P_1 and P_2. Suppose that the weight of the beam acts at a

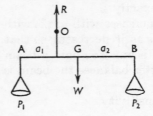

Fig. 11.18

distance x from the fulcrum O (Fig. 11.18) but that the beam remains horizontal when the balance is unloaded.

Then
$$P_1 a_1 = Wx + P_2 a_2. \tag{i}$$

Now suppose a weight W_1 on pan P_1 requires a weight W_2 on pan P_2 to make the beam horizontal; we get

$$(P_1 + W_1)a_1 = Wx + (P_2 + W_2)a_2 \tag{ii}$$

Now place W_1 in pan P_2 and find the weight W_3 which must be put in pan P_1 to balance it; we get

$$(P_1+W_3)a_1 = Wx+(P_2+W_1)a_2 \tag{iii}$$

From (i) and (ii), $W_1a_1 = W_2a_2.$

From (i) and (iii), $W_3a_1 = W_1a_2.$

From these equations $W_1{}^2 = W_2W_3$

or $W_1 = \sqrt{(W_2W_3)}$

i.e. the true weight of the body is the geometric mean of the weights required to balance it when it is placed in each pan in turn.

Also, $\dfrac{a_1}{a_2} = \dfrac{W_2}{W_1} = \dfrac{W_1}{W_3}$

giving the ratio of the arms.

11.23. The common steelyard

This consists of a heavy rod AB (Fig. 11.19) supported at a fixed fulcrum O, nearer to one end than the other.

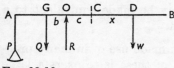

Fɪɢ. 11.19

A scale pan is attached to the end of the shorter arm to carry the body whose weight is required. A movable weight w can slide along the longer arm OB, which is graduated

Let $P =$ the weight of the scale pan

$Q =$ the weight of the rod, acting at G

$a =$ OA

$b =$ OG.

Let C be the point at which w must be placed to keep the rod horizontal when there is no weight in the scale pan, and OC $= c$.

Then $wc = Pa+Qb. \tag{i}$

If a weight W be placed in the scale pan the weight w will balance it, when moved to D, a distance x from C, given by

$$w(c+x) = (P+W)a+Qb. \tag{ii}$$

From (i) and (ii) $wx = Wa.$

Hence if from C we mark off distances a, $2a$, $3a$, etc., a weight in the pan which balances w at the first mark is equal to w; if it balances w at the second mark its weight is $2w$ and so on.

If w has a mass of 1 kg, the graduations correspond to kilogrammes in the pan, and they can be subdivided to show grammes.

At a distance $10a$ from C the sliding weight is equivalent to a mass of 10 kg in the pan, i.e. the steelyard can weigh anything with a mass between 0 and 10 kg.

In many cases a carrier is attached to the end of the longer arm, and slotted weights can be placed on the carrier. In this case C will again be the point at which the sliding weight w must be placed to keep the rod horizontal, when there is no weight in the pan.

The graduations are made in the same way as before, but if with w at C, a weight X on the carrier balances a weight W on the pan, then

$$X \times \text{OB} = W \times \text{OA}.$$

In this way a small weight may be made equivalent to a much larger weight in the scale pan.

11.24. The principle of the lever is made use of in many practical appliances. The usual object of these is to exert a large force at one point by applying a smaller force at another point.

Thus with a bar AB pivoted at C, where BC $= 20 \times$ AC (Fig. 11.20), a weight of 20 N at A can be supported by a force

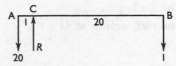

Fig. 11.20

of 1 N at B, and a slightly greater force will lift the weight at A. Scissors and cutting pliers are examples of double levers of this type.

If the rod AB is pivoted at A, a force of 1 N at B directed upwards, can support a weight of 21 N at C. A wheelbarrow or a beam with one end on the ground used for lifting a heavy girder are examples of this arrangement. A pair of nut-crackers is one example of a double lever of this type used for producing a large crushing force at C.

If AB is pivoted at A and a force F applied to C it can overcome a force of $\frac{1}{21} F$ oppositely directed at B. The end B, however, moves through twenty-one times the distance moved by C, and this arrangement is used to magnify movement, e.g. in the treadle of a lathe the foot is applied to C, and the end B is caused to move through a considerable distance by a small movement of the foot.

EXAMPLES 11.4

1. Explain how the position of the zero marks and the distance between the graduations for the sliding weight are determined in a common steelyard. If the sliding weight has a mass of 100 g, and if 50 g at the end of the longer arm of the steelyard balances 4 kg at the end of the shorter arm when the sliding weight is at zero mark, find what fraction of the length of the longer arm is the distance between the graduations for the sliding weight to measure consecutive kg at the end of the shorter arm.   (I.A.)

2. Prove that if the fulcrum of a balance be not immediately above the centre of gravity but the arms are equal a correct result is obtained by weighing the body alternately in the two pans and taking the arithmetic mean of the results. Show further that if, in addition, the arms be unequal and differ by an amount h, the total span being l, then, to obtain a correct result the arithmetic mean must be diminished by $\frac{1}{2}(W_1 \sim W_2)(h/l)$, where W_1, W_2 are the apparent weights in the two cases.

3. A weighing machine is constructed as follows: A stiff beam ABCD is pivoted at C, BC being less than CD. Equal rods BF, DE are suspended from B and D, and their ends F and E are joined by a rod of length equal to BD, the rods being freely jointed at B, D, E, F; a scale pan is attached to the middle point of FE. The counterpoise is a weight P which can slide along AC. If M is the position of P when the machine is in equilibrium without any load, show how to graduate the machine.   (I.A.)

4. A tradesman has a pair of scales, which do not quite balance, and makes them balance by attaching a small weight to one of the pans. Show that if he tries to serve a customer with any weight of a commodity by weighing part of it against half the weight on one pan, and the rest against half the weight in the other pan, he will always cheat himself.   (H.S.C.)

5. A uniform rod 0·9 m long is smoothly pivoted on a fixed horizontal peg at its centre C; strings attached to its ends A and B pass respectively through fixed smooth rings A′ and B′ and carry weights of masses 7 kg each; A′ is vertically above C and B′ vertically below C, each being 45 cm from C. A weight of mass x kg is hung on the rod at A. Prove that if the rod is to rest in other than a vertical position x must not be less than a certain value, and determine for what value of x the rod will be in equilibrium in a horizontal position.   (I.A.)

6. A balance having light arms of unequal length and scale pans of unequal weight does not balance when unloaded. A body known to weigh a units appears to weigh x units, and another body known to weigh b units appears to weigh y units. Show that the true weight of a body which appears to weigh z units is

$$\frac{bx - ay + (a-b)z}{x-y}.$$ (H.S.D.)

7. A heavy non-uniform bar of length 3 m can be balanced about its mid-point when a mass of 2 kg is suspended from one end; if a mass of 6 kg is suspended from the same end the bar will balance about a point 0·3 m from the centre. Find the weight of the bar and the position of its centre of gravity. Show how the bar might be graduated as a steelyard with a movable fulcrum, and prove that the distances of the graduations measured from the end at which the masses are weighed form a series in harmonical progression.   (I.E.)

8. Two uniform rods AB, BC of the same material and thickness are rigidly jointed together at B so that the angle ABC is 120°. The bent lever so formed is then pivoted at B so that it is free to turn in a vertical plane, and in the position of equilibrium BC is horizontal. Show that if a weight is attached to C so that in equilibrium AB becomes horizontal this weight must be $\frac{3}{2}$ of the weight of BC.   (I.S.)

9. ABC is a horizontal lever pivoted at its mid-point B and carrying a scale pan of weight W_0 at C; AD is a light bar pivoted at A to the lever and at D, vertically above A, to a horizontal bar FDE, which is freely movable about its end F, which is fixed. The weight of this bar is W_1, and its centre of gravity is at a distance d from F and FD = c. Show how to graduate this bar with a movable weight w for varying weights W placed in the scale pan at C. If cm graduations correspond to weights of mass 200 g and the mass of $w = 100$ g, find the value of c. In this case find the relation between W_0 and W_1 when $d = 2$ cm, and the zero mark is 2 cm from F.   (I.E.)

CHAPTER TWELVE

FORCES IN A PLANE ACTING ON A RIGID BODY

12.1. Rigid body subject to three forces

We shall consider first problems where there are only three forces acting on a body.

If a rigid body is in equilibrium under the action of three forces in a plane the lines of action of these forces must all be parallel or all meet in a common point.

Let P, Q, R be the forces. If they are not all parallel two of them, say P and Q, must meet in some point O.

The resultant of P and Q must then be some force passing through O.

But since the three forces are in equilibrium, this resultant must balance R.

Hence R must be equal and opposite to the resultant of P and Q, and in the same straight line with it, and must therefore pass through O.

If the forces are all parallel the resultant of any two of them must be equal and opposite to, and in the same straight line as, the third force.

12.2. *From the preceding theorem we see that, unless the three forces are parallel, we can use the methods which apply to forces acting on a particle,* i.e. we can use Lami's Theorem, or the triangle of forces graphically, or we can resolve in two directions at right angles. In some cases it may be quicker to take moments about some convenient point. In all cases it is important to draw a figure with the three forces appropriately shown, either all parallel or meeting in a point.

12.3. The following points, some of which have been mentioned earlier, must be carefully remembered, as they are of fundamental importance:

(i) The weight of a body acts vertically downwards through its centre of gravity.

(ii) When a body is leaning against a *smooth* surface the reaction on the body is normal to the surface.

(iii) When a rod is resting on a *smooth* peg the reaction of the peg on the rod is perpendicular to the rod.

(iv) The tension in a light string is the same throughout the string, and this tension is unaffected by the string passing over *smooth* pegs or pulleys. If the pulley is rough the tension is different on the two sides of the pulley.

(v) The resultant of two equal forces bisects the angle between them. Thus, when a string passes over a smooth peg the thrust on the peg bisects the angle between the portions of the string on each side of the peg.

(vi) When a rigid body is *freely* suspended from a fixed point O the centre of gravity G of the body must lie in the vertical through O.

The resultant reaction at O must balance the weight, and for this to be possible the two forces must be in the same straight line. This result follows whether O is a point in the body itself, as in Fig. 12.1, or whether the body is attached to O by two strings, as in Fig. 12.2. If other forces act on the body G is not necessarily vertically below O.

FIG. 12.1   FIG. 12.2

The above considerations, together with the fact that when there are only three non-parallel forces they must meet in a point, enable us to draw an accurate figure showing the position of the body. This is illustrated in the examples given below.

EXAMPLE (i)

A uniform beam AB, 6 m long, has a mass of 40 kg. The end A, about which the beam can turn freely, is attached to a vertical wall, and the beam is kept in a horizontal position by a rope attached to a point of the beam 1·25 m from A and to a point of the wall vertically above A. If the tension of the rope is not to exceed the weight of a mass of 120 kg, show that the height above A of the point of attachment of the string to the wall must not be less than $1\frac{2}{3}$ m.   (I.S.)

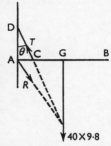

FIG. 12.3

Let G (Fig. 12.3) be the centre of the beam, C and D the points of attachment of the rope to the beam and to the wall.

Let $AD = x$ m and let the angle $ADC = \theta$.

Then
$$\cot \theta = \frac{x}{1\cdot 25} = \tfrac{4}{5}x$$

∴
$$\operatorname{cosec}^2 \theta = 1 + \frac{16x^2}{25} \text{ or } \sin \theta = \frac{5}{\sqrt{(25+16x^2)}}.$$

The reaction R N acting on the beam at A must pass through the point of intersection of the tension T acting at C and the weight.

Taking moments for the beam about A, if T N be the tension in the rope, we get

$$T \times x \sin \theta = 3 \times 40 \times 9\cdot 8$$

∴
$$T = \frac{120 \times 9\cdot 8}{x \sin \theta}$$

Now $T \not> 120 \times 9\cdot 8$, and hence

$$\frac{120}{x \sin \theta} \not> 120$$

∴
$$x \sin \theta \not< 1$$

∴
$$5x \not< \sqrt{(25+16x^2)}$$

$$25x^2 \not< 25 + 16x^2$$

∴
$$x \not< \tfrac{5}{3} \text{ or } 1\tfrac{2}{3}.$$

EXAMPLE (ii)

A heavy uniform rod AB, of weight W, is hinged at A to a fixed point. It is pulled aside by a horizontal force P so that it rests inclined at an angle of 30° to the vertical. Find the magnitude of the force P and the reaction at the hinge.

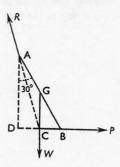

FIG. 12.4

Let G (Fig. 12.4) be the mid-point of the rod. The weight W acts vertically downwards through G.

Let the verticals through G and A cut the line of action of P in C and D, then the reaction R at A must pass through C, the point of intersection of W and P.

Method (a). Taking moments about A for the rod, we get

$$P \times AD = W \times CD.$$

Now $AD = AB \cos 30°$ and $CD = \tfrac{1}{2}AB \sin 30°.$

$\therefore$ $P = W \dfrac{\frac{1}{4}AB}{\frac{\sqrt{3}}{2}AB} = \dfrac{\sqrt{3}}{6}W.$

Also, if X and Y are the horizontal and vertical components of R

$$X = P = \frac{\sqrt{3}}{6}W$$

and $Y = W$

$\therefore$ $R = \sqrt{(X^2 + Y^2)} = W\sqrt{(\tfrac{3}{36}+1)} = W\sqrt{\tfrac{13}{12}}.$

If θ is the inclination of R to the horizontal,

$$\tan \theta = \frac{Y}{X} = \frac{6}{\sqrt{3}} = 2\sqrt{3}.$$

Method (*b*). The triangle ADC has its sides parallel to the forces *W*, *P*, *R* taken in order, and can therefore be used as a triangle of forces.

$$\therefore \qquad \frac{P}{DC} = \frac{R}{AC} = \frac{W}{AD}.$$

As above
$$AD = \frac{\sqrt{3}}{2} AB \text{ and } CD = \tfrac{1}{4}AB.$$

Also
$$AC^2 = AD^2 + CD^2 = (\tfrac{3}{4} + \tfrac{1}{16})AB^2$$

$$\therefore \qquad AC = \frac{\sqrt{13}}{4} AB$$

$$\therefore \qquad P = W \frac{\tfrac{1}{4}AB}{\frac{\sqrt{3}}{2}AB} = \frac{\sqrt{3}}{6} W$$

and
$$R = W \frac{\frac{\sqrt{13}}{4}AB}{\frac{\sqrt{3}}{2}AB} = W\sqrt{\tfrac{13}{12}}.$$

Also
$$\tan ACD = \frac{AD}{DC} = \frac{\frac{\sqrt{3}}{2}AB}{\tfrac{1}{4}AB} = 2\sqrt{3}.$$

EXAMPLE (iii)

A uniform heavy rod AB has the end A in contact with a smooth vertical wall, and one end of a string is fastened to the rod at a point C, such that AC = ¼AB, and the other end of the string is fastened to the wall vertically above A. Find the length of the string, if the rod rests in a position inclined to the vertical.

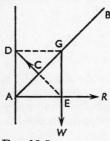

Fig. 12.5

Draw the rod AB inclined to the wall as in Fig. 12.5, and let G be its mid-point.

Since the wall is smooth, the reaction at A is normal to the wall, i.e. horizontal.

Let this normal meet the line of the weight in E; then, since this reaction, the weight and the tension of the string are the only forces acting on the rod, they must meet in a point.

Hence the direction of the string must pass through E. Join EC and produce it to meet the wall in D, then D must be the point of attachment to the wall and CD is the length of the string.

Now, since GEA, EAD are right angles, and C is the mid-point of AG, it is clear that the figure AEGD is a rectangle, and that AG and ED are its diagonals.

$$\therefore \qquad\qquad CD = AC,$$

i.e. the length of the string is 0·25 of the length of the rod.

The tension in the string and the reaction at A can be found by resolving horizontally and vertically, or by using the triangle ADE to serve as the triangle of forces. They will involve the inclination of the rod to the vertical, which may have any value less than 90°.

Note. If the rod rests with B uppermost, as in Fig. 12.5, it is clear that the point where the string is attached to the rod must lie between A and G. For the line joining E to this point must meet the wall in the point where the string is attached to the wall, and this is obviously impossible if C is at or above G.

If the string is attached between G and B or at B the end B must be lower than A, as in the following example.

EXAMPLE (iv)

A uniform rod AB, of length a, hangs with one end A against a smooth vertical wall, being supported by a string, of length l, attached to the other end of the rod and to a point of the wall vertically above A. Show that, if the rod rests inclined to the wall at an angle θ,

$$\cos^2 \theta = \frac{l^2 - a^2}{3a^2}.$$

Since the wall is smooth, the reaction R at A (Fig. 12.6) is horizontal.

Now the line of the string has to pass through the point where the line of the weight meets R, and this is obviously impossible unless B is below A.

Hence draw AB downwards and let G be its middle point. Let the vertical through G meet R in D, join BD and produce it to meet the wall in C, then BC represents the string and BC = l.

Let AC = h, then DG = $\frac{1}{2}h$, since G is the mid-point of AB and GD is parallel to AC.

In the triangle AGD,

$$\cos \theta = \frac{GD}{AG} = \frac{\frac{1}{2}h}{\frac{1}{2}a} \qquad \text{(i)}$$

In the triangle ACB,

$$\cos CAB = \frac{h^2 + a^2 - l^2}{2ah}$$

but $$\cos CAB = -\cos \theta$$

∴ $$-\cos \theta = \frac{h^2 + a^2 - l^2}{2ah}.$$

Substituting $h = a \cos \theta$ from (i), we get

$$-\cos \theta = \frac{a^2 \cos^2 \theta + a^2 - l^2}{2a^2 \cos \theta}$$

∴ $$-2a^2 \cos^2 \theta = a^2 \cos^2 \theta + a^2 - l^2$$

∴ $$\cos^2 \theta = \frac{l^2 - a^2}{3a^2}.$$

Again, the tension in the string and the reaction R at A can be found by resolving horizontally and vertically, or by using the triangle CAD as the triangle of forces.

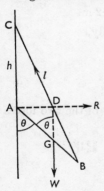

FIG. 12.6

EXAMPLE (v)

A rectangular board, 1·8 m by 1·2 m, is suspended with its longer sides horizontal by means of a light string 4·8 m long passing through smooth rings at the upper corners and over a smooth peg. Find the tension of the string and the thrust on each ring if the weight of the board is W.

Let ABCD (Fig. 12.7) represent the board, and O the position of the peg, the rings being at A and B.

Since the string is continuous and only passes over smooth surfaces, the tension T is the same throughout.

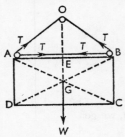

FIG. 12.7

The resultant of the two tensions at O bisects the angle AOB, and it must also balance the weight W acting vertically through G, the centre of gravity of the board.

Hence G must be vertically below O.

If OG cut AB in E, AE = 0·9 m.

Also $\qquad$ AO+OB = 3 m, and OA = OB,

∴ $\qquad$ AO = 1·5 m

∴ $\qquad$ OE = $\sqrt{(2 \cdot 25 - 0 \cdot 81)} = 1 \cdot 2$ m.

If the angle AOE = θ, then resolving vertically,

$$2T \cos \theta = W$$

and $\qquad \cos \theta = \frac{4}{5}$

∴ $\qquad T = \frac{5}{8} W.$

The thrust R on the ring at A is the resultant of the two forces T acting at an angle OAE, where cos OAE = $\frac{3}{5}$.

∴ $\qquad R^2 = T^2 + T^2 + 2T^2 \times \frac{3}{5} = \frac{16}{5} T^2 = \frac{16}{5} \times \frac{25}{64} W^2$

∴ $\qquad R = \frac{\sqrt{5}}{2} W.$

The direction of R bisects the angle OAE.

EXAMPLE (vi)

A heavy uniform rod, 26 cm long and of mass 10 kg, is suspended from a fixed point by strings fastened to its ends, their lengths being 24 cm and 10 cm. Find the angle at which the rod is inclined to the vertical and the tensions in the strings.

Let AB (Fig. 12.8) represent the rod, and O the point of suspension. The weight of the rod is 98 N.

Since there are only three forces acting on the rod, the line of the weight must pass through O, i.e. the mid-point G of the rod must be vertically below O.

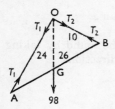

FIG. 12.8

Let $\angle OAB = \theta$.

Since $24^2 + 10^2 = 26^2$

the angle AOB is a right angle, and

$$GO = GA = GB$$

∴ $\angle AOG = \theta.$

Let T_1 and T_2 N be the tensions in OA and OB. Resolving along OA and OB, we have immediately

$$T_1 = 98 \cos \theta = \tfrac{12}{13} \times 98 = 90{\cdot}5$$
$$T_2 = 98 \sin \theta = \tfrac{5}{13} \times 98 = 37{\cdot}7.$$

EXAMPLE (vii)

A rod whose centre of gravity divides it into two portions, a and b, rests inside a smooth sphere in a position inclined to the horizontal. Show that, if θ be its inclination to the horizontal and 2α the angle it subtends at the centre of the sphere,

$$\tan \theta = \frac{b-a}{b+a} \tan \alpha.$$

Let AB (Fig. 12.9) be the rod, C the centre of the sphere. Since the sphere is smooth, the reactions at A and B must be normal to the sphere, and therefore pass through C. Hence the line of the weight must pass through C, i.e. the centre of gravity G must be vertically below C.

The result then follows from the geometry of the figure.

Let $AG = a$, $GB = b$. Since the angle $ACB = 2\alpha$, the angles A and B are each equal to $90° - \alpha$.

Draw CD perpendicular to AB. Then angle $GCD = \theta$. Also $AD = \frac{1}{2}(a+b)$ and $GD = \frac{1}{2}(a+b)-a = \frac{1}{2}(b-a)$.

Hence
$$\tan \theta = \frac{GD}{CD}$$

$$= \frac{\frac{1}{2}(b-a)}{\frac{1}{2}(b+a) \cot \alpha} = \frac{b-a}{b+a} \tan \alpha.$$

If the reactions are required they can now be found by taking moments, or by resolving in two perpendicular directions.

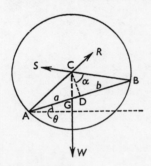

FIG. 12.9

Let R, S be the reactions at A and B respectively.
Taking moments for the rod about A, we get

$$S(a+b) \sin (90°-\alpha) = Wa \cos \theta$$

$$\therefore \qquad S = W \frac{a \cos \theta}{(a+b) \cos \alpha}.$$

Taking moments about B, we get

$$R(a+b) \sin (90°-\alpha) = Wb \cos \theta$$

$$\therefore \qquad R = W \frac{b \cos \theta}{(a+b) \cos \alpha}.$$

EXAMPLE (viii)

A rod, which is not uniform, rests in a vertical plane with its lower end A on a smooth plane inclined at an angle α to the horizontal, and the upper end B against a smooth vertical wall. If G is the centre of gravity of the rod, and β its inclination to the horizontal, show that

$$\frac{AG}{GB} = \frac{\sin \alpha \sin \beta}{\cos (\alpha+\beta)}. \qquad \text{(H.S.D.)}$$

Let the reactions at A and B, which are normal to the plane and wall respectively, meet at C (Fig. 12.10). Then G must be vertically below C.

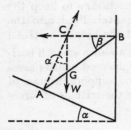

FIG. 12.10

Now $\angle CBG = \beta$, $\angle ACG = \alpha$, and $\angle CAG = 90° - \beta - \alpha$.

Hence
$$\frac{AG}{\sin \alpha} = \frac{CG}{\sin CAG} = \frac{CG}{\cos (\alpha + \beta)}$$

and
$$\frac{GB}{\sin 90°} = \frac{CG}{\sin \beta}$$

∴
$$\frac{AG}{GB} = \frac{\sin \alpha \sin \beta}{\cos (\alpha + \beta)}.$$

Note. In most of these problems the result follows from the geometry of the figure, if it is drawn so that the three forces meet at a point.

EXAMPLES 12.1

1. A uniform rod can turn freely about a hinge at one of its ends, and is pulled aside from the vertical by a horizontal force acting at the other end of the rod and equal to half the weight of the rod. Find the inclination to the vertical at which the rod will rest.

2. If, in Question 1, the horizontal force is three-quarters the weight of the rod, find the inclination to the vertical, and also the reaction at the hinge.

3. A ladder AB rests against a smooth vertical wall at A and is supported by a socket in which its lower end B is placed; the vertical through G (the centre of gravity of the ladder and the load) meets the horizontal through A in K, and the same horizontal cuts the vertical through B in L. Prove that the triangle BKL will serve as a triangle of forces for the weight and the reactions at A and B.   (I.S.)

4. A uniform beam AB of weight W can turn in a vertical plane about a hinge at A, and to the other end B is tied a rope which passes over a smooth pulley C vertically above A so that AC = AB. Find the tension of the rope necessary to keep the beam at an angle of 60° with the horizontal. Find also the direction and magnitude of the reaction at the hinge.   (I.A.)

5. AB is a uniform bar of weight W, movable about a smooth horizontal axis fixed at A; to B is attached a light cord which passes over a pulley C fixed vertically over A, and supports a mass of weight P at its free end. Show by applying the triangle of forces that, in the position of equilibrium,

$$\text{CB} = 2\frac{P}{W} \times \text{AC}.$$ (I.A.)

6. A uniform heavy rod AB freely hinged to a fixed point A in a smooth wall is kept in a horizontal position parallel to the wall by a light cord, attached to its free end B and fastened to a point P in the line LM in which the wall meets the ceiling. Prove that for various positions of P on LM (the length of the cord being adjusted so that the rod is always horizontal) the tension in the cord is proportional to its length BP.   (H.S.D.)

7. A pole rests with its lower end P in a socket, and is supported by a rope joining a point Q of the pole to a point R vertically above the socket. Prove that if the vertical through the centre of gravity of the pole cuts QR in S, the triangle PRS forms a triangle of forces for the weight, the tension in the rope, and the reaction of the socket.   (H.C.)

8. A uniform rod 3 m long is suspended by a light string of length 5 m passing over a smooth peg, and rests horizontally, the string being attached to the ends of the rod. If the rod has a mass of 7 kg, find the tension of the string.   (H.C.)

9. A uniform rod AB of mass 10 kg is smoothly hinged at A and rests in a vertical plane with the end B against a smooth vertical wall. If the rod makes an angle of 40° with the wall, find the pressure on the wall and the magnitude and direction of the reaction at A.   (H.C.)

10. A uniform lamina of weight W in the form of an isosceles triangle ABC right-angled at B is freely hinged to a fixed point at A and rests with AC vertical and C above A, equilibrium being maintained by a horizontal string attached to C. Find the tension in the string and the magnitude and direction of the reaction at A.   (H.C.)

11. A uniform equilateral triangular lamina ABC of weight W has the vertex A hinged to a fixed point, about which it can turn freely in a vertical plane, and rests with AB vertical, B being above A, and the vertex C in contact with a smooth vertical wall. Find the reaction between the lamina and the wall, and the magnitude and direction of the reaction at A. (H.C.)

12. A uniform rod ACB of weight W is supported with its end A against a smooth vertical wall, with the end B uppermost; by means of a string attached to C and to a point D in the wall on the same level as B. If the inclination of CD to the wall is 30°, find the tension of the string and the reaction at the wall, and prove that $AC = \frac{1}{3}AB$. (H.C.)

13. A uniform rod AB is in equilibrium at an angle α with the horizontal with its upper end A resting against a smooth peg and its lower end B attached to a light cord, which is fastened to a point C on the same level as A. Prove that the angle β at which the cord is inclined to the horizontal is given by the equation

$$\tan \beta = 2 \tan \alpha + \cot \alpha,$$

and that $$AC = \frac{AB \sec \alpha}{1+2 \tan^2 \alpha}.$$ (H.S.C.)

14. A uniform heavy rod, whose length is equal to the diameter of a smooth hemispherical bowl which is fixed with its axis vertical, rests with one end in the bowl and the other end outside the bowl. Prove that the inclination of the rod to the horizontal is about 32° 32′. (I.S.)

15. A sphere of mass 5 kg and radius 63 cm is hung by a string 24 cm long from a point in a smooth vertical wall. Find the tension in the string. (H.S.D.)

16. A uniform flagstaff, 12 m long and of mass 120 kg, has its lower end attached to the ground by a swivel; it is being raised by a rope attached to its highest point. If the inclination of the rope to the horizontal is 20° when that of the flagstaff is 50°, find graphically or otherwise, the tension of the rope and the magnitude and direction of the reaction of the swivel. (I.A.)

17. A uniform bar AB, of weight $2W$ and length l, is free to turn about a smooth hinge at its upper end A, and a horizontal force is applied to the end B so that the bar is in equilibrium with B at a distance a from the vertical through A. Prove that the reaction at the hinge is equal to

$$W \left[\frac{4l^2 - 3a^2}{l^2 - a^2} \right]^{\frac{1}{2}}.$$ (I.S.)

18. A rectangular block hangs suspended from a support by two wires of equal length attached to two points symmetrically situated on the upper face, the upper ends being attached to the same point of the support. Show that the tension in the wires is increased if their lengths are shortened. If the block is cubical, of edge 0·9 m and mass 2000 kg, and the points of attachment of the wires are 0·6 m apart, find the shortest possible length of the wires, given that the breaking strain of each is 15 000 N. (I.E.)

19. A uniform circular plate of weight W, whose centre is C and plane vertical, is freely movable in its own plane about a horizontal axis fixed at a point A of the circumference. The line AC is to be kept at a given inclination α to the vertical by causing the plate to rest against a fixed smooth peg at a point B on the circumference. Find the position of B such that the pressure on the peg is least, and find this least pressure.   (I.A.)

20. A uniform circular hoop, of radius a and weight W, free to move in a vertical plane, passes through a smooth fixed ring at P, and a point Q of the hoop is attached by an inextensible string of length l to a fixed point O vertically above P. Prove that in the equilibrium position the tension of the string is $W(l+a)/\text{PO}$, provided that $\text{PO}>l$.   (I.A.)

21. A picture of mass 5 kg is hung from a nail by a cord 1·5 m long fastened to two rings 0·9 m apart. Find the tension in the cord.   (I.A.)

22. A uniform ladder of mass 20 kg rests at an angle 25° with the vertical, with one end against a smooth vertical wall and the other end on a rough horizontal floor, the vertical plane through the ladder being perpendicular to the wall. Find the magnitudes of the reactions at the floor and the wall.   (H.S.D.)

23. A sphere, of radius a and weight W, rests on a smooth inclined plane supported by a string of length l with one end attached to a point on the surface of the sphere and the other end fastened to a point on the plane. If the angle of inclination of the plane to the horizontal be α, prove that the tension of the string is

$$\frac{W(a+l)\sin\alpha}{\sqrt{(l^2+2al)}}.\qquad\text{(H.S.D.)}$$

24. A uniform rod AB can turn freely in a vertical plane about the end A, which is fixed, and the rod is held at an inclination θ to the vertical by means of a string attached to B. Find the direction of the string that the tension in it may be as small as possible, and determine the reaction of the hinge in this case.

25. An equilateral triangular lamina is suspended by threads fastened to two of its angular points. The direction of the threads pass through the centre of gravity of the lamina, and one of them is horizontal and has a tension of 5 N. Find the tension of the other thread and the weight of the lamina.

26. A uniform rod, 3 m long and of mass 20 kg, is placed on two smooth planes inclined at 30° and 60° to the horizontal. Find the pressures on each plane and the inclination of the rod to the horizontal when in equilibrium.

12.4. Rigid body subject to more than three forces

We have now to consider the general case where there are more than three coplanar forces acting on a rigid body. The forces need not meet in a point.

From the principle of the transmissibility of force we assume that the point of application of any force may be taken as **any** point on its line of action. For example, if four forces act on a rigid body at the points A, B, C, and D, as shown in Fig. 12.11,

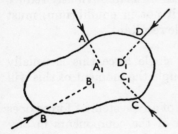

FIG. 12.11

they may be assumed to act at A_1, B_1, C_1, and D_1, points on the lines of action of the four forces. It follows that what is important is not the shape or size of the body but the magnitudes of the forces and their relative positions.

The conditions of equilibrium therefore depend only on the forces and not on the body. For this reason we frequently speak of the conditions of equilibrium of a given system of forces without specifying the body on which they act.

Questions are often set asking for the resultant of certain forces acting round the sides of a square or polygon. The sides of the figure merely fix the lines of action of the forces, which need not be acting on a body of that shape; their resultant will be the same whatever the shape of the body on which they act, provided it is rigid.

We shall first deduce the conditions of equilibrium for any number of coplanar forces from the theorem in the next paragraph. A more general method of treatment is given in 12.21.

12.5. Any system of coplanar forces acting on a rigid body, and not in equilibrium, can be reduced either to a single force or a single couple

We can always reduce any three of the forces, say P, Q, and R, to two. For we can always compound P with either Q or R, unless P forms a couple with each of them.

In this case Q and R are equal, parallel, and *like* forces (for each is in the opposite direction to P), and therefore Q and R can be compounded.

By taking another force of the system with the two forces obtained from P, Q, and R, we can again reduce the three forces to two, and by repeating this process we shall obviously reduce the system to two forces which, if not in equilibrium, must either form a couple or have a single resultant.

12.6. If the system reduces to a single force this is usually denoted by R; if it reduces to a couple the moment of this will be denoted by G.

It is evident that the reduction of any system of forces does not cause any change in the sum of the components in any direction, for on compounding any two forces the component of the resultant is equal to the sum of the components of the two forces. Hence, on reducing a system of forces, the sum of the components of the last two forces in any direction is equal to the sum of the components of the original forces in that direction, and is also equal to the component of the single resultant R to which the system finally reduces. If the system reduces to a couple the sum of the components of the original forces in any direction must be zero.

In the same way the sum of the moments about any point is unaffected by the process of reduction; the moment of R or of the couple about any point is equal to the sum of the moments of the separate forces about that point. (*Cf.* 11.13.)

It is clear that R is given in magnitude and direction by the vector sum of the system of forces. If the vector sum is zero, $R = 0$; the system will then, in general, reduce to a couple of moment G. If in addition $G = 0$ the system will be in equilibrium.

12.7. Conditions of equilibrium

Now, if R is zero its component in any direction must be zero; but to ensure, conversely, that R *is* zero we must know that its components in *two* different directions are zero. If we know that the component in one direction only is zero this direction *might* be perpendicular to the direction of R, but if the component in a second direction is also zero, then R must be zero.

Also, if the components of R in any two directions are zero the sums of the components of the separate forces in these directions must also be zero.

Since the moment of a couple is the same about all points in its plane, we see that, if G is to be zero, the sum of the moments of the separate forces of the system about *any* point in their plane must be zero.

Conversely, if the sum of the moments of the forces about *any* point in their plane is zero the system cannot reduce to a couple.

It must be noted, however, that the sum of the moments about one or two points being zero does not prove that the system is in equilibrium, for these two points might happen to be on the line of action of the single resultant. If, however, the sum of the moments about three points, not in the same straight line, is zero, then the system must be in equilibrium, as it cannot reduce to either a force or a couple.

The necessary conditions for a system of forces to be in equilibrium are (i) that the sum of the components in any given direction should be zero, and (ii) the sum of the moments about any given point should be zero, but they are not separately *sufficient* to ensure that the forces *are* in equilibrium.

12.8. The simplest set of conditions which is *sufficient* to ensure that a system of forces is in equilibrium is as follows:

(i) the sums of the components of the forces in any *two* directions must be zero; *and*

(ii) the algebraic sum of the moments of the forces about any point in their plane must be zero.

An alternative form of (i) is that the vector sum of all the forces must be zero.

Condition (i) ensures that the system does not reduce to a single force, and condition (ii) ensures that it does not reduce to a couple.

It is clear that (i) and (ii) are really equivalent to *three* conditions.

Another set of conditions already mentioned above is that the sums of the moments of the forces about three points not in the same straight line must be zero. This, again, is equivalent to three conditions.

12.9. In solving problems in Statics we are dealing with a system of forces in equilibrium, and we can therefore use one of the sets of conditions mentioned above.

As a rule we obtain three equations connecting the unknown forces and angles as follows:

(a) Equate to zero the algebraic sum of the components of all the forces in some convenient direction.

(b) Equate to zero the algebraic sum of the components of all the forces in some other direction (usually perpendicular to the direction in (a)).

(c) Equate to zero the algebraic sum of the moments of the forces about any point in their plane.

Note. The directions chosen in (a) and (b) are usually, but not necessarily, the horizontal and vertical. The point about which we take moments is usually chosen so as to exclude as many forces as possible, i.e. the point through which most of the forces pass.

12.10. The method of obtaining the equations mentioned in the last paragraph is illustrated in the following examples.

It will be noticed that there are, in some cases, geometrical relations between lengths or angles involved which give additional equations to those obtained by resolving and taking moments. In some problems the difficulties are not really in applying mechanical principles but in the geometrical and trigonometrical knowledge required to obtain the result asked for.

EXAMPLE (i)

A heavy uniform beam, hinged to a vertical wall, has a mass of 150 kg and is 4·5 m long. A tie attached to the other end keeps the beam horizontal, and is fixed to the wall 3·6 m above it. A mass of 200 kg is hung from this end. Find the tension of the tie and the thrust on the beam.

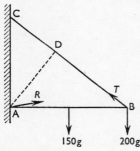

FIG. 12.12

Let AB (Fig. 12.12) represent the beam, AC the wall, and BC the tie. Since

$$AB = 4·5 \text{ m}, \quad AC = 3·6 \text{ m}$$
$$BC = 0·9\sqrt{41} \text{ m, and } \sin ABC = 4/\sqrt{41}.$$

If AD is the perpendicular from A to BC,

$$AD = AB \sin ABC = 18/\sqrt{41} \text{ m}.$$

The forces acting on the beam are shown, R being the reaction at the hinge A, and T the force at B equal to the tension in the tie. Taking moments about A so as to eliminate R, we get

$$\frac{18}{\sqrt{41}}T = 150 \text{ g} \times 2·25 + 200 \text{ g} \times 4·5$$

$$\therefore \qquad T = \frac{275 \times 9·8 \times 4·5}{18}\sqrt{41} = 673·75\sqrt{41} \text{ N}.$$

The only horizontal forces acting on the beam are the horizontal components of the tension in the tie and of the reaction at A. These must be equal and opposite, and the thrust on the beam must be equal to either of them.

Hence the thrust is

$$T \cos ABC = 673·75\sqrt{41} \times \frac{5}{\sqrt{41}}$$

$$= 3368·75 \text{ N}.$$

EXAMPLE (ii)

One end of a uniform rod of weight W is attached to a hinge, and the other end is supported by a string attached to the other end of the rod and to a point on the same level as the hinge, the rod and string being inclined at the same angle to the horizontal. Find the tension in the string and the action at the hinge.

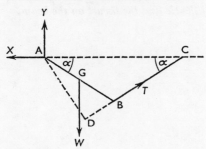

FIG. 12.13

Let AB (Fig. 12.13) be the rod, G its mid-point, and BC the string, AC being horizontal.

Let $\angle BAC = \angle BCA = \alpha$ and $AB = l$.

Then $AC = 2l \cos \alpha$, and if AD be the perpendicular from A to BC we get $AD = 2l \cos \alpha \sin \alpha$.

Hence, if T be the tension in the string, taking moments about A,

$$T \times 2l \cos \alpha \sin \alpha = W \frac{l}{2} \cos \alpha \text{ or } T = \frac{W}{4 \sin \alpha}.$$

If X and Y be the horizontal components of the reaction at A, then resolving horizontally,

$$X = T \cos \alpha = \frac{W \cos \alpha}{4 \sin \alpha}$$

and resolving vertically,

$$Y = W - T \sin \alpha = \tfrac{3}{4} W.$$

If R is the resultant reaction at A,

$$R = \sqrt{(X^2 + Y^2)} = \frac{W}{4} \sqrt{(9 + \cot^2 \alpha)}.$$

If θ is the inclination of R to the horizontal,

$$\tan \theta = \frac{Y}{X} = \tfrac{3}{4} \times \frac{4 \sin \alpha}{\cos \alpha} = 3 \tan \alpha.$$

EXAMPLE (iii)

A pole with one end resting on the ground is kept vertical by two ropes attached to fixed points on the ground at equal distances d from the foot of the pole, and in the same plane with it. The ropes are fastened to the pole at heights a, b, and the tensions are adjusted so that the vertical reaction on the ground is twice the weight of the pole. Prove that the total reaction on the ground makes an angle θ with the vertical, where

$$\tan\theta = \tfrac{1}{4}d\left(\frac{1}{a}\sim\frac{1}{b}\right).$$

Let OAB (Fig. 12.14) be the pole, O the lower end, and A and B the points of attachment of the ropes AC, BD, so that OC = OD = *d*.

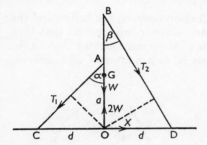

Fig. 12.14

Let AO = *a*, OB = *b*, $\angle$OBD = β, $\angle$OAC = α, and let the tensions in AC and BD be T_1 and T_2.

Taking moments about O,

$$T_1 d \cos\alpha = T_2 d \cos\beta. \tag{i}$$

Now since the vertical reaction on the ground is $2W$, where W is the weight of the pole, the sum of the vertical components of the tensions must be equal to W.

$$\therefore \qquad T_1 \cos\alpha + T_2 \cos\beta = W. \tag{ii}$$

Hence, using (i),

$$T_1 \cos\alpha = T_2 \cos\beta = W/2.$$

The horizontal component, X, of the reaction on the ground must equal the difference between the horizontal components of the tensions, for resolving horizontally we get:

$$X = T_1 \sin\alpha - T_2 \sin\beta = \frac{W}{2}(\tan\alpha - \tan\beta)$$

$$= \frac{W}{2}\left(\frac{d}{a} - \frac{d}{b}\right).$$

The vertical reaction is $2W$, so that

$$\tan \theta = \frac{X}{2W} = \frac{d}{4}\left(\frac{1}{a} - \frac{1}{b}\right).$$

EXAMPLE (iv)

A roller of 42 cm radius lies on the ground; a uniform plank 60 cm long rests flat on the roller with one end on the ground and the other projecting over the roller, the length of the plank being at right angles to the axis of the roller. If the roller and the plank are prevented from slipping by a cord 70 cm long attached to the axle of the roller and to that end of the plank which lies on the ground, prove that the tension of the cord is $\frac{9}{50}$ of the weight of the plank.

Note. No mention is made of friction between the bodies and the ground or between themselves. As, however, we are told that they are prevented from slipping by the cord we must assume that all the contacts are smooth. The problem is, as a matter of fact, indeterminate otherwise.

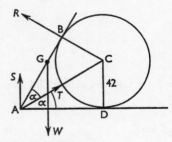

FIG. 12.15A

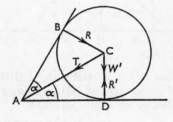

FIG. 12.15B

Let C (Fig. 12.15) be the centre of the roller, D its point of contact with the ground, AB the plank touching the roller at B, G the mid-point of the plank, and let $\angle CAD = \alpha$.

Since $CD = 42$ cm, and $AC = 70$ cm

$$AD = \sqrt{(70^2 - 42^2)} = 56 \text{ cm},$$

∴ $AB = 56$ cm.

Figure 12.15A shows the forces acting on the plank and Fig. 12.15B the forces on the roller.

The reaction R acting on the plank at its contact with the roller is along the radius CB, and the weight W of the plank acts vertically through G.

Taking moments about A for the plank, to eliminate the reaction S at the ground and the tension T, we get

$$56R = W \times 30 \cos 2\alpha.$$

Now $\sin \alpha = \frac{3}{5}$, $\cos \alpha = \frac{4}{5}$ and $\cos 2\alpha = \cos^2 \alpha - \sin^2 \alpha = \frac{7}{25}$

$$\therefore \qquad R = W \times \frac{30 \times 7}{56 \times 25} = \frac{3}{20}W.$$

The forces tending to move the roller horizontally are the horizontal components of R and of the tension T in the cord. Since these must be equal and opposite, we get

$$T \cos \alpha = R \sin 2\alpha$$

$$\therefore \qquad T = 2R \sin \alpha = 2 \times \frac{3W}{20} \times \frac{3}{5} = \frac{9W}{50}.$$

EXAMPLE (v)

A uniform rod of weight W and length 2a is free to turn about one end A. It is supported by means of a light string of length l, one end of which is attached to a point vertically above and at a distance h from A, while the other end is attached to a smooth ring of weight w through which the rod passes. Show that in the equilibrium position the string is inclined at an angle θ to the vertical, where

$$Wal(h \cos \theta - l) = w(l^2 - 2lh \cos \theta + h^2)^{\frac{3}{2}}.$$

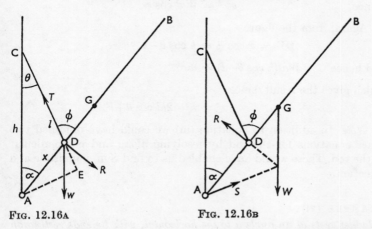

FIG. 12.16A   FIG. 12.16B

Let C (Fig. 12.16) be the upper end of the string, D the position of the ring, G the mid-point of the rod, and let the angle CAD = α, the angle CDG = ϕ, and AD = x.

Draw AE (Fig. 12.16A) perpendicular to CD, then AE $= h \sin \theta$.
Let T be the tension in the string.

Figure 12.16A shows the forces acting on the ring, and Fig. 12.16B the forces on the rod. S is the reaction acting on the rod at the hinge. Equal and opposite forces R act on the ring and rod perpendicular to the rod.

For the ring, resolving along and perpendicular to AB, we get

$$T \cos \phi = w \cos \alpha \tag{i}$$

and $\qquad\qquad T \sin \phi = w \sin \alpha + R. \tag{ii}$

For the rod only, taking moments about A, we get

$$Rx = Wa \sin \alpha. \tag{iii}$$

Substituting in (ii), for T from (i) and R from (iii), we get

$$w \cos \alpha \tan \phi = w \sin a + W \frac{a}{x} \sin \alpha$$

$\therefore \qquad wx(\cos \alpha \tan \phi - \sin \alpha) = Wa \sin \alpha$

$\therefore \qquad wx \sin (\phi - \alpha) = Wa \sin \alpha \cos \phi$

$\therefore \qquad wx \sin \theta = Wa \sin \alpha \cos \phi.$

But from the figure

$$\frac{x}{\sin \theta} = \frac{l}{\sin \alpha}.$$

Hence, $\qquad\qquad wx^2 = Wal \cos \phi.$

Again, from the figure

$$\mathrm{DE} = x \cos \phi = h \cos \theta - l$$

and hence $\qquad Wal(h \cos \theta - l) = wx^3$

which gives the result, since

$$x^2 = h^2 - 2hl \cos \theta + l^2.$$

Note. In addition to equation (iii) we could have obtained two other equations for the rod by resolving along and perpendicular to the rod. These would have enabled us to find S in magnitude and direction.

EXAMPLE (vi)

A ladder rests at an angle α to the horizontal, with its ends resting on a smooth floor and against a smooth vertical wall, the lower end being joined by a string to the junction of the wall and the floor. Find the tension of the string, and the reaction at the wall and the ground. Find

*also the tension of the string when a man, whose weight is equal to that
of the ladder, has ascended the ladder three-quarters of its length.*

Let AB (Fig. 12.17) be the ladder, C the junction of the wall and
the floor, and G the mid-point of the ladder.

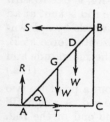

FIG. 12.17

Since the surfaces are smooth, the reactions at A and B are
normal to the ground and wall; let these be R and S.

Let W be the weight of the ladder, acting vertically through G,
and let T be the tension in the string.

Resolving vertically, $R = W.$ (i)

Resolving horizontally, $S = T.$ (ii)

Taking moments about B,

$$T \times AB \sin \alpha = R \times AB \cos \alpha - W \frac{AB}{2} \cos \alpha.$$ (iii)

Substituting for R from (i),

$$T \sin \alpha = W \cos \alpha - \tfrac{1}{2} W \cos \alpha$$

$\therefore$ $\qquad\qquad\qquad T = \tfrac{1}{2} W \cot \alpha.$

From (ii) $S = T = \tfrac{1}{2} W \cot \alpha.$

When the man is at D, where $AD = \tfrac{3}{4} AB$, equations (i) and (iii)
become

$$R = W + W = 2W$$

and $\quad T \times AB \sin \alpha = R \times AB \cos \alpha - W \frac{AB}{2} \cos \alpha - W \frac{AB}{4} \cos \alpha$

$\therefore$ $\qquad\qquad T \sin \alpha = 2W \cos \alpha - \tfrac{3}{4} W \cos \alpha$

$\therefore$ $\qquad\qquad\qquad T = \tfrac{5}{4} W \cot \alpha.$

EXAMPLES 12.2

1. A heavy bar AB, of mass 20 kg and length 2·4 m, is hinged at A
to a point in a vertical wall, and is maintained in a horizontal
position by means of a chain attached to B and to a point in

the wall 1·5 m above A. If the bar carries a load of 10 kg at a point 1·8 m from A, calculate the tension in the chain, and the magnitude and direction of the action at A between the bar and the wall.   (I.E.)

2. A uniform rod ACB, 1·8 m long and of mass 4 kg, is free to turn about a hinge at C, which is 0·6 m from A. The rod is kept at an inclination of 45° to the vertical with A downwards by a downward vertical force of 49 N at A, and a horizontal force at B. Find the magnitude of the force at B, and the magnitude and direction of the reaction at the hinge C.   (I.E.)

3. A heavy uniform rod of weight W is hung from a point by two equal strings, one attached to each end of the rod. A weight W is hung half-way between the centre and one end of the rod. Prove that the ratio of the tensions in the strings is

$$\frac{2W+3w}{2W+w}.$$ (H.S.C.)

4. A door 2·25 m in height is hung from two hinges placed 25 cm from the top and bottom. The door has a mass of 18 kg, and its centre of gravity is 67·5 cm distant from the line of the hinges. Find the total force on each hinge, it being assumed that half the weight of the door is supported by each hinge.   (I.S.)

5. A gate hangs from two hinges A, B, its centre of gravity being G, and the vertical through G meets the horizontal through B in K. Prove that if the whole weight is supported at A the triangle ABK will serve as a triangle of forces to determine the reactions at A, B; also modify this construction when the weight is equally divided between A and B.   (I.S.)

6. A uniform beam rests with its ends on two smooth inclined planes which make angles of 30° and 60° with the horizontal respectively. A weight equal to twice that of the beam can slide along its length. Find the position of the sliding weight when the beam rests in a horizontal position.   (I.A.)

7. A smooth uniform ladder rests with its extremities against a vertical wall and a horizontal plane, and is held by a rope, one end of which is attached to a rung of the ladder one-quarter of the way up, the other end being fixed to a point of the base of the wall, vertically below the top of the ladder. Show that if the base and top of the ladder be distant a and b respectively from the base of the wall the ratio of the reactions P and Q between the ladder and the ground and wall respectively is given by

$$Q/P = 3a/5b.$$ (I.A.)

8. A ladder, 3 m long and of mass 17·5 kg, rests with the end A against a smooth vertical wall, and the other end B on the ground, which is smooth, at a distance of 1·8 m from the wall; it is maintained in this position by a horizontal cord attached at B. Find the tension of the cord if the centre of gravity of the ladder is 1·2 m from B. Find also the magnitude and direction of the force which, applied at A, will keep the ladder in position without the help of the cord. (I.S.)

9. A uniform plank AB, 1·8 m long and of given weight, is supported horizontally by two pegs at C and D respectively, where AC = BD = 20 cm. Another exactly equal plank A′B′ is placed over the first so that A′ projects 27·5 cm beyond A. Find the pressures R_1 and R_2 at C and D. A vertical force P is now applied at A′, but so that equilibrium is still maintained; if $R_1′$ and $R_2′$ are the new pressures at C and D, show that

$$\frac{R_1′ - R_1}{R_2 - R_2′} = \frac{75}{19}.$$ (H.S.D.)

10. The centre of gravity of a hemispherical bowl is on the radius round which the bowl is symmetrical, and divides this radius in the ratio $m : n$. If the bowl is placed with its curved surface in contact with a plane, rough enough to prevent sliding, inclined at an angle θ to the horizontal, find the inclination of the rim of the bowl to the horizontal. It is found that the bowl rests in equilibrium, with the plane of its rim vertical, when θ is approximately 25°. Calculate the ratio $m : n$. (I.S.)

11. A man wishes to pull a smooth lawn roller of diameter 50 cm and mass 100 kg over a kerbstone 10 cm high. Find the direction in which he should pull, in any position of the roller, so as to raise the roller with the least effort; and show that the greatest force he need exert is 784 N. (H.C.)

12. It is required to pull a garden roller of weight W and radius r, whose centre of gravity lies on its axis, up a step of height $\frac{1}{4}r$. The force is applied to a handle which acts directly on the axis of the roller. What is the best direction in which to pull the handle? Compare the force required to move the roller, when applied in this direction, with that required when the handle is pulled horizontally. Is there any tendency for the roller to slip on the step or ground? (H.S.D.)

13. A uniform bar AB, 0·9 m long and of mass 2 kg, has a cord 1·5 m long attached to its ends. The cord passes through a smooth ring O fixed in a smooth vertical wall, and the rod is placed in a vertical plane perpendicular to the wall with the end A against

the wall and vertically below O. Prove that the rod will be in equilibrium if OA is 0·6 m, and show that the tension of the string is 14·7 N. (H.C.)

14. A telegraph pole carries six wires, of which three go south, two go north-east, and one west. If all the wires are in one horizontal plane and are stretched to a tension of 900 N, find the pull they exert on the pole. The wires are each 12 m above the ground and a stay fixed to the pole at a point 9 m up is made fast to the ground 4·5 m from the foot of the pole. Find the tension in this stay if there is no tendency for the pole to overturn. (N.U.S.)

15. A triangular lamina ABC in which the angles at B and C are 45° is of mass 3 kg and is hung from the mid-point of the side BC. Masses of 2 and 8 kg respectively are hung from A and B and a mass M is hung from C. Find the value of M if the side BC makes an angle of 60° with the vertical. (Q.E.)

12.11. Jointed rods

We shall now consider some problems where two or more rigid bodies are involved, and, in particular, cases where a number of heavy rods are smoothly jointed together.

We shall not consider the stresses in the material of the rods.

In the ordinary problems on the equilibrium of jointed heavy rods we only consider the forces acting at the joints (and, of course, the weights of the rods), i.e. we consider the equilibrium of the rods under the action of their own weight and the forces exerted on their *ends* by the hinges.

12.12. Consider a heavy rod AB (Fig. 12.18) freely jointed at A and B.

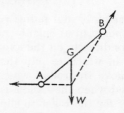

Fig. 12.18

Its weight acts vertically through its centre of gravity G, and it is obvious that, to keep it in equilibrium by means of forces applied at A and B, these forces must either be vertical or they must meet, as shown, on the line of action of the weight. i.e. the vertical through G.

In neither case can they act along the rod (unless it is vertical). If, however, the rod is *light*, then forces applied at the ends which keep it in equilibrium must be equal and opposite and act *along the rod.*

It is the confusion between the cases of the heavy rod and the light rod which causes most of the trouble experienced by students in problems on heavy rods. In the case of a heavy rod the one direction in which the forces at the ends *cannot* act is along the rod. We usually consider the horizontal and vertical components of the force exerted by a hinge on the rod, and in order to show these clearly in the diagram, it is better in drawing it not to make the rods meet, but to leave a space between them.

12.13. EXAMPLE (i)

Two equal uniform rods AC and CB are smoothly jointed at C, and have their other ends attached to supports at two points, A and B, at the same level. If each rod has a mass of 40 kg and is inclined at 60° to the horizontal, find the action on the hinge C.

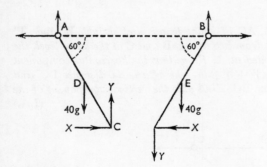

FIG. 12.19

Let D, E (Fig. 12.19) be the mid-points of the rods; then the weights of 40g N act vertically at D and E.

Let X, Y be the horizontal and vertical components of the action of the hinge at C on the rod AC. Its action on BC will consist of components equal to those on AC but in opposite directions. These forces and the forces acting on the rods at the supports at A and B are shown in the figure.

Let *l* be the length of each rod.

Taking moments about A for AC,

$$Xl \sin 60° + Yl \cos 60° = 40 \text{ g} \frac{l}{2} \cos 60°$$

∴ $X \tan 60° + Y = 20 \text{ g}.$ (i)

Taking moments about B for BC,

$$Xl \sin 60° - Yl \cos 60° = 40 \text{ g} \frac{l}{2} \cos 60°$$

$$X \tan 60° - Y = 20 \text{ g}.$$ (ii)

From equations (i) and (ii) it is obvious that $Y = 0$.

Hence the reaction at C consists only of a horizontal force X N whose value is given by

$$X \tan 60° = 20 \text{ g}$$

∴ $X = \dfrac{196}{\sqrt{3}} = \dfrac{196}{3}\sqrt{3}.$

Note. Since the whole system is symmetrical about the vertical through C, we might have argued without writing down any equations that Y must be zero. It is clear from Fig. 12.19 that the forces on the two rods are identical only if Y is zero; otherwise the symmetry is destroyed.

EXAMPLE (ii)

Two uniform bars AB, AC *of equal length and weight* W *and* W' *hang in a vertical plane from two hinges* B *and* C *at the same level, the bars being smoothly jointed at* A. *Prove that the horizontal component of the reaction at* A *is* $\frac{1}{4}(W + W')a/h$, *where* 2a *is the distance* BC, *and* h *is the depth of* A *below* BC. *Find also the vertical component of the reaction.*   (I.A.)

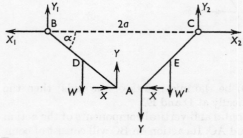

FIG. 12.20

Let D, E (Fig. 12.20) be the mid-points of the rods, and X, Y the horizontal and vertical components of the action of the hinge at A on the rods.

These must be in opposite directions on the two rods, but it does not matter whether we show them as in the figure or in reversed directions. If we take them in the opposite directions to those in which they really act we shall simply obtain *negative* values for them.

Let the angle ABC $= \alpha$, then the angle ACB $= \alpha$ also. Let l be the length of each rod.

Taking moments about B for AB, we get:

$$X \, l \sin \alpha + Yl \cos \alpha = W \frac{l}{2} \cos \alpha$$

$$\therefore \qquad X \tan \alpha + Y = \tfrac{1}{2} W. \qquad \text{(i)}$$

Taking moments about C for AC, we get:

$$Xl \sin \alpha - Yl \cos \alpha = W' \frac{l}{2} \cos \alpha$$

$$\therefore \qquad X \tan \alpha - Y = \tfrac{1}{2} W'. \qquad \text{(ii)}$$

Adding (i) and (ii),

$$2X \tan \alpha = \tfrac{1}{2}(W + W')$$

$$\therefore \qquad X = \tfrac{1}{4}(W + W') \cot \alpha$$

$$\therefore \qquad X = \frac{(W + W')a}{4h}, \text{ since } \cot \alpha = \frac{a}{h}.$$

Subtracting (ii) from (i)

$$2Y = \tfrac{1}{2}(W - W') \text{ or } Y = \tfrac{1}{4}(W - W').$$

Note. The other four equations obtained by resolving horizontally and vertically for the rod AB and for the rod BC would enable us to find X_1, Y_1 and X_2, Y_2, the components of the reactions on the rods at the hinges B and C.

EXAMPLE (iii)

A square figure ABCD is formed of four equal heavy uniform rods jointed together, and the system is suspended from the joint A, and kept in the form of a square by a string connecting the joints at A and C. Find the tension in the string, and the magnitude and direction of the action at either of the joints B or D.

Draw the diagram as in Fig. 12.21, leaving gaps at A, B, C, and D. All the forces acting on AD and CD are shown; identical sets of forces act on AB and BC from symmetry.

Let X, Y be the horizontal and vertical components of the action of the hinge at D on AD. The reaction on CD will consist of components equal to those on AD but in opposite directions.

The forces acting on AD are the forces X, Y at D, its weight W and certain forces at A. Since the supporting force R acting on the whole system at A is $4W$, by symmetry $2W$ acts on AD and $2W$ acts on AB. Similarly, a force $\frac{1}{2}T$, equal to half the tension in the string,

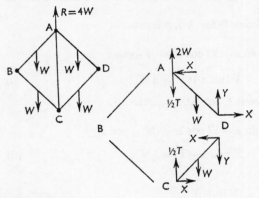

Fig. 12.21

acts downwards on AD at A. In addition, there is the reaction at the hinge A; the vertical component of this is zero from symmetry, and the horizontal component must equal X in the direction shown, since the only other horizontal force acting on AD is X at D.

Resolving vertically,

$$2W + Y = W + \tfrac{1}{2}T \tag{i}$$

and taking moments about A, if l is the length of the rod, we get

$$Xl \cos 45° + Yl \sin 45° = W(\tfrac{1}{2}l \sin 45°)$$

$$\therefore \qquad\qquad X + Y = \tfrac{1}{2}W. \tag{ii}$$

The forces acting on CD are the forces X, Y at D as shown, its weight W, the tension $\frac{1}{2}T$ upwards as explained above, and the reaction at the hinge C. The vertical component of this reaction is zero from symmetry, and its horizontal component must equal X in the direction shown, since the only other horizontal force acting on CD is X at D.

Resolving vertically

$$\tfrac{1}{2}T = W + Y \tag{iii}$$

and taking moments about C we get

$$Xl \cos 45° - Yl \sin 45° = W(\tfrac{1}{2}l \cos 45°)$$

$$\therefore \qquad\qquad X - Y = \tfrac{1}{2}W. \tag{iv}$$

From (ii) and (iv) $Y = 0$ and $X = \frac{1}{2}W$. (We could not foresee here that $Y = 0$.)

Substituting in (i) or (iii), $T = 2W$.

EXAMPLE (iv)

Four equal uniform rods are freely jointed to form a rhombus ABCD. The rhombus is suspended from the joint A, and is maintained in the form of a square by means of a rod of negligible weight joining the midpoints of AC and CD. Find the vertical and horizontal components of the reactions at the joints B and D.

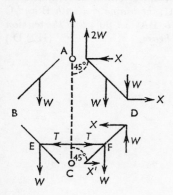

FIG. 12.22

Since EF has no weight, the forces exerted on it by the rods at E and F must be along its length and equal and opposite (Fig. 12.22). Also since the figure would tend to collapse so that B and D moved inwards, it is evident that there is a thrust T in EF.

Since the supporting force on the whole system at A is $4W$, by symmetry $2W$ acts on AD and $2W$ acts on AB.

The vertical component of the reaction on AD at the joint A is zero from symmetry; the horizontal component is denoted by X as shown. At the other joint D the horizontal component of the reaction on AD must also be X in the direction shown, and the vertical component must be W downwards (resolving vertically).

Taking moments about A for the rod AD, if l is the length of AD we get

$$Xl \cos 45° = Wl \sin 45° + W(\tfrac{1}{2}l \sin 45°)$$

$$\therefore \qquad\qquad X = \tfrac{3}{2}W$$

The vertical and horizontal components of the reaction at D are therefore W and $\frac{3}{2}W$, and by symmetry they will be the same at B.

If we were asked for the thrust in EF we could find it by taking moments about C for CD; this gives

$$T\frac{l}{2}\cos 45° + W\frac{l}{2}\sin 45° = \tfrac{3}{2}W \times l\cos 45° + W \times l\sin 45°$$

$$\therefore \qquad \tfrac{1}{2}T + \tfrac{1}{2}W = \tfrac{3}{2}W + W$$

$$\therefore \qquad\qquad T = 4W.$$

EXAMPLE (v)

Two equal heavy beams AB, AC are smoothly jointed at A, and B is joined by a string to the mid-point of AC; the beams rest with B and C on a smooth horizontal plane; if the angle BAC = 60°, find the tension in the string in terms of the weight of a beam. (H.S.D.)

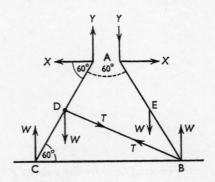

FIG. 12.23

Let D (Fig. 12.23) be the mid-point of AC, E that of AB.

Since AB = AC and the angle BAC = 60°, the triangle ABC is equilateral. Hence BD is perpendicular to AC.

Since the beams are of equal weight W and the lines of action of the weights are equidistant from B and C, the vertical reactions at B and C are each equal to W.

(This can also be shown by taking moments about C and B for *both beams*.)

Let T be the tension in the string, and l the length of each beam.

Taking moments about A for AC,

$$T \times \frac{l}{2} + W \times \frac{l}{4} = W \times \frac{l}{2}$$

$$\therefore \qquad\qquad \frac{T}{2} = \frac{W}{4} \text{ or } T = \frac{W}{2}.$$

If we required the reaction at A it could be obtained as follows:

Let X, Y be the horizontal and vertical components of the action of the hinge at A on AC.

Resolving horizontally for AC,

$$X = T \cos 30° = \frac{\sqrt{3}}{4} W.$$

Resolving vertically for AC,

$$Y + W = W + T \sin 30°$$
$$\therefore \qquad Y = \tfrac{1}{2}T = \tfrac{1}{4}W.$$

The resultant reaction R at A is given by

$$R = \sqrt{(X^2 + Y^2)} = W\sqrt{(\tfrac{3}{16} + \tfrac{1}{16})} = \tfrac{1}{2}W.$$

It is inclined to the horizontal at an angle

$$\tan^{-1}\frac{Y}{X} = \tan^{-1}\frac{1}{\sqrt{3}}$$

i.e. at an angle of 30°.

EXAMPLE (vi)

Six equal weightless rods hinged together at their ends form a regular hexagon ABCDEF. The rod AB is held horizontally and a weight W is hung from the mid-point of DE, the hexagonal shape being maintained by a light rod CF. Find the stress in the rod CF.

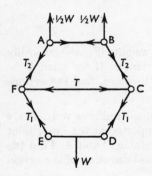

FIG. 12.24

Let ABCDEF (Fig. 12.24) represent the framework.

Since the rods are light and (except ED) acted on by forces at their ends only, the stresses in all the rods except ED must be along the length of the rods.

Let T_1 be the tension in CD and EF, and T_2 that in BC and FA. The rod ED is in equilibrium subject to its weight W and forces T_1 at E along EF and T_1 at D along DC. The vertical components of the tensions T_1 must support the weight W, and hence

$$2T_1 \cos 30° = W,$$

$$\therefore \qquad T_1 = \frac{W}{\sqrt{3}}.$$

The vertical stress at A and at B is evidently $\frac{1}{2}W$. Hence resolving vertically for the hinge B,

$$T_2 \cos 30° = \tfrac{1}{2}W$$

$$\therefore \qquad T_2 = \frac{W}{\sqrt{3}}.$$

If T is the thrust in CF, resolving vertically and horizontally for the hinge C, we get

$$T_1 \sin 60° = T_2 \sin 60° \text{ or } T_1 = T_2$$

and

$$T = T_1 \cos 60° + T_2 \cos 60°$$

$$= \frac{W}{2\sqrt{3}} + \frac{W}{2\sqrt{3}} = \frac{W}{\sqrt{3}}$$

$$\therefore \qquad T = W/\sqrt{3}.$$

EXAMPLES 12.3

1. Three equal uniform rods, each of weight W, are smoothly jointed so as to form an equilateral triangle. If the triangle be supported at the mid-point of one of its sides, find the actions at the joints.

2. A square ABCD is formed by four equal uniform rods, freely jointed together, and the system is supported at the lower joint C, and kept in shape by a light rod joining C and A. Find the thrust in the rod, and the magnitude and direction of the action at either of the joints B or D.

3. A rhombus ABCD is formed by four equal uniform rods freely jointed together, and the system is suspended from the joint A, and kept in shape, with the angle CAD = 30°, by a string connecting A and C. Find the tension in the string and the magnitude and direction of the reaction at B or D.

4. AB and BC are two uniform exactly similar rods, each of weight W, freely hinged together at B, and carrying small rings of negligible weight which enable the ends A and C to move without friction on a fixed horizontal wire. The rods are placed so as to include a right angle, with the joint B below the wire, and are prevented from closing up by means of a rigid stay of negligible weight joining the mid-points of the rods. Find the stress in this stay and the reactions at A, B, and C. (H.C.)

5. AB and BC are two rods of equal length freely jointed at B, the weight of AB is W and that of BC is $2W$. They are placed in a vertical plane inclined to one another at 90° with the ends A and C on a horizontal plane. What horizontal forces must be applied at A and C to maintain equilibrium? (I.E.)

6. Two rods AB and BC, a m and b m long, of the same material and cross-section, are freely jointed at B and hang with their ends A and C attached to two points at the same level, and at such a distance apart that ABC is a right angle. If the material of the rods has a mass of M kg per m, find the reactions at the joint B, and at the points of attachment A and C. (I.E.)

7. Two uniform ladders, each of length a and weight W, are hinged at their upper ends, and stand on a smooth horizontal plane. A weight W is hung from a rung of one of the ladders at a distance b from its lower end, and the ladders are prevented from slipping by means of a rope of length $2c$ attached to their lower ends. Find the pressure of each ladder on the ground, and the tension in the rope.

8. Two uniform rods AB, BC of the same material and thickness, but of different lengths, are freely jointed at B, and the ends A and C are fixed in the same vertical line. Show that the stress at the joint B acts along BD, the bisector of the angle ABC, and that its magnitude is

$$\tfrac{1}{2} W \frac{BD}{AC}$$

where W is the weight of the two rods.

9. A step-ladder of weight $2W$ consists of two equal parts, jointed at the top, and held together by a rope half-way between the top and bottom, so that when the rope is tight the angle between the two halves of the ladder is $2 \tan^{-1} \tfrac{6}{13}$. A man of weight $5W$ mounts the ladder and then stops two-thirds of the way up. Neglecting the friction between the ladder and the ground, find the tension in the rope and the reaction at the hinge. (I.S.)

10. Two uniform boards rest against smooth parallel walls, their lower ends being in contact on a smooth horizontal floor. Prove that if the weights of the boards are w, w', and their inclinations to the vertical θ, θ', the condition for equilibrium is

$$w \tan \theta = w' \tan \theta'. \qquad \text{(I.A.)}$$

11. Two heavy plane rectangular areas, of the same lengths, but of different widths, are hinged together along their equal sides and placed on a smooth horizontal plane with the hinge horizontal and uppermost. They are kept from sliding by a string attached to the mid-points of their lower edges. If their weights are W_1, W_2, and their inclinations to the plane are θ and ϕ respectively, prove that the action between them at the hinge makes an angle with the horizontal whose tangent is

$$\frac{W_1 \tan \phi - W_2 \tan \theta}{W_1 + W_2}. \qquad \text{(H.S.D.)}$$

12. AB, BC, CD, DE, EA are five equal uniform rods, each of weight W, freely jointed at their extremities and suspended from the joint A in the form of a regular pentagon, this configuration being maintained by light strings joining A to C and to D. Find the reactions at B and E, and show that the tension in either string is $2W \cos 18°$. (H.S.D.)

13. Three equal rods AB, BC, CD and a rod AD of double their length are freely hinged together at A, B, C, D, and the framework is suspended from the mid-point of BC. If w is the weight of each of the equal rods and $2w$ that of the longest rod, find the magnitudes of the forces on the hinges. Show that the line of action of the forces at A and B meet at a depth $BC/\sqrt{3}$ below BC. (H.S.C.)

14. A frame is formed of three uniform rods, BC, CA, AB of lengths 1·5, 2, 2·5 m and of mass 1 kg per m, smoothly joined by weightless pins at their ends. It is suspended from such a point D in the longest side AB that it rests in equilibrium with AB horizontal. Find the distance of D from the mid-point of AB and the stresses at the joints. (Ex.)

15. AC and BC are two light rods freely jointed at C, and freely jointed to a wall at A and B so that AC is horizontal and the angle $ACB = \alpha°$, and the point B is vertically below A. A weight W is suspended from C. Find the tension in AC and the thrust in BC. Prove that the tension in AC, if also a weight W' be suspended from the mid-point of BC, is $\frac{1}{2}(W' + 2W) \cot \alpha$. (H.S.D.)

16. A disc of radius a and weight W rests, as shown in Fig. 12.25, between two light rods which are smoothly hinged together at O with their ends A, B resting on a smooth table, and are maintained in equilibrium by a string AB; OA = OB = c, $\angle AOB = 2\alpha$; the whole figure is in a vertical plane. Find the tension in the string. (H.S.C.)

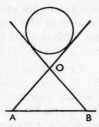

Fig. 12.25

17. BA, AC are heavy uniform rods, of mass 6 kg and 3 kg respectively, smoothly hinged to each other at A and to a light rod BC. The hinges at B and C are supported by vertical strings so that BC is horizontal with A below BC; the perpendicular from A on BC is of length 0·9 m, and its foot divides BC so that BD is 0·6 m and DC is 1·2 m. Prove that the reaction at A is horizontal; find the reaction and also the thrust in BC. (H.S.D.)

18. Two uniform rods AB, BC, alike in all respects and each of weight W, are rigidly jointed at B so that ABC is a right angle, and the end A is hinged freely to a fixed point from which the two rods hang in equilibrium. Show that AB makes an angle $\tan^{-1}\frac{1}{3}$ with the vertical. If the rods are freely jointed at B, but A and C are connected by a light inextensible string of such length that ABC is a right angle, show that the tension in the string is $3W/2\sqrt{5}$. (H.C.)

19. AB and BC are two uniform rods of weights W and W' respectively. They are freely hinged together at B and the end A is freely pivoted to a fixed point A, while the end C is constrained to move on a fixed horizontal wire, passing through A, by means of a small, smooth ring of negligible mass. Show that the horizontal force which must be applied at C to keep the rods in the position in which the angles CAB and ACB are θ and ϕ and B is below AC, is

$$\tfrac{1}{2}(W+W')\cos\phi\cos\theta\operatorname{cosec}(\theta+\phi). \qquad \text{(H.C.)}$$

20. A straight rod ABC of negligible weight is horizontal, and is pivoted at a smooth hinge A. A load of mass 100 kg hangs from C.

The rod is supported at its mid-point B by a uniform rigid rod BD of negligible weight, D being a smooth hinge fixed vertically below A, with AD = AB. Find the horizontal and vertical components of the stresses at D and B.

21. Two uniform rods AB, BC, of equal lengths but of different weights, are freely jointed at B, and jointed at A and C to two fixed points in the same horizontal line, at such a distance apart that ABC is a right angle. Show that the tangent of the angle which the direction of the reaction at B makes with the rod BA is the ratio of the weight of AB to that of BC. (I.S.)

22. Two uniform rods AB, AC, of weight W_1, W_2, and of equal length, are smoothly hinged at A, and rest with B, C on a smooth horizontal plane, being kept in equilibrium by an inextensible string joining BC. A weight w is suspended from a point in AC at a distance of $\frac{3}{4}$AC from A. Prove that the tension of the string is

$$\tfrac{1}{4}(W_1 + W_2 + \tfrac{1}{2}w) \tan \tfrac{1}{2}A. \qquad \text{(I.S.)}$$

23. Each half of a step-ladder is 1·65 m long, and the two parts are connected by a cord 70 cm long attached to points in them distant 40 cm from their free extremities. The half with the steps has a mass of 8 kg and the other half a mass of 2 kg. Find the tension in the cord when a man of mass 77 kg is standing on the ladder 45 cm from the top, it being assumed that the cord is fully stretched and that the reactions between the ladder and ground are vertical. (I.S.)

24. Two uniform bars AB, BC are smoothly jointed at B and the end C is pivoted to a point on a wall by a smooth pivot. The bar AB is 1·5 m long and has a mass of 10 kg, the bar BC is 1·2 m long and has a mass of 5 kg. The two bars are kept in a horizontal line by a prop placed under AB. Find the position of the prop and the reaction at C. (N.U.3)

25. Two equal uniform rods AB and AC, each of length 1·2 m and mass 1·5 kg, are smoothly jointed at A. They are placed symmetrically on a smooth fixed sphere of radius 0·3 m, so that A is vertically above the centre. Show that the angle between the rods when in equilibrium is a right angle, and find the magnitude of the reaction at the joint. (N.U. 3 and 4)

26. A uniform rod, of length $2a$ and mass m, is pivoted at its lower end to a fixed point O. A light string fastened at one end to a fixed point at a distance $2a$ vertically above O passes over a small smooth groove in the free upper end of the rod and supports a mass M at its other end. Find the inclination of the upper part of the string to the vertical in the position of equilibrium. (N.U.3)

27. A circular cylinder is maintained in equilibrium, with its axis horizontal and touching along its length an inclined plane, by means of a rod AB of weight equal to that of the cylinder hinged to the plane below the cylinder at A and being a tangent to the cylinder at its upper end B. The vertical plane through the rod intersects the inclined plane in a line of greatest slope, and contains the centre of gravity of the cylinder. If all the surfaces are smooth prove that

$$\tan \alpha = \frac{\sin 2\theta}{5 - \cos 2\theta}$$

where α is the inclination of the plane to the horizontal and θ is the angle which the rod AB makes with the plane.   (H.S.D.)

28. Two uniform rods AB and CD, each of weight W and length a, are smoothly jointed together at O, where $OB = OD = b$. The rods rest in a vertical plane with the ends A and C on a smooth table, and the ends B and D connected by a light string. Prove that the reaction at the joint is $(aW/2b) \tan \alpha$, where α is the inclination of either rod to the vertical.   (C.W.B.)

12.14. Resultant of coplanar forces

In Chapter 10 we showed how to find the resultant of any number of forces acting on a particle. We shall now consider the more general problem that arises when the forces act on a rigid body.

Usually we shall require to find the resultant of a number of forces whose magnitudes and lines of action are given.

Often we shall not be told on what the forces are acting, for as already mentioned, their resultant is independent of the shape and size of the body, provided it is rigid.

The magnitude of the resultant is, as a rule, best obtained by resolving the forces in two directions at right angles, adding the components in these directions, and compounding the two components so obtained into a single force.

The ratio of these two components gives the direction of the resultant, i.e. the tangent of the angle made by it with one of the directions in which the forces were resolved.

To fix the position of the line of action we can either find one point on it, and give this and the direction, or in some cases it is easier to find the points in which the resultant cuts two given lines; the latter are often conveniently obtained by taking moments. No general method should be laid down; the shortest method of obtaining the required result differs considerably in different cases.

Various methods are used in the following examples.

EXAMPLE (i)

Find the magnitude, direction, and line of action of the resultant of three forces 1, 2, 3 units acting in order round the three sides of an equilateral triangle of side 2a.

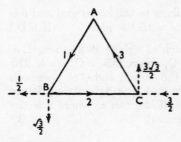

Fɪɢ. 12.26

Let the forces 1, 2, 3 act along the sides AB, BC, CA of the equilateral triangle ABC, as shown in Fig. 12.26.

Resolve the forces along and perpendicular to BC.

The force 1 is equivalent to $\frac{1}{2}$ acting at B in the direction CB, and $\sqrt{3}/2$ acting at B perpendicular to BC and downwards.

The force 3 is equivalent to $\frac{3}{2}$ acting at C in the direction CB, and $3\sqrt{3}/2$ acting at C perpendicular to BC and upwards.

The components along BC balance the force 2, and we are left with unlike parallel forces $\sqrt{3}/2$ at B and $3\sqrt{3}/2$ at C.

Their resultant is $\sqrt{3}$ acting upwards perpendicular to BC, at a point D in BC produced such that

$$\frac{3\sqrt{3}}{2}CD = \frac{\sqrt{3}}{2}BD$$

or $$3CD = BD$$

or $$CD = \tfrac{1}{2}BC = a.$$

EXAMPLE (ii)

ABCD is a given quadrilateral; forces are represented in magnitude, lines of action, and senses by the sides AB, BC, DC (cyclical order interrupted), and DA. What are the magnitude and line of action of the resultant?
(I.S.)

The resultant of the forces AB, BC (Fig. 12.27) is equal and parallel to AC and acts at B.

The resultant of this force and the force DA is equal and parallel to DC, and acts at E, where a parallel to CA through B meets DA produced.

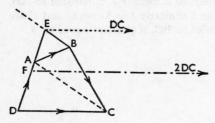

FIG. 12.27

We now have two parallel forces, each equal to DC, one acting along DC and one parallel to DC at E.

Their resultant is a force 2DC acting at F the mid-point of DE.

Alternatively, we may proceed as follows:

The magnitude and direction of the resultant of the four forces is given by their vector sum, viz.

$$\mathbf{AB+BC+DC+DA} = \mathbf{DC}+(\mathbf{DA+AB+BC})$$
$$= \mathbf{DC}+\mathbf{DC}$$
$$= \mathbf{2DC}.$$

The resultant is therefore a force **2DC** and its line of action may be found by taking moments about any point, say D.

Suppose the resultant **2DC** cuts DA at F. Its moment about D is clockwise and is represented by $4\triangle$ FDC. But the moment of the four given forces about D is also clockwise and is represented by $2\triangle$ ABD $+2\triangle$ BCD.

$$\therefore \qquad 4\triangle \text{FDC} = 2(\triangle \text{ABD} + \triangle \text{BCD})$$
$$= 2(\text{quad. ABCD})$$
$$= 2\triangle \text{EDC}, \text{ since BE is parallel to CA.}$$
$$\therefore \qquad 2\text{FD} = \text{ED},$$

that is, F is the mid-point of DE.

EXAMPLE (iii)

Four forces P, Q, R, and S act along the sides of a rectangle ABCD in the directions AB, BC, CD, DA respectively. If AB = a *and* AD = b, *find the magnitude of the resultant of the system of forces and the distance from* A *of the points in which ᵗʰe line of action of the resultant cuts the sides* AB, AD.

Draw the rectangle ABCD and insert the forces as in Fig. 12.28. The forces P and R are equivalent to a force $P-R$ parallel to AB, provided P is not equal to R, and similarly the forces Q and S are equivalent to a force $Q-S$ parallel to BC, if Q is not equal to S.

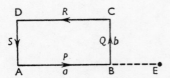

FIG. 12.28

The magnitude of the resultant is therefore

$$\sqrt{[(P-R)^2+(Q-S)^2]}$$

If the resultant cuts AB produced at a point E distant x from A, then since E is on the line of action of the resultant, the sum of the moments of the forces about it is zero,

$$\therefore \qquad Q(x-a) = Rb+Sx$$
$$\therefore \qquad x(Q-S) = Rb+Qa$$
$$\therefore \qquad x = \frac{Rb+Qa}{Q-S}.$$

Similarly, if the resultant cuts DA produced at a point F distant y from A, taking moments about F, we get

$$Py = Qa+R(b+y)$$
$$\therefore \qquad y(P-R) = Qa+Rb.$$
$$\therefore \qquad y = \frac{Qa+Rb}{P-R}.$$

Note.

If P is greater than R (as assumed above), F will be below A.

If R is greater than P the above value of y will be negative and F will be above A.

If S is greater than Q, E will be to the left of A instead of to the right, as shown in Fig. 12.28.

If $R = P$ and $S = Q$, the system reduces to a couple of moment $Pb+Qa$.

EXAMPLE (iv)

ABCDEF *is a regular hexagon; forces* P, $2P$, $3P$, $5P$, $6P$ *act along* AB, BC, DC, EF, AF *respectively; show that a force can be determined to act along* ED *so that the six forces are equivalent to a couple, and find the moment of the couple.* **(I.S.)**

Draw the hexagon and insert the forces as in Fig. 12.29.

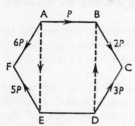

FIG. 12.29

Method (i)

A force along ED will form a couple with the given forces provided these forces have a resultant parallel to DE.

Now, sum of the components of the forces perpendicular to
$$ED = 5P \cos 30° - 6P \cos 30° - 2P \cos 30° + 3P \cos 30° = 0.$$

Also, sum of the compounds of the forces parallel to
$$ED = -5P \sin 30° - 6P \sin 30° + 2P \sin 30° + 3P \sin 30° = -2P.$$

Hence the resultant of the five forces is a force of magnitude $2P$ parallel to DE. Its position can be found by taking moments about some point.

Suppose this resultant is at a perpendicular distance x above the centre of the hexagon, and that the length of each side is a.

Taking moments about the centre, we get:
$$2P \times x = (-5P + 6P - P - 2P + 3P)a\sqrt{3}/2$$
$$\therefore \qquad x = a\sqrt{3}/4.$$

Hence the perpendicular distance of the resultant from
$$ED = a\sqrt{3}/4 + a\sqrt{3}/2 = 3a\sqrt{3}/4.$$

Hence with a force $2P$ along ED the five forces will form a couple of moment $2P(3a\sqrt{3}/4) = 3\sqrt{3}Pa/2$ in a counter-clockwise direction.

Method (ii)

The force $5P$ is equivalent to a force $5P \cos 30° = 5P\sqrt{3}/2$ along EA and $5P \sin 30° = 5P/2$ along DE.

The force $6P$ is equivalent to a force $6P \cos 30° = 3P\sqrt{3}$ along AE and $6P \sin 30° = 3P$ along BA.

The force $2P$ is equivalent to a force $2P \cos 30° = P\sqrt{3}$ along BD and $2P \sin 30° = P$ along AB.

The force $3P$ is equivalent to a force $3P \cos 30° = 3P\sqrt{3}/2$ along DB and $3P \sin 30° = 3P/2$ along ED.

In all, the five forces are equivalent to $5P/2-3P/2 = P$ along DE, $3P-P-P = P$ along BA, $P\sqrt{3}/2$ along AE and $P\sqrt{3}/2$ along DB.

The forces P along DE and BA have a resultant $2P$ parallel to DE through the centre of the hexagon, and the forces $P\sqrt{3}/2$ along AE and DB form a couple of moment $(P\sqrt{3}/2)a$ in a counter-clock-wise direction.

If therefore we introduce a force $2P$ along ED the six forces are equivalent to two couples of moments $2P(a\sqrt{3}/2)$ and $Pa\sqrt{3}/2$ respectively, both counter-clockwise. Hence, the moment of the resultant couple is $3Pa\sqrt{3}/2$.

EXAMPLES 12.4

1. A, B, C are three points on a line ABCD, such that $AB = BC = a$. Forces of 3, 6, and 4 N respectively act at A, B, C in directions making angles of 60°, 120°, and 270° with AD. Show that they reduce to a single force, and find where its line of action cuts AD. (I.S.)

2. A, B, C, D are four points in a straight line at equal intervals of 0·6 m. At A, B, D forces 2, 3, and 4 N respectively act perpendicular to AD upwards; at C a force of 9 N acts perpendicular to AD downwards. Show that the system is equivalent to a couple, and find where the 3-N force should have been applied to produce equilibrium. (I.S.)

3. Forces 3, 3, and 5 N act respectively along the sides BA, AC, BC of an equilateral triangle of altitude 1·2 m. Find the distance from A of the line of action of the resultant. (I.A.)

4. ABCD is a square, E and F are the mid-points of BC and CD respectively. Find the magnitude and direction of the resultant of the forces, 2, 5, 10, 1 units along AB, AE, FA, AD respectively.

5. ABC is an equilateral triangle, forces of 4, 2, and 1 unit act along the sides AB, AC, BC respectively, in the directions indicated by the letters. Prove that their resultant is a force of $3\sqrt{3}$ units in a direction at right angles to BC, and find the point in which the line of action meets BC. (I.A.)

6. Find the resultant of the following forces acting along the sides of a square ABCD; 21 N along CD, 15 N along DA, 3 N along BA, 9 N along CB; and show that its line of action bisects two of the sides of the square. (I.S.)

7. Find the magnitude of the resultant of the following forces acting along the sides of a square ABCD; 11 N along DA, 7 N along CB, 19 N along CD, 5 N along BA; and prove that its line of action bisects AD and trisects CD. (I.A.)

8. AD is an altitude of triangle ABC in which BC = 6, CA = 7, AB = 5. A force of 12 N along DA is equilibrated by parallel forces at B and C. If the directions of all the forces are rotated about A, B, C respectively through the same angle so as to be perpendicular to AB, prove that the resultant of the forces is a couple and find its moment. (I.S.)

9. ABCD is a trapezium in which the parallel sides AD and BC are in the ratio 2 : 3, and AB = AD = DC; find the magnitude and position of the resultant of forces, $3P$ from B towards C, P from B towards A, $2P$ from D towards A, and $2\frac{1}{2}P$ from D towards C. (I.E.)

10. A unit force acts along the side AB of a square ABCD. Find the magnitudes and directions of the forces which must act along the remaining three sides in order to maintain equilibrium. Find the resultant if: (i) the force along BC is reversed; (ii) the forces along BC and AD are both reversed. (H.S.D.)

11. ABCD is a rectangular board in which AB = DC = 0·9 m, BC = AD = 1·8 m. One rope pulls it along AD with a force of 15 units, another rope pulls it along BC with a force of 25 units, a third rope pulls it along CD with a force of 16 units. Find what force along AB will make the resultant pass through G, the mid-point of the rectangle ABCD, and calculate the resultant completely. (I.S.)

12. ABCD is a square, of side a, traced on a lamina; E, F are points on BA and BC produced through A and C respectively, so that BE = 3a, BF = 3a. A system of forces acting on the lamina consists of P along AB, $2P$ along BC, $3P$ along CD, $4P$ along DA, and $2\sqrt{2}P$ along EF. Prove that the resultant of the system is a couple of moment Pa. (H.S.D.)

13. Forces 1, 2, 3, 4 N respectively act along the sides AB, BC, CD, DA of a square of side 1 m. Find the distance from the centre of the square of the line of action of the resultant. What additional force along the diagonal BD will make the whole system have a resultant passing through A? (H.S.D.)

14. A rectangle ABCD can turn freely in a horizontal plane about its centre, which is fixed, and forces of 1, 2, and 3 N act along AB, BC, and DC respectively. If AB = 0·3 m, BC = 0·6 m, determine the force which must be applied along AD to keep the rectangle at rest.

15. A square lamina ABCD on a smooth horizontal table can turn about a smooth peg fixed at the point of trisection of the diagonal BD, which is nearer to B. It is acted on by a force of 5 units along AD and a force of 3 units along CB. Find the force which, acting at A in the direction AB, will keep it in equilibrium and the resultant pressure on the peg.   (H.S.C.)

16. Forces $3P$, $2P$, P, $2P$ act along the sides AB, CB, CD, AD of a square ABCD in the directions indicated by the order of the letters. Find the magnitude and the line of action of the resultant.   (H.C.)

12.15. *The resultant of two forces, acting at a point* O *in directions* OA *and* OB *and represented in magnitude by* $l \times$ OA *and* $m \times$ OB *is represented in magnitude and direction by* $(l+m)$OC, *where* C *is a point in* AB *such that* $l \times$ CA $= m \times$ CB.

For let C (Fig. 12.30) divide AB so that

$$l \times \text{CA} = m \times \text{CB}.$$

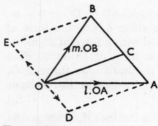

Fɪɢ. 12.30

Complete the parallelograms OCAD and OCBE.

The force $l \times$ OA is equivalent to forces represented by $l \times$ OC and $l \times$ OD.

The force $m \times$ OB is equivalent to forces represented by $m \times$ OC and $m \times$ OE.

Hence the forces $l \times$ OA and $m \times$ OB are equivalent to a force represented by $(l+m)$OC, and forces represented by $l \times$ OD and $m \times$ OE.

But OD = CA and OE = CB and $l \times CA = m \times CB$.

Therefore these two latter forces are equal and opposite and are therefore in equilibrium.

Hence the resultant of $l \times OA$ and $m \times OB$ is represented by $(l+m)OC$.

In vector notation the resultant of the two forces is given by their vector-sum. We write

$$l\mathbf{OA}+m\mathbf{OB} = l(\mathbf{OC}+\mathbf{CA})+m(\mathbf{OC}+\mathbf{CB})$$
$$= (l+m)\mathbf{OC}+l\mathbf{CA}+m\mathbf{CB}$$
$$= (l+m)\mathbf{OC}$$

provided $\qquad l \times CA = m \times CB.$

If $l = m = 1$, we get $\mathbf{OA}+\mathbf{OB} = 2\mathbf{OC}$ provided CA = CB, that is, the resultant of forces OA, OB is a force 2OC, where C is the mid-point of AB. This is also obvious from the fact that in this case OC is half the diagonal of the parallelogram, of which OA and OB are adjacent sides.

EXAMPLE (i)

Forces represented by 2BC, CA, BA *act along the sides of a triangle* ABC. *Show that their resultant is* represented by 6DE, *where* D *bisects* BC *and* E *is a point on* CA *such that* CE = $\frac{1}{3}$CA. (H.C.)

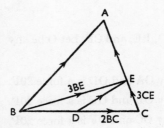

FIG. 12.31

In Fig. 12.31 the resultant of forces 2BC and BA is a force 3BE, where E is a point in AC such that 2CE = EA, i.e. CE = $\frac{1}{3}$CA.

Also CA = 3CE, and the resultant of forces 3BE along BE and 3CE along CA is a force 6DE along DE, where D is the mid-point of BC.

Alternatively, we may proceed as follows:
The vector sum of the three forces is

$$2\mathbf{BC}+\mathbf{CA}+\mathbf{BA} = \mathbf{CA}+(2\mathbf{BC}+\mathbf{BA})$$
$$= \mathbf{CA}+3\mathbf{BE} \text{ if } 2\mathbf{CE} = \mathbf{EA},$$
$$= 3\mathbf{CE}+3\mathbf{BE}$$
$$= 6\mathbf{DE} \text{ if } \mathbf{BD} = \mathbf{DC}.$$

Since the sum of the moments of the three given forces about D is zero, the resultant must pass through D and is therefore represented in magnitude, direction, and line of action by **6DE**.

EXAMPLE (ii)

ABCDEF *is a regular hexagon and* O *is any point. Prove that the resultant of forces represented by* OA, OB, OC, OD, OE, OF *is a force* 6OP, *where* P *is the centre of the circumcircle of the hexagon.*

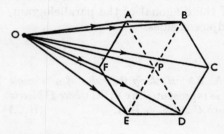

FIG. 12.32

In Fig. 12.32 P is the mid-point of AD, BE, and CF. Let O be any point and join OP.

The resultant of forces represented by OA and OD is a force 2OP.

The resultant of forces represented by OB and OE is a force 2OP.

The resultant of forces represented by OC and OF is a force 2OP.

Therefore the resultant of forces represented by OA, OB, OC, OD, OE, OF is a force represented by 6OP.

EXAMPLE (iii)

M *is the point of trisection of the side* AC *of a triangle* ABC *which is nearer to* A, *and* N *is the point of trisection of the side* AD *which is nearer to* B. *Resolve a force, represented in magnitude and direction by* MN, *into three forces acting each along a side of the triangle.* (I.S.)

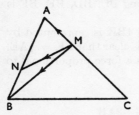

FIG. 12.33

Join MB (Fig. 12.33).

Since N divides AB in the ratio 2 : 1, the force MN is equivalent to forces $\frac{2}{3}$MB and $\frac{1}{3}$MA acting at M.

The latter is along CA and equal to $\frac{1}{3}$CA.

Since M divides AC in the ratio 1 : 2, a force MB is equivalent to forces $\frac{2}{3}$AB and $\frac{1}{3}$CB acting at B.

Hence a force $\frac{2}{3}$MB is equivalent to forces $\frac{4}{9}$AB and $\frac{2}{9}$CB acting at B.

The force MN is therefore equivalent to forces

$$\frac{4}{9}AB, \ \frac{2}{9}CB, \ \frac{1}{3}CA,$$

acting along the corresponding sides.

EXAMPLE (iv)

ABCDEF *is a plane lamina in the form of a regular hexagon. Forces act from* A *and* B *towards the other four vertices proportional in magnitude to the distance from them. Prove that the resultant is proportional to* 6AE, *and find the line of action.*

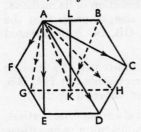

FIG. 12.34

The resultant of forces proportional to AF and AE (Fig. 12.34) is a force proportional to 2AG, where G is the mid-point of EF.

Similarly, the resultant of forces proportional to AC and AD is a force proportional to 2AH, where H is the mid-point of CD.

The resultant of forces proportional to 2AG and 2AH is a force proportional to 4AK, where K is the mid-point of GH.

Similarly, the resultant of the forces along BC, BD, BE, BF is a force represented by 4BK.

Finally, the resultant of forces 4AK and 4BK is represented by 8LK, where L is the mid-point of AB, and it is clear that LK = $\frac{3}{4}$AE.

Hence the resultant of the eight forces is a force proportional to 6AE and acts along LK.

Vectorially we write

$$AF+AE+AD+AC = 2AG+2AH$$
$$= 4AK$$

and the resultant passes through A.

Also

$$BF+BE+BD+BC = 2BG+2BH$$
$$= 4BK$$

and the resultant passes through B.

Hence the eight forces are equivalent to a force 4AK along AK and a force 4BK along BK, which in turn are equivalent to a force 8LK acting along LK.

EXAMPLES 12.5

1. The sides BC and DA of a quadrilateral ABCD are bisected in F and H respectively. Show that if two forces parallel and equal to AB and DC act at a point their resultant is parallel to HF and equal to 2HF.

2. ABC is a triangle and G the point of intersection of its medians; if O is any point in the plane of the triangle, prove that the resultant of forces represented by OA, OB, OC is represented by 3OG.

3. If O is the circum-centre, and H the ortho-centre of a triangle ABC, prove that the resultant of forces represented by HA, HB, HC will be represented in magnitude and direction by 2HO.

4. ABCD is a quadrilateral, of which A and C are opposite vertices. Two forces acting at A are represented in magnitudes and directions by AB and AD; and two forces acting at C are represented in magnitudes and directions by CB and CD. Show that the resultant force is represented in magnitude and direction by four times the line joining the mid-points of the diagonals of the quadrilateral.

5. ABCD is a quadrilateral; forces are completely represented by the lines AB, BC, AD, DC. Prove that their resultant is represented in magnitude and direction by 2AC, and that its line of action bisects BD.

6. O is any point in the plane of a triangle ABC, and D, E, F are the mid-points of the sides. Show that the system of forces represented by OA, OB, OC is equivalent to the system represented by OD, OE, OF.

7. ABCD is a quadrilateral and O is any point in its plane, E, F, G, H are the mid-points of AB, BC, CD, DA respectively. Prove that the resultant of forces represented by OA, OB, OC, OD is represented by 4OK where K bisects EG.

8. A point P on the circumference of a circle is joined to fixed points A and B on the circle. Forces 2PA, 3PB act along PA, PB respectively, and their resultant is represented in direction and magnitude by PQ. Find the locus of Q as P moves round the circle. (H.S.C.)

9. Three forces AB, 2BC, 2AC act, in the directions indicated by the letters, along the sides of a triangle ABC. Find their resultant, and deduce that the line joining the mid-point of AB to the point of trisection of BC nearer to C cuts AC produced in E where AC = CE. (I.S.)

10. A and B are fixed points; P moves in such a way that the resultant of forces represented by PA and PB is always double the former force. Find the locus of P.

11. If the resultant of forces represented by lines drawn from a point P to the corners of a quadrilateral be of constant magnitude, prove that the locus of P is a circle, and find its centre and radius.

12. ABCD is a parallelogram and E is a point in AD. Find a point F in BC such that the resultant of forces represented by AE and AF may act in the direction AC.

13. Forces equal to **AB**, **AC**, and **CB** act in the sides of a triangle ABC. Prove that their resultant acts in ED and is equal to **4ED**, where D, E are the mid-points of the sides BC, CA respectively.

14. O is any point on a median of a triangle ABC. Forces act from O towards A, B, and C proportional to the distances of O from these points. Prove that their resultant is represented in magnitude and direction by 3OG, where G is the centroid of the triangle.

15. Forces completely represented by AB, CB, CD, AD act in the sides of a quadrilateral ABCD. Prove that their resultant is

completely represented by 4HK, where H and K are the mid-points of AC and BD respectively.   (C.W.B.)

16. ABC is an equilateral triangle and G is its centroid. Forces 1, 1, 4, 2, 2, 1 N act along BC, CA, AB, AG, BG, CG respectively. Determine the magnitude and direction of their resultant and the distance from A at which it cuts AB.   (I.S.)

17. Prove that the resultant of any number of concurrent forces $l \times OA$, $m \times OB$, $n \times OC$ ... is $(l+m+n+ ...)OG$, where G is the centre of gravity of masses proportional to l, m, n, ... placed at A, B, C, ... respectively.   (H.S.C.)

18. ABCD is a trapezium with AB parallel to DC. Show that forces represented in magnitude, direction, and line of action by **AD,** **DC**, **CB**, **BA**, **AC** and **BD** have a resultant represented in magnitude and direction by 2EF, where E and F are the mid-points of AB and CD respectively. Show that the line of action cuts BA produced at a distance $\frac{1}{2}$CD from A.

19. Forces are represented in magnitude, direction, and line of action by 3**BC**, 2**AC**, and 7**BA**. The line of action of the resultant cuts AB at F and AC at E. Show that 2AF = 3FB, 7AE = 3EC, and that the resultant is represented in magnitude and direction by (50/3)**FE**.   (H.S.C.)

20. If AD, BE are medians of any triangle ABC, show that the five forces represented in magnitude, direction, and line of action by **AB**, 2**CB**, 3**CA**, **BE**, and **DA** have a resultant represented completely by 5**CH**, where H is the point dividing AB internally in the ratio 3 : 7.

21. Forces are represented in magnitude, direction, and line of action by **BC**, **AC**, and 3**BA** in a parallelogram ABCD. Show that their resultant is represented in magnitude and direction by 2**BD** and find its line of action.

22. A point P lies in the plane of the rectangle ABCD. Forces represented completely by **AB**, 2**DC**, l**PA**, l**BP**, m**CP**, m**PD** are in equilibrium. Find l in terms of m.

    Prove that P can lie at any point of a line parallel to AB and find the ratio in which this line divides AB.

12.16. Composition of couples

We have seen (11.14) that the moment of a couple is the same about any point in its plane. We shall now prove the following theorem, which enables us to obtain the resultant of any number of couples in one plane.

Two couples acting in the same plane are equivalent to a single couple whose moment is the algebraic sum of the moments of the separate couples.

Case (i). When the lines of action of the forces are all parallel.

Let P, P, Q, Q be the forces of the couples acting as in Fig. 12.35, and draw a straight line OABCD perpendicular to their lines of action to meet them in A, B, C, D.

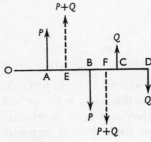

FIG. 12.35

The force P and Q at A and C are equivalent to a parallel force $(P+Q)$ at a point E in AC such that $P \times \text{AE} = Q \times \text{EC}$.

The forces P and Q at B and D are equivalent to a parallel force $(P+Q)$ at a point F in BD, such that $P \times \text{BF} = Q \times \text{FD}$, and this force is in the opposite direction to the first one.

Hence the two couples are equivalent to a single couple.

Also the moment of the resultant couple

= the sum of the moments about O of the two forces $P+Q$ at E and F.

But the moment of $P+Q$ at E about O

= the sum of the moments about O of P at A and Q at C.

Similarly, the moment of $P+Q$ at F about O

= the sum of the moments about O of P at B and Q at D.

Hence the moment of the resultant couple

= the sum of the moments of the four forces of the couples,

= the sum of the moments of the original couples.

Case (ii). When the lines of action of the forces are not all parallel.

Let P, P, Q, Q be the forces of the couples; and let one of the forces P meet one of the forces Q in O (Fig. 12.36), and the other two forces meet in O'.

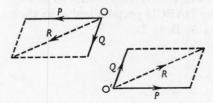

Fig. 12.36

The forces P, Q at O can be combined into a single force R, and so can the forces P and Q at O'. Also these single forces will be equal, parallel, and opposite, for they are both resultants of forces P and Q acting at the same angle but in opposite directions.

Hence the two couples are equivalent to a single couple.

Now, the moment of this resultant couple

= the moment about O of R at O'

= the sum of the moments about O of P and Q at O'

= the sum of the moments of the original couples.

The theorem having been proved for two couples, it follows that any number of couples in a plane are equivalent to a single couple whose moment is the algebraic sum of the moments of the separate couples.

12.17. From the theorem of the last paragraph we can deduce the following:

1. *Two couples acting in a plane, whose moments are equal and opposite, balance one another.*

For their resultant is a couple of zero moment, which means that the forces of the couple are each zero, or its arm is zero, and in the latter case it must consist of two equal and opposite forces in the same straight line which are obviously in equilibrium.

2. *Any two couples of equal moment and in the same plane are equivalent.*

This follows by reversing the directions of the forces of one of the balancing couples in (1).

12.18. *A force P acting at any point A of a rigid body may be transferred parallel to itself, to act at any other point B of the body, by introducing a couple whose moment is Pp, where p is the perpendicular distance of B from the line of action of P. This couple acts so as to turn the body about B in the same direction as P, acting at A, tends to move it.*

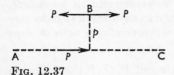

FIG. 12.37

Let AC (Fig. 12.37) be the line of action of P.

Apply at B two equal and opposite forces P acting along the line through B parallel to AC.

One of these, the one acting towards the right, is the original force P transferred to act at B.

The other forms with the original force a couple whose moment is Pp, where p is the perpendicular distance of B from AC.

12.19 EXAMPLE (i)

Prove that the combination of a couple with a force in the same plane is equivalent to changing the position of the line of action of the force.

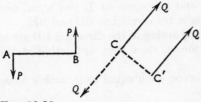

FIG. 12.38

Let the couple be formed by two forces P acting at A and B (Fig. 12.38), and let Q be the force acting at C.

We can replace the couple by any other couple of equal moment in the same plane.

We choose a couple of which the forces are of magnitude Q, one acting at C in the opposite direction to the force Q already acting there. The other force of the couple will act at C′, where CC′ is perpendicular to the direction of the original force Q, and CC′ = (P/Q)AB.

We now have two forces at C balancing each other, and a single force Q at C′.

The result is therefore to move the line of action of Q parallel to itself through a distance M/Q, where M is the moment of the couple.

EXAMPLE (ii)

If three forces acting on a rigid body be represented in magnitude, direction, and line of action by the sides of a triangle taken in order they are equivalent to a couple whose moment is represented by twice the area of the triangle.

Let ABC (Fig. 12.39) be the triangle and P, Q, R the forces, so that P, Q, R are represented completely by the sides BC, CA, AB respectively.

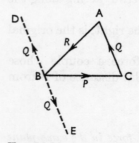

Fig. 12.39

Draw DBE parallel to AC, and introduce at B two equal and opposite forces, equal to Q, acting in the directions BD and BE.

The forces P, R and the force Q acting in the direction BD are in equilibrium by the triangle of forces, since they are acting at the point B.

We are thus left with two forces, each equal to Q, acting along the lines CA and BE.

These form a couple whose moment is $Q \times$ the perpendicular distance of B from CA.

Also, since CA represents Q, this moment is represented by CA × the perpendicular distance of B from CA, i.e. by twice the area of the triangle ABC.

Alternatively, we can say that the vector-sum of the three forces, **AB**+**BC**+**CA**, is zero. Hence the forces are equivalent to a couple. The moment of the couple is obtained by taking moments about any point, say B, and the result follows as above.

EXAMPLE (iii)

*Forces represented in magnitude and direction by l***AB**, *m***BC**, *l***CD**, *m***DA** *act along the corresponding sides of a quadrilateral ABCD. Show that they are equivalent to a couple if l = m or if ABCD is a parallelogram.*

If the four forces reduce to a couple their vector sum must be zero. The vector sum is

$$l\mathbf{AB}+m\mathbf{BC}+l\mathbf{CD}+m\mathbf{DA}$$
$$= l(\mathbf{AB}+\mathbf{BC}+\mathbf{CD}+\mathbf{DA})+(m-l)(\mathbf{BC}+\mathbf{DA})$$
$$= (m-l)(\mathbf{BC}+\mathbf{DA}).$$

This is zero if $l = m$ or if $\mathbf{BC}+\mathbf{DA} = 0$. If the latter condition is satisfied BC is equal and parallel to AD, so that ABCD is a parallelogram.

When either of these conditions is satisfied the moment of the four forces about any point, D say, is clearly not zero, and hence the forces reduce to a couple.

EXAMPLES 12.6

1. A uniform rod AB of length $2a$ and weight W can rotate about a smooth fixed horizontal axis at A. If a couple of moment N is applied to it and maintains it at an angle of 30° to the vertical, find N.

2. A uniform bar AB of length 3·6 m and mass 5 kg is clamped at the end A in a horizontal position, and a mass of 2·5 kg is suspended from the end B. Find the force and the couple that must act on the bar where it is clamped.

3. A uniform ladder of length l and weight W is held with its upper end resting against a smooth vertical wall, and with its lower end on a smooth horizontal surface. A man of weight W' stands on the ladder at a distance l' from its lower end. Show that if the ladder is kept from slipping by means of a couple, the moment of the couple is equal to

$$(\tfrac{1}{2}Wl+W'l)\sin\theta$$

where θ is the inclination of the ladder to the vertical.   (H.C.)

4. Prove that two couples whose forces are coplanar are in equilibrium if their moments are equal in magnitude and opposite in sign.

A uniform square plate ABCD of weight W is kept in equilibrium with the corner A against a rough vertical wall by means of a horizontal force W acting at C, the point B being above A. Prove that the coefficient of friction cannot be less than unity, and find the inclination of AB to the vertical.   (N.U.)

5. A uniform heavy bent rod ABCD, whose parts AB, BC, CD form three sides of a square, is smoothly hinged to a point fixed at A in a smooth wall and is supported in a vertical plane perpendicular to the wall, with AB, CD horizontal and CD below AB, by the pressure of the wall against D. Find the reactions of the hinge at A and of the wall at D.

Show that the stresses in the rod at B and C each consist of a force and a couple; find the reactions of the parts AB, DC on the part BC, and verify the equilibrium of BC.   (H.C.)

6. Forces $3P$, $4P$, and $5P$ respectively act along the sides of a right-angled triangle of sides 3 m, 4 m, 5 m, in the same circular sense viewed from any point of the triangle. Find the forces which, acting at the ends of the side 5 m long and at right angles to it, will maintain equilibrium with these forces.

7. ABCDEF is a regular hexagon. Show that forces represented completely by AB, CD, and EF are equivalent to a couple of moment equal to the area of the hexagon.

8. P, Q, R are the mid-points of the sides AB, BC, CA of a triangle ABC. Find the value of k if the forces **AB**, **BC**, **CA**, k**PQ**, k**QR**, k**RP** are in equilibrium.   (L.A.)

9. ABCD is a square of side a m. Forces of 10, 5, 10, 15 N act along AB, BC, CD, DA respectively. Show that there are two forces such that if either is combined with these four forces the system will reduce to a couple of moment $5a$ N m.   (L.A.)

10. ABCD is a rectangle with AB $= a$, BC $= b$. M is the mid-point of BC. Three forces are represented completely by k**AM**, k**MC**, k**CD**, where k is positive. Find the magnitude and direction of their resultant and the distance from A of its line of action.

Find the magnitude of the couple that must be combined with the three forces in order that the resultant of the system shall pass through the mid-point of AB.   (L.A.)

12.20. Resultant of coplanar forces

We shall now consider another method of reducing a system of coplanar forces.

From the theorem proved in the next paragraph we can deduce the theorem of 12.5, and also easily obtain the various sets of conditions necessary and sufficient for a system of forces to be in equilibrium.

12.21. *Any system of coplanar forces acting on a rigid body can, in general, be replaced by a single force acting at an arbitrary point in the plane of the forces together with a couple.*

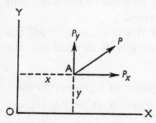

FIG. 12.40

Let the forces $P_1, P_2, \ldots P_n$ act at the points $A_1, A_2, \ldots A_n$, and let O (Fig. 12.40) be any point in the plane of the forces. Take O as origin of coordinates, and let the coordinates of A_1, $A_2, \ldots A_n$, referred to rectangular axes through O be (x_1, y_1), $(x_2, y_2), \ldots (x_n, y_n)$.

Consider any one of the forces P acting at the point A (x, y).

Resolve P into its components P_x, P_y, parallel to OX, OY.

We can transfer P_x parallel to itself to act at O by introducing a couple whose moment is yP_x, and we can transfer P_y parallel to itself to act at O by introducing a couple xP_y.

These couples are in opposite senses, and the algebraic sum of their moments is $xP_y - yP_x$.

Similarly for all the forces.

Let X be the algebraic sum of all the components of the forces transferred to act along the axis of x, and Y the sum of those components acting along the axis of y.

These can be compounded into a single resultant R acting at O, and the couples can be added (with their proper signs) to form a single couple of moment G, say, equal to the sum of the moments of all the couples.

If the resultant R makes an angle θ with the axis of x,

$$R^2 = X^2 + Y^2 \text{ and } \tan \theta = Y/X.$$

It should be noticed that the values of R and θ are independent of the position of the point O, since they do not contain the coordinates of any of the points A_1, A_2, . . . A_n. In fact, R is given in magnitude and direction by the vector sum of the forces P_1, P_2, . . . P_n.

The moment of the resultant couple is

$$G = \sum(xP_y - yP_x)$$

where P_x, P_y are the components of P parallel to the axis, and the $\sum$ denotes summation for all the forces.

It is evident that G is the sum of the moments of all the forces about the origin O, and its value will depend on the position of O.

12.22. *Conditions of equilibrium for a system of coplanar forces*

Let the forces be reduced to a single force R at any arbitrary point O and a couple G.

Then for equilibrium we must have $R = 0$ and $G = 0$.

If $R = 0$ we must have both $X = 0$ *and* $Y = 0$.

This gives us *three* conditions, which can be stated as follows:

The algebraic sums of the components of the forces in any two directions which are not parallel must be zero, and the algebraic sum of the moments of all the forces about any arbitrary point must be zero.

We obtained these conditions earlier (12.8).

12.23. *Change of base*

If we take another point O′ with coordinates (x', y') as base instead of the origin the moment of the couple for this base may be obtained from that for the origin O by writing $x - x'$ and $y - y'$ for x and y in the value for G.

$$\therefore \quad G' = \sum(x - x')P_y - \sum(y - y')P_x$$
$$= \sum xP_y - \sum yP_x - \sum x'P_y + \sum y'P_x$$
$$= G - x'\sum P_y + y'\sum P_x$$

since x', y' are constant.

$$\therefore \quad G' = G - x'Y + y'X.$$

In this result G is the sum of the moments of the forces about the origin, x', y' are the coordinates of the base, X and Y the sums of the components of the forces parallel to the axes.

12.24. *Line of action of resultant*

If the system is not in equilibrium, and we reduce it to a force R at the point (x', y'), and a couple G', then

$$R^2 = X^2 + Y^2$$

and
$$G' = G - x'Y + y'X.$$

Now if R is zero, $X = 0$ and $Y = 0$, and the system reduces to a couple G, since this cannot vanish too.

If R is not zero we may, by properly choosing the base, make the couple G' vanish, so that the system reduces to the single force R. This is the case when the coordinates (x', y') of the base satisfy the equation

$$G - xY + yX = 0$$

i.e. the base must lie on this line.

Now this line makes an angle $\tan^{-1} Y/X$ with the axis of x, and is therefore parallel to R, and since R acts at the base (x', y'), this straight line is the line of action of R. The equation of the line of action of the resultant is therefore

$$G - xY + yX = 0.$$

12.25. Other forms of the conditions of equilibrium

(1) *A system of coplanar forces will be in equilibrium if the sum of the moments of all the forces about two different points (say* O *and* C*) is zero, and the sum of the components in some one direction, not perpendicular to* OC*, is also zero.*

Taking O as origin, C as base (x', y'), we have

$$G = 0$$

and
$$G' = G - x'Y + y'X = 0$$

and
$$X = 0.$$

These give $X = 0$, $Y = 0$, $G = 0$, provided x' is not zero, i.e. provided C is not on the y axis (so that X is perpendicular to OC).

(2) *A system of coplanar forces will be in equilibrium if the sum of the moments about three different points*, O, C, D, *not all in the same straight line, are each zero.*

Taking O as origin, C as (x', y'), and D as (x'', y''), these conditions give

$$G = 0$$

and $$G - x'X + y'X = 0$$

and $$G - x''Y + y''X = 0$$

∴ $$-x'Y + y'X = 0$$

and $$-x''Y + y''X = 0.$$

Therefore $X = 0$ and $Y = 0$, unless $x'y'' - x''y' = 0$, i.e. unless O, C, D are in a straight line.

12.26. EXAMPLE (i)

Forces 2, 2, 3, 2 *units act along the sides* AB, CD, ED, EF *respectively of a regular hexagon* ABCDEF *in the directions indicated by the order of the letters. Find the magnitude of the resultant and prove that it acts along* AB. (I.S.)

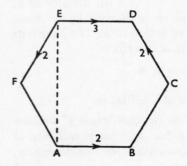

FIG. 12.41

Fig. 12.41 shows the forces acting along the sides of the hexagon. Take axes along and perpendicular to AB with A as origin. Let the side of the hexagon $= a$.

Sum of the components of the forces parallel to AB

$$= 2 - 2 \cos 60° + 3 - 2 \cos 60° = 3$$

and the sum of the components of the forces perpendicular to AB

$$= 2 \sin 60° - 2 \sin 60° = 0$$

which together show that the resultant has magnitude 3 and is parallel to AB.

But the sum of the moments of the forces about A

$$= 2 \times 2a \sin 60° - 3 \times 2a \sin 60° + 2 \times a \sin 60° = 0$$

and hence the resultant must pass through A.

Therefore the resultant has magnitude 3 units and acts along AB.

EXAMPLE (ii)

A force acting in the xy plane has moments −60 *Nm,* −156 *Nm, and* 84 *Nm, about the origin, the point* (8, 0) *and the point* (0, 10) *respectively, the coordinates being in metres. Find the magnitude of the force and the points in which it cuts the coordinate axes.* (I.E.)

Let X, Y N be the components of the force along the axes and G Nm its moment about the origin.

The moment about the point (x, y) is $G - xY + yX$ in Nm.

$$\therefore \qquad\qquad G = -60$$

and $\qquad\qquad -60 - 8Y = -156$

and $\qquad\qquad -60 + 10X = 84.$

$$\therefore \qquad Y = 12 \text{ and } X = 14 \cdot 4$$

$$\therefore \qquad R = \sqrt{(X^2 + Y^2)} = \sqrt{[14 \cdot 4^2 + 12^2]}$$

$$= 12\sqrt{(1 \cdot 44 + 1)} = 18 \cdot 72 \text{ N.}$$

The equation of the line of action of the force R is

$$-60 - 12x + 14 \cdot 4y = 0.$$

When $y = 0$, $x = -5$, and when $x = 0$, $y = 60/14 \cdot 4 = 4 \cdot 2$.

Hence the line of action of the force cuts the axes at the points $(-5, 0)$ and $(0, 4 \cdot 2)$.

12.27. Other examples on coplanar forces

EXAMPLE (i)

Forces 1, 2, 3, 4 *act in the sides* AB, BC, CD, DA *of a square* ABCD. *Reduce the system to a force through* A *and a force in* BC.

Figure 12.42A shows the forces acting in the sides of the square ABCD. Fig. 12.42B shows the system replaced by a force R at A making an angle θ with AB, and a force F in BC. The two systems are equivalent if the sum of the components of each set of forces in any two perpendicular directions is the same, and if the sum of the moments of each set about any point is the same.

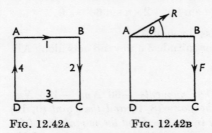

FIG. 12.42A   FIG. 12.42B

Resolving parallel and perpendicular to AB we get

$$R \cos \theta = 1-3 \tag{i}$$

$$R \sin \theta - F = 4-2 \tag{ii}$$

and taking moments about A

$$F \times a = 2a + 3a \tag{iii}$$

where a is the side of the square.

From equation (iii) $F = 5.$

Hence from equations (i) and (ii)

$$R \cos \theta = -2$$

$$R \sin \theta = 7.$$

Therefore $R = \sqrt{53}$ and $\tan \theta = -3.5$ (θ lies between 90° and 180°). Hence the force R has magnitude $\sqrt{53}$ and makes an angle of $\tan^{-1} 3.5$ with BA produced.

EXAMPLE (ii)

An equilateral triangular lamina ABC resting on a smooth horizontal plane is acted upon by a force of 5 N along BC, 3 N along AC, and 2 N along AD, where AD is perpendicular to BC. Find the force at B and the couple which will keep the lamina at rest.

Draw the triangle and insert the forces as in Fig. 12.43.

Let the additional force be R N at an angle θ to BC and the couple be of moment N Nm in a counterclockwise direction as shown.

Since the lamina is at rest when subject to all these forces, resolving parallel and perpendicular to BC we get:

$$R \cos \theta + 5 + 3 \cos 60° = 0 \tag{i}$$

$$R \sin \theta - 2 - 3 \sin 60° = 0 \tag{ii}$$

since the sum of the components of the two forces constituting the couple is zero.

Also taking moments about B,

$$N-2\times\tfrac{1}{2}a-3\times a \sin 60° = 0 \qquad \text{(iii)}$$

where a = side of the triangle ABC.

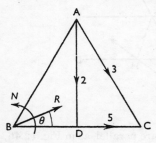

FIG. 12.43

From (iii) $\qquad N = a+3a\sqrt{3}/2 = 3.598a.$

From (1) and (ii)

$$R \cos \theta = -5-\tfrac{3}{2} = -\tfrac{13}{2}$$

and $\qquad\qquad R \sin \theta = 2+3\sqrt{3}/2$

∴ $\qquad\qquad R^2 = \tfrac{169}{4}+4+\tfrac{27}{4}+6\sqrt{3} = 53+6\sqrt{3}$

∴ $\qquad\qquad R = 7.962.$

Also, $\qquad \tan \theta = -\dfrac{4+3\sqrt{3}}{13} = -0.7074.$

Since $\sin \theta$ is positive and $\cos \theta$ is negative, θ lies between 90° and 180° and, in fact, equals $180°-35° \ 16' = 144° \ 44'.$

EXAMPLE (iii)

Show that a given force may be resolved into three components, acting in three given lines which are not all parallel or concurrent.

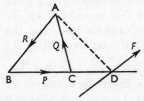

FIG. 12.44

Let the three lines form a triangle ABC (Fig. 12.44), and suppose the given force F cuts BC in D.

Then F can be resolved into two components acting along DA and BC respectively, and the force along DA can be resolved into two components along AB and CA respectively. The resolutions can be effected graphically, as in Fig. 12.45, where the dotted line is parallel to DA.

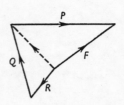

FIG. 12.45   FIG. 12.46

Similarly, if two of the lines AB, CD are parallel, as in Fig. 12.46, and EG is the third line.

Let F cut CD in H.

Then F can be resolved into two components along CD and HE respectively.

The force along HE can be then resolved into two components acting along GE and BA respectively.

EXAMPLES 12.7

1. Ox, Oy are rectangular axes, and P is a point whose coordinates are (3, 4). Find the intercepts made on Ox, Oy by the line of action of the resultant of a force of 7 units along OP, and a counterclockwise couple of moment 21 units.   (I.S.)

2. Forces of magnitudes 1, 2, 3, 4, 5, 6 units act in the same sense along the sides of a regular hexagon taken in order, and a force acts at the centre of the hexagon. If the several forces are equivalent to a couple, find the moment of the couple, and the magnitude and direction of the force at the centre.   (H.S.D.)

3. Forces of magnitude F, $2F$, $3F$, $4F$ act along the sides BA, BC, CD, DA of a quadrilateral ABCD in the directions indicated by the order of the letters, the quadrilateral being such that AB and BC are two sides of a square ABCE and D is the mid-point of CE. Find the magnitude and direction of the resultant, and find the distances from B at which its line of action meets AB and BC.   (I.E.)

4. Forces of magnitude F, $2F$, $3F$, $4F$, $5F$, $6F$ act along the sides of a regular hexagon, taken in order. Show that they are equivalent to a single force $6F$ acting parallel to one of the given forces, the distance of the line of action of that force and of the resultant from the centre of the hexagon being in the ratio $2 : 7$. (I.E.)

5. A system of forces acts on a plate in the form of an equilateral triangle of side $2a$ units. The moments of the forces about the three vertices are G_1, G_2, G_3 units respectively. Find the magnitude of the resultant. (H.S.C.)

6. A number of forces act in a plane, and the sum of the x components is X, the sum of the y components is Y, and the sum of the moments about the origin is N. Find the equation of the line of action of the resultant. (H.S.D.)

7. ABCD is a square whose side is 2 m, P is the mid-point of AD and Q of CD. Forces of magnitude 10, 10, 30, 40 act along AB, CD, QB, CP in the directions indicated by the order of the letters. Find the magnitude of the resultant, and the distances from A of the points where its line of action meets AB and AD.

8. ABCDEF is a regular hexagon. Forces of 1, 3, 2, and 4 N act along AB, BE, ED, and DA respectively. Find the magnitude of the resultant. Take AB as x axis and AE as y axis, and find the equation of the line of action. Indicate by an arrow the direction of the resultant. (I.E.)

9. A force in the plane of two rectangular axes has components X and Y in the directions of the axes of x and y respectively, and its line of action passes through the point (x', y'). Prove that it is equivalent to a force whose components are X and Y acting at the origin, together with a couple of moment $x'Y - y'X$. Parallel forces, P_1, P_2, P_3, . . . act in the plane of these axes at points (x_1, y_1), (x_2, y_2), (x_3, y_3), . . . respectively. Prove that the forces are in equilibrium whatever their common direction, if $\Sigma P = 0$, $\Sigma Px = 0$, $\Sigma Py = 0$. (H.C.)

10. ABCD is a rectangle in which AB $= 5$ m, BC $= 3$ m. Forces of 2 N, 4 N, 3 N, 11 N act along AB, BC, DC, DA respectively, the sense in each case being indicated by the order of the letters. If this system is reduced to a force acting at the point of intersection of AC and BD, together with a couple, determine the magnitude and direction of the force, and the moment and sense of the couple. (I.S.)

11. Forces act at the corners of a square of side 8 cm, as shown in Fig. 12.47. Find by calculation the magnitude and direction of the resultant force acting at the centre and the resultant couple.

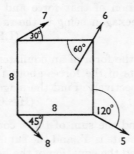

Fig. 12.47

12. A plane regular hexagon OABCDE has a side of 5 cm. Forces of 1, 2, 3, 4, 5, and 6 N act along the sides OA, AB, BC, CD, DE, and EO respectively, in the sense indicated by the order of the letters. Find the resultant force at O and the resultant moment about O.   (I.C.)

13. Prove that a system of coplanar forces is in equilibrium if the sum of the moments about each of three non-collinear points is zero. A couple of 10 Nm units acts on a square board ABCD of side 2 m. Replace the couple by forces acting along AB, BD, CA.   (N.U.3)

14. ABC is a triangle in which AB = AC = 4 cm, BC = 3 cm. E is the mid-point of AB, F a point on BC such that CF = 1 cm. Find three forces along the sides of the triangle ABC which will to-gether be equivalent to a force of 4 N along EF, representing them in an accurate diagram on a scale of 1 N to 2 cm.   (Ex.)

15. ABC is a triangular lamina with AC = 6 cm, BC = 8 cm, and C a right angle. A force 10 N acts along AB. Prove that this can be completely balanced by two forces acting perpendicular to AC, BC respectively at their mid-points. Find the magnitudes of these forces.   (N.U.)

16. A system of forces acting on a rigid lamina in a plane is reduced, firstly, to a single force acting at a point A in the lamina, and secondly, to a single force acting at another point B and a couple of moment G. Prove that if the system were reduced to a single force acting at the mid-point of AB and a couple the moment of the couple would be $\frac{1}{2}G$.   (N.U.3)

17. Forces 3, 4, 2, 1 N act respectively along the sides AB, BC, CD, DA of a square ABCD of side 1 m. Reduce the system to: (i) a force at A and a couple; (ii) two parallel forces through B and C.

18. A, B are any two points in a lamina, on which a system of forces coplanar with it are acting, and when the forces are reduced to a single force at each of these points and a couple the moments of the couples are G_a and G_b respectively. Prove that when the reduction is made to a force at the mid-point of AB and a couple the moment of the couple is $\frac{1}{2}(G_a+G_b)$.　　　　(C.W.B.)

19. Forces P, Q, P, Q act along the sides AB, BC, CD, DA respectively of a square; if these four forces and a fifth force R of given magnitude in the same plane have a resultant which passes through the centre of the square, prove that the line of action of R touches a fixed circle.　　　　(I.S.)

20. A uniform square lamina ABCD, of side 0·6 m, and of mass 7 kg, can turn freely in a vertical plane about A, which is fixed and is kept in equilibrium with the diagonal AC horizontal by means of a pull exerted in a horizontal string through its highest point D, together with a couple. Find the moment of the couple when the magnitude of the reaction at A is 100 N.　　　　(I.S.)

21. Forces P, $4P$, $2P$, $6P$ act along the sides AB, BC, CD, DA of a square ABCD of side a. Find the magnitude of their resultant, and prove that the equation of its line of action referred to AB and AD as coordinate axes is

$$2x-y+6a = 0.　　　　\text{(H.C.)}$$

22. Forces 1, 3, 5, 7, $9\sqrt{2}$ act along the sides AB, BC, CD, DA, and the diagonal BD of a square of side a, the senses being indicated by the order of the letters. Taking AB and AD as axes of x and y respectively, find the magnitude of the resultant and the equation of its line of action.　　　　(H.C.)

23. ABC is an equilateral triangle; forces of 4, 2, and 2 units act along the sides AB, AC, BC in the directions indicated by the letters. Prove that if E is the point where the perpendicular to BC at B meets CA produced and if F bisects AB, the resultant is $2\sqrt{7}$ units acting along EF.　　　　(H.C.)

24. ABCD is a quadrilateral in which AB = BC, CD = DA, A and C are right angles, B is 60°, D is 120°. Equal forces $\sqrt{3}P$ act along AD and DC; equal forces P act along CB and BA. Find the magnitude of their resultant, and the point in which it cuts BD produced.　　　　(H.C.)

25. ABCD is a square; four forces, whose algebraic magnitudes form an arithmetical progression, act along the sides taken in order. Show that, if their resultant passes through a corner of the square, the progression is a diminishing one, in which, if the common difference is $2P$ the greatest force is $5P$ or $3P$. (H.C.)

12.28. Moment of a force about an axis

So far we have dealt only with coplanar forces, and have considered their moments about a *point* in their plane.

Suppose now that we have a rigid body which is free to rotate about some *axis* fixed in the body.

Any force (whose line of action is not parallel to, or does not pass through, this axis) will tend to turn the body about it. This introduces the idea of the *moment of a force about an axis*.

For the present we shall consider only cases where the force is perpendicular to the axis. In this case the moment of the force about the axis is defined as the product of the force and the perpendicular distance between the force and the axis. As earlier, we shall regard the moment as positive if the force tends to rotate the body about the axis in a counterclockwise direction.

It can be shown that the principle of moments holds for moments about a fixed axis.

12.29. EXAMPLE (i)

A square table stands on four legs placed at the mid-points of its sides; find the greatest weight which can be put at one of the corners of the table without upsetting it, the total weight of the table and legs being W.

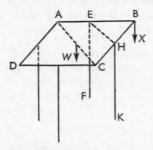

FIG. 12.48

Let ABCD (Fig. 12.48) represent the table and suppose the weight X be put at B.

This will tend to tilt the table about the line FK, joining the points of contact with the floor of the legs EF, HK. The weight W acts at the mid-point of AC, and its line of action is therefore at the same distance from FK as the line of action of the weight X.

Hence the greatest value of X is W.

EXAMPLE (ii)

A uniform circular plate is supported horizontally at three points in its edge, whose distances apart are l, m, n; find the proportion of the weight of the plate carried by each support.

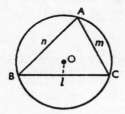

FIG. 12.49

Let A, B, C (Fig. 12.49) be the points of support, $BC = l$, $CA = m$, $AB = n$.

The weight of the plate acts at the centre of the circle O, which is the circumcircle of the triangle ABC.

The distance of O from BC is $R \cos A$, where R is the radius of the circle, and the distance of A from BC is $m \sin C$. Hence if P_A is the reaction at A, taking moments about BC, we get

$$P_A \times m \sin C = W \times R \cos A.$$

Also
$$R = \frac{l}{2} \operatorname{cosec} A$$

$\therefore$
$$P_A = W \frac{l}{2} \times \frac{\cos A}{m \sin C \sin A}$$

$$= \frac{Wl^2}{2mn} \times \frac{\cos A}{\sin^2 A}, \text{ since } \sin C = \frac{n}{l} \sin A.$$

This result should be expressed in terms of l, m, and n.
Using the formula

$$\sin A = \frac{2}{bc} \sqrt{[s(s-a)(s-b)(s-c)]}$$

and remembering that $a = l, b = m, c = n$,

$$\sin^2 A = \frac{4}{m^2 n^2} \times \frac{(l+m+n)(m+n-l)(l+n-m)(l+m-n)}{16}$$

Also

$$\cos A = \frac{m^2+n^2-l^2}{2mn}.$$

$$\therefore \qquad P_A = \frac{Wl^2}{2mn} \times \frac{(m^2+n^2-l^2)}{2mn}$$

$$\times \frac{4m^2n^2}{(l+m+n)(m+n-l)(l+n-m)(l+m-n)}$$

$$= W\frac{l^2(m^2+n^2-l^2)}{(l+m+n)(m+n-l)(l+n-m)(l+m-n)}$$

and there are similar expressions for the reactions at B and C.

12.30. Work done by a couple

Let the forces of the couple be each P and let the arm AB (Fig. 12.50) be of length p.

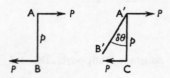

FIG. 12.50

Suppose the rigid body on which the couple acts is displaced so that AB moves to the position A'B', where the angle between AB and A'B' is the small angle $\delta\theta$.

We may suppose the motion to take place in two stages.

First, suppose the forces to move parallel to themselves as AB moves to the parallel position A'C. The total work done by the equal and opposite forces P during this displacement is zero.

Second, suppose the body to turn through the angle $\delta\theta$ about A' so that A'C now coincides with A'B'; to maintain the moment of the couple constant, suppose the forces to turn through the angle $\delta\theta$ about A'.

The force P at A' does no work, as its point of application does not move. The displacement of the point of application of the other force P at C is $p\,\delta\theta$, since $\delta\theta$ is indefinitely small, and the total work done is therefore $Pp\,\delta\theta$, i.e. *the moment of the couple multiplied by the elementary angle turned through.*

If the moment of the couple M remains constant the work done in turning through an angle θ is $M\theta$, i.e. the moment of the couple multiplied by the angle turned through. If the moment of the couple varies with θ the work done is given by the expression $\int_0^\theta M d\theta$.

EXAMPLES 12.8

1. A uniform circular table, resting on four equal legs placed symmetrically round its edge, has a mass of 50 kg. Find the least weight which will just upset the table when hung from its edge.

2. A circular table stands symmetrically on three vertical legs distant 1 m from one another and attached to the table top at the vertices of the equilateral triangle ABC. The table-top has a mass of 40 kg, and a mass of 60 kg is placed at L (within the triangle ABC) distant 15 cm and 25 cm from BC and CA respectively. Calculate the pressures on each leg.   (H.D.)

3. Show how to find the resultant of three parallel forces not in the same plane. A light table stands on three equal vertical legs, and a weight is placed at the centre of the circle inscribed in the triangle formed by the points of intersection of the legs. Show that the pressures on the legs are proportional to the opposite sides of the triangle.   (I.S.)

4. A circular table of mass 20 kg is 1·2 m in diameter; it is supported by three equally spaced legs at its edge. Find the load that can be placed diametrically opposite one leg at the edge of the table, so that the whole weight of the table and the load is carried by the other two legs.   (C.E.)

5. A round table 1·5 m in diameter has three symmetrically placed legs each 0·6 m from the centre. If the table has a mass of 25 kg, find the least weight which, placed on the edge of the table, will cause it to overbalance. What is the greatest weight which can be placed on the edge without overbalancing it?

6. A stool of mass 4 kg has a circular top of diameter 0·6 m. It is supported symmetrically in a horizontal position by three legs, 0·6 m long, each making an angle 60° with the ground, and fixed into the circular top at the vertices of an equilateral triangle, the lengths of its sides being 0·3 m. Calculate the least weight which, when placed on the edge of the stool, will cause it to topple over.   (Q.E.)

7. A pulley of radius 0·6 m is supported with its axis horizontal, and is rotated by applying a force of 49 N tangentially to the rim of the pulley. Find the work done in one revolution. What is the gain of kinetic energy after one revolution if a frictional couple of moment 12 Nm acts at the axis?

8. A couple of moment M Nm acts on a rigid body, which can rotate about a fixed axis. Find the work done in one complete rotation of the body when M equals: (i) 10, and (ii) $10 - \frac{1}{2}\theta$, where θ is the angle turned through at any instant.

9. A solid flywheel of radius r m and mass M kg is rotating at a speed of n rev sec^{-1}. It is brought to rest by a constant frictional couple of moment N Nm. Show that the number of revolutions it will make before coming to rest is $\pi M r^2 n^2 / 2N$.

10. A helical spring, fixed at one end, is twisted by applying to the free end a torsional couple of moment $k\theta$, where θ is the angle of twist. Show that the work done in giving the spring a twist ϕ is $\frac{1}{2}k\phi^2$.

REVISION EXAMPLES D

1. (i) Prove that the resultant of two forces P and Q which meet at an angle α is $\sqrt{(P^2+2PQ\cos\alpha+Q^2)}$.

   (ii) ABCDEF is a regular hexagon of centre O. Forces 2, 4, P, Q act from O along OA, OC, OE, OG respectively, where G is the mid-point of AB, and are in equilibrium. Find the values of P and Q.   (I.S.)

2. Particles of weights w_1 and w_2 lie at rest at the points A and B respectively on the upper half of a smooth circular wire whose plane is vertical, equilibrium being maintained by a light inextensible string which connects the particles and lies along the minor arc joining A to B. This arc subtends an angle α at the centre O of the circle. Prove that the tangent of the acute angle which OA makes with the vertical is

$$\frac{w_2\sin\alpha}{w_1+w_2\cos\alpha}.$$

Show the heavier particle is nearer the highest point of the circle than the lighter particle.   (I.S.)

3. Prove that if three concurrent forces are in equilibrium each force is proportional to the sine of the angle between the other two. Three forces, P, Q, R are in equilibrium. P is given in magnitude and direction. The magnitude of Q is not given, but its direction makes an angle θ with the direction of P. Find the direction of R when its magnitude is least, and determine the corresponding magnitudes of Q and R.   (I.S.)

4. Two particles of weights $2W$, $3W$, fastened to the ends of a light inextensible string which passes over two smooth pegs on the same level distant a apart, are kept in equilibrium by a third particle of weight W' fastened to the part of the string between the pegs. If the angle between the oblique portions of the string is $120°$, prove that $W' = \sqrt{7}W$ and that the depth of W' below the level of the pegs is $2a/7\sqrt{3}$.   (I.S.)

5. Two rings of equal weight, connected by a string, can slide on two fixed rough rods which are in the same vertical plane and inclined to the downward vertical at equal angles of $45°$ on opposite sides of it. If the coefficient of friction is $\frac{1}{3}$, prove that the maximum angle which the string can make with the horizontal, the rings remaining at rest, is θ, where $\tan\theta = \frac{3}{4}$.   (I.S.)

6. Prove that the algebraic sum of the moments of a number of concurrent coplanar forces about a point in their plane is equal to the moment of their resultant about that point.

   (i) If three forces X, Y, Z, acting along the internal bisectors of the angles of the triangle ABC in order, are in equilibrium, prove that $X : Y : Z = \cos\frac{1}{2}A : \cos\frac{1}{2}B : \cos\frac{1}{2}C$.

   (ii) Forces P, Q, R act along the sides BC, CA, AB respectively, of a triangle ABC and their resultant acts along the line joining the incentre and the orthocentre. Prove that

   $P : Q : R = \sec B - \sec C : \sec C - \sec A : \sec A - \sec B.$

   (C.W.B.)

7. Obtain the conditions of equilibrium of a system of coplanar forces. A uniform square lamina ABCD is suspended by two strings attached to A and B which slope away from one another and make angles 30° and 45° respectively with the vertical. Find the inclination of AB to the horizontal. (C.W.B.)

8. A uniform square lamina ABCD of weight W is freely suspended at A. A weight w is attached to the lamina at B, and the system rests in equilibrium with AB inclined to the vertical at an angle of 30°. Find the ratio of w to W. If now an additional weight $2w$ is attached to the lamina at D, find an equation for the inclination of AD to the vertical in the new position of equilibrium. Prove that this inclination is greater than 30°.

9. To the end B of a uniform rod AB, of weight W, is attached a particle of weight w. The rod and particle are suspended from a fixed point O by two light strings OA, OB of the same length as the rod. Prove that, in the position of equilibrium, if T, T' are the tensions in OA, OB

   $$\frac{T}{W} = \frac{T'}{W+2w}.$$

   Prove also, that if OA makes angle α with the vertical,

   $$\tan \alpha = \frac{(W+2w)\sqrt{3}}{3W+2w}.$$

   (H.C.)

10. A uniform rod AB of length $2a$ and weight W lies along a line of greatest slope of a plane inclined at angle θ to the horizontal, B being above A. The coefficient of friction between the rod and the plane is $\tan \lambda$, where λ is greater than θ. A cord, attached to A, passes over a small pulley at height a vertically above the mid-point of the rod and supports a scale-pan in which gradually increasing weights are placed. Prove that if λ is greater than $45° - \frac{1}{2}\theta$ the rod will tilt before it slides. (I.E.)

11. A thin rod of length a is in equilibrium with its ends resting on the inner rim of a smooth circular hoop, of radius a, fixed with its plane vertical. If the centre of gravity of the rod divides its length in the ratio 3 : 4, prove that its inclination to the vertical is $\tan^{-1} 7\sqrt{3}$.

    Determine the ratio of the reaction on the lower end of the rod to that on the upper end. (L.A.)

12. Two equal smooth cylinders of radius a and weight W lie in contact along generators on a horizontal table. A third equal cylinder is placed symmetrically upon them, and the system is kept in equilibrium by a band which passes round the cylinders in a plane perpendicular to the generators. Find the tension of the band if the lower cylinders are just about to separate. If the band is elastic and its natural length is $12a$, prove that the tension of the band at any extension x would be

$$\frac{Wx}{4\sqrt{3}(\pi-3)a}.$$ (H.C.)

13. Two uniform ladders, each of weight W and length $2b$, are hinged smoothly at their upper ends and stand on a smooth horizontal plane. A weight w is hung from a rung of one of the ladders at a distance d from its lower end, and the ladders are prevented from slipping by means of a light rope of length $2a$ attached to their lower ends. Find the pressure of each ladder on the ground and prove that the tension in the rope is

$$\frac{a(2Wb+wd)}{4b(4b^2-a^2)^{\frac{1}{2}}}.$$ (I.S.)

14. Three equal uniform rods, AB, BC, CD, each of length $2a$ and weight W, are smoothly jointed at B and C and rest with AB, CD in contact with two smooth pegs at the same level. In the position of equilibrium AB and CD are inclined at an angle α to the vertical, BC being horizontal. Prove that the distance between the pegs is $2a(1+\frac{2}{3}\sin^3\alpha)$. If β is the angle which the reaction at B makes with the vertical, prove that

$$\tan\alpha\tan\beta = 3.$$ (H.C.)

15. A pentagon ABCDE of smoothly jointed uniform rods, each of weight W and of the same length, is supported symmetrically in a vertical plane with CD horizontal and AB and AE in contact with smooth pegs at the same horizontal level and at such a distance apart that the pentagon is regular. From the equilibrium of the pentagon find the reactions on the pegs, and by considering the equilibrium of the rods BC, CD, DE, show that the

horizontal components of the reactions at B, C, D, E are equal and of magnitude $W \cot (2\pi/5)$. Show further that the reaction at A is a horizontal force

$$\left(\frac{5}{2} \tan \frac{\pi}{5} - \cot \frac{2\pi}{5}\right) W.$$ (H.S.C.)

16. A square ABCD is formed from four equal uniform rods, each of weight W, freely jointed at their ends. The square is suspended freely from A and a weight $3W$ is hung from the lowest point C, the square shape being maintained by a light horizontal strut joining the mid-points of AB and AD. Prove that the thrust in this strut is $10W$.   (L.A.)

17. Two uniform bars AB and BC, each of length $2a$ and weight W, are smoothly jointed together at B. A light ring is attached to C and threaded on a fixed smooth horizontal rod, and A is freely jointed to a fixed point at depth $3a$ vertically below the rod. Prove that equilibrium is possible if, and only if, one of the bars is vertical. Find the reaction at C when the system is in equilibrium: (i) with AB vertical; (ii) with BC vertical.   (L.A.)

18. Each of the two legs of a step-ladder is 2 m long, is uniform, and has a mass of 9 kg. The legs are smoothly hinged together at one end of each, and the mid-points are connected by an elastic cord of unstretched length 1 m and modulus λ. The ladder stands on smooth horizontal ground with its feet apart and supports a mass of 75 kg at the hinge. If, in the equilibrium position, the extension in the cord is 10 cm, calculate the value of λ.

19. ABCD is a plane quadrilateral with AB $= 0.9$ m, BC $= 1.2$ m, CD $= 3.6$ m, DA $= 3.9$ m and AC $= 1.5$ m, B and D being on opposite sides of AC. AB is vertical and B is below A. CD, DA, AC, and CB represent four light rods smoothly jointed together to form a framework, A and B being fixed points in a vertical wall. A load of mass 75 kg is suspended from D. Find the force in each of the four rods.   (L.A.)

20. Two equal uniform rods AB, BC, each of weight W, are freely jointed together at B. They rest in contact with a smooth solid circular cylinder which is fixed with its axis horizontal, the plane of the rods being at right angles to this axis. In the position of equilibrium the rods are at right angles; show that the length of each rod is equal to twice the diameter of the cylinder.   (L.A.)

21. Two uniform rods AC, BC, whose weights are proportional to their lengths, are freely jointed together at C, and the ends A and B are freely hinged to two points in a vertical line. Show

that the reaction between the rods at C acts along the bisector
of the angle ACB. (L.A.)

22. ABCD is a rectangle with AB = a, BC = b. M is the mid-point
of BC. Three forces are represented completely by kAM, kMC,
kCD, where k is positive. Find the magnitude and direction of
their resultant and the distance from A of its line of action.

Find the magnitude of the couple that must be combined
with the three forces in order that the resultant of the system
shall pass through the mid-point of AB. Indicate the sense of
this couple in a diagram. (L.A.)

23. Forces P, Q act along the lines BA, CA in the directions indicated
by the order of the letters. Write down the equivalent pair of
forces acting along the internal and external bisectors of the
angle A, where $\angle$BAC = 2α.

The triangle ABC is isosceles and right-angled at A; BCD is
an equilateral triangle on the other side of BC. Forces of 3, 2, 3,
10, 14 N act along AB, BC, CA, BD, CD in the directions indicated by the order of the letters. Prove that the line of action of
the resultant force is at a distance $(\sqrt{3}/15)$ AB from A. (L.A.)

24. Prove that a coplanar system of forces which is not in equilibrium may be reduced to a single force or to a couple.

ABCD is a square; forces of magnitude 3, 2, 4, 3, P units act
along AB, CB, CD, AD, DB respectively in directions indicated
by the order of the letters. If the system is equivalent to a
couple, find the value of P. (L.A.)

25. A system of coplanar forces has anticlockwise moments M,
$2M/3$, $3M/2$, respectively about the points $(0, 0)$; $(a, 0)$; $(0, 2a)$
in its plane. Calculate the magnitude of the resultant of the
forces and prove that the equation of its line of action is

$$3y - 4x + 12a = 0.$$ (L.A.)

26. Show that a system of coplanar forces, not in equilibrium, can
be reduced either to a single force or to a couple.

Forces 4, 3, 3 N act respectively along the sides AB, BC,
CA of an equilateral triangle ABC of side 0·6 m. Find the magnitude and direction of their resultant and obtain the perpendicular distance of its line of action from C.

An additional force is introduced at C in the plane ABC. If the
system is now equivalent to a couple, find its moment and the
magnitude and direction of the additional force. (L.A.)

27. Show that the moment of a couple is the same about all points
in its plane. Prove that a force F and a couple of moment M
acting in the same plane are equivalent to a single force.

Forces of magnitudes 3, 4, 6, 7 units act along the sides AB, BC, CD, DA of a square ABCD of side a, the directions of the forces being indicated by the order of the letters. In addition, a couple acts in the plane of the square. If the whole system is equivalent to a force acting through the centre of the square, find the magnitude and sense of this couple. Find also the magnitude and line of action of this force.   (L.A.)

28. ABCD is a square plate acted upon by the following forces in its plane: $5\sqrt{2}$ N at C along AC produced; $15\sqrt{2}$ N at B along DB produced; 10 N at D along a line making an angle of 30° with AD produced on the side remote from BC. A force P is to be placed at A so that the whole system reduces to a couple. Find the magnitude and direction of P, and the moment of the couple if the side of the square is of length 1 m.   (I.E.)

29. Prove that two coplanar couples of equal and opposite moment are in equilibrium. Show that the resultant of any number of coplanar couples is a couple whose moment is the algebraic sum of the moments. ABCDE is a regular pentagon. Five forces each equal to P act along AE, ED, DC, CB, BA. Five forces each equal to Q act along AC, CE, EB, BD, DA. Prove that the ten forces will be in equilibrium if P and Q are in a certain ratio and find the ratio.   (C.W.B.)

30. A force acting at the point (x, y) has components (X, Y) parallel to the axes of coordinates. Prove that it may be replaced by a force X along the axis of x, a force Y along the axis of Y, and a couple $xY - yX$. Forces of magnitudes 1, 5, 9, 11, 7, 3 act in the sides AB, BC, CD, DE, EF, FA of a regular hexagon of side a in the senses indicated by the order of the letters. Taking as axes OA and OH, where O is the centre of the hexagon and H is the mid-point of BC, find the forces along the axes and the couple by which the system may be replaced. Prove also that the system is equivalent to a single force which meets the axes at the points $(-9a/4, 0)$ and $(0, -9\sqrt{3}a/2)$.   (H.C.)

CHAPTER THIRTEEN

GRAPHICAL CONSTRUCTIONS

13.1. The magnitude and direction of the resultant of any number of coplanar forces can be found graphically by means of the polygon of forces. When the forces act at a point the resultant must pass through this point, so that we know its line of action. When the forces are acting on a rigid body we can still find the magnitude and direction of the resultant by drawing the polygon of forces, but we require a further construction to determine the line of action.

We shall now consider how this may be done, and also how to apply the graphical method to determine the stresses in a framework of light rods acted on by given forces.

13.2. To find, graphically, the resultant of any number of coplanar forces

Let the lines of action of the forces P, Q, R, S be as in Fig. 13.1A.

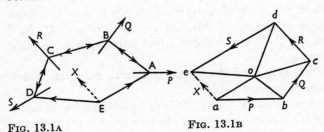

FIG. 13.1A   FIG. 13.1B

Draw the figure $abcde$ (Fig. 13.1B) having its sides ab, bc, cd, de parallel and proportional to P, Q, R, S respectively. Join ae.

By the polygon of forces ae represents the resultant of P, Q, R, and S in magnitude and direction. We will denote the resultant by X.

To find the line of action of the resultant, take any point o and join it to a, b, c, d, and e.

Take any point A on the line of action of P (Fig. 13.1A) and draw AE and AB parallel to oa and ob, and let AB meet the line of action of Q in B. P is equivalent to forces represented by ao and ob acting along EA and BA respectively.

Through B draw BC parallel to oc to meet R in C.

Q is equivalent to forces bo, oc acting along AB, CB respectively; the former of these balances the force ob along BA.

From C draw CD parallel to od to meet S in D.

R is equivalent to forces co, od acting along BC, DC respectively; the former balances the force oc acting along CB.

From D draw DE parallel to oe to meet AE in E.

S is equivalent to forces do, oe acting along CD and ED respectively; the former balances the force od acting along DC.

Hence the forces P, Q, R, and S are equivalent to forces ao, oe acting along EA, ED respectively, and since these intersect in E, their resultant must pass through E.

The resultant is therefore a force X passing through E, parallel to ae and represented in magnitude by ae.

We have therefore determined the line of action of the resultant as well as its magnitude and direction.

The figure $abcde$ is called the *Force Polygon* for the given system, and the figure ABCDE is called a *Link* or *Funicular Polygon*.

If the link polygon were formed of strings it would be kept in equilibrium in the shape ABCDE by the forces P, Q, R, S acting at A, B, C, D and a force equal and opposite to their resultant acting at E.

This is the origin of the name funicular polygon, which means a rope polygon.

It is evident that by taking different positions for A and o the shape of the funicular polygon can be varied in any number of ways, but the final point of intersection of AE and DE will always lie on the same straight line, the line of action of the resultant.

13.3. If the point e of the force polygon coincides with a the polygon is said to close, and the resultant force vanishes.

This does not ensure, however, that the forces are in equilibrium.

For in this case oe and oa coincide, and AE, DE will be parallel, and the forces acting along them will be equal and opposite.

Hence, unless DEA is a straight line, i.e. unless the funicular polygon closes, we are left with a couple.

This means that *if the forces are in equilibrium, both the force polygon and the funicular polygon must close.*

13.4. EXAMPLE

ABC *is a triangle whose sides* AB, BC, CA *are respectively* 12, 10, *and* 15 *cm long, and* BD *is the perpendicular from* B *on* CA. *Find graphically the magnitude and line of action of the resultant of the following forces:* 8 *from* A *to* C, 4 *from* C *to* B, 3 *from* B *to* A, 2 *from* B *to* D.

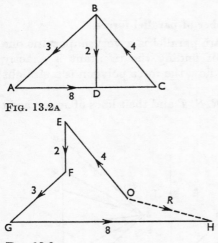

FIG. 13.2A

FIG. 13.2B

The forces are shown in Fig. 13.2A. Their resultant can be found in magnitude and direction by drawing a force-polygon, as in Fig. 13.2B, where the vectors OE, EF, FG, GH represent the forces 4, 2, 3, 8 respectively. The resultant of the forces, R, is represented by the closing side OH.

By measurement, $R = 3·4$ and the angle it makes with GH, that is, with AC, equals 13° approximately.

To find the line of action of R, it is not necessary in this case to draw a funicular polygon. For, since three of the forces act through B, their resultant passes through B, and its magnitude and direction is represented by the vector OG in Fig. 13.2B.

If therefore we draw through B a line parallel to OG to meet CA produced at X, say, the resultant of the four forces must pass through this point.

13.5. Bow's Notation

Graphical constructions involving coplanar forces are often facilitated by the use of Bow's notation. According to this, the plane in which the forces act may be regarded as divided up into spaces or compartments by the lines of action of the forces. The spaces are lettered, for example, A, B, C, D, . . . and the force along the line dividing space B from space C is denoted by *bc* and so on.

It is specially convenient in dealing with frameworks, as will be shown later (13.10).

13.6. Resultant of any number of parallel forces

The case when the forces are parallel is a very important one in practice. The method of finding the resultant is exactly similar to that in 13.2, but now the force polygon is a straight line.

Let the forces be P, Q, R, S, T and their lines of action as in Fig. 13.3A.

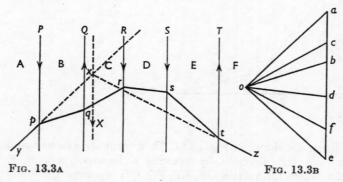

Fig. 13.3A　　　　　　　　　　　　　　Fig. 13.3B

Letter the spaces A, B, C, D, E, F as shown, and on a line parallel to the direction of the forces mark off *ab* downwards to represent P to scale (Fig. 13.3B), *bc* upwards to represent Q, *cd*, *de* and *ef* to represent R, S, and T.

Then *af* represents the resultant in magnitude and direction, and its line of action can be found as follows.

Take any point *o* and join *oa*, *ob*, *oc*, *od*, *oe*, and *of*.

Take any point *p* on the line of action of P and draw *py*, *pq* parallel to *ao*, *ob*, and let *pq* meet the line of action of Q in *q*.

P is equivalent to forces *ao*, *ob* along *py* and *pq*.

From q draw qr parallel to oc to meet R in r.

Q is equivalent to forces bo, oc acting along qp, qr, and the former balances the force ob along pq.

From r draw rs parallel to od to meet S in s.

R is equivalent to forces co, od acting along rq, rs, and the former balances the force oc acting along qr.

From s draw st parallel to oe to meet T in t.

S is equivalent to forces do, oe acting along sr, st, and the former balances the force od acting along rs.

From t draw tz parallel to of.

T is equivalent to forces eo, of, acting along ts, tz, and the former balances the force oe along st.

We are thus left with a force ao along py and a force of along tz.

Produce yp and zt to meet in x; then the resultant of the forces must pass through x.

The resultant is a force X represented in magnitude and direction by af and passing through x.

It might be noted that this method applied to *two* forces is equivalent to the one used earlier in 11.2. In fact, the polygon HABK (Fig. 11.1) may be regarded as the funicular polygon for the two forces P and Q.

EXAMPLE (i)

A light beam having given weights attached to it at given points of its length is supported at its ends. To find the reactions on the supports.

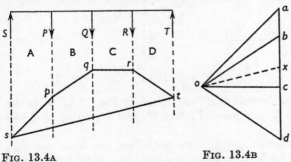

FIG. 13.4A   FIG. 13.4B

Let the weights be P, Q, R acting as shown in Fig. 13.4A, and let S, T be the reactions on the beam at the supports.

Letter the spaces A, B, C, D, as shown, and draw the force polygon $abcd$ (Fig. 13.4B). Take any point o and join oa, ob, oc, od.

Take any point p in the line of action of P, and draw ps parallel to oa to cut S in s and pq parallel to ob to cut Q in q.

From q draw qr parallel to oc to cut R in r, and from r draw rt parallel to od to cut T in t.

The forces P, Q, R are equivalent to forces represented by ao and od acting along ps and rt.

Join st and draw ox parallel to st to cut ad in x.

The force ao acting along ps is equivalent to a force represented by ax acting downwards along the line of S, and a force xo acting along ts.

The force od acting along rt is equivalent to xd acting downwards along the line of T and a force ox acting along st. This latter force balances the force xo acting in the direction ts, and we are left with vertical forces represented by ax and xd acting along the lines of S and T.

The reactions on the beam at the ends must be equal and opposite to these forces and are therefore equal and opposite to ax and xd.

EXAMPLE (ii)

PQRS *is a light string attached to two fixed points* P *and* S, *and carrying weights at* Q *and* R. *Determine the ratio of these weights if* PQ *is inclined at 30° to the vertical,* QR *at 60° to the vertical, and* RS *is horizontal.*

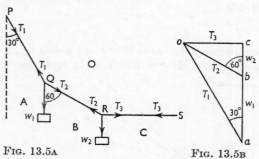

FIG. 13.5A   FIG. 13.5B

The form of the string PQRS is shown in Fig. 13.5A. It is the funicular polygon for the parallel forces W_1 and W_2 acting at Q and R respectively.

From this funicular polygon we can draw the force polygon. For in Fig. 13.5B let ba represent the weight W_1; draw lines from a and b parallel to the strings QP and QR respectively, and let them meet at o. Then this triangle abo is the triangle of forces for the forces W_1, T_1, and T_2 acting at Q.

If now we draw oc parallel to the string RS, that is, horizontal, then the triangle *bco* is the triangle of forces for the forces W_2, T_2, and T_3 acting at R.

Hence *cb* represents W_2 on the same scale as *ba* represents W_1, and therefore $W_1/W_2 = ab/bc$.

But $ac = oc \tan 60° = oc\sqrt{3}$

and $bc = oc \tan 30° = oc/\sqrt{3}$

∴ $ac = 3bc$

∴ $W_1 + W_2 = 3W_2$ or $W_1 = 2W_2$.

This result can also be obtained by resolving the forces acting at Q and R horizontally and vertically as follows:

For Q, $T_1 \cos 30° - T_2 \cos 60° = W_1$

and $T_1 \sin 30° - T_2 \sin 60° = 0$.

Also for R, $T_2 \cos 60° = W_2$

and $T_2 \sin 60° - T_3 = 0$

leading to $W_1 = 2W_2$.

EXAMPLE (iii)

Forces of 5, 9, −7, 3, and −10 N act along parallel straight lines, and their distances apart, in the order given, are 10, 5, 7, 3 cm. Find by means of the vector and link polygons the magnitude and sense of the resultant couple.

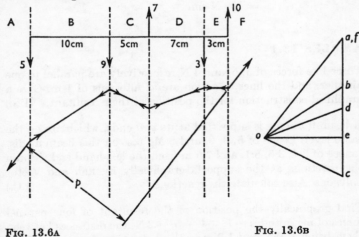

FIG. 13.6A   FIG. 13.6B

Draw the space diagram as in Fig. 13.6A, and letter it as shown.

Draw the force polygon as shown in Fig. 13.6B. In this figure $ab = 5$, $bc = 9$, $cd = 7$, $de = 3$, and ef or $ea = 10$, i.e. the polygon closes.

Construct the funicular by drawing in the compartments A, B, C, D, E, F of the space-diagram lines parallel to *oa, ob, oc, od, oe, of* respectively.

Each of the parallel forces can be resolved into two components acting along sides of the funicular polygon, as shown in Fig. 13.6A. These components balance in pairs except the first and the last, which are equal and parallel and in opposite directions and so form a couple.

The magnitude of these forces is represented by *oa* in the force-diagram, and their distance apart, *p* say, can be obtained from the space-diagram, in Fig. 13.6A.

The moment of the couple is therefore given by $oa \times p$, and is counterclockwise.

From the figures $oa = 12 \cdot 7$ N and $p = 15 \cdot 7$ cm. Hence the moment of the couple is $12 \cdot 7 \times 15 \cdot 7 = 199$ N cm.

This value can be checked by taking the moments of all the forces about some point, for example, a point on the line of action of the force 5. We get

$$-9 \times 10 + 7 \times 15 - 3 \times 22 + 10 \times 25$$

$$= -90 + 105 - 66 + 250$$

$$= 199 \text{ N cm.}$$

EXAMPLES 13.1

1. Three like forces of 3, 5, and 4 N respectively are parallel to one another, and the lines of action are at intervals of 1 m. Give a graphical construction for the position of their resultant.   (I.S.)

2. A beam 9 m long is supported at its two ends, which are on the same level. Loads of 5, 3, 9, and 2 Mg rest on this beam at distances of $2 \cdot 4$, $3 \cdot 6$, $5 \cdot 1$, and $7 \cdot 5$ m from the left-hand end. Obtain the reactions at the supports graphically by link and vector polygons. Also calculate the reactions.   (I.C.)

3. Find graphically the position of the resultant of four parallel forces of magnitudes $+7$, $+4$, -5, $+2$ N, the distances between them being 1, $0 \cdot 5$, and $1 \cdot 2$ m in the order given.   (I.E.)

4. Loads of mass 2, 3, and 5 kg are placed on a beam 3 m long at distances of $0 \cdot 3$, $0 \cdot 9$, and $1 \cdot 5$ m from one end. Find graphically the line of action of the resultant.

5. A horizontal beam 20 m long is supported at its ends and carries loads of mass 2, 3, 6, and 4 kg at distances of 3, 6, 12, and 15 m respectively from one end. Find graphically the thrusts on the ends.

6. Weights of mass 8, 3, 2, and 6 kg are suspended at distances of 2, 3, 6, and 8 m from one end of a light beam 10 m long supported at its ends. Find graphically the thrusts on the supports.

7. Like parallel forces of 2, 4, 6, 8, and 10 N act at distances of 1 m apart. Find graphically the position of the line of action of their resultant.

8. The loads on the wheels of a locomotive are the weights of 10, 10, 18, 16, 8, and 8 Mg respectively, and their distances apart are 1·2, 3, 2·4, 1·8, and 1·2 m respectively. Find graphically the magnitude and position of the resultant thrust on the rails, and check the result by calculation.

9. A horizontal bar 10 m long carries weights of mass 4, 5, 6, and 7 kg at distances respectively 2, 5, 7, and 9 m from one end; give graphical constructions (i) for the resultant of the weights, (ii) for the pressures on the supports when the bar is supported at its two ends, neglecting the weight of the bar itself.   (Q.E.)

10. The spaces between and the loads taken by the axles of a locomotive are as follows, reading from front to rear:

Spaces		2·7		3		2·4		3		m
Loads	12		12		25		25		5 units

Find by a graphical construction the horizontal distance of the centre of gravity of the locomotive from its front axle.   (Q.E.)

11. A uniform beam, AB, of mass 50 kg and length 6 m, is supported at A and at a point 1·2 m from B. It carries loads of mass 30 kg at points 1·5 m and 2·4 m from A and a load of mass 40 kg at B. Find *graphically* the pressures on the supports.

12. A light string is fastened to a fixed point A and passed over a smooth pulley D at the same level as A, and carries a known weight W at its end. If unknown weights W_1 and W_2 are fastened to points B and C of the string between A and D, show how W_1 and W_2 can be found from the directions of the portions AB, BC, and CD of the string in the equilibrium position.

13. ABCD is a light string. The ends A, D are fastened to fixed points in the same horizontal line. Weights of mass 2·5 kg and P kg are attached at B and C. Determine graphically the value of P and the tensions in the portions AB, BC, CD if AB and CD make angles of 60° and 45° respectively with the horizontal and the angle BCD is 140°.

14. Forces 1, 3, −4 N act in order round the sides of an equilateral triangle ABC of side 5 cm drawn on a rigid lamina. Give a graphical construction for the magnitude, direction, and position of their resultant. (C.W.B.)

15. Forces, 3 N, 2 N, −3·5 N act in order round three consecutive sides of a regular hexagon of side 5 cm drawn on a rigid lamina. Give a graphical construction for the magnitude, direction, and line of action of their resultant. (N.U.3)

13.7. Frameworks

In most cases in which a graphical method is used it is known that the forces are in equilibrium. The forces are usually acting on some sort of framework, and the problem is to find the stresses in the various parts or 'members' of this framework. The method of modifying the construction of the preceding paragraphs for this purpose are illustrated in the following examples.

In considering the equilibrium of a *light* rod it is evident that, if the only forces acting on it are applied at the ends, these forces must be directed along the rod or they cannot balance one another; they must also, of course, be equal and opposite. The stress in a *light* rod, acted on by forces at the ends only, must therefore consist of a thrust or a tension along the length of the rod.

A rod which is in a state of thrust is called a *Strut*, and a rod in a state of tension is called a *Tie*.

13.8. *A closed polygon of light rods, freely jointed at their extremities, is in equilibrium under the action of a given system of forces applied at the joints; to find the stresses in the rods.*

Let AB, BC, CD, DE, EA represent the rods freely jointed at their ends, and let forces P, Q, R, S, and T act at the joints as in Fig. 13.7A.

Let the resulting forces acting on the joints along the rods be T_1, T_2, T_3, T_4, T_5 respectively. The forces on the rods are equal and opposite to these.

Draw the force polygon $abcde$ (Fig. 13.7B) having its sides parallel and proportional to P, Q, R, S, and T respectively. Since the forces are in equilibrium, this polygon must close.

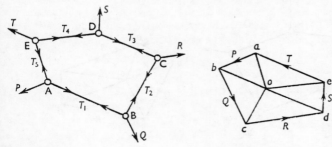

FIG. 13.7A   FIG. 13.7B

Through a draw ao parallel to AE, and through b draw bo parallel to AB. The triangle boa has its sides parallel to the forces P, T_1, and T_5 which act on the joint at A. Its sides are therefore proportional to these forces, and the sides bo and oa must represent T_1 and T_5 on the same scale that ab represents P.

Join oc, od, oe.

The sides ob, bc of the triangle obc represent two of the forces T_1 and Q, which act at B. Hence co represents the third force acting at B, i.e. T_2, and must therefore be parallel to BC.

Similarly do represents T_3 and eo represents T_4.

The lines oa, ob, oc, od, oe therefore represent, in magnitude and direction, the forces along the sides of the framework.

13.9. It is clear that, of the figures in the last paragraph, $abcde$ is the force polygon and ABCDE a funicular polygon for the system of forces P, Q, R, S, T.

Also if $abcde$ represents a jointed framework acted on by forces oa, ob, oc, od, oe, then ABCDE is the force polygon for this system of forces, $abcde$ being the funicular polygon.

Hence either of these polygons may be the framework or funicular polygon, and then the other is the corresponding force polygon. For this reason such figures are said to be *Reciprocal*.

13.10. Bow's Notation

As explained in 13.5, there is another system of lettering the figures which may be used. It is known as Bow's notation. Consider the framework of 13.8.

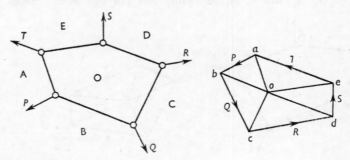

Fɪɢ. 13.8

Draw the framework and forces as in Fig. 13.8, and instead of lettering the corners of the framework, letter the *spaces* or *compartments* between the forces and bars, e.g. let the space between T and P be called A, that between P and Q be called B, that between Q and R be called C, and so on.

The line of action of P is the boundary between the spaces A and B, and in the force polygon the line representing P is called *ab*, that representing Q is called *bc* and so on.

The force polygon is then *abcde*.

Calling the pole of the force polygon *o* the space within the funicular is then called O.

A small letter attached to a vertex of the force polygon corresponds to a big letter attached to a space of the funicular.

EXAMPLE (i)

ABCD *is a quadrilateral formed of four light rods freely jointed at their extremities. The angles at* A *and* B *are each right angles, the angle* ADC *is* 60° *and* AD = CD. *It is stiffened by a rod* AC, *and at* B *and* D *act forces of* 40 N, *in such a manner that the frame is in equilibrium. Find the tensions or thrusts in the rods.*

Since AD = DC and ADC = 60°, the triangle ADC is equilateral and the angle CAB = 30°.

Draw AB as in Fig. 13.9, and AC, making BAC = 30° to cut the perpendicular to AB at B in C. Then construct the triangle ACD on AC.

Since the two forces of 40 N balance they must act in the same straight line, i.e. along BD, and in opposite directions. Take them as acting outwards.

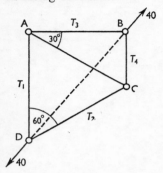

Fig. 13.9

Method (i)

Draw the triangle of forces for the corner D, and obtain the tensions in AD and DC, denoted by T_1 and T_2 ($T_1 = 15 \cdot 1$, $T_2 = 30 \cdot 2$).

Draw the triangle of forces for the corner B, and obtain the tensions in AB and BC, denoted by T_3 and T_4 ($T_3 = 26 \cdot 2$, $T_4 = 30 \cdot 2$). The thrust in AC is found by drawing the triangle of forces for A or C. (This thrust is $30 \cdot 2$.)

The triangles of forces for each joint can be combined compactly in one diagram as explained below.

Method (ii)

Using Bow's notation, we letter the compartments of the diagram (Fig. 13.10A) P, Q, R, S as shown.

To draw the force polygon we start at one of the corners, say B, where one of the known external forces acts, and draw pq to represent the 40 N force in magnitude and direction. We then draw ps parallel to the rod (AB) between the compartments P and S, and qs parallel to the rod (BC) between the compartments Q and S. Then psq is the triangle of forces for the forces acting at the joint B, and since the 40 N force is in the direction q to p, the directions of the other forces acting at B must be as shown in Fig. 13.10A.

Proceeding to the neighbouring joint A, we draw pr parallel to the rod (AD) between the compartments P and R, and sr parallel to the rod (AC) between the compartments S and R. Then prs is the triangle of forces for the forces acting on the joint A, and since the direction of the force *ps* is known, the direction of the others can be found and are as shown in Fig. 13.10A.

If we now join *qr* the triangle *pqr* is the triangle of forces for the forces acting on the joint D, and the directions of the forces are as shown in Fig. 13.10A.

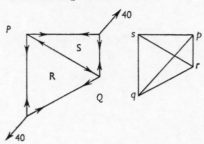

FIG. 13.10A   FIG. 13.10B

The forces acting on the joint C are represented by the triangle *rqs*, and the directions are as shown. It is clear that this triangle is equilateral, and hence the three forces acting on the joint C are equal.

The magnitudes of all the forces may be obtained by measuring the sides of the figure *pqrs*, and using the scale that *pq* represents 40 N.

The forces in the rods are equal and opposite to those acting on the hinges at their ends; consequently (reversing the directions shown in Fig. 13.10A) the rods AB, BC, CD, DA are in tension and the rod AC in thrust.

EXAMPLE (ii)

ABC *is a triangular framework of light rods freely jointed together and placed on supports at A and B so that AB is horizontal and C above AB, and the plane ABC is vertical. BC = 6·6 m, CA = 5·4 m, AB = 6 m. A weight of mass 200 kg is suspended from C. Find by the methods of graphical statics the thrusts or tensions in the three rods.* (H.S.D.)

Draw the framework to scale as in Fig. 13.11, with the lines of action of the external forces *outside the framework*. The external forces are the 200g N, and the vertical reactions of the supports P and Q at A and B.

The reactions P and Q may be found graphically as in 13.6.

In this simple case, however, there is no need to find P and Q initially: they may be found as follows from the triangle of forces for each joint.

Letter the spaces formed by the lines of action of the external forces and the bars of the framework, X, Y, Z, W, as shown.

The space Y extends indefinitely to the left, being separated from the other spaces by the $200g$ N force, the bar AC, and the force P.

Similarly, the space X extends indefinitely to the right.

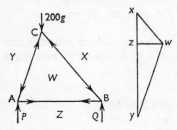

FIG. 13.11

Starting with the joint C; it is acted upon by the $200g$ N and the stresses along AC and CB. Now draw xy vertically downwards to represent $200g$ N; complete the triangle of forces for C by drawing yw parallel to AC and xw parallel to CB. Since the forces $200g$ N represented by xy is vertically downwards, the directions of the forces acting on the joint C are therefore as shown.

Considering next the joint B, we complete the triangle of forces xwz by drawing wz parallel to BA. zx must therefore represent the reaction Q and wz the stress in AB.

Similarly, yzw is the triangle of forces for the joint A and yz represents the reaction P. Again the directions of the forces acting at the joint A can be found from the triangle yzw, since the force P represented by yz is upwards.

Since the directions of the forces acting on the joints are as shown, the bar AB is in tension and the bars BC and CA in thrust.

The tensions and thrusts can be denoted by arrows, as shown, or by putting — for a tension and + for a thrust. Sometimes they are distinguished by putting one and two strokes through the bar. Great care must be taken to remember that in obtaining the directions of the forces from the triangle of forces we must go round the triangle in order, e.g. for A, since yz represents P, zw represents the force acting on the joint A along AB, i.e. it acts towards the right away from A. To find the nature of the stresses in the rods the arrows may be reversed.

EXAMPLE (iii)

A framework of seven rods is in the form of three equilateral triangles ABC, BCD, CDE. *It rests on smooth vertical supports at* A *and* E, with BD *and* ACE *horizontal, and* BD *above* ACE, *and carries loads of 5 units at* B, *5 units at* C, *and 10 units at* D. *Neglecting the weights of the rods, find the reactions at* A *and* E, *and determine, preferably by means of a stress diagram, the stresses in each of the rods, indicating which are thrusts and which are tensions.*

Draw the framework and insert the external forces as in Fig. 13.12.

The reactions P and Q acting on the framework at A and E can be found graphically, but in this case it is much easier to find them by taking moments.

Taking moments about A we get

$$4Q = 5 \times 1 + 5 \times 2 + 10 \times 3 = 45$$

∴ $$Q = 11\tfrac{1}{4} \text{ and } P = 8\tfrac{3}{4}.$$

We then letter the spaces as in Fig. 13.12 (all the external forces being drawn *external* to the framework), and draw the force polygon as described below.

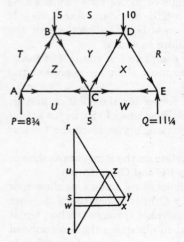

FIG. 13.12

On a vertical line with scale 2 cm = 5 units, mark off $rs = 10$, $st = 5$, and then $tu = 8\tfrac{3}{4}$ upwards to represent P. Now mark off $uw = 5$ to represent the weight of 5 units at C. wr represents Q the reaction at E.

Construct the triangle of forces for the forces acting on the joint A by drawing uz parallel to AC and tz parallel to AB. uz represents the stress along AC and zt the stress along AB. The directions of the forces acting on the joint A are shown. AC is in tension and AB in thrust.

Of the force polygon for B we have already st and tz, and to complete it we draw zy parallel to BC and sy parallel to BD.

zy represents the stress in BC (a tension) and ys the stress in BD (a thrust).

Of the force polygon for D we have already rs and sy and to complete it we draw yx parallel to DC and rx parallel to DE.

yx represents the stress in CD (a tension), and xr the stress in DE (a thrust).

Since wr represents Q and rx the thrust on E due to DE, wx must be the third side of the triangle of force for E, i.e. wx must be parallel to CE and xw represents the stress in CE (a tension).

We notice that we have also a closed polygon $yzuwx$ for the joint C. The directions of the forces acting on this joint can be checked since the force uw is downwards.

The stresses in the various rods can be found by measuring the corresponding sides of the force-diagram. They are approximately as follows, a positive sign denoting a thrust and a negative sign a tension.

Stresses in $AB = +10$, $AC = -5$, $BC = -4\frac{1}{4}$, $BD = +5$, $CD = -1\frac{3}{4}$, $CE = -6\frac{1}{4}$, $DE = +13$.

EXAMPLE (iv)

A crane, as in Fig. 13.13, is pinned at A and kept vertical by a horizontal pressure at B.

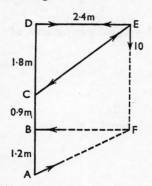

FIG. 13.13

If a load of mass 10 Mg be suspended from E, show how to find the reactions at A, B, and the forces in CE, DE graphically. Also calculate the reactions and forces.

Method (i)

Draw the figure to scale, say 1 cm = 1 m.

Since the rod AD is acted on by forces at points other than its ends, the stress in it will not be a simple thrust or tension. To find the reactions at A and B we consider all the external forces acting on the crane, i.e. these two reactions and the weight of 10 units. The unit is the weight of 1 Mg.

Draw BF horizontal to meet the vertical through E in F, then the reaction at A must pass through F.

Join AF. The triangle ABF will serve as a triangle of forces for the reactions and the load. The lengths of BA, AF, FB, are 1·2, $1·2\sqrt{5}$, 2·4 cm, and these represent 10 units, the reaction at A and the reaction at B respectively.

Hence the reaction at A is $10\sqrt{5}$ units, and the reaction at B is 20 units.

The triangle DCE is a triangle of forces for the corner E.

The lengths of DC, CE, ED are 1·8, 3, and 2·4 cm, and these represent 10 units, the stress in CE and the stress in ED respectively. Hence the stress in CE is $\frac{50}{3}$ units (a thrust), and the stress in ED is $\frac{40}{3}$ units (a tension).

Method (ii)

To *calculate* the reaction at B and A.

Let P units be the reaction at B, then, taking moments about A for the whole frame,

$$1·2P = 2·4 \times 10$$
$$\therefore \qquad P = 20.$$

Let X, Y units be the horizontal and vertical components of the reaction at A, then

$$X = P = 20$$
and $$Y = 10.$$

If R is the resultant reaction,

$$R = \sqrt{[20^2 + 10^2]} = 10\sqrt{5} \text{ units.}$$

R is inclined to the horizontal at an angle $\tan^{-1} \frac{1}{2}$.

To calculate the stresses in CE, ED.

Let T_1 units be the thrust in CE.

Resolving vertically for the corner E,

$$T_1 \sin CED = 10$$
$$\therefore \qquad \tfrac{3}{5}T_1 = 10 \text{ or } T_1 = \tfrac{50}{3}.$$

Let T_2 units be the tension in ED.

Resolving horizontally for the corner E,

$$T_2 = T_1 \cos CED = \tfrac{50}{3} \times \tfrac{4}{5} = \tfrac{40}{3}.$$

EXAMPLES 13.2

1. A framework is built up of rigid bars AB = AD = 0·6 m., BC = CD = 37·5 cm, smoothly hinged together. The framework is placed on a horizontal table in such a manner that the angle BAD = 60°, and A, C are on opposite sides of BD. B and D are joined by a string capable of supporting a weight of mass 14 kg. Find the greatest forces which can be applied to A and C so that the framework is in equilibrium in the given position with the string intact, and determine the corresponding stresses in the members of the framework, stating whether they are tensions or compressions.   (H.S.D.)

2. A rod AB 3 m long, hinged to a wall at B and carrying a weight of mass 50 kg at A, is supported by a cord attached to the middle point C of the rod and carried to a point D of the wall 2·1 m above B, the length of CD being 1·8 m. Draw a diagram to scale, and from a triangle of forces estimate the tension in the cord and the magnitude and direction of the reaction of the hinge B.

3. A uniform beam AB, of mass 50 kg, is supported by strings AC and BD, the latter being vertical and the angles CAB and ABD, being each 105°. The rod is maintained in this position by a horizontal force F applied at B. Show that the value of F is about 122 N.

4. Five equal light rods are freely jointed together at their extremities to form a pentagon ABCDE. The system is suspended from the joint A, and a load w is suspended from the joint C, the shape of a regular pentagon being kept by rods BE, BD. Draw a diagram showing graphically the magnitudes of the stresses in the various rods, and find which of the rods are in compression and which in tension.   (I.S.)

5. An equilateral triangle ABC formed of three light rods, each 0·6 m long jointed at their ends, is supported at a point in AC which is 37·5 cm from A, and a weight of mass 6·5 kg is hung from a point in AB 17·5 cm from A. Find (by graphical or other method) the tension in the rod BC, and the action between the other two rods at A.   (I.A.)

6. Three light bars are jointed together to form a triangular framework ABC in which the angles A and C are each 30°. The framework can turn in a vertical plane about the point B, and is kept in equilibrium with AB horizontal by a weight of mass 50 kg hung at C and a vertical force P at A. Find, graphically or otherwise, the magnitudes of the force P and of the stresses in the rods.   (H.S.D.)

7. Five light rods form a parallelogram ABCD and its diagonal BD. The sides AD and BC of the parallelogram are twice as long as the other two sides, and the angles at A and C are 60°. Two equal and opposite forces of magnitude F are applied at A and C along the diagonal AC so that the parallelogram remains in equilibrium. Find the stresses in all the rods.   (I.S.)

8. The framework shown in Fig. 13.14 is formed by smoothly jointed rods, the length of AB and AD is 0·9 m, of BC and DC 1·2 m, the distance AC is 1·5 m, and E is the point mid-way between A and C. Forces of 40 N act at C and E as shown. Find the tension or compression in each rod of the framework. (Q.E.)

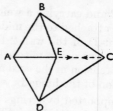

Fig. 13.14

9. A regular pentagon ABCDE (Fig. 13.15) jointed at the angles is stiffened by two jointed bars AC, AD. Two equal and opposite forces, each equal to 15 N, are applied at B and E. Find the stress in each bar of the framework, stating whether it is tensile or compressive.   (Q.E.)

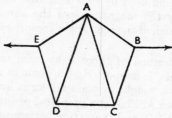

Fig. 13.15

10. A rectangle ABCD in which the sides AB, BC are respectively 8 and 12 cm is formed by smoothly jointed rods, and is made stiff by a diagonal BD; the frame is hung up from A and a weight of mass 10 kg is fastened at C; draw a stress diagram for the forces in the rods (which are supposed to be light), and hence find the stresses, distinguishing between thrusts and tensions.

                                                                        (I.S.)

11. Figure 13.16 represents a framework of nine smoothly jointed bars supported by ropes at A, B in the directions shown and carrying loads at X, Y. Find *graphically* the forces in each bar, indicating the results in your figure, and showing whether they are tensions or thrusts. (Neglect the weight of the bars.)

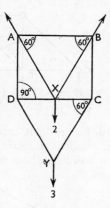

12. Four rods AB, BC, CD, and DE of a framework ABCDE form sides of a regular hexagon, and the framework is stiffened by rods joining AC, AE, and CE. Equal forces of 20 units are applied at the joints B and D from outside along directions perpendicular to AC and CE respectively, and the frame is kept in equilibrium by forces applied at A and E along AB and ED respectively. Find the magnitude of these forces and the stresses in the various members of the frame. (N.U.)

FIG. 13.16

13. Three equal strings of negligible weight are knotted together to form an equivalent triangle ABC. A mass of 30 units is suspended from A, while the triangle and weight are supported by strings at B and C so that BC is horizontal. If the supporting strings are equally inclined at an angle of 135° to BC, find the tensions in the strings by a graphical method. (N.U. 3 and 4)

14. Figure 13.17 represents the framework of a roof whose weight may be regarded as distributed in the manner shown. Find the stress in each of the nine members and indicate its nature.

$$AE = EC = ED = 2CF = 2FD = 2FB.$$

Weight at E = 200 units, at F = 100 units, at C = 150 units, and ACB is a right angle.

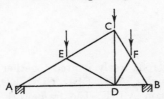

FIG. 13.17

15. The framework ABCDEF (Fig. 13.18) is composed of light rods, smoothly jointed; it is hung from smooth pins at A, B, and carries weights as shown. Find the stresses in all the rods to the

nearest unit, and mark with a double line the rods which are under a thrust.

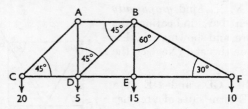

Fig. 13.18

16. Figure 13.19 represents a framework of nine light rods loaded as indicated, resting on vertical supports at A, B with AB horizontal. Find the reactions at A and B and the stresses in all the rods.

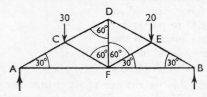

Fig. 13.19

17. The framework in Fig. 13.20 consists of four light bars, AB, BC, CD, DB freely jointed at B, C, D and attached to a vertical wall at A and D. A weight of 10 units is suspended from C. Find the stresses in all the bars and the reactions at A and D. Mark the struts with double lines.

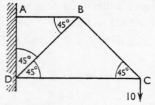

Fig. 13.20

18. A framework of nine equal light rods freely jointed together is formed by four equilateral triangles, ABC, CBD, CDE, EDF, the whole forming a parallelogram ABFE. The framework is placed in a vertical plane with the lowest rod AB horizontal, a weight of 20 units is suspended from F and vertical forces at A and B maintain equilibrium. Draw a force diagram to show the stresses in the rods.

19. Figure 13.21 represents a framework of light bars smoothly jointed so as to form three isosceles right-angled triangles. The frame is hinged at A to a fixed point and kept in position by a

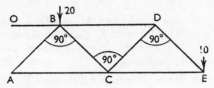

FIG. 13.21

light horizontal rod OB hinged to it at B and to a fixed point O; it is loaded as shown. Find the reaction at A and the tension in OB, and draw a stress diagram to give the stresses in all the bars.

20. The framework in Fig. 13.22 consists of nine smoothly jointed light rods, smoothly hinged to a fixed point at A, kept in position

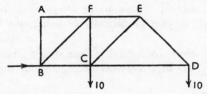

FIG. 13.22

by a horizontal reaction at B, and loaded with 10 units each at C and D, the angles in the figure are all 45° or 90°. Determine the stresses in the rods, marking the struts with a double line.

21. Figure 13.23 represents a loaded framework of light rods, attached to a vertical wall at A and B, with ADF, BCE horizontal. The angles are all 45° or 90°. Assuming that the reaction at B

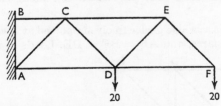

FIG. 13.23

is wholly along BC, find the magnitude and direction of the reaction at A, and find the stresses in all the rods, indicating which are in a state of thrust and which are in a state of tension. Measurements in a stress diagram will be sufficient. (I.S.)

22. ABCDE (Fig. 13.24) is a light smoothly jointed vertical frame held so that ED is horizontal, the angles and lengths being as

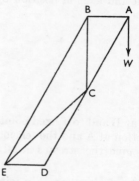

follows. ABED is a parallelogram, AB = 2 m, BC = 4 m, ABC is a right angle, and AC = CD. A weight W is hung at A. Find the stresses in the six rods, specifying their nature in each case.   (I.S.)

Fig. 13.24

23. Draw a triangle AET with AT = AE. Let AE represent to scale the horizontal, and AT the vertical part of a structure in which AT = 12 m. Divide AE into four equal parts, and letter the dividing points, B, C, D. Join TB, TC, TD, and let these lines with TE represent tie bars. Consider AB, BC, CD, DE to be rigid, weightless bars, and suppose loads of 1 unit to be suspended from the points B, C, D, and E. Obtain graphically or otherwise the tensions in the tie bars.   (I.E.)

24. Figure 13.25 represents a crane composed of four freely jointed, light bars, AC, BC, BD, CD in a vertical plane, supporting a

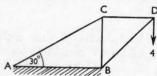

Fig. 13.25

weight of 4 units at D; AB and CD are horizontal, and BC vertical. Find graphically or otherwise, the force acting along each bar.

25. Figure 13.26 represents a bridge girder freely supported at A and E; CF and CH are squares, and AB = BF = DE. Loads of 10,

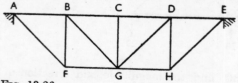

Fig. 13.26

15, and 12 units are applied at B, C, and D. Determine the stresses in AB, BF, BG, FG, and CG.   (I.E.)

26. Draw a rectangle ABCD with AB = DC = 15 cm, AD = BC = 5 cm. Bisect DC in E, and trisect AB in F and G, F being nearer to A than to B. Join DF, EG, FE, CG, and let the figure represent a bridge truss to scale. Determine the forces in all the members when the truss is supported at A and B with AB level, and loaded with 1 unit at F. (I.E.)

27. In the frame ABCDE (Fig. 13.27) of freely jointed bars,

$$AD = DC = CE = EB = DE,$$

and $$AC = CB = 1\cdot8AD.$$

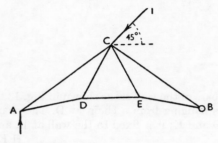

Fig. 13.27

It is freely supported at A, and B is hinged to a support at the same level. A force of 1 unit acts at C as shown; find the reactions at A and B, and show how to draw a stress diagram for the bars. (I.E.)

28. The frame of smoothly jointed rods represented in Fig. 13.28 is supported at A and B, AB being horizontal, and weights of 8 and

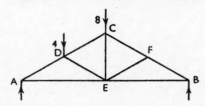

Fig. 13.28

4 units are suspended from C and D. The acute angles in the figure are 30° or 60°. Find by a stress diagram the stresses in each member of the frame. (I.S.)

29. Three equal light bars are jointed together to form a triangular framework ABC. The framework is suspended from A, and

weights of 4 units and 5 units are attached at B and C. Find, graphically or otherwise, the angle which AB makes with the vertical and the force along BC. (H.S.D.)

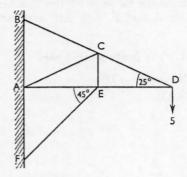

FIG. 13.29

30. Find the stresses in the bars of the wall crane shown in Fig. 13.29 due to a load of 5 units hanging from a chain at D. The chain passes over pulleys at D and E; it is fixed to the wall at F, and AE = ED. (I.E.)

CHAPTER FOURTEEN

FRICTION

14.1. The laws of Friction and their application to the equilibrium of a particle on a rough surface were considered in Chapter Ten. We shall now consider cases where bodies other than particles are in equilibrium under frictional as well as other forces.

Before proceeding to discuss particular problems, there are one or two general points in connection with friction which are worth noticing.

14.2. Friction plays an important part in everyday mechanics. When a person is walking there is a tendency for the feet to slip backwards; this is prevented by the friction between the feet and the ground, which acts in the forward direction. The force of friction is really the propelling force; without friction it would be impossible to walk.

A railway engine cannot move forward, even without a train behind it, unless there is an external force acting in the forward direction. The engine can only cause its own driving wheels to rotate. If these are resting on smooth rails they will revolve without causing any forward motion. In practice, the friction between the driving wheel and the rail tends to prevent rotation or rather to prevent slipping at the point of contact C (Fig.

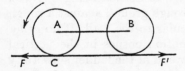

Fig. 14.1

14.1). The wheel is thus made to roll along the rail, and the friction force F called into play acts in a forward direction. This friction gives the magnitude of the tractive force of the engine. The other wheels of the engine or the wheels of a carriage of the train are drawn forward by a force applied to the axle as at B. Such wheels on smooth rails would simply skid forward *without turning*; the effect of friction which acts in the *backward direction*, as F' in Fig. 14.1, causes them to roll.

14.3. *Action of brakes*

The brakes on a motor car tend to stop the wheels rotating. If they actually lock the wheels (i.e. prevent them rotating altogether) sliding friction acts at the points of contact with the ground and reduces the car to rest.

In most cases, however, the brakes merely check the rotation of the wheels, which still keep rolling, and in this case it is not perhaps obvious how the force tending to stop the car is produced.

It is clear that checking the rotation of the wheel cannot, in itself, produce a retarding force on the car. If the ground were smooth, then even locking the wheels would have no such effect.

When a wheel, whose centre is A (Fig. 14.1) and point of contact C, is rolling freely there is no slipping at C. The backward velocity of C relative to A is equal to the forward velocity of A so that C is instantaneously at rest. Hence if the rotation of the wheel is checked the backward velocity of C is diminished, so that C tends to move forward with A. This brings into play a backward friction force at C, and it is this force which retards the forward motion of the wheel.

14.4. Problems involving friction can be classified roughly as follows:

1. Those in which the body is rigid and equilibrium can be broken only by sliding, the direction of motion being obvious. For example, a ladder resting on rough ground against a rough wall in a vertical plane perpendicular to the wall. If no other forces act it is obvious that if motion ensues in the vertical plane it will be such that the lower end of the ladder slips away from the wall and the upper end slips downwards at the same time. One end cannot slip without the other.

2. Those in which equilibrium may be broken either by sliding or tilting. For example, a block or cylinder resting on a rough plane which is gradually tilted. If the vertical through the centre of gravity comes outside the base before sliding commences the body will topple over before sliding.

3. Those in which we have a non-rigid body such as two jointed rods AB, BC (Fig. 14.2) freely jointed at B and with the ends A and C resting on a rough horizontal plane. In this case it is not necessary for slipping to occur at *both* A and C. The friction may be limiting at A or at C without being limiting at both. It *may*, of course, be limiting at both. If there are no external forces other than the weights of the rod and weights placed on them, then, in equilibrium, the frictions at A and C must be equal and opposite, since they are the only horizontal forces acting.

Care must be taken, however, not to assume that either of them is limiting, i.e. equal to μR.

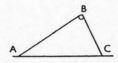

FIG. 14.2

4. More difficult problems where the direction of motion is not obvious; or where equilibrium may be broken by sliding or rolling, e.g. a ladder resting on rough ground and against a rough wall, but not in a vertical plane perpendicular to the wall; or a rough cylinder resting on two others, which in turn rest on a rough horizontal plane.

Examples of various kinds are illustrated in the following paragraphs.

14.5. EXAMPLE (i)

One end of a uniform ladder, of weight W, rests against a smooth wall, and the other end on rough horizontal ground, the coefficient of friction being μ. Find the inclination of the ladder to the horizontal when it is on the point of slipping, and the reactions at the wall and ground.

Let AB (Fig. 14.3) be the ladder, G its centre of gravity, C the intersection of the wall and the ground. Since the wall is smooth, the reaction R at B must be perpendicular to the wall.

If S is the normal reaction on the ladder at A, then, since the ladder is on the point of slipping, the friction at A is μS towards the wall.

Method (i)

There are thus four forces acting on the ladder, and by resolving horizontally and vertically, and taking moments about C or A, we obtain three equations to find the unknown reactions R and S, and the angle θ.

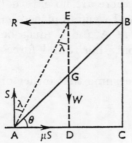

FIG. 14.3

Resolving horizontally $\qquad\qquad\qquad R = \mu S$ $\qquad\qquad$ (i)

Resolving vertically, $\qquad\qquad\qquad S = W$ $\qquad\qquad$ (ii)

Taking moments about C,

$$Rl \sin\theta + W\frac{l}{2}\cos\theta = Sl\cos\theta \qquad\qquad\text{(iii)}$$

where l is the length of the ladder.

From (i) and (ii) $R = \mu W = W\tan\lambda$, where λ is the angle of friction.

From (iii) $\qquad W\tan\lambda\sin\theta + \tfrac{1}{2}W\cos\theta = W\cos\theta$

$\therefore \qquad\qquad\qquad\qquad W\tan\lambda\tan\theta = \tfrac{1}{2}W.$

$\therefore \qquad\qquad\qquad\qquad\qquad \tan\theta = \tfrac{1}{2}\cot\lambda.$

The resultant reaction at the ground is $\quad \sqrt{(S^2 + \mu^2 S^2)}$

$$= S\sqrt{(1 + \tan^2\lambda)}$$
$$= W\sec\lambda.$$

Method (ii)

The angle of inclination of the ladder can also be found by considering the *resultant* reaction of the ground at A instead of the two components S and μS. This reduces the number of forces acting on the ladder to three, which must therefore meet in a point, viz. the point E, where the vertical through G cuts the line of action of R.

Also since the ladder is on the point of slipping, the resultant reaction at A makes an angle λ, the angle of friction, with the normal at A.

If (Fig. 14.3) the vertical EG cuts AC at D we have

$$\tan \theta = \frac{BC}{AC} = \frac{ED}{2AD} = \tfrac{1}{2} \cot \lambda.$$

The geometrical method is particularly useful when we require only the *position* of a body in limiting equilibrium, as we obtain the result without introducing the reactions and having to solve equations. Even when reactions are required, it is sometimes useful to use this method to find the position of the body and then find the reactions by resolving or taking moments.

EXAMPLE (ii)

One end of a uniform ladder, of weight W, rests against a rough wall, and the other end on rough horizontal ground, the coefficient of friction at the ground and wall being μ and μ' respectively. Find the inclination of the ladder to the horizontal when it is on the point of slipping, and the reactions at the wall and ground.

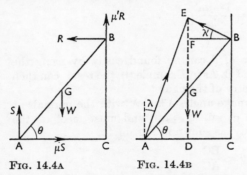

Fig. 14.4A   Fig. 14.4B

Let AB (Fig. 14.4A) be the ladder, G its centre of gravity, R and S the normal reactions acting on the ladder at the wall and ground. Since both ends are on the point of slipping, we have a force of friction $\mu' R$ acting *upwards* at B, and μS acting *towards* the wall at A.

Method (i)

Let θ be the inclination of the ladder to the ground, and $2l$ its length. Resolving horizontally,

$$\mu S = R. \tag{i}$$

Resolving vertically, $S + \mu' R = W.$ (ii)

Taking moments about C,

$$Wl \cos \theta = S2l \cos \theta - R2l \sin \theta$$

or $W \cos \theta = 2S \cos \theta - 2R \sin \theta.$ (iii)

From (i) and (ii) we have

$$S(1+\mu\mu') = W,$$

∴ $$S = \frac{W}{1+\mu\mu'}, \text{ and } R = \frac{\mu W}{1+\mu\mu'}.$$

Substituting μS for R in (iii),

$$W \cos \theta = 2S(\cos \theta - \mu \sin \theta)$$

$$= \frac{2W}{1+\mu\mu'} (\cos \theta - \mu \sin \theta)$$

∴ $$1 = \frac{2}{1+\mu\mu'} (1 - \mu \tan \theta)$$

∴ $$\frac{1+\mu\mu'}{2} = 1 - \mu \tan \theta$$

or $$\mu \tan \theta = \frac{1-\mu\mu'}{2}$$

or $$\tan \theta = \frac{1-\mu\mu'}{2\mu}.$$

Method (ii)

In this case the value of θ can be found easily by using the resultant reactions at A and B. As in Example (i), the result can then be derived from the geometry of the figure.

These reactions must make angles λ and λ' with the normals at A and B (where $\tan \lambda = \mu$, $\tan \lambda' = \mu'$), and must meet on the vertical through G, at E say, as shown in Fig. 14.4B.

Hence, $$\tan \theta = \frac{BC}{AC}$$

$$= \frac{ED-EF}{AC}$$

$$= \frac{ED}{2AD} - \frac{EF}{2FB}$$

$$= \tfrac{1}{2}(\cot \lambda - \tan \lambda')$$

$$= \tfrac{1}{2}\left(\frac{1}{\mu} - \mu'\right)$$

$$= (1-\mu\mu')/2\mu.$$

We can then find R and S by resolving as above.

EXAMPLE (iii)

One end of a uniform ladder, of weight W, rests against a smooth wall, and the other end on rough ground, which slopes down from the wall at an angle α to the horizontal. Find the inclination of the ladder to the horizontal when it is on the point of sliding, and show that the reaction of the wall is then W tan (λ−α), where λ is the angle of friction.

Let AB (Fig. 14.5) be the ladder, G its centre of gravity, and θ the inclination to the horizontal.

Since the wall is smooth, the reaction R at B is perpendicular to the wall.

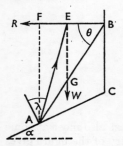

FIG. 14.5

When the ladder is on the point of slipping the resultant reaction at A makes an angle λ with the normal at A, and also passes through E, where the line of action of R meets the vertical through G.

Draw AF perpendicular to BE produced.

Then
$$\tan \theta = \frac{EG}{EB} = \frac{\frac{1}{2}AF}{FE}$$
$$= \tfrac{1}{2} \cot FAE$$
$$= \tfrac{1}{2} \cot (\lambda - \alpha)$$

which gives θ, the inclination of the ladder to the horizontal.

If $2l$ be the length of the ladder, then, taking moments about A,

$$R2l \sin \theta = Wl \cos \theta$$
$$\therefore \qquad R = \frac{W}{2} \cot \theta = \frac{W}{2} \times 2 \tan (\lambda - \alpha)$$
$$= W \tan (\lambda - \alpha).$$

EXAMPLE (iv)

A uniform ladder rests with its lower end on rough horizontal ground and its upper end against a rough vertical wall, the ground and wall being equally rough, and the angle of friction λ. Show that the greatest inclination of the ladder to the vertical is 2λ.

When the ladder is in this position can it be ascended without slipping?

Let AB (Fig. 14.6) be the ladder, G its centre of gravity, θ the inclination to the vertical. When the ladder is on the point of slipping the resultant reactions at A and B make angles equal to λ

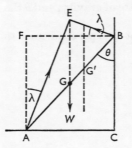

FIG. 14.6

with the normals at those points, and they must also meet at some point E on the vertical through G. The geometry of the figure gives

$$\angle AEG = \lambda, \angle GEB = 90° - \lambda, \angle AEB = 90°,$$

and hence the semicircle AFEB has centre G.

$\therefore$ $\qquad\qquad \theta = \angle EGB$

$\qquad\qquad\quad = 2\angle AEG$, since AG = GE,

$\therefore$ $\qquad\qquad \theta = 2\lambda.$

If an additional weight is placed anywhere on the ladder between A and G the centre of gravity of the ladder and added weight is moved to a point below G. The vertical through the new centre of gravity will then be to the left of that shown in the figure, and it is clear that the reactions at A and B can still meet on this vertical without their inclination to the normals at A and B being greater than λ; they will, as a matter of fact, be less than λ, so that the equilibrium is no longer limiting.

When the added weight reaches G the equilibrium is again limiting.

When the added weight gets above G the centre of gravity of the ladder and weight moves *above* G (say to G′) and the reactions at A and B cannot meet on the vertical through G′, as this would require one of the inclinations to the normal to be greater than λ. The ladder can therefore be ascended only as far as its centre.

If an additional weight is added at the foot of the ladder (as by someone standing on the bottom rung) the centre of gravity is brought below G. In this case the ladder can be ascended by another person above G, but only to such a height as to bring the centre of gravity of the ladder and the two added weights back to G.

EXAMPLE (v)

The upper end of a uniform ladder rests against a rough vertical wall and the lower end on a rough horizontal plane, the coefficient of friction in both cases being $\frac{1}{3}$. *Prove that if the inclination of the ladder to the vertical is* $\tan^{-1}\frac{1}{2}$, *a weight equal to that of the ladder cannot be attached to it at a point more than* $\frac{9}{10}$ *of the distance from the foot of it without destroying equilibrium.*

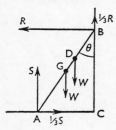

FIG. 14.7

Let AB (Fig. 14.7) be the ladder, G its centre of gravity, W its weight, and D the position of the extra weight W when the ladder is *on the point of slipping.*

Method (i)

If R, S are the normal reactions at the wall and ground the frictions at these points are $\frac{1}{3}R$ and $\frac{1}{3}S$.

Resolving horizontally $\qquad R = \frac{1}{3}S \qquad\qquad$ (i)

Resolving vertically, $\qquad S + \frac{1}{3}R = 2W \qquad\qquad$ (ii)

$\therefore \qquad\qquad S + \frac{1}{9}S = 2W \text{ or } S = \frac{9}{5}W$

and $\qquad\qquad\qquad R = \frac{3}{5}W.$

Taking moments about A, if $2l$ is the length of the ladder, $AD = x$ and $\angle ABC = \theta$, where $\tan\theta = \frac{1}{2}$, we get

$\therefore \qquad Wl\sin\theta + Wx\sin\theta = R2l\cos\theta + \frac{1}{3}R2l\sin\theta$

$\therefore \qquad W\sin\theta + W\frac{x}{l}\sin\theta = \frac{6}{5}W\cos\theta + \frac{2}{5}W\sin\theta$

$\therefore \qquad\qquad \frac{x}{l} = \frac{6}{5}\cot\theta + \frac{2}{5} - 1$

$\qquad\qquad\qquad = \frac{12}{5} - \frac{3}{5} = \frac{9}{5}$

$\therefore \qquad x = \frac{9}{5}l = \frac{9}{10}$ of the length of the ladder.

Method (ii)

This problem can also be dealt with by the geometrical method.

For equilibrium it is necessary that the resultant reactions at A and B should meet on the vertical through the centre of gravity of the ladder and any added weight.

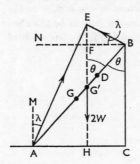

Fɪɢ. 14.8

If G (Fig. 14.8) is the centre of gravity of the ladder alone and G′ that of the ladder and added weight in the limiting position, then the reactions at A and B will meet the vertical through G′ in E so that

$$\tan AEG' = \cot G'EB = \tfrac{1}{3}$$

∴ $AH = \tfrac{1}{3}EH$ and $EF = \tfrac{1}{3}FB.$

Hence, $BC = EH-EF$

$$= 3AH-\tfrac{1}{3}FB.$$

But $BC = 2AC$ since $\tan \theta = \tfrac{1}{2}$

∴ $2AC = 3AH-\tfrac{1}{3}FB$

∴ $2(AH+HC) = 3AH-\tfrac{1}{3}HC$

∴ $3AH = 7HC$

∴ $AH = \tfrac{7}{10}AC.$

Hence, $AG' = \tfrac{7}{10}AB = 7l/5.$

Also, if x is the distance of the added weight W above A, since the centre of gravity of this and the ladder is at G′, we have, taking moments about A,

$$Wx+Wl = 2W \times \tfrac{7}{5}l,$$

∴ $x = \tfrac{9}{5}l = \tfrac{9}{10}$ of the length of the ladder.

EXAMPLE (vi)

A uniform rod rests in limiting equilibrium inside a rough hollow sphere, the rod being in a vertical plane through the centre of the sphere. Show that the rod makes with the horizontal an angle

$$\tan^{-1} \frac{\sin 2\epsilon}{\cos 2\alpha + \cos 2\epsilon}$$

where ϵ is the angle of friction, and 2α the angle subtended at the centre of the rod.

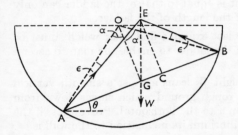

FIG. 14.9

Let AB (Fig. 14.9) be the rod, G its centre of gravity, O the centre of the sphere. Then the reactions at A and B meet at a point E on the vertical through G, and are inclined at the same angle ϵ to the radii OA, OB, since these are the normals to the sphere at A and B.

Draw EC perpendicular to AB. Then if θ is the inclination of AB to the horizontal, we get

$$\tan \theta = \frac{GC}{EC} = \frac{\frac{1}{2}(AC - CB)}{EC}$$

$$= \tfrac{1}{2}(\tan AEC - \tan CEB).$$

But, $\quad$ angle AEC $= \alpha + \epsilon$ and angle CEB $= \alpha - \epsilon$

$\therefore \qquad 2 \tan \theta = \tan(\alpha + \epsilon) - \tan(\alpha - \epsilon)$

$$= \frac{\sin(a+\epsilon)}{\cos(\alpha+\epsilon)} - \frac{\sin(\alpha-\epsilon)}{\cos(\alpha-\epsilon)}$$

$$= \frac{\sin 2\epsilon}{\cos(\alpha+\epsilon)\cos(\alpha-\epsilon)}$$

$\therefore \qquad \tan \theta = \dfrac{\sin 2\epsilon}{\cos 2\alpha + \cos 2\epsilon}.$

EXAMPLES 14.1

1. A uniform ladder rests with one end on horizontal ground and the other against a vertical wall, the coefficients of friction being respectively $\frac{3}{5}$ and $\frac{1}{3}$. Find the inclination of the ladder to the vertical when it is about to slip.

2. A uniform ladder rests with one end on rough horizontal ground, the coefficient of friction being $\frac{5}{8}$, and the other end against a smooth vertical wall. If the inclination of the ladder is 45°, show that a man whose weight is equal to that of the ladder can only ascend three-quarters of the length of the ladder.

3. In the case given in the last example find what weight must be placed on the bottom of the ladder to enable the man to ascend to the top.

4. A uniform ladder of weight W leans against a smooth vertical wall, and its foot is on rough ground which slopes down from the wall at an inclination α to the horizontal. Prove that, if the ladder is in limiting equilibrium, its inclination to the wall is

$$\tan^{-1}[2 \tan (\epsilon - \alpha)],$$

where ϵ is the angle of friction. Prove also that the resultant reaction with the ground is then $W \sec (\epsilon - \alpha)$.   (I.S.)

5. A uniform stick of length l is placed in the rough ring of an umbrella-stand at a height h above the ground. It rests also on a smooth floor. Show that equilibrium is impossible unless the stick is vertical, if the coefficient of friction is less than

$$\frac{h}{\sqrt{(l^2 - h^2)}}.$$ (I.E.)

6. A uniform rod of length l rests in a vertical plane against (and over) a smooth horizontal bar at a height h, the lower end of the rod being on level ground. Show that if the rod is on the point of slipping when its inclination to the horizontal is θ, then the coefficient of friction between the rod and the ground is

$$\frac{l \sin 2\theta \sin \theta}{4h - l \sin 2\theta \cos \theta}.$$ (I.E.)

7. A uniform thin heavy rod AB rests between two planes OA, OB inclined at 45° to the vertical and meeting in a horizontal line. The end A of the rod and the plane OA are rough, the other end B and the plane OB are smooth. Show that the rod will rest in any position in which it makes an angle θ with the smooth plane, provided that $\tan \theta$ lies between $1 - 2\mu$ and $1 + 2\mu$.

8. Two equal uniform rods AB, BC, of length $2l$, are rigidly connected at B, so that ABC is a right angle. Prove that if the rods rest in limiting equilibrium in contact with a fixed circular hoop radius a, so that AB is a horizontal, and BC a vertical tangent to the circle, then
$$2a(1-\mu) = l(1+\mu^2),$$
where μ is the coefficient of friction between the rods and the hoop. (I.S.)

9. A uniform ladder rests, with one end on the ground and the other end against a vertical wall, in a plane perpendicular to the line of intersection of wall and ground. The coefficients of friction at the wall and ground are both equal to $\tan 15°$. Show that the inclination of the ladder to the ground cannot be less than $60°$. Show that the ladder can just rest at an inclination of $30°$ if a weight $\frac{1}{2}(\sqrt{3}+1)$ of its own is attached to its lower end. (H.C.)

10. A uniform rod rests in limiting equilibrium equally inclined to two planes, the one horizontal and the other inclined at $120°$ to it. If the angle of friction between the rod and the inclined plane is $30°$, show that the coefficient of friction between the rod and the horizontal plane is $\frac{1}{5}\sqrt{3}$. (H.S.D.)

11. A uniform plank AB, of length 2.4 m and mass 10 kg, rests with one end A on a rough floor, leaning at an inclination $\tan^{-1}\frac{4}{3}$ to the horizontal, against the edge of a smooth table of height 1.2 m. Show that the coefficient of friction μ between the plank and the floor is greater than $\frac{48}{89}$. If $\mu = \frac{3}{4}$, find what weight can be hung from the end B of the plank without it slipping. (H.S.D.)

12. A uniform heavy rod of weight W rests inclined at $45°$ to the horizontal with one end on the ground and the other against a vertical wall, the vertical plane through the rod being at right angles to the wall. The ground and wall are equally rough, the coefficient of friction between each of them and the rod being $\frac{1}{2}$. Show that the friction at the lower end of the rod may have any value between $\frac{1}{2}W$ and $\frac{1}{3}W$, and find the corresponding values of the frictions at the upper end. Discuss the case in which each coefficient of friction is $\sqrt{2}-1$. (H.S.C.)

13. A ladder of mass 50 kg rests with one end on the rough ground and the other against a smooth vertical wall. If the inclination of the ladder to the horizontal is $60°$, determine the frictional force necessary to keep the ladder at rest. If the coefficient of friction between the ladder and the ground be $\sqrt{3}/4$, determine the greatest weight which can be suspended from the top of the ladder without causing it to slip.

14. A uniform rod is placed inside a rough cylindrical drum which is fixed with its axis horizontal. If the rod rests in a vertical plane perpendicular to the axis of the drum, show that its least possible inclination to the vertical is $\tan^{-1}$ ($\cot 2\lambda + \cos \gamma$ cosec 2λ), where λ is the angle of friction between the rod and the drum, and γ is the angle the rod subtends at the nearest point of the axis of the drum.   (N.U.3)

15. The foot of a ladder, of length 9 m and mass 25 kg, rests on a rough horizontal surface, while the upper end rests in contact with a rough vertical wall, the ladder being in a vertical plane perpendicular to the wall. If the first rung of the ladder is 30 cm from the foot and the rest are at intervals of 30 cm, find the highest rung to which a man of mass 75 kg can climb without causing the ladder to slip, when the ladder is inclined at 60° to the horizontal and the coefficient of friction at each end is 0·25.   (N.U. 3 and 4)

16. A uniform ladder of length $2a$ rests on a rough horizontal plane at a point O, and is held inclined at an angle α to the vertical by a rope tied at its top end and passing over a pulley fixed at a point distant $2a$ vertically above O. Prove that equilibrium is possible only if the coefficient of friction between the ladder and the plane is greater than $\tan \frac{1}{2}\alpha$.   (C.W.B.)

17. Show that if the coefficients of friction with a vertical wall and a horizontal floor are respectively $\frac{1}{2}$ and $\frac{1}{3}$ the least inclination to the horizontal at which a uniform ladder can rest in a vertical plane with one end on the floor and the other against the wall is about 51° 20′.   (C.W.B.)

18. A uniform rod rests in limiting equilibrium equally inclined to two planes, the one horizontal and the other inclined at an angle of 135° to it. If the angle of friction between the rod and the inclined plane is $22\frac{1}{2}$°, show that the coefficient of friction between the rod and the horizontal plane is $\frac{1}{17}(3\sqrt{2}+1)$.

(H.S.D.)

19. A uniform rod AB rests with one end A in contact with a rough inclined plane, which makes 30° with the horizontal; the rod makes an angle 30° with the upward direction of the plane, and is in a vertical plane through the line of greatest slope. It is kept in equilibrium by means of a string attached to the other end B, and pulled parallel to the plane. Prove that the angle of friction at A must be at least $\tan^{-1}$ ($\frac{2}{3}\sqrt{3}$).   (H.S.D.)

20. To one end A of a uniform heavy wire AB there is attached
a light ring which can slide along a fixed rough horizontal rod.
The other end B is joined by a light inextensible string to a fixed
point C of the rod. If the wire is in limiting equilibrium when
inclined at an angle α to the vertical and with the angle
ABC $= 90°$, prove that the coefficient of friction μ between the
ring and the rod is given by

$$\mu(1+\cos^2\alpha) = \sin\alpha\cos\alpha. \qquad \text{(L.A.)}$$

14.6. EXAMPLE (i)

*A cone, of radius r and height h, rests on a rough plane, and the inclina-
tion of the plane to the horizontal is gradually increased; show that the
cone will slide before it topples over if the coefficient of friction is less
than 4r/h.*

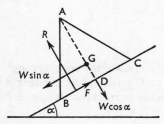

FIG. 14.10

Let W be the weight of the cone, G (Fig. 14.10) its centre of
gravity, α the inclination of the plane. Let R denote the normal
reaction, and F the frictional force acting on the cone. If the cone
slides $F = \mu R$, and if the cone topples about B the reaction R must
act at B.

The cone will slide if $W\sin\alpha > \mu W\cos\alpha$, i.e. if $\tan\alpha > \mu$.

Taking moments about B, the cone will topple over if

$$W\sin\alpha \times \frac{h}{4} > W\cos\alpha \times r$$

i.e. if $\tan\alpha > \dfrac{4r}{h}.$

If μ is less than $4r/h$, and α is gradually increased, $\tan\alpha$ reaches
the value μ before it reaches the value $4r/h$, and the cone will slide.

If μ is greater than $4r/h$, $\tan\alpha$ reaches the value $4r/h$ first and the
cone will topple over.

If $\mu = 4r/h$ the cone begins to slide and topple over at the same
time.

EXAMPLE (ii)

A block in the form of a cube of side 2a stands on a horizontal plane, the coefficient of friction between the block and plane being μ. A gradually increasing horizontal force is applied to a vertical face of the cube, at right angles to it, and in a vertical plane through the centre of gravity of the cube. Show that if μ < ½ the cube will tend to slide without upsetting, but that if μ > ½ the cube will tend to upset without sliding, if the point of application of the force is at a height above the plane greater than a/μ.

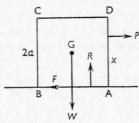

FIG. 14.11

Let ABCD (Fig. 14.11) be the vertical section of the cube, through its centre of gravity G, in which the force P acts, and let the height of P above the plane be x. Let R denote the normal reaction, and F the frictional force.

For sliding $P > \mu W$, since $F = \mu R$ and $R = W$.

For tilting, R must act at A and

$$Px > Wa, \text{ or } P > Wa/x.$$

Since the least value of a/x is $a/2a$ or $\frac{1}{2}$, as P increases it will reach the value μW first if $\mu < \frac{1}{2}$, so that in this case the cube slides without tilting.

If $\mu > \frac{1}{2}$ the cube will tilt or slide first according as

$$\mu > \text{ or } < \frac{a}{x}$$

i.e. as $x > \text{ or } < \frac{a}{\mu}$.

Hence, if $x > a/\mu$ the cube will upset without sliding.

EXAMPLES 14.2

1. A uniform cylinder, of radius r and height h, is placed with its plane base on a rough plane whose inclination to the horizontal is gradually increased. Show that the cylinder will topple over before it slides if $2r/h$ is less than the coefficient of friction.

2. A right cone is placed with its base on a rough inclined plane; if 0·25 be the coefficient of friction, find the angle of the cone when it is on the point of slipping and turning over at the same time.

3. An equilateral triangle rests in a vertical plane with one side on a rough horizontal plane; a gradually increasing horizontal force acts on its highest vertex in the plane of the triangle. Prove that the triangle will slide before it tilts if the coefficient of friction be less than $\frac{1}{3}\sqrt{3}$.

4. A rectangle of sides a and h rests in a vertical plane with one of the sides of length a on a rough horizontal table. A gradually increasing horizontal force acts along the upper side in the plane of the rectangle. Find the condition that the rectangle shall tilt before it slides.

5. A right cone rests on a rough horizontal plane and is acted on by a gradually increasing horizontal force at its vertex. Show that the cone will turn over, or slide, according as the coefficient of friction is $>$ or $< r/h$, where r is the radius and h the height of the cone.

6. A triangular lamina ABC, right-angled at C, stands with BC on a rough horizontal plane. If the plane is tilted round an axis in its own plane perpendicular to BC, so that C is lower than B, show that the lamina will begin to slide, or tilt, according as the coefficient of friction is less, or greater than, tan A.

7. A uniform cubical block is supported on a rough inclined plane by a rope parallel to the line of greatest slope attached to the mid-point of the upper edge of the cube, which is horizontal. Show that the inclination of the plane must be less than $\tan^{-1}(1+2\mu)$, where μ is the coefficient of friction. (I.S.)

8. A cube rests on a rough plane of inclination α ($\alpha < \frac{1}{4}\pi$), with two of its upper and two of its lower edges horizontal. Show that it will not be possible to drag the cube up the plane without upsetting it, by means of a rope attached to the mid-point of the uppermost edge and pulled parallel to the greatest slope of the plane, if the coefficient of friction between the plane and the cube exceeds $\frac{1}{2}(1-\tan\alpha)$. (H.C.)

9. A uniform cube, of edge $4a$, stands on a rough horizontal plane. A gradually increasing horizontal force is applied to one of its vertical faces at a height a vertically above the centre of the face. Determine how equilibrium will be broken

    (i) when the coefficient of friction between the plane and cube is 0·5.

    (ii) when the coefficient is 0·7.   (H.C.)

10. The triangle ABC, in which BC is horizontal and AB and AC are equal and greater than BC, represents the cross-section of a triangular prism standing on a rough horizontal plane on one of its rectangular faces, and the face represented by AB is subject to wind pressure. Show that when this pressure, assumed normal to AB, becomes sufficiently great the prism will topple over or slide according as the angle of friction is greater or less than $\pi - 2\alpha$, where α is the inclination of either sloping face to the base. (I.E.)

11. A cubical box, of edge a and weight W, stands on a rough horizontal plane, and a heavy bar of length b and weight w rests at an inclination of $45°$ with one end on the plane and the other against a vertical face of the box, the vertical plane through the bar passing through the centre of the box. If the lower end of the bar is prevented from slipping, find the least possible value of the coefficient of friction between the box and the plane in order that the box may not slide, friction between the bar and the box being neglected. Find also the ratio between the weights of the bar and the box if the latter is on the point of toppling over. (I.E.)

12. A uniform cube of edge $4a$ and weight W stands on a rough horizontal plane. A gradually increasing force P is applied inwards at right angles to a face F of the cube at a point distant a vertically above the centre of that face. Prove that equilibrium will be broken by sliding or by tilting according as the coefficient of friction between the cube and the plane is less than or greater than a certain value, and find this value.

If P has not reached a value for which equilibrium is broken, and $P = \frac{1}{2}W$, find how far from the face F of the cube the normal reaction acts. (H.C.)

14.7. EXAMPLE

Two uniform beams AB, BC, of equal length, are freely jointed at B, and rest in equilibrium in a vertical plane with the ends A and C on a rough horizontal plane. If the weight of AB is twice that of BC, show that there cannot be limiting friction both at A and C, and that if there is limiting friction at either of these points it is at C. Find also the coefficient of friction if the greatest angle that the rods can make with each other is a right angle.

The friction forces at A and C (Fig. 14.12) must be equal, since they are the only external horizontal forces acting on the beams. If

$\angle ABC = 2\theta$, and the reactions at A and C be R and S, then taking moments about A for *both* beams,

$$S \times 4l \sin \theta = W \times 3l \sin \theta + 2Wl \sin \theta$$

where $2l = $ length of AB or BC.

$\therefore \qquad\qquad S = \frac{5}{4}W$ and hence $R = \frac{7}{4}W$.

Now, if the friction is limiting at A its value must be μR or $\frac{7}{4}\mu W$, while if it is limiting at C its value must be μS or $\frac{5}{4}\mu W$. But the frictional force has the same value at A and C, and hence it cannot be limiting at both these points, for $\frac{5}{4}\mu W$ cannot equal $\frac{7}{4}\mu W$.

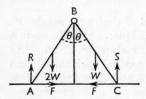

FIG. 14.12

It is also clear that F will reach the value $\frac{5}{4}\mu W$ before it reaches $\frac{7}{4}\mu W$, so that if it is limiting at either point it will be at C.

When $2\theta = 90°$ the point C will be on the point of slipping but A will not. The frictional force at both C and A will be $\frac{5}{4}\mu W$.

Hence, taking moments about B for the rod BC,

$$\tfrac{5}{4}\mu W \times 2l \cos \theta = S \times 2l \sin \theta - W \times l \sin \theta$$
$$\therefore \qquad\qquad \tfrac{5}{2}\mu W = 2S \tan \theta - W \tan \theta.$$
$$\therefore \qquad\qquad \tfrac{5}{2}\mu W = 2 \times \tfrac{5}{4}W - W = \tfrac{3}{2}W$$
$$\therefore \qquad\qquad \mu = \tfrac{3}{5}.$$

EXAMPLES 14.3

1. Two uniform rods AB and BC of the same thickness and material, and of length 0·9 m and 0·6 m respectively, are freely hinged together and rest in a vertical plane with the ends A and C on a rough horizontal plane. If the greatest possible value of $\angle ABC$ consistent with equilibrium is 90°, find the coefficient of friction between the rods and ground, and determine how equilibrium will be broken if the inclination of the rods is slightly increased beyond 90°. (H.S.C.)

2. Two equal uniform rods AB and BC of the same weight, freely jointed at B, rest in a vertical plane with the end A and C in a rough horizontal plane. If equilibrium is possible when ABC is any angle not exceeding a right angle, find the coefficient of friction between the rods and the plane. (H.S.C.)

3. Two uniform ladders, AB, BC of equal lengths and weights W, W' ($W > W'$) are hinged together at the top B and will stand on rough ground when containing an angle 2θ. Show that the total reaction at A makes a smaller angle with the vertical than at C. Assuming the coefficients of friction at A and C are each equal to μ, show that, as θ is increased, slipping will occur at C, and that

$$\mu = [(W + W')/(W + 3W')] \tan \alpha$$

where α is the value of θ for which slipping first occurs.   (H.S.D.)

4. AB and BC are two equal uniform rods of the same weight W, freely jointed at B. They rest in a vertical plane with the ends A and C in contact with a rough plane of inclination α, on a line of greatest slope of the plane with the rod BC horizontal. Find the pressures on the plane at the points A and C, and the friction at these points. Show that $\cos^2 \alpha$ must be $> \frac{1}{3}$, and that the friction at C is acting up or down the plane, according as $\cos^2 \alpha <$ or $> \frac{2}{3}$. If $\alpha = 30°$, and the friction at either of the points A and C is limiting, determine at which of these it is limiting and find the coefficient of friction.   (H.S.C.)

5. Two equal uniform rods AB, BC, smoothly jointed at B, are in equilibrium with the end C resting on a rough horizontal plane and the end A held above the plane. Prove that, if α and β are the inclinations of CB and BA to the horizontal, the coefficient of friction must exceed

$$\frac{2}{\tan \beta - 3 \tan \alpha}.$$ (I.S.)

6. The two sides of a pair of steps are of the same length, but unequal weights, and they are freely jointed together at the top. If the steps are gradually opened out while standing on a rough horizontal plane, prove that the lighter side will tend to slip first, and that this will happen when the inclination of each side to the vertical is

$$\tan^{-1}\frac{(3w_1 + w_2)\mu}{w_1 + w_2}$$

where w_1, w_2 are the respective weights of the two sides ($w_1 < w_2$), and μ is the coefficient of friction at each point on the ground.   (C.W.B.)

14.8. EXAMPLE (i)

*A uniform sphere is held in equilibrium on a rough inclined plane
of angle α by a force of magnitude $\frac{1}{2}W \sin \alpha$ applied tangentially to its
circumference, where W is the weight of the sphere. Prove that the force
must act parallel to the plane, and that the coefficient of friction must be
not less than $\frac{1}{2} \tan \alpha$.*

Let A (Fig. 14.13) be the point of contact of the sphere, C its
centre, and a its radius. Then, if the sphere is not to roll about A
the moment of the force $\frac{1}{2}W \sin \alpha$ about A must equal the moment
of the weight about A, i.e. $Wa \sin \alpha$.

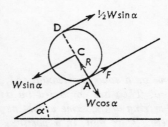

FIG. 14.13

Hence the force $\frac{1}{2}W \sin \alpha$ must be at a distance $2a$ from A, and
must therefore act parallel to the plane at D, the other end of the
diameter through A.

If there is to be no slipping, resolving parallel to the plane

$$F + \tfrac{1}{2}W \sin \alpha = W \sin \alpha$$

where $F \leqslant \mu R$ and $R = W \cos \alpha$

∴ $\tfrac{1}{2}W \sin \alpha \leqslant \mu W \cos \alpha.$

∴ $\mu \geqslant \tfrac{1}{2} \tan \alpha.$

EXAMPLE (ii)

*A heavy chain is placed on a rough plane inclined to the horizontal
at an angle α equal to the angle of friction, with a portion a m long along
a line of greatest slope and the remainder of length b m hanging vertically
over the top of the plane. If the chain is on the point of slipping, show
that b is either zero or 2a sin α.*

Let ABC (Fig. 14.14) represent the chain, and let w be its weight
per unit length. The frictional force acting on AB is $\mu aw \cos \alpha$, and
this equals $aw \sin \alpha$ since $\mu = \tan \alpha$.

If A is on the point of moving down

$$wa \sin \alpha - wa \sin \alpha = bw, \qquad \therefore \ b = 0.$$

If A is on the point of moving up,

$$bw = wa \sin \alpha + wa \sin \alpha,$$
$$\therefore \qquad b = 2a \sin \alpha.$$

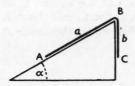

FIG. 14.14

EXAMPLE (iii)

Two rings of equal weight are free to move on a rough horizontal rod, the coefficient of limiting friction being μ. They are connected by a smooth string of length l, on which another ring of the same weight as the other two rings together can move freely. Prove that, in a position of equilibrium of the system, the two rings on the rod cannot be further apart than $2\mu(1+4\mu^2)^{-\frac{1}{2}}l$.

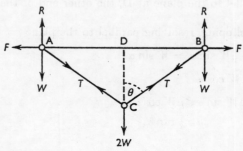

FIG. 14.15

Let W be the weight of each ring A and B (Fig. 14.15), $2W$ that of C.

Then, since C is free to slide on the string the tension is the same throughout the string and the vertical CD through C bisects the angle ACB. Let $\angle$DCB $= \theta$.

Resolving vertically for C,

$$2T \cos \theta = 2W.$$

The normal reaction R between A and the rod is

$$W + T \cos \theta = 2W,$$

and therefore the maximum friction at A is $2\mu W$.

For equilibrium $\qquad T \sin \theta = \mathrm{F} \not> 2\mu W$

or $\qquad\qquad\qquad\qquad W \tan \theta \not> 2\mu W$

or $\qquad\qquad\qquad\qquad\quad \tan \theta \not> 2\mu.$

If DB $= x$, DC$^2 = (l^2/4) - x^2$, and $\tan \theta = x/\mathrm{DC}$

$\therefore\qquad\qquad\qquad\qquad \dfrac{x^2}{\frac{1}{4}l^2 - x^2} \not> 4\mu^2$

$\therefore\qquad\qquad\qquad\qquad x^2 \not> \mu^2 l^2 - 4x^2\mu^2$

$\therefore\qquad\qquad\qquad x^2(1 + 4\mu^2) \not> \mu^2 l^2$

$\therefore\qquad\qquad\qquad\qquad x \not> \dfrac{\mu l}{\sqrt{(1 + 4\mu^2)}}.$

EXAMPLES 14.4

1. A heavy plank of length a lies on a rough horizontal plane. To one end is attached a rope which is kept inclined to the horizontal at an angle α. The end of the plank is gently raised. Show that the other end will slip at once if cot $\alpha > \mu$, the coefficient of friction; and find the ratio of the tension of the rope to the weight of the plank, if $\mu \tan \alpha$ exceeds unity, when the slipping commences. (I.E.)

2. A body of weight W rests on a horizontal plane with which the coefficient of friction is μ. A horizontal force nW, which is $< \mu W$, is applied to the weight, and another horizontal force P, perpendicular to W is also applied. Find the least value of P which will just cause the weight to move, and find the inclination of the direction of motion to the direction of P. (I.E.)

3. A rigid square frame made of uniform heavy wire rests in a vertical plane on a rough horizontal cylinder of radius a, two of its sides being in contact with the cylinder. Show that the limiting angle of inclination of a diagonal to the vertical is given by the equation

$$b \sin \theta = a\sqrt{2} \sin \epsilon \cos (\theta + \epsilon),$$

where ϵ is the angle of friction and b is the distance of the centre of the square from the axis of the cylinder. (I.S.)

4. An equilateral triangle formed of wire is placed in a vertical plane with one side horizontal. On each side is strung a bead of weight W, and the beads are connected by an endless string, in tension, and passing through small smooth rings at the corners of the triangle. Prove that, if a gradually increasing horizontal force be applied to the bead on the horizontal side, the system will begin to move when the force is equal to $2\mu W$, where μ is the coefficient of friction between the beads and the wire. (I.S.)

5. Two equal uniform rods, AB, CD, each of weight W, are freely jointed at their mid-points, and are placed in a vertical plane with the ends A and C on a rough horizontal plane of coefficient of friction μ. A string having weights, each equal to W, attached to its ends is passed over B and D. Prove that in the limiting position of equilibrium the rods are inclined to the horizontal at an angle $\tan^{-1}[3/(1+2\mu)]$. (H.S.C.)

6. A wedge of weight W, lying on rough ground, has its thin end pushed against a smooth vertical wall, the sloping face of the wedge making an angle 2θ with the wall. A smooth right circular cylinder of weight W_1 lies between the wedge and the wall. Find the relation between W and W_1 when the wedge is just on the point of sliding, the coefficient of friction between the ground and wedge being μ. (H.S.D.)

7. A light rod AD passes over a rough peg at B and under another rough peg at C in the same horizontal line, and has weights of 15 N and 9 N attached to it at A and D. The lengths AB, BC, CD are 0·9 m, 0·6 m, and 0·3 m. If the least horizontal force which will move the rod is 6 N, find the coefficient of friction, assuming the pegs equally rough. (I.S.)

8. A wedge of mass M, whose faces are inclined at an angle α, is placed with one face in contact with a horizontal plane. A small object of mass m is placed in contact with the other face and is just prevented from sliding down by a horizontal force. If $\mu(<\tan\alpha)$ is the coefficient of friction for the object and the wedge, find the least value of the coefficient for the wedge and the plane in order that the wedge may remain at rest.

9. A rough circular cylinder of diameter d is fixed on an equally rough horizontal plane, and a uniform rod of length $2l$ rests tangentially against the cylinder in a vertical plane, which is perpendicular to the axis of the cylinder, one end of the rod being on the rough plane. If the friction is limiting at both ends of the rod, when the rod is inclined at 30° to the vertical, prove that the angle of friction is $\frac{1}{2}\sin^{-1}(l/d)$. (H.S.D.)

10. Two equal particles, each of weight W, are placed on a rough horizontal table and connected by a taut inextensible string. Prove that the least horizontal force that can be applied to one of them in a direction making an angle θ with the string so as to cause them both to be on the point of motion is $2\mu W \cos \theta$, where μ is the coefficient of friction between either particle and the table. (H.S.C.)

11. Figure 14.16 represents the central section ABCD of a child's box filled with sand and being dragged forward by a horizontal force applied at C. The box is attached to two crossbars at A and B,

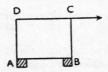

Fig. 14.16

and the whole is dragged across a rough floor whose coefficient of friction with the crossbars at A and B is μ. Given $AB = l$, $BC = h$, and the weight of the box and sand to be W, prove that the vertical reactions at A and B are

$$\frac{l-2\mu h}{2l} W \quad \text{and} \quad \frac{l+2\mu h}{2l} W$$

respectively. (H.S.D.)

12. A heavy uniform rod is placed over a rough peg at A and under another rough peg at B, at a higher level than A, so that the rod lies in a vertical plane; show that the length of the shortest rod that will rest in this position is

$$a(1+\tan \alpha \cot \lambda),$$

where a is the distance between the pegs, α is the angle of inclination to the horizontal of the line joining the pegs, and λ is the angle of friction.

13. A uniform circular lamina of radius a and weight W rests with its plane vertical on two fixed rough planes each inclined at an angle of 45° to the horizontal, their line of intersection being perpendicular to the plane of the lamina. If the coefficient of friction at each contact is $\frac{1}{2}$, prove that the least couple required to rotate the lamina in its plane about its centre is of moment $2\sqrt{2}Wa/5$. (L.A.)

14. A sphere is placed on a rough plane inclined at an angle α to the horizontal. A force is applied tangentially to the sphere at a point of its circumference and in the vertical plane containing the centre of the sphere and a line of greatest slope of the plane. The direction of this force makes an angle β with the horizontal (in the same sense as α). If the coefficient of friction is μ, prove that, for the sphere to rest in equilibrium,

$$\mu \geqslant \frac{\sin \alpha}{\cos \alpha + \cos \beta}.$$

If β is variable, prove that the least value of μ for which equilibrium is possible is $\tan \frac{1}{2}\alpha$.

If, however, the applied force is to be a minimum, prove that the least possible value of μ is $\frac{1}{2} \tan \alpha$. (H.C.)

15. A wheel situated in a vertical plane is free to turn about its centre C. A uniform rod AB, weight W, is smoothly hinged at A, which is at the same level as C, and rests in contact with the wheel at D. Prove that to turn the wheel a couple of moment greater than

$$\frac{\mu W \times AB \times CD}{2 \, AC}$$

is required, μ being the coefficient of friction between the rod and the wheel. Prove also that, when the wheel rotates so that the point in contact with the rod at D moves towards B, the reaction at A will be vertical, if the inclination of the rod to the horizontal is $\tan^{-1} \mu$. (H.C.)

16. A circular cylinder of weight W, with its axis horizontal, is supported in contact with a rough vertical wall by a string wrapped partly round it and attached to a point of the wall, and making an angle α with the wall. Show that the coefficient of friction must not be less than cosec α, and that the normal pressure on the wall is $W \tan \frac{1}{2}\alpha$. (H.C.)

17. A sphere of weight W is placed on a rough plane inclined at 45° to the horizon, and is kept in equilibrium, if possible, by a horizontal force P applied at the highest point of the sphere.

(1) Show that equilibrium is impossible if μ, the coefficient of friction between the plane and the sphere, is less than $\sqrt{2}-1$.

(2) Show that equilibrium is possible if μ is equal to or greater than $\sqrt{2}-1$; find the value of P, and determine whether equilibrium is limiting or not when μ is greater than $\sqrt{2}-1$. (H.C.)

18. A thin hemispherical shell rests with its curved surface in contact with a rough horizontal plane, whose coefficient of friction is μ, and with a rough vertical plane, whose coefficient is μ'. If the shell is on the point of slipping when the plane of the rim makes $30°$ with the horizontal, find the relation connecting μ and μ'; and prove that if $\mu' < \frac{1}{3}$, μ must lie between $\frac{1}{5}$ and $\frac{1}{4}$. (The centre of gravity of a thin hemispherical shell bisects the radius.)

(H.C.)

19. A uniform thin hemispherical bowl rests with its curved surface on a rough horizontal plane (coefficient of friction μ) and leans against a smooth vertical wall. Prove that when the bowl is on the point of slipping the inclination of the axis of the bowl to the vertical is $\sin^{-1} 2\mu$.

(H.S.D.)

20. A uniform rod AB rests with one end A in contact with a rough inclined plane, which makes $30°$ with the horizontal; the rod makes an angle $45°$ with the upward direction of the plane, and is in a vertical plane through the line of greatest slope. It is kept in equilibrium by means of a string attached to the other end B, and pulled parallel to the plane. Prove that the angle of friction at A must be at least $\tan^{-1}\left(\dfrac{\sqrt{3}+1}{2\sqrt{3}}\right)$.

(H.S.D.)

CHAPTER FIFTEEN

MACHINES

15.1. We shall now consider some simple examples of machines. A machine is a piece of apparatus in which work is done *on* the machine by applying a force, called the *Power or Effort*, at one part, and work is done *by* the machine in overcoming some external force, called the *Weight or Resistance*, at another part.

In most cases the machine is so arranged that, by applying a small force or effort a larger force is overcome.

15.2. Thus an inclined plane may be used as a simple machine.

Suppose we have a weight W resting on a smooth inclined plane AB (Fig. 15.1) connected to a weight P hanging freely by a light string passing over a smooth pulley at the top of the plane. P may be regarded as the *effort* used to raise a *weight W*.

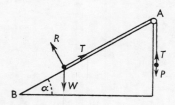

Fig. 15.1

If W rests in equilibrium on the plane, then the tension in the string T must equal $W \sin \alpha$. But $T = P$, and hence $P = W \sin \alpha$. Any force P slightly in excess of $W \sin \alpha$ will cause W to move up the plane. Thus the weight W can be raised vertically by applying a force less than W, which makes the inclined plane a useful machine. Indeed, historically it was one of the earliest machines used by man.

We notice that when P moves downwards a distance x, W moves a distance x along the plane, that is, it is raised a distance $x \sin \alpha$ *vertically*. Hence the work done *by* P is Px, and this equals the work done *on* W, which is $Wx \sin \alpha$. (If the plane were rough Px would be greater than $Wx \sin \alpha$, since $P = W \sin \alpha + F$, where F is the frictional force called into play.) This result follows, of course, from the law of conservation of energy. In an ideal machine no energy is lost, and the work done *by* P is then equal to the work done *on* W, or in other words, the total work done *by* P and W is zero. This is sometimes known as the *Principle of Work.* In practice, however, the work done by P usually exceeds the work done on W, that is, more work has to be done as a result of using the machine (to overcome friction and to move certain parts of the machine). The great convenience of the machine is that usually P is less than W.

The following definitions are important.

15.3. If a force P applied to a machine causes it to exert a force W, the ratio W/P is called the **mechanical advantage** of the machine. The ratio of the distance moved by the effort P to that moved by the weight W is called the **velocity ratio**. These two ratios are related, as we shall now show.

If there is no friction, and the parts of the machine are weightless, then, by the principle of work,

$P \times$ distance through which P moves

$\qquad = W \times$ distance through which W moves,

$$\therefore \quad \frac{W}{P} = \frac{\text{distance through which } P \text{ moves}}{\text{distance through which } W \text{ moves}}$$

$\qquad = $ velocity ratio,

i.e. in an ideal machine whose parts are weightless, and in which there is no friction,

$\qquad$ Mechanical Advantage $=$ Velocity Ratio.

Thus in all cases when the effort is less than the weight the effort has to move through a distance greater than the distance moved by the weight.

Occasionally a machine is arranged to give increased movement, and in this case the effort has to be greater than the weight moved.

In practical machines where there is friction the mechanical advantage is *less* than the velocity ratio.

15.4. The **efficiency** of a machine is measured by the ratio

$$\frac{\text{Useful work done by the machine}}{\text{Work supplied to the machine}}.$$

In an ideal machine the efficiency is therefore unity. The ratio giving the efficiency is often expressed as a percentage, and then the efficiency of an ideal machine is 100 per cent.

The efficiency may be determined experimentally by measuring the effort P required to raise a weight W and also the distances x and y moved through by P and W respectively.

$$\text{Efficiency} = \frac{Wy}{Px} = \frac{W/P}{x/y}$$

$$= \frac{\text{Mechanical advantage}}{\text{Velocity ratio}}.$$

In most cases the efficiency varies with the load.

It should be noticed that the only quantity connected with a machine which can be *calculated* from its dimensions is the velocity ratio.

The mechanical advantage and efficiency must be determined by experiment, except in the case of an ideal machine.

In actual machines it is often found that W and P are connected by a linear relation of the form

$$P = a + bW,$$

where a and b are constants.

This relation is often called the 'Law of the Machine'.

Clearly b is positive, but a may have any value. If a is zero, than $P = bW$ or $W/P = 1/b$, that is, the mechanical advantage, and therefore the efficiency, do not vary with W. This is the ideal case, and b is the reciprocal of the velocity ratio.

If a is positive, as it usually is (since even when $W = 0$, P is positive owing to friction), then the mechanical advantage increases as W increases. For

$$W/P = W/(a+bW) = 1 \bigg/ \left(\frac{a}{W} + b \right)$$

and this increases as W increases, if a is positive, and is less than $1/b$ for all values of W. Thus the efficiency increases with the load, but is always less than $1/br$, where r is the velocity ratio.

If a is negative W/P diminishes as W and P increase, i.e. the efficiency diminishes with the load. This is explained by the fact that with greater loads the friction between the various parts of the machine is increased.

EXAMPLE

A machine for lifting weights has a velocity ratio of 16, and it is found that efforts of 11 N and 19 N are needed to lift with it loads of 56 N and 112 N respectively. What is the efficiency in each case? Assuming a straight-line graph for load and effort, find the effort necessary to lift 224 N.

In the first case the mechanical advantage is $\frac{56}{11}$, and in the second case it is $\frac{112}{19}$.

Since $\qquad \text{Efficiency} = \dfrac{\text{Mechanical advantage}}{\text{Velocity ratio}},$

the efficiencies are $\dfrac{56}{11 \times 16}$ and $\dfrac{112}{19 \times 16}$, that is, $\frac{7}{22}$ and $\frac{7}{19}$.

Expressed as percentages, these are 31·8 per cent and 36·8 per cent.

Assuming that, since the relation between W and P is linear,

$$P = a + bW,$$

where a and b are constants, we have

$$11 = a + 56b$$

and $\qquad\qquad 19 = a + 112b$

whence $\qquad\qquad a = 3 \text{ and } b = \frac{1}{7}.$

$\therefore \qquad\qquad P = 3 + \frac{1}{7}W.$

When $W = 224$, we get

$$P = 3 + 32.$$

$\therefore \qquad\qquad Effort = 35 \text{ N}.$

15.5. *System of pulleys with a single string*

In this system there are two blocks each containing pulleys, the upper block being fixed to a support and the lower block, which has the weight attached, being movable.

Figure 15.2A shows such a system when the number of pulleys in each block is the same, and Fig. 15.2B shows one where the number of pulleys in the upper block is greater than the number in the lower block.

In the first case one end of the string must be fastened to the upper block, and in the second case it must be fastened to the lower block.

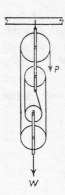

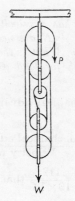

Fig. 15.2A   Fig. 15.2B

The relation between P and W may be obtained in two ways,

(i) by considering the equilibrium or uniform motion of the lower block; or

(ii) by the principle of work.

Let the weight of the lower block be w, and neglect friction.

(i) Since the pulleys are smooth, the tension is the same throughout the string and equal to P.

If there are n portions of string at the lower block the total upward force on this block is nP. Therefore for equilibrium or motion with uniform speed

$$W + w = nP.$$

We note that this is of the form $P = a + bW$, where a and b are positive constants. Further, $W/P = n - w/P$, which is always less than n, the velocity ratio of the system.

We have assumed that all the portions of the string not in contact with the pulleys are vertical. If this is not the case the resultant of the two tensions P due to a string passing round one of the pulleys is not $2P$, but depends on the angle at which the two portions are inclined. In practice, the strings are not exactly parallel, but usually they are very nearly so.

(ii) If the load W and the whole of the lower block is raised a distance x, then in the first figure a length of string $2x$ will pass round the upper pulley of the lower block, a further length $2x$ round the lower one, and so on for any number of pulleys in the lower block.

Hence to keep the string taut P must move a distance $2x \times$ the number of pulleys at the lower block. But there are two portions of string to each pulley, and so the distance moved by P is nx, where n is the number of portions of string at the lower block. The velocity ratio is therefore n. By the principle of work

$$(W+w)x = Pnx,$$

$\therefore$ $$W+w = nP,$$

as obtained above.

In the second figure a length of string $3x$ will pass round the upper pulley of the lower block, and an additional length of $2x$ for each other pulley. If p be the number of pulleys P must move $(2p+1)x$, but $2p+1 = n$, the number of strings, and we have the same relation between W, w, and P as before.

This system is often called the Block and Tackle.

EXAMPLE

A pulley system in which the same string passes round all the pulleys consists of six pulleys, the string being attached to one of the upper pulleys. When on the point of motion the tension of the string as it passes over each pulley is increased by 25 per cent. Find the force which will just lift a weight of 300 N, neglecting the weights of the pulleys themselves. Show also that the useful work done is about half that expended.   (H.S.D.)

The arrangement is shown in Fig. 15.3.

Let T be the tension in the end of the string attached to the upper block. The tension after passing round the first lower pulley is $(5/4)T$, and over the first upper pulley $(5^2/4^2)T$, and so on.

The tension at the free end is $\dfrac{5^6}{4^6}T$.

$\therefore$ $$\frac{5^6}{4^6}T = P.$$

For the equilibrium of the weight

$$T\left(1+\frac{5}{4}+\frac{5^2}{4^2}+\frac{5^3}{4^3}+\frac{5^4}{4^4}+\frac{5^5}{4^5}\right) = 300$$

$$\therefore \qquad T\frac{\dfrac{5^6}{4^6}-1}{\tfrac{1}{4}} = 300$$

$$\therefore \qquad \frac{4^6}{5^6}\left(\frac{5^6}{4^6}-1\right)P = 75$$

$$\therefore \qquad \left(1-\frac{4^6}{5^6}\right)P = 75$$

$$\therefore \qquad P = \frac{5^6\times 75}{61\times 189} = 101\cdot6 \text{ N.}$$

If the lower block moves a distance x m, P moves a distance $6x$ m.

$$\therefore \qquad \text{Work expended} = 101\cdot6\times 6x = 609\cdot6x \text{ J}$$

and $\qquad\qquad$ Useful work $= 300x$ J.

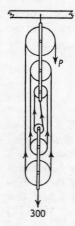

Fig. 15.3

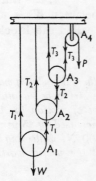

Fig. 15.4

15.6. *System of pulleys when each string is attached to the support*
This arrangement is as shown in Fig. 15.4. The weight is attached to the lowest pulley.

The fixed pulley A_4 is usually inserted so that the effort P may be applied in a downward direction; it does not affect the mechanical advantage.

As before, we suppose that all portions of the strings not in contact with the pulleys are vertical, and that there is no friction. We shall neglect the weights of the pulleys.

(i) Let T_1, T_2, ... be the tensions in the strings passing round A_1, A_2, ...

From the equilibrium of the pulleys, A_1, A_2, ... we have

$$W = 2T_1$$
and $$T_1 = 2T_2$$
and $$T_2 = 2T_3$$
$$\therefore \qquad W = 2^3 T_3 = 2^3 P$$

and clearly for n movable pulleys,

$$W = 2^n P.$$

(ii) If P moves a distance x the upper movable pulley moves $x/2$.

The next moves $x/2^2$ and so on.

Hence with n movable pulleys the lowest one, and therefore the weight, moves a distance $x/2^n$.

From the principle of work

$$W \times (x/2^n) = Px$$
or $$W = 2^n P, \text{ as before.}$$

EXAMPLE

A man of mass 70 kg supports a weight of mass 45 kg by means of three movable pulleys arranged in the system where each pulley hangs in the loop of a separate string. The pulleys have masses 2, 4, and 5 kg respectively. What is the thrust of the man on the ground?

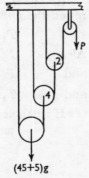

We shall assume that the end of the string on which the man pulls is passed over a fixed pulley as in Fig. 15.5, so that he pulls downwards. His thrust on the ground will be the difference between his weight and the pull he exerts.

If P moves a distance x the upper movable pulley moves $x/2$, and the work done is $2g \times x/2$.

The next moves $x/4$ and the work done is $4g \times x/4$.

The lower pulley moves $x/8$ and the work done is $50g \times x/8$.

FIG. 15.5

Hence from the principle of work,

$$Px = \left(1+1+\frac{50}{8}\right)g\,x = 8{\cdot}25g\,x,$$

$$\therefore \qquad P = 8{\cdot}25g \text{ N.}$$

Hence the thrust on the ground is $61{\cdot}75g$ N.

EXAMPLES 15.1

1. If there are four movable pulleys whose masses, commencing with the lowest, are 4, 3, 2, and 1 kg respectively, what force will support a weight of mass 500 kg?

2. If there are three movable pulleys whose masses, commencing from the lowest are 4, 4, and 2 kg respectively, what force will support a weight of mass 56 kg?

3. If there are four movable pulleys, each of weight w, and the effort be P, show that the stress on the beam is $15P-11w$ (P is supposed to act upwards, the string to which it is applied not passing over a fixed pulley).

4. When there are four movable pulleys find the effort necessary to support a weight of mass 400 kg, neglecting the weights of the pulleys. Find also the pull of each string on the beam; and if the sum is not equal to the weight, explain the difference.

15.7. *System of pulleys with each string attached to the weight*

This arrangement is shown in Fig. 15.6. The weight is suspended from a bar AB to which each string is attached.

The free portions of the strings are assumed to be parallel, and we shall neglect the weights of the pulleys.

(i) Let T_1, T_2, . . . be the tensions in the strings passing round the pulleys A_1, A_2, . . .

$$T_1 = P, \text{ since } A_1 \text{ is smooth.}$$

Also $\qquad T_2 = 2T_1 = 2P$, since A_1 is in equilibrium,

and $\qquad T_3 = 2T_2 = 2^2P$ since A_2 is in equilibrium,

and $\qquad T_4 = 2T_3 = 2^3P$ and so on.

If there are n pulleys,

$$\begin{aligned}
W &= T_1 + T_2 + \ldots + T_n \\
&= P(1+2+2^2+\ldots+2^{n-1}) \\
&= P\frac{2^n-1}{2-1} = P(2^n-1).
\end{aligned}$$

(ii) If AB is raised a distance x a length of string x passes over the uppermost pulley A_4; this lowers the next pulley A_3 a distance x. Since this pulley descends a distance x and the bar rises x, the string from the pulley to the bar shortens by $2x$, hence the next pulley A_2 descends a distance $2x+x = 3x$. The string from A_2 to the bar therefore shortens by $4x$, and the next pulley A_1 descends $4x+3x = 7x$.

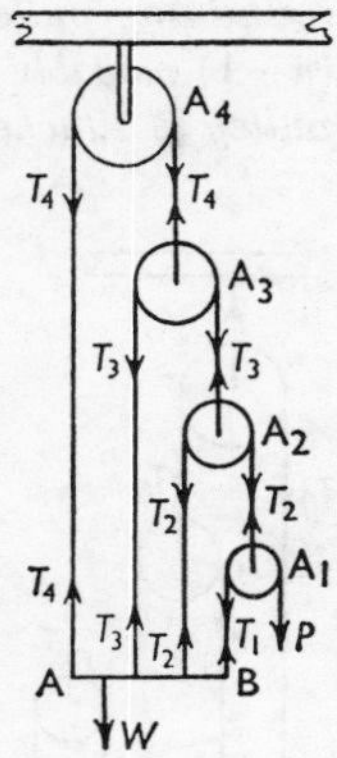

The string from A_1 to the bar therefore shortens by $8x$, and the weight P descends $8x+7x = 15x$.

In the case shown there are four pulleys, and this distance is $(2^4-1)x$. With n pulleys the distance moved by P would be $(2^n-1)x$, and from the principle of work,

$$Wx = P(2^n-1)x$$
or
$$W = P(2^n-1).$$

FIG. 15.6

The system of pulleys is not used in practice for raising weights. It is used to give a short strong pull on the bar AB, which is fixed, the uppermost pulley being attached to the object, such as the top of a mast, on which it is required to exert a pull. It is evident that as the tensions in the strings attached to the bar are not equal, that if the bar is free, as shown in the figure, it will not remain horizontal unless the weight is attached at a particular point.

If the pulleys are of equal size the distances between the points of attachment of the strings will be equal, and the condition for the bar to remain horizontal is obtained by taking moments about one end.

In the case shown, $T_4 = 8P$, $T_3 = 4P$, $T_2 = 2P$, and $W = 15P$.

If a is the distance between the strings the sum of the moments of the tensions about B is

$$24Pa+8Pa+2Pa = 34Pa.$$

Hence, to keep the bar horizontal, W must be attached at a point distant x from B, where

$$15Px = 34Pa$$
or
$$x = \tfrac{34}{15}a.$$

EXAMPLE

In a system of n equal weightless pulleys, in which the string passing round any pulley has an end attached to a weightless bar AB, there are $(n-1)$ movable pulleys and one fixed pulley; the string round the fixed pulley is attached to the bar at A and that round the last movable pulley is attached to the bar at B and has a weight P at the other extremity. The bar AB is kept in horizontal equilibrium by a weight W attached at A and another weight at B: prove that

$$W = \frac{(n-2)2^n+2}{n-1}P. \qquad \text{(H.S.C.)}$$

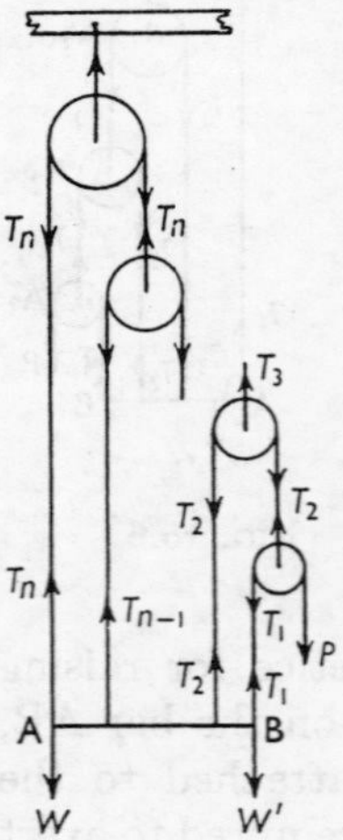

The arrangement will be as in Fig. 15.7.

Since the pulleys are of equal size, the points of attachment of the strings to AB will be equidistant; let the distance between them be a.

Let T_1, T_2, ... T_n be the tensions in the strings, then their distances from B will be 0, a, $2a$, ... $(n-1)a$ respectively.

Also $T_2 = 2T_1 = 2P,$

and $T_3 = 2T_2 = 2^2T_1 = 2P^2,$

$\qquad \cdot \qquad \cdot \qquad \cdot \qquad \cdot \qquad \cdot$

and $T_n = 2^{n-1}P.$

Fig. 15.7

Hence, taking moments for the bar about B,

$$W(n-1)a = 2P \times a + 2^2P \times 2a + 2^3P \times 3a \ldots + 2^{n-1}P(n-1)a$$
$$= Pa[2 + 2^2 \times 2 + 2^3 \times 3 + \ldots + 2^{n-1}(n-1)].$$

To sum the series in the bracket, let

$$S = 2 + 2^2 \times 2 + 2^3 \times 3 + \ldots + 2^{n-1}(n-1)$$

$\therefore \qquad 2S = \qquad 2^2 \times 1 + 2^3 \times 2 + \ldots + 2^{n-1}(n-2) + 2^n(n-1)$

$\therefore \qquad -S = 2 + 2^2 + 2^3 + \ldots + 2^{n-1} - 2^n(n-1)$

$$= \frac{2(2^{n-1}-1)}{1} - 2^n(n-1)$$

$\therefore \qquad S = 2^n(n-2) + 2$

$\therefore \qquad W = \frac{2^n(n-2)+2}{n-1}P.$

15.8. *The Weston differential pulley*

The upper block A (Fig. 15.8) of this system has two grooves side by side, one of which has a slightly greater diameter than the other.

The weight is attached to the lower pulley B. An endless chain passes round the larger groove on the upper block, then round the lower pulley and the smaller groove on the upper block; the remainder of the chain hangs slack.

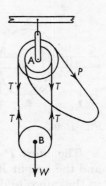

The chain is prevented from slipping by small projections or recesses in the groove.

The effort P is applied as in the figure.

(i) If T be the tension of the portions of the chain which support the lower pulley and the weight W we have (assuming that these portions are vertical and neglecting the weight of the chain and lower pulley)

Fig. 15.8

$$2T = W.$$

If R and r be the radii of the larger and smaller grooves we have, taking moments about the centre of the upper block,

$$P \times R + T \times r = T \times R$$

$$\therefore \qquad P = T\frac{R-r}{R} = W\frac{R-r}{2R}$$

$$\therefore \qquad \frac{W}{P} = \frac{2R}{R-r}.$$

By making R and r nearly equal a large mechanical advantange can be obtained.

(ii) Suppose the upper block is turned through an angle θ so that P moves downward; P moves a distance $R\theta$. The string on the left of B is shortened by $R\theta$, but an extra length $r\theta$ is let down on the right of B, owing to the smaller groove of A turning. Hence W rises $\frac{1}{2}(R\theta - r\theta)$ and, by the principle of work,

$$\frac{W}{2}(R-r)\theta = PR\theta$$

$$\therefore \qquad \frac{W}{P} = \frac{2R}{R-r}.$$

15.9. *The wheel and axle*

This consists of a wheel AB and an axle CD, which rotate together round the same axis as in Fig. 15.9A. Figure 15.9B shows a sectional view.

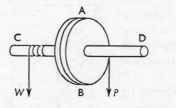
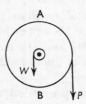

FIG. 15.9A   FIG. 15.9B

The effort P is applied to a string wound round the wheel, and the weight W is attached to a string wound round the axle in the opposite direction.

Let a, b be the radii of the wheel and axle respectively.

(i) Taking moments about the common axis,

$$Pa = Wb$$

$$\therefore \quad \frac{W}{P} = \frac{a}{b}.$$

(ii) If the wheel and axle be wound through an angle θ (in radians) so that P descends, P moves a distance $a\theta$, while W moves up a distance $b\theta$.

Hence, by the principle of work,

$$Wb\theta = Pa\theta$$

$$\therefore \quad \frac{W}{P} = \frac{a}{b}.$$

The mechanical advantage is limited in practice by the facts that if a is too large the machine is unwieldy, while if b is too small the axle may break.

A capstan and windlass are similar in action. In these there is only one cylinder, corresponding to the axle, the effort being applied at the ends of bars or at the end of a long handle perpendicular to the axle.

15.10. *The differential wheel and axle*

In this modified form of the wheel and axle the axle is made of two parts, having different radii; the weight is attached to a pulley, and the rope supporting this is wound in opposite directions on the two parts of the axle, the pulley hanging in the loop between the two parts as in Fig. 15.10.

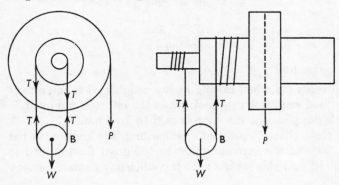

FIG. 15.10

As P descends, the rope round the pulley B is wound up on the larger axle and unwinds on the smaller.

Let a, b, c be the radii of the wheel and the larger and smaller portions of the axle respectively, and T the tension in the rope supporting B (Fig. 15.10).

We assume that the portions of the rope round B are both vertical, and neglect the weights of the rope and the pulley.

(i) From the equilibrium of W

$$2T = W, \text{ or } T = \tfrac{1}{2}W.$$

Taking moments about the common axis,

$$P \times a + T \times c = T \times b$$

$$\therefore \qquad P = T\frac{b-c}{a} = W\frac{b-c}{2a},$$

$$\therefore \qquad \frac{W}{P} = \frac{2a}{b-c}.$$

By making b and c nearly equal a large mechanical advantage can be obtained without making the wheel too large or the axle too thin.

(ii) If the wheel turns through an angle θ radians so that P descends, P moves down a distance $a\theta$.

The larger axle winds up a length $b\theta$ of rope, while the smaller axle unwinds a length $c\theta$.

Hence the weight rises a distance $\frac{1}{2}(b-c)\theta$, and from the principle of work,

$$\frac{W}{2}(b-c)\theta = Pa\theta$$

$$\therefore \qquad \frac{W}{P} = \frac{2a}{b-c}.$$

15.11. *Overhauling*

In many cases (as when raising heavy weights) it is important that the load shall not run back when the effort is removed.

If this happens the machine is said to 'overhaul'.

It is clear that, to prevent overhauling, the friction in the various parts of the machine must be too great for the load to overcome it, and this means that the efficiency cannot be very great.

Suppose an effort P just raises a load W, and that when P is removed W remains at rest.

When P is raising W the friction acts against P, and when P is removed it just supports W.

For small displacements x and y of P and W let the work done by the friction be F, then when the machine is worked

$$Px = Wy + F.$$

Now if the same displacement is given to W when F is supporting it, then

$$Wy = F.$$

Hence F must not be less than Wy, so that

$$Px \not< 2Wy,$$

$$\therefore \qquad \frac{Wy}{Px} \not> \tfrac{1}{2}$$

i.e. the efficiency must not be greater than $\frac{1}{2}$ or 50 per cent.

Any machine whose efficiency is less than 50 per cent will not overhaul. The usefulness of the Weston pulley, apart from its large velocity ratio, is due to the fact that its efficiency is usually less than 50 per cent.

EXAMPLES 15.2

1. The drum of a windlass is 10 cm in diameter, and the effort is applied to the handle 60 cm from the axis. Find the effort necessary to support a weight of mass 120 kg.

2. A wheel and axle is used to raise a load of mass 50 kg. The radius of the wheel is 50 cm, and while it makes seven revolutions the load rises 3·3 m. What is the smallest force that will support the load?

3. An anchor of mass 1 Mg is being raised by its chain being wound round a capstan of 22·5 cm diameter, which is turned by six men who work at the ends of capstan bars of 1·5 m effective length. Assuming that each exerts the same effort, find what that effort must be, if the efficiency is 56 per cent. (Neglect the weight of the chain.) (N.U.)

4. A differential pulley, the two parts of which have respectively twenty-four and twenty-five teeth, is used to raise a weight of mass 500 kg. Show by a sketch how the apparatus is used, and determine its velocity ratio. Find also what effort must be exerted if the efficiency is 60 per cent. (N.U.)

15.12. *The screw*

A screw consists of a bolt of circular section with a projecting *thread* running round it in a spiral curve, the inclination of this thread to a plane perpendicular to the axis of the bolt being the same at all points.

The distance between two consecutive threads, measured parallel to the axis, is called the *pitch* of the screw.

The screw works in a nut or fixed support, along the inside of which is cut out a hollow groove of the same shape as the thread of the screw and along which the thread slides.

The only movement possible for the screw is a rotation about its axis, and at the same time a motion parallel to the axis due to the thread sliding in its groove. In one complete revolution the screw moves parallel to its axis a distance equal to the pitch.

If the thread and groove are smooth and the axis of the screw inclined to the horizontal its weight will tend to cause it to move downwards and rotate. In practice, of course, friction is sufficient to prevent this.

In a screw-press or screw-jack one end of the screw is placed against the body on which a force is to be exerted, and the screw is driven forward in its support by means of a bar attached to the other end (Fig. 15.11).

Let a be the length of the arm at which the effort P is applied, and p the pitch of the screw.

In one revolution P moves a distance $2\pi a$, while the screw moves forward a distance p.

$$\therefore \qquad \text{the velocity ratio} = \frac{2\pi a}{p}.$$

If the screw is smooth this is also the mechanical advantage. Theoretically the velocity ratio can be made very large by making a large and p very small. The former, however, causes the machine to be unwieldy, while a very small pitch means a thin thread and consequent weakness.

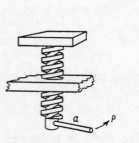

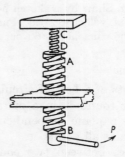

Fig. 15.11   Fig. 15.12

15.13. *The differential screw*

This machine gives a large velocity ratio without the drawbacks of a very long arm or small pitch.

One screw AB (Fig. 15.12) works in a fixed block.

The inside of this screw is hollow and a second screw DC of smaller pitch works inside it. The smaller screw is fastened to a block at C so that it cannot rotate, but can only move in the direction of its length.

When the effort arm has made one revolution the screw AB has advanced a distance equal to its pitch p_1, while the smaller screw goes into AB a distance equal to its pitch p_2.

Hence the smaller screw, and therefore the weight, has advanced a distance $p_1 - p_2$.

If a is the length of the effort arm the velocity ratio is

$$\frac{2\pi a}{p_1 - p_2}.$$

This can be made very large by making p_1 and p_2 nearly equal.

EXAMPLES 15.3

1. In the system of pulleys in which there is only one string it is found that weights of 5 and 6 units respectively will support weights of 18 and 22 units at the lower block. Find the number of strings and the weights of the lower block.

2. In the system of pulleys in which there is only one string it is found that a weight of 3 units supports a weight of 15 units and a weight of 5 units supports a weight of 27 units. Find the weight of the lower block, and also what would be the mechanical advantage if the lower block were weightless.

3. In the system of pulleys in which there is only one string there are five portions of the string at the lower block. What is the velocity ratio? If the efficiency of the apparatus is 50 per cent, what force is required to support a weight of 60 N?

4. With a machine of which the velocity ratio is 60, it is found that efforts of 21, 35, 49 units are necessary to lift loads of 400, 800, 1200 units. Find graphically, or otherwise, the probable effort required to lift a load of 2240 units, and find the efficiency of the machine for each load.

5. Find the condition of equilibrium in the system of pulleys in which each string is attached to a bar carrying the load, assuming that there are three movable pulleys, each of weight w, an effort P, and that the weight of the bar (including the attached weight) to which the four strings are attached is W. If the radius of each pulley, including the fixed pulley, is a, show that for the bar to remain horizontal and the strings vertical, the horizontal distance of the centre of gravity of the bar and weight from the point of attachment of the longest string must be equal to $\dfrac{11P + 5w}{W}a$.

6. If there are four pulleys in the system in which each string is attached to the weight, and each pulley weighs 2 N, what weight can be raised by an effort of 20 N?

7. In a system of pulleys in which each string is attached to the support there are three movable pulleys, each of mass 1 kg. The effort required to support a certain weight is twice that which would be required if these pulleys were weightless. Find the weight.

8. Find the condition of equilibrium for a system of pulleys in which each pulley hangs in the loop of a separate string, the strings being all parallel, and each string attached to the beam. The weights of the pulleys are to be taken into account. If there are five pulleys and each has a mass of 1 kg, what weight will a force of $5g$ N support on such a system, and what will be the total pull on the beam?   (I.S.)

9. In a system of n pulleys in which the same string passes round all the pulleys, show that, if the weight of the pulleys is neglected, the mechanical advantage is n. A man of mass 80 kg uses such a system consisting of seven pulleys, each of mass 1·5 kg, to raise a weight of mass 200 kg. If he pulls vertically downwards, what pressure does he exert on the ground?   (H.S.D.)

10. A string with one end attached to a fixed point A passes under a heavy pulley P, then over a fixed pulley B, then under a heavy pulley Q, and has its other end attached to the centre of the pulley P, all the hanging parts of the string being vertical. By means of the principle of virtual work, or otherwise, find the ratio of the weights of P and Q when the system is in equilibrium.   (H.S.D.)

11. A Weston differential pulley consists of a lower block and an upper block which has two cogged grooves, one of which has a radius of 10 cm and the other a radius of 9 cm; the efficiency of the machine is 40 per cent. Calculate the effort required to raise a load of 1500 N.   (H.S.D.)

12. In a differential wheel and axle the radius of the wheel is 30 cm, and the radii of the axle are 5 cm and 7·5 cm. It requires an effort of 600 N to lift a weight of mass 1 Mg; calculate the efficiency of the machine for this load.   (I.E.)

13. A man of mass 65 kg sits in a seat of mass 7 kg, which is suspended from a smooth pulley supported by the two parallel portions of a rope which is coiled in opposite directions round the two drums of a differential wheel and axle of radii 38 cm and 30 cm respectively. He raises himself by pulling one side of the rope. State which side, and show that to raise himself he must exert a pull exceeding $8·5g$ N.   (I.E.)

14. Find the force necessary to sustain three movable pulleys, each of weight W, in that system of pulleys in which each movable pulley hangs in the loop of a separate string, the hanging parts of the strings being vertical, and one end of each string being attached to a fixed point. A, B are two such movable pulleys, each of weight W; a third pulley, also of weight W, hangs in the loop of a string whose ends are attached one to the axle of A and the other to the axle of B. If B is the upper of the pair A, B, what force must be applied to the free end of the string which passes under B so as to maintain equilibrium ? (I.A.)

15. If the fixed pulleys of a Weston differential block have ten and eleven teeth, and the effect of friction in the machine is to increase the effort by an amount which is a fixed proportion of the load, find that proportion when the efficiency is $\frac{1}{3}$. (I.E.)

16. It is found that a couple of 35 N cm applied to a screw which has two threads to the cm can produce a force of 100 N. What is the efficiency of the screw ? (H.S.D.)

17. A copying press has a lever 50 cm long fastened at its centre to a screw, the thread of which makes 12 complete turns per 10 cm of length. Forces equal to 48 N (in opposite directions) are applied at the two ends of the lever; by the principle of virtual work, or otherwise, find the force exerted by the press. (I.A.)

18. If an effort of 50 N, acting at the end of an arm 0·6 m long, produces in a screw press a thrust of 10^4 N, what is the pitch of the screw ?

19. If the two screws in a differential screw have pitches of 0·8 cm and 1·2 cm respectively, and a couple of moment 3000 N cm applied to the larger screw produces a thrust equal to the weight of a mass of 500 kg, calculate the efficiency of the machine.

(I.S.)

20. A bucket is lowered into a well by means of a windlass and a pulley. The end of the rope of the windlass (which in the more usual arrangement is attached to the bucket) is here attached to the frame of the windlass, and the pulley, with bucket attached, slides in the loop of the rope, the hanging parts of the rope being vertical. Neglecting friction and the weight of the rope, determine by the principle of virtual work, or otherwise, the force that must be applied at the arm of the windlass to maintain the bucket in equilibrium, having given the weight W of the bucket and its load, b the diameter of the barrel of the windlass, and a the length of the arm. In a practical machine friction cannot be neglected. What is the *efficiency* of this machine if the force that will just raise the bucket is nW ? (I.S.)

21. In a pair of pulley blocks there are three sheaves in each block, the mass of each block is 12 kg, and a weight of mass 132 kg is hung from the lower block. The efficiency is 60 per cent. Find the effort required to raise the weight and the reaction on the hook supporting the apparatus, neglecting the weight of the rope.

22. Two wheels of a radii a and b $(a>b)$ are fixed to the same axle which is rotated by an arm of length c at right angles to the axis. A light cord has one end fastened to a point on the circumference of the larger wheel and the other to a point on the circumference of the smaller, so that when the arm is turned the cord is wound on one wheel and off the other. The cord passes under a smooth light pulley supporting a load W.

Equilibrium is maintained by a force P applied at the end of the arm and at right angles to it in the plane in which it moves. Assuming that there is no friction and that the hanging parts of the string are vertical, find the relation between P and W.

If, on the other hand, there is friction and the efficiency of the machine is 45 per cent, find the load W which can be just raised by a force P of 120 N, given that a, b, c are respectively 15 cm, 10 cm, and 40 cm.   (H.C.)

CHAPTER SIXTEEN

CENTRE OF GRAVITY

16.1. In Chapter Eleven we found the position of the centre of gravity of some bodies of simple form. We shall now show how to find the position of this point in a few other cases, and then how to obtain general formulae by means of which the centre of gravity may be found in more difficult cases.

16.2. Three rods forming a triangle

Let AB, BC, CA be three uniform rods of the same thickness and material forming a triangle ABC (Fig. 16.1).

Let D, E, F be the mid-points of BC, CA, AB.

Joine DE, EF, FD.

The centres of gravity of the rods are at D, E, and F, and their weights, which are proportional to their lengths a, b, and c, may be taken to act at these points.

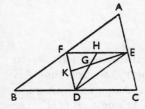

FIG. 16.1

The centre of gravity of the rods AB and AC is therefore at a point H in EF such that

$$c \times FH = b \times HE,$$

or

$$\frac{FH}{HE} = \frac{b}{c}.$$

But

$$b = 2DF \text{ and } c = 2DE$$

∴

$$\frac{FH}{HE} = \frac{DF}{DE}$$

∴ DH bisects the angle FDE.

Also the centre of gravity of the weight a at D and $b+c$ at H must lie on DH.

Hence the centre of gravity of the three rods must lie on DH. Similarly, the centre of gravity must lie on EK, which bisects the angle DEF.

The centre of gravity is therefore at G, where these bisectors intersect, and this point is the centre of the circle inscribed in the triangle DEF.

16.3. Tetrahedron

Let ABCD (Fig. 16.2) be a tetrahedron made of uniform material, E the mid-point of BD, and G_1 the centre of gravity of the base BCD.

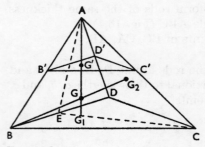

Fig. 16.2

Let B'C'D' be any section of the tetrahedron parallel to BCD. Then, from known results in geometry, we see that AE passes through the mid-point of B'D' and AG_1 passes through the intersection of the medians of the triangle B'C'D', i.e. through its centre of gravity G'.

Hence by considering the tetrahedron as built up of triangular slices parallel to BCD, it follows, since the centre of gravity of each slice lies in AG_1, that the centre of gravity of the whole lies in AG_1.

Similarly, it may be shown that the centre of gravity lies on the line joining B to the centre of gravity G_2 of the opposite face ACD.

Now it is also known that these lines intersect in a point G such that

$$G_1G = \tfrac{1}{4}G_1A$$

and

$$G_2G = \tfrac{1}{4}G_2B.$$

Hence the centre of gravity lies on the line joining the centre of gravity of any face to the opposite angular point at a distance equal to one-quarter of this line from the face.

Note. The centre of gravity of a tetrahedron is the same as that of four equal particles placed at its vertices.

For equal weights w placed at the vertices of the triangle BCD are equivalent to a weight $3w$ at G_1, the centre of gravity of BCD. Also $3w$ at G_1 and w at A are equivalent to $4w$ at G_1, since $G_1G = \frac{1}{4}G_1A$.

16.4. Pyramid on any base. Solid cone

Let OABCDE (Fig. 16.3) represent a uniform pyramid on any rectilinear base ABCDE. Let H be the centre of gravity of the base, and h the height of the pyramid.

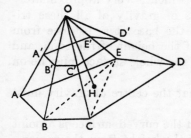

FIG. 16.3

Any plane parallel to the base will cut the pyramid in an area A'B'C'D'E' similar to the base, and its centre of gravity will be similarly placed to that of the base and lie on OH.

By considering the pyramid to be made up of thin slices parallel to the base, since the centres of gravity of all these slices lie on OH, the centre of gravity of the whole pyramid must lie on OH.

By dividing the base into triangles such as ABE, BEC, CED, we can divide the pyramid into tetrahedra.

The centre of gravity of each of these is at a height $h/4$ above the base, and therefore the centre of gravity of the whole pyramid is at a height $h/4$ above the base.

Hence the centre of gravity is on the line joining the vertex to the centre of gravity of the base and one-quarter of the way up that line.

Since a right circular cone may be considered as the limiting case of a pyramid when the base is a regular polygon and the number of sides is increased indefinitely, the result just obtained applies to a solid cone.

The centre of gravity of a solid right circular cone is in the line joining the vertex to the centre of the base and at a distance from the base equal to one-quarter of the height of the cone.

For *any* solid cone the centre of gravity is in the line joining the vertex to the centre of gravity of the base and one-quarter of the way up this line from the base.

16.5. Curved surface of a right circular cone

By joining the vertex to points on the edge of the base indefinitely close together, we can divide the surface into an infinite number of parts, each of which is very approximately a triangular lamina. The centres of gravity of all these triangles lie on a plane parallel to the base at a distance from the vertex equal to two-thirds of the height of the cone, and therefore the centre of gravity of the whole surface must lie on this plane.

We can see, by symmetry, that the centre of gravity must lie on the axis of the cone.

Hence the centre of gravity of the curved surface is a point on the axis distant two-thirds of the height from the vertex.

16.6. Centre of gravity of a number of particles

Let a number of particles of weights w_1, w_2, w_3, ... w_n be placed in a plane at points A_1, A_2, A_3, ... A_n (Fig. 16.4), and

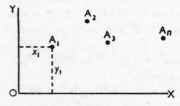

Fig. 16.4

let the coordinates of these points referred to two rectangular axes OX, OY in the plane be (x_1, y_1), (x_2, y_2), (x_3, y_3), ... (x_n, y_n).

Suppose the plane placed horizontally, so that the weights act perpendicularly to it, i.e. in the figure they are acting perpendicular to the plane of the paper.

The resultant of the weights is a weight $w_1+w_2+w_3+ \ldots +w_n$ or $\sum w$, and we know that the moment of this resultant about either of the axes OX or OY is equal to the sum of the moments of the separate weights about that axis.

Now the sum of the moments of the weights about OY is

$$w_1x_1+w_2x_2+ \ldots +w_nx_n \text{ or } \sum wx.$$

Hence if $\bar{x}$ is the distance of the line of action of the resultant from OY,

$$\bar{x}\sum \mathbf{w} = \sum \mathbf{wx}$$

$$\therefore \qquad \bar{x} = \frac{\sum \mathbf{wx}}{\sum \mathbf{w}}.$$

Similarly, if $\bar{y}$ is the distance of the resultant from OX,

$$\bar{y} = \frac{\sum \mathbf{wy}}{\sum \mathbf{w}}.$$

The line of action of the resultant weight therefore passes through a point G in the plane whose coordinates are $\bar{x}$ and $\bar{y}$, and this point must be the centre of gravity of the particles, which we know is a point in the plane.

This formula for the position of the centre of gravity will clearly apply also when $w_1, w_2, \ldots w_n$ are the weights of bodies whose centres of gravity are at $A_1, A_2, \ldots A_n$.

Since $w = mg$, where m is the mass of the particle, the above formulae can also be written.

$$\bar{x} = \frac{\sum mx}{\sum m} \quad \text{and} \quad \bar{y} = \frac{\sum my}{\sum m}.$$

The point thus found by considering the *masses* of the particles instead of their weights is the *Centre of Mass*. The centre of mass and centre of gravity are usually considered to be the same (as they are in the case of bodies small in comparison with the earth). The position of the centre of mass of a body of uniform density depends only on its shape, that is, it is determined entirely by the geometry of the body.

16.7. When we are given a finite number of particles of known weight and position the summations involved in finding the values of $\sum wx$ and $\sum wy$ are effected by ordinary addition.

In the case of a rigid body the number of particles is infinite. We then imagine the body as made up of strips or slices, the positions of whose centres of gravity are known. In a few simple cases, such as those already considered, we can, by taking the strips or slices in two different directions, show that the centre of gravity of the whole body must be at the point of intersection of two straight lines.

In many cases, however, although it is easy to see one line in which the centre of gravity must lie, we have to determine the position in this line by using the formula,

$$\bar{x} = \frac{\sum wx}{\sum w},$$

where w now represents the weight of a strip or slice, and x the distance of its centre of gravity from some fixed point in the line. The value of Σwx must be obtained by integration, as we are dealing with an infinite number of strips.

In the case of a plane surface of area A, if x and y are the distances of any element δA of its area from two fixed axes, the

$$\bar{x} = \frac{\sum x\delta A}{A} \quad \text{and} \quad \bar{y} = \frac{\sum y\delta A}{A}$$

formulae give the position of the *Centroid* of the surface.

In the case of a thin *uniform* lamina (in which the mass is proportional to the area) the centroid is the same as the centre of mass. If the lamina is *not* uniform these points will not be the same.

The centre of gravity, centre of mass, and centroid are usually the same, and the three terms are frequently used as if they really meant the same point. It must be remembered, however, that this is not true except in the case of uniform bodies in which the directions of the weights of the particles are considered parallel.

EXAMPLES 16.1

1. Particles of mass 2, 3, 6, and 9 kg are placed in a straight line AB at distances 1, 2, 3, 4 cm respectively from A. Find the distance of their centre of gravity from A.

2. A uniform rod AB is 4 m long and has a mass of 6 kg, and masses are attached to it as follows: 1 kg at A, 2 kg at 1 m from A, 3 kg at 2 m from A, 4 kg at 3 m from A, and 5 kg at B. Find the distance from A of the centre of gravity of the system.

3. Weights of mass 3, 4, and 5 kg are placed at the corners A, B, C respectively of an isosceles triangle in which AB = AC = 12 cm, BC = 8 cm. Find the distance of the centre of gravity of the weights from BC and from AD, the perpendicular from A to BC.

4. Weights of mass 1, 2, 3, 4 kg are placed at the corners A, B, C, D respectively of a square ABCD of side 8 cm. Find the distance of the centre of gravity of the system from AB and AD.

5. Weights of mass 1, 2, and 3 kg are placed at the corners of an equilateral triangle of side 9 cm. Find the distance of their centre of gravity from the first weight.

6. Weights of mass 5, 6, 9, and 7 kg are placed at the corners A, B, C, D of a square of side 27 cm. Find the distance of their centre of gravity from A.

7. ABC is an equilateral triangle of side 4 m. Weights of mass 5, 1, and 3 kg are placed at A, B, and C respectively, and weights of mass 2, 4, and 6 kg are placed at the mid-points of BC, CA, and AB. Find the distance of their centre of gravity from B.

8. Weights of mass 1, 5, 3, 4, 2, and 6 kg are placed at the angular points of a regular hexagon taken in order. Show that their centre of gravity is at the centre of the hexagon.

9. Weights of mass 5, 1, 3, 2, 4, and 15 kg are placed at the angular points of a regular hexagon taken in order. Find the distance of their centre of gravity from the 15 kg weight.

10. Weights of mass 1, 2, 3, 4, 5, and 6 kg are placed at the angular points of a regular hexagon taken in order. Find the distance of their centre of gravity from the centre of the hexagon, the length of the side being 14 cm.

11. ABC is an isosceles triangular lamina in which AB = AC = 15 cm, BC = 24 cm. The mass of the lamina is 24 kg, and weights of mass 6, 6, and 4 kg are placed at the corners A, B, and C respectively. Find the distance of the centre of gravity of the system from BC.

12. Masses of 1, 2, 3, 4 kg are placed respectively at the corners A, B, C, D of a rectangle; AB = 6 m, BC = 12 m. Find the perpendicular distances of the centre of gravity from AB and BC.

16.8. Centre of gravity of a compound body

If we know the weights and the centres of gravity of each of two parts of a body we can find the centre of gravity of the whole as follows.

Let G_1, G_2 (Fig. 16.5) be the centres of gravity of the two parts, W_1 and W_2 their weights.

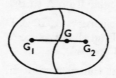

FIG. 16.5

These weights are like parallel forces acting at G_1 and G_2, and their resultant is equal to $W_1 + W_2$ and acts at a point G in $G_1 G_2$ such that

$$W_1 \times G_1 G = W_2 \times G G_2$$

$$\therefore \quad \frac{G_1 G}{W_2} = \frac{G G_1}{W_1} = \frac{G_1 G_2}{W_1 + W_2}$$

$$\therefore \quad G_1 G = \frac{W_2}{W_1 + W_2} G_1 G_2 \quad \text{and} \quad G G_2 = \frac{W_1}{W_1 + W_2} G_1 G_2.$$

This result may also be obtained by applying the general formula, or the method employed in proving the formula, which is really an application of the principle of moments.

We know that the resultant of W_1 at G_1 and W_2 at G_2 is $W_1 + W_2$, acting at some point G in $G_1 G_2$.

Taking G_1 as origin and moments about this point, we have

$$(W_1 + W_2) G_1 G = W_2 \times G_1 G_2$$

$$\therefore \quad G_1 G = \frac{W_2}{W_1 + W_2} G_1 G_2.$$

16.9. Centre of gravity of a remainder

If we know the weight and centre of gravity of a body, and the weight and centre of gravity of a part of it which is removed, the centre of gravity of the remainder is obtained as follows.

In the figure of the last paragraph let G be the centre of gravity of the whole body, W its weight, G_2 and W_2 the centre of gravity and weight of the part removed.

The centre of gravity of the remainder must obviously be in the same straight line as G_2 and G.

Also the sum of the moments of the weights of the two parts about any point in the line must equal the moment of the weight of the whole about that point.

Hence the moment of the remainder is equal to the moment of the whole, less the moment of the part removed.

If G_1 is the centre of gravity of the remainder, taking moments about G_2, we have

$$(W - W_2)G_2G_1 = W \times G_2G$$

$$\therefore \qquad G_2G_1 = \frac{W}{W - W_2}G_2G.$$

16.10. If a compound body is made up of several parts, or several parts are removed from a body, we take two axes and proceed as in obtaining the general formulae.

It is better to use the principle of moments directly, rather than quote the formulae.

For a body made up of several parts we have, about either axis,

Moment of whole = Sum of moments of parts.

Similarly for the remainder, after removing parts of a body, we have

Moment of remainder = Moment of whole
—Sum of moments of parts removed.

These methods are illustrated in the following examples.

It should be noticed that the position of the centre of gravity depends only on the *relative* values of the weights. It is often more convenient to use quantities *proportional* to the weights than the actual weights themselves.

16.11. EXAMPLE (i)

In a circular disc of 18 cm diameter a circular hole of 6 cm diameter is cut, the centre of the hole being 4 cm from the centre of the disc. Find the position of the centre of gravity of the remainder of the disc.

Let G, G_1 (Fig. 16.6) be the centres of the disc and hole. It is clear that the centre of gravity of the remainder must be in G_1G, on the side of G opposite to G_1.

It is convenient here to take moments about G; the moment of the whole disc is then zero, and the moments of the part removed and the remainder are equal and opposite.

FIG. 16.6

Tabulating weights and distances, we have

	Weight	Distance of C.G. from G
Disc	81	0
Part removed	9	4 cm
Remainder	72	x cm

Taking moments about G, we have

$$72x = 36$$

$$\therefore \qquad x = \tfrac{1}{2}.$$

Note. The squares of the radii are taken to represent the weights. This avoids introducing π and the density of the disc.

EXAMPLE (ii)

A sheet of metal is in the shape of a square ABCD with an isosceles triangle described on the side BC; if the side of the square be 12 cm, and the height of the triangle be 9 cm, find the distance of the centre of gravity of the sheet from the line AD.

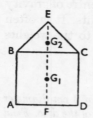

FIG. 16.7

Let ABECD (Fig. 16.7) represent the sheet, and draw EF perpendicular to AD. The centre of gravity of the square is at G_1, where $FG_1 = 6$ cm. The centre of gravity of the triangle is at G_2, in EF, where $EG_2 = \frac{2}{3} \times 9 = 6$ cm, so that $FG_2 = 15$ cm. The weights are proportional to the areas, i.e. to 144 and 54. Tabulating the weights and distances of the centres of gravity from the axes, we get

	Weight	Distance of C.G. from AD
Square	144	6 cm
Triangle	54	15 cm
Whole figure	198	x cm

Taking moments about AD,

$$198x = 144 \times 6 + 54 \times 15$$
$$= 93 \times 18,$$
$$\therefore \qquad x = 8\tfrac{5}{11}.$$

EXAMPLE (iii)

The radii of the faces of a frustum of a cone are 2 m and 3 m, and the thickness of the frustum is 4 m. Find the distance of the centre of gravity from the larger face.

Let ABCD (Fig. 16.8) represent a section of the frustum through its axis EF.

Produce AD, BC, EF to meet in O, the vertex of the cone from which the frustum is cut.

By similar triangles OFC, OEB, we have

$$\frac{OE}{OF} = \frac{EB}{FC} = \frac{3}{2}.$$

$$\therefore \qquad \frac{OF+4}{OF} = \frac{3}{2}$$

$$\therefore \qquad \frac{4}{OF} = \frac{1}{2} \text{ or } OF = 8 \text{ m.}$$

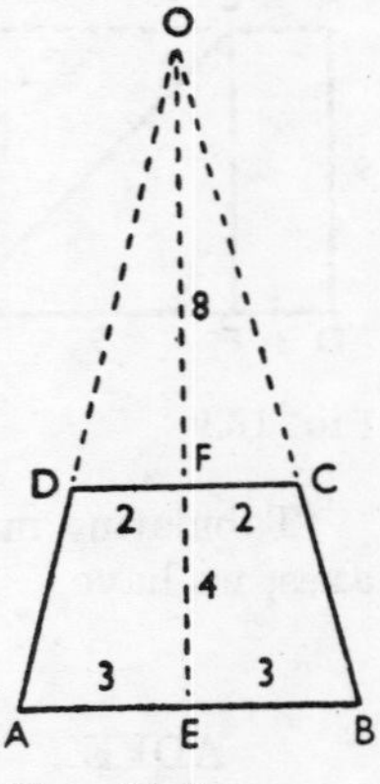

FIG. 16.8

Now the volumes of similar solid figures are proportional to the cubes of corresponding dimensions,

$$\frac{\text{Volume of cone ODC}}{\text{Volume of cone OAB}} = \frac{8^3}{12^3} = \frac{8}{27}.$$

The weights of the whole cone, the upper cone which is removed, and the frustum are therefore proportional to 27, 8, and 19 respectively.

The centres of gravity of all three lie in OE.

Tabulating weights and distances of C.G.s from O, we get

	Weight	Distance of C.G. *from* O
Whole cone	27	9 m
Part removed	8	6 m
Frustum	19	x m

Taking moments about O, we have

$$19x = 27 \times 9 - 48 = 195$$
$$\therefore \quad x = \tfrac{195}{19}.$$

Hence the distance of the centre of gravity from E is

$$12 - \tfrac{195}{19} = \tfrac{33}{19} \text{ m}.$$

EXAMPLE (iv)

A sheet of paper is in the shape of a rectangle, 9 cm wide and 12 cm long; one of the shorter sides is folded down, so as to lie entirely along one of the longer sides. Find the position of the centre of gravity of the whole sheet thus folded.

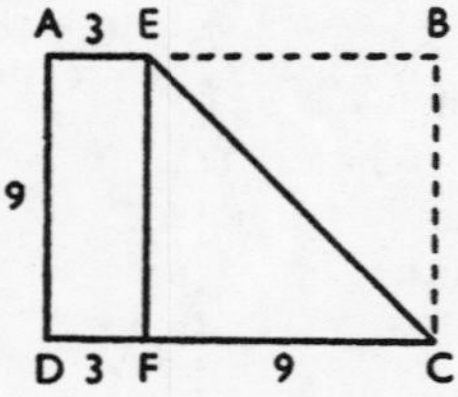

Fig. 16.9

Let AECFD (Fig. 16.9) represent the folded sheet, so that the triangular portion EFC is double.

It will be convenient to take DC, DA as axes of x and y.

The mass of ADFE is proportional to 27, that of EFC to 81.

Tabulating masses and distances of centres of gravity from the axes, we have

	Mass	Distance of C.G. *from* DA	*from* DC
ADFE	27	$\tfrac{3}{2}$ cm	$\tfrac{9}{2}$ cm
EFC	81	$3+3 = 6$ cm	3 cm
Whole figure	108	x cm	y cm

Taking moments about DA, we have

$$108x = 486 + \tfrac{81}{2} = \tfrac{1053}{2}$$
$$\therefore \quad x = \tfrac{1053}{216} = 4\tfrac{7}{8}.$$

Taking moments about DC, we have

$$108y = 243 + \tfrac{243}{2} = \tfrac{729}{2}$$
$$\therefore \quad y = \tfrac{729}{216} = 3\tfrac{3}{8}.$$

EXAMPLE (v)

ABCD *is a trapezium in which* AB, CD *are parallel, and of lengths* a, b. *Prove that the distance of the centre of mass from* AB *is* $\frac{1}{3}h\frac{a+2b}{a+b}$, *where h is the distance between* AB *and* CD.

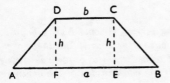

FIG. 16.10

Method (a)

Draw CE, DF perpendicular to AB (Fig. 16.10).
We then have

	Area	Distance of C.G. *from* AB
ABCD	$\frac{1}{2}(a+b)h$	x
DCEF	bh	$\frac{1}{2}h$
ADF	$\frac{1}{2}$AF $\times h$	$\frac{1}{3}h$
CEB	$\frac{1}{2}$EB $\times h$	$\frac{1}{3}h$

Hence, taking moments about AB,

$$\tfrac{1}{2}(a+b)hx = b \times \frac{h^2}{2} + \tfrac{1}{2} \times \text{AF} \times \frac{h^2}{3} + \tfrac{1}{2} \times \text{EB} \times \frac{h^2}{3}$$

$$= \frac{h^2}{2}\left(b + \frac{\text{AF}+\text{EB}}{3}\right).$$

But

$$\text{AF}+\text{EB} = a-b$$

$$\therefore \quad \tfrac{1}{2}(a+b)hx = \frac{h^2}{2}\left(b + \frac{a-b}{3}\right) = \frac{h^2}{2} \times \frac{2b+a}{3}$$

$$\therefore \quad x = \tfrac{1}{3}h\frac{a+2b}{a+b}.$$

Method (b)

The position of the centre of mass can also be found by supposing the trapezium divided into two triangles ADC, ACB, whose areas are $\frac{1}{2}bh$ and $\frac{1}{2}ah$ respectively, and then replacing them by particles of masses $\frac{1}{6}bh$ and $\frac{1}{6}ah$ at the vertices.

This gives $\frac{1}{6}(a+b)h$ at A and C, $\frac{1}{6}ah$ at B, and $\frac{1}{6}bh$ at D.

Taking moments about AB,

$$\tfrac{1}{2}(a+b)hx = [\tfrac{1}{6}bh+\tfrac{1}{6}(a+b)h]h$$
$$= \tfrac{1}{6}[a+2b]h^2$$
$$\therefore \qquad x = \tfrac{1}{3}h\frac{a+2b}{a+b}.$$

EXAMPLE (vi)

A uniform rectangular board ABCD has AB = 10 cm, AD = 8 cm. Two square holes, each of side 2 cm, are cut in the board, and these are filled to the original thickness with metal whose specific gravity is nine times that of the material of the board. If the coordinates of the centres of the holes referred to AB, AD as axes of x and y and measured in centimetres are (4, 3), (7, 4) respectively, find the coordinates of the centre of gravity of the loaded board.

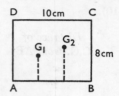

FIG. 16.11

Let G_1, G_2 (Fig. 16.11) be the centre of the holes.

The area of each hole is 4 cm², and its relative weight is 36. It is convenient to consider the loaded board as made up of the uniform board with added weights of 32 at G_1 and G_2, we then have,

	Weight	Distance of C.G. from AD	Distance of C.G. from AB
Unloaded board	80	5 cm	4 cm
Load at G_1	32	4 cm	3 cm
Load at G_2	32	7 cm	4 cm
Loaded board	144	x cm	y cm

Taking moments about AD, we have

$$144x = 400+128+224 = 752$$
$$\therefore \qquad x = \tfrac{752}{144} = 5\tfrac{2}{9}.$$

Taking moments about AB, we have

$$144y = 320+96+128 = 544.$$
$$\therefore \qquad y = \tfrac{544}{144} = 3\tfrac{7}{9}.$$

EXAMPLES 16.2

1. A sheet of paper in the shape of a rectangle ABCD, with an isosceles triangle described on the side BC, has the following dimensions: AB = 12 cm, AD = 8 cm, and the height of the triangle is 12 cm. Find the distance of the centre of gravity of the sheet from AD.

2. In a circular disc of 12 cm radius a circular hole of 2 cm radius is cut, the centre of the hole being 6 cm from the centre of the disc. Find the position of the centre of gravity of the remainder of the disc.

3. In a circular disc of 12 cm radius two circular holes of 2 cm radius are cut, the centres of the holes lying on two perpendicular diameters of the disc at a distance of 6 cm from the centre of the disc. Find the position of the centre of gravity of the remainder of the disc.

4. A sheet of paper is in the shape of a rectangle ABCD in which AB = 12 cm, AD = 8 cm. E is the mid-point of AD and the triangle CED is removed. Find the distance of the centre of gravity of the remainder of the sheet from AD and AB.

5. ABCD is a square board of side 12 cm, and E is a point in AD such that DE = 3 cm. The triangle CED is removed. Find the distance of the centre of gravity of the remainder of the board from AB and AD.

6. In a triangle ABC the mid-point of BC is D. A straight line is drawn through the centre of mass of the triangle parallel to BC, cutting the sides AB, AC in E and F respectively. Prove that the centre of mass of the quadrilateral BEFC lies in AD at a distance $\frac{7}{45}$AD from D.   (I.A.)

7. ABCD is a square lamina of side 9 cm. E, F are points in BC, CD such that EC, CF are each 3 cm. Find the centroid of the part ABEFDA of the lamina.   (I.A.)

8. ABCDEF is a sheet of thin cardboard in the form of a regular hexagon. Prove that if the triangle ABC is cut off and superposed on the triangle DEF the centre of gravity of the whole is moved a distance $\frac{2}{9}a$, where a is the side of the hexagon.   (I.S.)

9. ABCD is a rectangular plate; AB = 8 cm, BC = 12 cm, and E is the mid-point of BC. If the triangular portion ABE is removed from the plate and the remainder is then suspended from A, find the inclination of the side AD to the vertical.   (I.E.)

10. ABCD is a rectangular lamina, such that $AB = CD = 2a$, $AD = BC = 2b$; P and Q are the mid-points of BC and CD respectively. The triangular portion PCQ of the lamina is cut off. Prove that the perpendicular distances of the centre of gravity of the remainder from the sides AD, AB are $19a/21$ and $19b/21$ respectively.

(H.S.D.)

11. A triangular plate is made up of two metals whose dividing line is parallel to a side and one-third up the median of that side. The ratio of the densities of the triangular and trapezoidal parts being 5 : 4, find the position of the mass centre of the compound plate.

(I.E.)

12. Three rectangular areas, 60 cm by 5 cm, 90 cm by 5 cm, 30 cm by 4 cm, are fitted together to form an I figure, the longest and shortest areas forming the cross-pieces. Find the distance of the centroid of the figure from the outer edge of the smallest area.

(I.E.)

13. A uniform square plate of 30 cm side has two circular holes punched in it, one of radius 2 cm, and coordinates of centre (10, 13) cm referred to two adjacent sides of the plate as axes, the other of radius 1 cm, and coordinates of centre (20, 3) cm, find the coordinates of the centre of mass of the remainder of the plate.

(I.S.)

14. Prove that, if ABCD is a trapezium with parallel sides AB, CD, its centre of gravity divides the line joining the mid-points of AB and CD in the ratio $AB+2CD : 2AB+CD$.

(I.S.)

15. ABC is a triangle, in which $AB = AC$; D, E, F are the mid-points of BC, CA, AB respectively, and G is the centre of gravity of the triangle. If the portion AFGE is removed, find the distance from A of the centre of gravity of the remainder of the triangle given that $AD = 0.9$ m.

(I.S.)

16. A uniform rectangular plate ABCD has a triangular portion removed by a straight cut through the mid-points of CB and CD. Show that the centre of gravity of the remaining portion is at a distance $\frac{1}{21}$ AC from the centre of the rectangle.

(I.S.)

17. Two right circular cones have the same base, and their axes in opposite directions. Show that the centroid of the spindle-shaped solid formed of these two cones is midway between the centre of their base and the point bisecting the distance between the vertices.

(I.S.)

18. ABC is a uniform equilateral triangular lamina of side 20 cm and mass 240 g, and masses of 30, 40, 50 g are placed at the corners A, B, C respectively. Find the distance of the centre of gravity of the whole system from the side BC.

(H.S.D.)

19. The radii of the circular ends of a frustum of a solid circular cone are in the ratio 2 : 3. Prove that the distances of the centroid of the frustum from the ends are in the ratio 43 : 33.   (H.S.D.)

20. A piece of cardboard is in the form of a rectangle, ABCD, where AB = 5 cm and BC = 8 cm. A piece of the cardboard ABE in the form of an equilateral triangle on AB as base is cut out. Calculate the distance of the centre of gravity of the remaining cardboard from DC.   (H.S.D.)

21. A haystack has the form of a right circular cone standing on a circular cylinder. If the diameter of the base is 10 m, the height of the cylinder 4·8 m, and the length of the slant side of the cone 6 m, calculate the height of the centre of gravity of the haystack above the ground.   (I.E.)

22. A closed regular tetrahedron is made of thin metal plate. Find the position of the centre of gravity when: (i) empty; (ii) filled with liquid whose weight is 3 times that of the tetrahedron. (I.E.)

23. A frustum of a cone has its circular ends of radii r_1 and r_2 and at a distance h apart. Its *curved surface* is covered with thin uniform material. Show that the height of the centre of gravity of the covering material above the end of radius r_2 is

$$\frac{h(2r_1+r_2)}{3(r_1+r_2)}.$$ (H.S.D.)

24. A uniform wooden triangular lamina in the form of an isosceles triangle of sides 12, 8, and 12 cm, has a thin metal band round it. If the weight of the metal band is twice that of the lamina, find the position of the centre of gravity of the lamina and band together.   (H.S.C.)

25. A uniform wire is bent in the form of a triangle ABC and is suspended at A. Prove that a plumb-line hung from A will cross BC at the point D, where

$$\frac{\text{BD}}{\text{DC}}=\frac{a+b}{a+c}$$

the sides of the triangle being a, b, c.   (H.S.D.)

26. The diameters of the plane ends of a frustum of a right circular cone are 30 cm and 90 cm respectively; the height of the frustum is 65 cm. Prove that its centre of gravity is 22·5 cm from the larger plane end.   (I.S.)

27. A line is drawn through the centre of gravity of a triangle, parallel to one of its sides. Prove that the centre of gravity of the quadrilateral portion divides the median of the triangle in the ratio 7 : 38.   (H.S.D.)

28. A tin can is in the form of right circular cone of semi-vertical angle 30°, with base, all made of uniform thin sheet metal. It is filled with liquid, whose total weight is twice that of the can. Find the ratio of the height of the centre of gravity above the base to the height of the cone. (H.S.D.)

29. A solid frustum of a uniform cone is of thickness h, and the radii of its end-faces are a and b ($a>b$). A cylindrical hole is bored through the frustum. The axis of the hole coincides with the axis of the cone, and the radius of the hole is equal to that of the smaller face of the frustum. Show that the centre of gravity of the solid thus obtained is at a distance from the larger face of the frustum equal to

$$\frac{h(a+3b)}{4(a+2b)}.$$

30. Prove that if the radius of one plane end-face of a frustum of a right circular cone is n times the radius of the other end-face the centre of gravity divides the axis of the frustum in the ratio

$$(3n^2+2n+1) : (n^2+2n+3).$$

31. Find the centre of gravity of a hollow right circular cone with a circular base formed of the same material as the curved surface. If the height and diameter of the base are equal, find the angle the axis makes with the vertical when the cone is suspended from a point on the rim of the base.

32. A hollow conical vessel made of thin sheet metal is closed at its base; if it is cut across by a plane parallel to the base at half the perpendicular height, and the upper cone removed, prove that the distance from the base of the centre of gravity of the remainder of the vessel is

$$2lh/3(3l+4r),$$

where h is the perpendicular height of the original vessel, l its slant height, and r the radius of the base. (I.S.)

33. Find the centre of gravity of an L-shaped uniform lamina, the outside height and breadth of the vertical arm being 10 cm and 1 cm, and the outside length and breadth of the horizontal arm being 6 cm and 2 cm respectively. (I.A.)

34. A corner is cut off from a solid wooden cube by means of a saw-cut through the mid-points of the edges that meet in that corner. Find the perpendicular distances of the centre of gravity of the remainder of the cube from the three uncut faces. (H.S.D.)

35. A regular tetrahedron of edge a is cut by a plane parallel to the base, and bisecting the perpendicular height of the tetrahedron. Find the position of the centre of mass of the frustum thus cut off.   (I.S.)

36. A four-sided plane lamina has the shape of a rectangle ABCD surmounted by a triangular part BEC, the side BE of which is a prolongation of AB. If the lengths of AB, AD, BE are a, b, c respectively, find how far the centre of gravity of the lamina is from AB and AD. Also prove that the centre of gravity will lie on BC if $c = a\sqrt{3}$.

37. There are four similar planks, each 3·6 m long, in a pile. The second plank projects 0·6 m beyond the first, the third 0·9 m beyond the second, and the fourth 1·8 m beyond the third; the sides are flush with each other. Find the centre of gravity of the four planks.   (I.A.)

38. A tank of sheet metal is a cube of side a, having in its base a central circular hole of diameter $a/4$; a cylinder of height $a/4$ is brazed externally to the edge of the hole and closed by a circular plate. The cube, cylinder, and plate being cut from the same sheet, find the mass centre.   (I.E.)

39. A solid cylinder of mass M and radius a has two small heavy discs, each of mass m, keyed to its ends so that the line joining the centres of the discs is parallel to the axis of the cylinder and at a distance c from it. Find where a cylindrical portion of radius b of the cylinder, with axis parallel to that of the cylinder, must be cut out in order that the centre of gravity of the remainder and the discs may be in the axis of the cylinder. What is the greatest value of the ratio m/M in order that this solution may be possible?   (I.E.)

40. A framework in the shape of a tetrahedron is made of six uniform rods, each rod being equal to its opposite rod. Show that the centre of gravity is at the same point as if the tetrahedron were solid.   (I.A.)

16.12. Quadrilateral lamina

The position of the centre of gravity of a quadrilateral is obtained most easily by dividing it into two triangles by drawing one of the diagonals, and considering each of these triangles to be replaced by three particles equal to one-third of its weight placed at the three vertices.

There are several ways of expressing the position of this centre of gravity, one of which is illustrated below.

Let ABCD (Fig. 16.12) represent any quadrilateral lamina, AC and BD its diagonals intersecting at E.

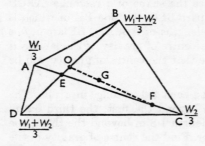

Fɪɢ. 16.12

Let W be the weight of the whole quadrilateral and W_1, W_2 the weights of the triangles ABD, BCD.

Since the areas ABD, BCD are in the ratio of AE to EC.

$$\frac{W_1}{W_2} = \frac{AE}{EC}.$$

Replacing ABD by equal particles $\frac{1}{3}W_1$ at A, B, D and replacing BCD by equal particles $\frac{1}{3}W_2$ at B, C, D we have $\frac{1}{3}W_1$ at A, $\frac{1}{3}W_2$ at C, and $\frac{1}{3}(W_1+W_2)$ at each of the corners B and D.

Now the centre of gravity of $\frac{1}{3}W_1$ at A and $\frac{1}{3}W_2$ at C is at a point F in AC such that

$$W_1 \times AF = W_2 \times CF$$

$$\therefore \qquad \frac{CF}{AF} = \frac{W_1}{W_2} = \frac{AE}{EC}.$$

Hence $\qquad\qquad CF = AE.$

The weights at A and C are equivalent to $\frac{1}{3}W$ at F.

The weights at B and D are equivalent to $\frac{2}{3}W$ at O, the mid-point of BD and the centre of gravity of the whole quadrilateral is therefore at G in OF, where $2OG = GF$.

EXAMPLE

G *is the centre of gravity of a uniform quadrilateral plate, G′ is the centre of gravity of four equal particles placed at its corners, and O is the intersection of its diagonals. Prove that O, G, and G′ are in the same straight line, and that $OG′ = 3GG′$.*   (H.S.D.)

Let ABCD (Fig. 16.13) be the quadrilateral.

Let W_1, W_2 be the weights of the triangles ABD, BCD respectively. Replace ABD by weights $\frac{1}{3}W_1$ at A, B, D, and replace BCD by weights $\frac{1}{3}W_2$ at B, C, D.

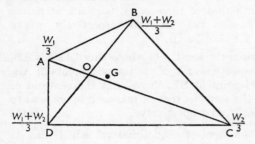

FIG. 16.13

G is therefore the centre of gravity of these particles, and the whole weight $W_1 + W_2$ acts there.

Now G' is the centre of gravity of these particles, together with particles $\frac{1}{3}W_2$ at A and $\frac{1}{3}W_1$ at C, which are equivalent to $\frac{1}{3}(W_1 + W_2)$ at O (since $W_1/W_2 = \text{AO/OC}$).

Hence G' is the centre of gravity of $W_1 + W_2$ at G and $\frac{1}{3}(W_1 + W_2)$ at O, and must therefore lie in OG, and OG' = 3GG'.

EXAMPLES 16.3

1. Show that the centre of gravity of a quadrilateral ABCD is the same as that of three particles of weights proportional respectively to AO, OC, 2AC placed at A, C, and the mid-point of BD, where O is the intersection of AC and BD.   (I.S.)

2. ABCD is a uniform plane quadrilateral whose diagonals intersect in L; M and N are points on the diagonals AC and BD respectively, such that AM = CL and BN = DL. Show that the centre of mass of the quadrilateral ABCD coincides with that of the triangle LMN.   (H.S.C.)

3. ABCD is a uniform plane quadrilateral lamina, in which AB is parallel to DC. The length of AB is a and the length of DC is b. Prove that the centre of gravity of the lamina coincides with that of four particles of weights proportional to a, $a+b$, b, $a+b$, placed at A, B, C, D respectively. If AD = BC = c, and $b>a$, find the coordinates of the centre of gravity referred to rectangular axes, of which one is DA and the other is the perpendicular to DA, drawn through D.

4. Calculate, to two decimal places, the coordinates of the centre of gravity of a uniform quadrilateral lamina whose angular points are (5, 0), (3, 7), (−2, 5), and (−5, 0).   (Ex.)

5. (i) Prove that the centre of gravity of a uniform triangular plate ABC coincides with that of three equal particles at points X, Y, Z on the sides BC, CA, AB respectively, where BX : XC = CY : YA = AZ : ZB.

   (ii) ABCD is a trapezium the lengths of whose parallel sides AB, DC are a and b respectively; E, F are the mid-points of AB, DC; H is the mid-point of EF. Prove that the centroid of the trapezium is the same as that of masses proportional to a, b, $2a+2b$, at E, F, H respectively.   (H.C.)

6. A uniform plate in the form of a quadrilateral ABCD has its diagonals AC, BD crossing at right angles at a point O, so that AO = 5 cm, OC = 10 cm, BO = 2·5 cm, OD = 7·5 cm. Find the distance of the centre of gravity of the quadrilateral from each of the diagonals.

7. AD, BE, CF are the medians of a triangle ABC, and G is their point of intersection. If the portion AFGE is removed, show that the centre of gravity of the remainder is on GD at a distance $\frac{7}{12}$GD from D.   (N.U.3)

8. ABCD is a quadrilateral, and it is 'reduced' to a triangle ABX of equal area by the usual construction (C being on the line BX). Prove that the centres of gravity of ABCD and of ABX are at the same distance from AC.   (Ex.)

9. ABCD is a plane quadrilateral lamina whose diagonals meet at O; AO is less than OC and DO than OB. S is the mid-point of BD, T the mid-point of AC, and OSKT is a parallelogram. Prove that the centre of gravity of the lamina ABCD coincides with that of three equal particles at S, T, and K.   (Ex.)

10. X, Y are the mid-points of two parallel sides of a quadrilateral whose lengths are a, b respectively. Show that G, the centroid of the quadrilateral, divides XY in the ratio $2b+a : 2a+b$. A uniform regular hexagonal area of side a has a part removed by a cut made parallel to one of the sides, and at a distance $\frac{1}{2}ka\sqrt{3}$ from it, where $k<1$. Prove that the centre of gravity of the remaining portion is at a distance from the centre of the complete area equal to

$$\frac{k(3-k^2)}{3(6-2k-k^2)}a\sqrt{3}.$$ (C.W.B.)

11. The mass centre of a uniform triangular plate ABC is G, and triangular pieces are cut from it by drawing parallels to BC, CA, AB cutting GA, GB, GC in the same ratio. Prove that the mass centre is unaltered. (C.W.B.)

12. A heavy quadrilateral lamina, weight $3W$, has a particle of weight W placed at the intersection of the diagonals. Prove that it will be in equilibrium in a horizontal position when four equal vertical forces support it, one at each corner. (Ex.)

16.13. *When a body is placed with its base in contact with a plane (rough enough to prevent sliding if inclined) it will be in equilibrium if the vertical line through its centre of gravity meets the plane within the area of the base.*

The forces acting on the body are its weight, acting vertically through its centre of gravity, and the reaction of the plane. If the plane is horizontal the reactions of the plane on the different parts of the base are all like parallel forces, and their resultant must obviously act at a point within the area of the base.

If the plane is inclined the resultant of the frictional forces on the different points of the base and the normal pressures of the plane must also have a resultant which acts at a point inside the area of the base.

Hence in both cases, if the resultant reaction of the plane is to balance the weight, the vertical through the centre of gravity must fall within the area of the base.

It should be noticed that if the base has re-entrant angles as in Fig. 16.14 the area of the base must be taken to mean the

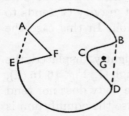

Fig. 16.14

area included in the figure which would be obtained by drawing a piece of thread tightly round the figure. Thus a point such as G would be within the area of the base.

16.14. *Stability of equilibrium*

If a rigid body be in equilibrium when one point only of the body is fixed it is clear that the centre of gravity of the body must be in the vertical line passing through the fixed point.

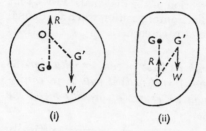

(i)   (ii)

FIG. 16.15

For let O (Fig. 16.15) be the fixed point, and G the centre of gravity of the body.

The only forces acting on the body are its weight acting vertically through G and the reaction R at the point O.

If these are to balance they must be in the same straight line, i.e. G must be in the vertical line through O.

This condition is satisfied in two cases, (i) when G is vertically below O, and (ii) when G is vertically above O.

Both these positions are positions of equilibrium, but there is a difference in the two cases.

In the first case, if the body is slightly displaced it will tend to return to its equilibrium position; the moment about O of the weight through the displaced centre of gravity G′ tends to bring the body back to its original position. In this case the equilibrium is said to be *Stable*.

In the second case, if the body is slightly displaced the moment about O of the weight acting through G′, Fig. 16.15 (ii), tends to increase the displacement, and the body does not tend to return to its original position. In this case the equilibrium is *Unstable*.

A body is said to be in stable equilibrium when it returns to its original position after a *small* displacement. The extent to which it can be displaced without upsetting is a measure of its *amount* or *degree* of stability, and this we shall not consider.

16.15. A right circular cone with its base resting on a horizontal plane is in stable equilibrium; if slightly displaced it tends to return to its original position.

If placed with its vertex in contact with a horizontal plane and its axis vertical it will be in unstable equilibrium; if slightly displaced it will fall over.

A right circular cylinder with a plane end in contact with a horizontal plane is in stable equilibrium; if placed with its curved surface in contact with a horizontal plane it will rest in *any position*.

In this case the equilibrium is said to be *neutral*.

A uniform sphere resting on a horizontal plane is also in neutral equilibrium.

In most cases it is quite easy to see whether a position of equilibrium is stable or unstable. In certain cases, however, it is a matter of considerable difficulty to determine whether a body in a position of equilibrium will return to this position when slightly displaced.

16.16 EXAMPLE (i)

A cubical block of edge a rests on a horizontal plane and is gradually undermined by cutting slices away by planes parallel to a horizontal edge, inclined at 45° to the horizontal. Find the centre of mass of the remainder when a length x has been removed from each of the four edges, and show that the block will fall when $9x = 5a$, approximately. (I.S.)

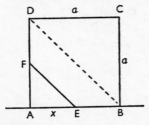

FIG. 16.16

Let ABCD (Fig. 16.16) represent a vertical section of the cube through its centre; the cutting plane will then be parallel to DB.

Let EF be the line in which the cutting plane meets ABCD, and $AE = x$. The centre of gravity of the prism removed will be at the centre of gravity of the triangle AEF.

The weights of the cube and part removed are proportional to the areas of the sections, a^2 and $\frac{1}{2}x^2$.

Tabulating the weights and distances of centres of gravity from BC and AB.

	Weight	Distance of C.G. from BC	from AB
Cube	a^2	$\frac{1}{2}a$	$\frac{1}{2}a$
Prism AFE	$\frac{1}{2}x^2$	$a-\frac{1}{3}x$	$\frac{1}{3}x$
Remainder	$a^2-\frac{1}{2}x^2$	X	Y

Taking moments about BC, we have

$$(a^2-\tfrac{1}{2}x^2)\mathrm{X} = \tfrac{1}{2}a^3-\tfrac{1}{2}x^2(a-\tfrac{1}{3}x)$$

$$\therefore \qquad \mathrm{X} = \frac{a^3-x^2(a-\frac{1}{3}x)}{2a^2-x^2}.$$

Taking moments about AB, we have

$$(a^2-\tfrac{1}{2}x^2)\mathrm{Y} = \tfrac{1}{2}a^3-\tfrac{1}{6}x^3$$

$$\therefore \qquad \mathrm{Y} = \frac{a^3-\frac{1}{3}x^3}{2a^2-x^2}.$$

The block will fall over if the centre of gravity comes to the left of E, i.e. if $\mathrm{X}>a-x$; hence it will be on the point of falling over when

$$a^3-x^2(a-\tfrac{1}{3}x) = (2a^2-x^2)(a-x)$$

or $\qquad a^3-ax^2+\tfrac{1}{3}x^3 = 2a^3-2a^2x-ax^2+x^3$

or $\qquad \tfrac{2}{3}x^3-2a^2x+a^3 = 0.$

Putting $x = \tfrac{5}{9}a$, the left side of this gives

$$\frac{250}{2187}a^3-\frac{10}{9}a^3+a^3 = \frac{250}{2187}a^3-\tfrac{1}{9}a^3$$

which is nearly zero.

Alternatively, we can write

$$x = \tfrac{1}{2}a+(x^3/3a^2).$$

Therefore as a first approximation, $x = \tfrac{1}{2}a$.

A second approximation is

$$x = \tfrac{1}{2}a+\frac{(\frac{1}{2}a)^3}{3a^2} = \tfrac{13}{24}a = 0\cdot54a.$$

EXAMPLE (ii)

Determine the position of the centre of gravity of a solid uniform prism, whose principal cross-section is shown in Fig. 16.17. *Determine whether such a prism can rest with the face* BC *in contact with a horizontal plane.*

(I.S.)

The centre of gravity lies in the section (since it was called the principal section), and from symmetry it is clear that it will lie in the line EF, joining the mid-points of AB and DC.

Draw AH, BK perpendicular to DC.

Then DH = 2, and AH = 2 tan 60° = $2\sqrt{3}$.

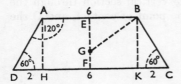

FIG. 16.17

The prism may now be regarded as made up of three prisms, whose principal sections are the two triangles and the rectangle in the figure, and the weights of the whole and parts will be proportional to the areas of ABCD, and the triangles and rectangle. Tabulating areas and distances of centres of gravity from DC.

	Area	*Distance of centre of gravity from* DC
ABCD	$16\sqrt{3}$	x
ABKH	$12\sqrt{3}$	$\sqrt{3}$
ADH	$2\sqrt{3}$	$\frac{2}{3}\sqrt{3}$
BCK	$2\sqrt{3}$	$\frac{2}{3}\sqrt{3}$

Taking moments about DC, we have

$$16\sqrt{3}x = 36+4+4 = 44$$

$$\therefore \qquad x = \frac{44}{16\sqrt{3}} = \frac{11\sqrt{3}}{12}.$$

The centre of gravity is therefore at G in EF, where FG = $\frac{11}{12}\sqrt{3}$

$$\therefore \qquad EG = 2\sqrt{3}-\tfrac{11}{12}\sqrt{3} = \tfrac{13}{12}\sqrt{3}.$$

Now the prism can rest on the face BC, provided ∠CBG is less than a right angle, i.e. provided ∠EBG is greater than 30°.

Now $$\tan EBG = \frac{EG}{EB} = \frac{13\sqrt{3}}{36}$$

and $$\tan 30° = \frac{\sqrt{3}}{3} = \frac{12\sqrt{3}}{36}$$

$$\therefore \qquad\qquad ∠EBG > 30°.$$

Therefore the prism can rest on the face BC.

EXAMPLE (iii)

A uniform cube rests with a face touching the highest point of a fixed rough sphere. Prove from fundamental principles that the equilibrium is stable if the edge of the cube is less than the diameter of the sphere.

Let AB (Fig. 16.18) represent the vertical section through the centre of gravity G of the cube, C the point of contact, and O the centre of the sphere (radius r).

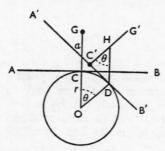

FIG. 16.18

The sphere is assumed to be rough enough to prevent sliding, and we only consider the stability for tilting.

Let the edge of the cube be $2a$, and let A′, C′, B′, G′ represent the positions of A, C, B, G, after tilting through a *small* angle θ, D being the new point of contact.

Now the cube will tend to return to its original position if G′ is to the left of the vertical through D.

Let C′G′ cut this vertical in H.

Since there is no slipping,

$$C'D = \text{arc } CD = r\theta.$$

Also the angle C′HD $= \theta$, and

$$C'H = C'D \cot \theta = r\,\frac{\theta}{\tan \theta}.$$

The equilibrium is therefore stable if

$$r\,\frac{\theta}{\tan \theta} > C'G'.$$

Now when θ is very small the ratio of θ to $\tan \theta$ is approximately unity, and since C′G′ $= a$, the equilibrium is stable if

$$r > a,$$

i.e. if the edge of the cube is less than the diameter of the sphere.

EXAMPLES 16.4

1. A triangular portion is cut from a square by a line parallel to a diagonal. Show that the remainder can stand on the remaining part of either of the cut sides, if that part is 0·5 of the side, but cannot stand if it is 0·4 of the side.   (I.S.)

2. ABCD is a vertical face of a rectangular block, the horizontal face which has BC for an edge being in contact with the ground; BC is 40 cm, CD is 25 cm; E is a point in BC, 15 cm from B. Find the position of a point F in CD, such that the block will be on the point of toppling over when a prism is cut from it by cutting along EF at right angles to the face ABCD.   (H.C.)

3. ABCD is a uniform plane quadrilateral lamina, in which AB is parallel to DC. The length of AB is a and the length of DC is b. Prove that the centre of gravity of the lamina coincides with that of four particles of masses proportional to a, $a+b$, b, $a+b$, placed at A, B, C, D respectively. If AD = BC = c, and $b>a$, find the coordinates of the centre of gravity, referred to rectangular axes, of which one is DA and the other is the perpendicular to DA drawn through D, and show that a uniform prism, which has such a quadrilateral for its cross-section, cannot rest on a horizontal plane with the faces corresponding to BC or AD in contact with the plane, if $2c^2(a+2b)$ is less than b^3-a^3.   (H.C.)

4. ABC is a vertical sheet of metal, A being a right angle and AC in contact with a horizontal plane; D is the mid-point of AC, and the triangle ABD is cut away. Show that the remaining portion of the sheet is just on the point of falling over.

5. A uniform right prism whose cross-section is an isosceles triangle BAC lies on the table with the face containing BC horizontal and in contact with the table; the prism is gradually sliced away by cutting slices parallel to the face in which AB lies, beginning from the edge through C. What fraction of the whole prism can be cut away without the remainder toppling over, AB, AC being the equal sides?   (H.S.C.)

6. ABCD is the section of a cube through its centre, and E is a point in AD. If the part cut off by the plane through EC, perpendicular to the section, be removed, find the distance from AB and AE of the centre of gravity of the remainder. If the block be placed on a horizontal plane, find the least length of AE that the block may not upset.

7. The cross-section of a uniform prism is the figure BDEC, where ABC is an equilateral triangle and D and E are the mid-points of the sides AB and AC. Determine in how many possible positions it may rest with a face in contact with a plane, rough enough to prevent sliding, which is inclined to the horizontal at an angle of 30°; all the cross-sections being in vertical planes through lines of greatest slope of the inclined plane.   (H.S.C.)

8. A regular tetrahedron rests with one face in contact with a plane, rough enough to prevent slipping, inclined at an angle α to the horizontal. Of the face in contact with the plane, one edge is horizontal and above the opposite vertex. Show that $\tan\alpha < 2\sqrt{2}$. (H.S.C.)

9. A solid hemisphere and a solid cylinder have the same radii and are made of the same homogeneous material, and one end of the cylinder is cemented to the base of the hemisphere. The height of the cylinder is $\frac{2}{3}$ of its radius. Show that the centre of gravity of the whole solid is $\frac{1}{48}$ of the radius from the common plane. (I.E.)

10. A hollow vessel, formed by uniformly thin material, is in the form of a frustum of a circular cone and has a flat base, the radius of the mouth being twice that of the base. If the semi-vertical angle of the cone is 30°, determine whether the vessel can rest with its curved surface in contact with a horizontal plane. (H.S.C.)

11. The height of a solid circular cone is three times the radius of its base. Another solid in the form of a hemisphere, of which the base of the cone is the plane boundary, is fastened to the cone. Find the least ratio of the specific gravities of the materials of the hemisphere and cone, if when the combined solid is placed on a horizontal table with the hemispherical surface in contact with the table it cannot be upset. (I.E.)

12. A hollow vessel, the material of which is of the same thickness throughout, consists of a hollow cone closed by a hollow hemisphere described on its base. Find the greatest possible ratio of the height of the cone to the radius of its base if the vessel can rest in stable equilibrium with the hemispherical surface in contact with a horizontal table. (The distance of the centre of gravity of a hollow hemisphere from its centre is half the radius.) (H.S.C.)

13. A pile in the shape of a flight of stairs is formed of n equal uniform cubical blocks, of edge a, each block being displaced a small distance c horizontally with reference to the block below. Determine the position of the centre of gravity of the pile and deduce that the pile must topple over if $(n-1)c > a$. (H.C.)

14. A body of uniform material consists of a solid right circular cone and a solid hemisphere on opposite sides of the same circular base of radius r. Find the greatest possible height of the cone if the body can rest on a horizontal plane in stable equilibrium with the cone uppermost. (C.S.)

15. A table consists of a 1 cm board, 60 cm square, and having at its corners legs of the same material, 60 cm long, and of 2 cm square section. Find the height of the centre of gravity and determine the greatest angle through which the table can be tilted on two legs without being overturned. (I.A.)

16. ABCD is a heavy uniform square plate, and the portion CBH is removed, where H is a point in AB. The remainder is placed with its plane vertical and AH in contact with a smooth horizontal plane. Show that equilibrium will be impossible unless AH : AB is greater than $\frac{1}{2}(\sqrt{3}-1)$. (C.W.B.)

16.17. Centre of gravity of a uniform circular arc

Let ACB (Fig. 16.19) be a circular arc of radius r, subtending an angle 2α at its centre O, and let C be the mid-point of the arc.

From symmetry it is clear that the centre of gravity will lie on OC, since the arc is uniform.

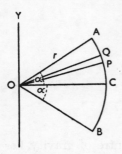

Fig. 16.19

Take OC as x-axis, and OY perpendicular to OC as y-axis.

Let PQ be an element of the arc such that $\angle POC = \theta$, and $\angle POQ = \delta\theta$. The length of the arc PQ is $r\delta\theta$, and its weight is $wr\delta\theta$, where w is the weight per unit of length.

Since the distance of PQ from OY is $r\cos\theta$, the moment of its weight about OY is $r\cos\theta \times wr\delta\theta$ or $wr^2\cos\theta \times \delta\theta$.

The sum of the moments of all the elements of the arc is the integral of this between the limits $\theta = -\alpha$ and $\theta = +\alpha$, i.e. $\int_{-\alpha}^{+\alpha} wr^2 \cos\theta \, d\theta$. The weight of the whole arc is $2wr\alpha$, and if the distance of its centre of gravity from OY is $\bar{x}$ we have, taking moments about OY,

$$2wr\alpha\bar{x} = wr^2 \int_{-\alpha}^{+\alpha} \cos\theta \, d\theta = wr^2 \Big[\sin\theta\Big]_{-\alpha}^{+\alpha} = 2wr^2 \sin\alpha$$

$$\therefore \qquad \bar{x} = r\frac{\sin\alpha}{\alpha}.$$

For a semicircular arc, in which $\alpha = \pi/2$, this becomes $2r/\pi$.

16.18. Centre of gravity of a sector of a circle

Let AOB (Fig. 16.20) be a sector of a circle of radius r whose centre is at O, and let $\angle AOB = 2\alpha$. Let C be the mid-point of the arc AB and OC the bisector of the angle AOB.

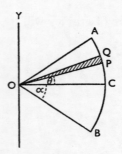

Fig. 16.20

From symmetry it is clear that the centre of gravity lies in OC.

Take OC as x-axis, and OY perpendicular to OC as y-axis.

Let POQ be an elementary sector, such that $\angle POC = \theta$, and $\angle POQ = d\theta$.

The area of this sector is $\frac{1}{2}r^2 \, d\theta$, and its weight is $\frac{1}{2}wr^2 \, d\theta$, where w is the weight per unit area, assumed constant.

Since PQ is very small, OPQ is very approximately a triangle, and its centre of gravity is at a distance $\frac{2}{3}r$ from O.

The distance of this centre of gravity from OY is therefore

$$\tfrac{2}{3}r \cos \theta.$$

The moment of the weight of POQ about OY is

$$\tfrac{2}{3}r \cos \theta \times \tfrac{1}{2}wr^2 \, \delta\theta = \tfrac{1}{3}wr^3 \cos \theta \, \delta\theta.$$

The sum of the moments of all the elementary sectors is

$$\int_{-\alpha}^{+\alpha} \tfrac{1}{3}wr^3 \cos \theta \, \mathrm{d}\theta = \tfrac{1}{3}wr^3 \int_{-\alpha}^{+\alpha} \cos \theta \, \mathrm{d}\theta.$$

The weight of the whole sector is $wr^2\alpha$, and if $\bar{x}$ is the distance of its centre of gravity from OY, then, taking moments about OY, we have

$$wr^2\alpha \times \bar{x} = \tfrac{1}{3}wr^3 \int_{-\alpha}^{+\alpha} \cos \theta \, \mathrm{d}\theta = \tfrac{2}{3}wr^3 \sin \alpha$$

$$\therefore \qquad \bar{x} = \frac{2r}{3} \times \frac{\sin \alpha}{\alpha}.$$

For a complete semicircle, $\alpha = \pi/2$, and the distance of the centre of gravity from the diameter of the semicircle is

$$4r/3\pi.$$

These formulae can also be obtained by making use of the result of the last paragraph. Suppose the area divided into concentric strips of breadth $\mathrm{d}x$. The weight of a strip of radius x is $2wx\alpha \, \mathrm{d}x$, and the distance of its C.G. from OY is $(x \sin \alpha)/\alpha$. Hence, taking moments about OY,

$$wr^2\alpha\bar{x} = \int_0^r 2wx\alpha \times x\frac{\sin \alpha}{\alpha}\mathrm{d}x = 2w \sin \alpha \left[\frac{x^3}{3}\right]_0^r$$

$$= \tfrac{2}{3}wr^3 \sin \alpha$$

$$\therefore \qquad \bar{x} = \frac{2r}{3}\frac{\sin \alpha}{\alpha}.$$

16.19. Centre of gravity of a segment of a circle

This is found most easily by considering the segment as the difference between a sector of a circle and a triangle.

Let ACB (Fig. 16.21) be a uniform segment of a circle of radius r, and O the centre of the circle.

The segment is the difference between the sector OAB and the triangle OAB.

Let $\angle$AOB $= 2\alpha$, and let OC bisect this angle.

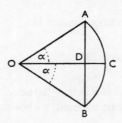

FIG. 16.21

From symmetry we see that the centre of gravity must lie in OC.

If w is the weight per unit area the weight of the sector is $wr^2\alpha$, and that of the triangle $\frac{1}{2}wr^2 \sin 2\alpha$.

Tabulating areas and distances of centres of gravity from O, we get

	Weight	*Distance of C.G. from O*
Sector	$wr^2\alpha$	$\dfrac{2r}{3}\dfrac{\sin \alpha}{\alpha}$
Triangle	$\frac{1}{2}wr^2 \sin 2\alpha$	$\frac{2}{3}r \cos \alpha$
Segment	$wr^2(\alpha - \frac{1}{2}\sin 2\alpha)$	x

Hence, taking moments about O, we have

$$wr^2(\alpha - \tfrac{1}{2}\sin 2\alpha)x = \tfrac{2}{3}wr^3 \sin \alpha - \tfrac{1}{3}wr^3 \sin 2\alpha \cos \alpha$$

$$\therefore \qquad x = \frac{2r}{3}\frac{\sin \alpha - \cos^2 \alpha \sin \alpha}{\alpha - \frac{1}{2}\sin 2\alpha}$$

$$= \frac{4r}{3}\frac{\sin^3\alpha}{2\alpha - \sin 2\alpha}.$$

If we are given the radius of the circle and height of the segment CD it is best to proceed as above and then express α, $\sin \alpha$, etc., in terms of CD and r.

When the segment is a semicircle and $\alpha = \pi/2$ the above result reduces to $4r/3\pi$, as obtained in the last paragraph.

16.20. Centre of gravity of a uniform solid hemisphere

Let ACB (Fig. 16.22) represent a section of the hemisphere perpendicular to the plane base, of which AB is a diameter and O the centre.

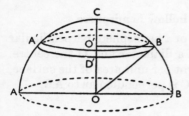

FIG. 16.22

Let r be the radius of the hemisphere, w the weight per unit volume, and C the highest point, so that OC is perpendicular to AB.

Suppose the hemisphere divided into infinitely thin slices parallel to the plane base.

From symmetry it is clear that the centres of gravity of all these slices, and therefore the centre of gravity of the hemisphere, will lie in OC.

If A'D'B' represents one of the slices, of thickness δx, and O' its centre then, if $OO' = x$,

$$O'B' = \sqrt{(r^2 - x^2)}.$$

The volume of the slice is therefore

$$\pi(r^2 - x^2)\,\delta x$$

and its weight is

$$w\pi(r^2 - x^2)\,\delta x.$$

This weight may be supposed concentrated at O', and its moment about O is

$$w\pi x(r^2 - x^2)\,\delta x.$$

Considering all the slices in the same way the sum of their moments about O is

$$\int_0^r w\pi(r^2 x - x^3)\,\mathrm{d}x = w\pi\left[\tfrac{1}{2}r^2 x^2 - \tfrac{1}{4}x^4\right]_0^r$$
$$= \tfrac{1}{4}w\pi r^4.$$

The weight of the whole hemisphere is $\frac{2}{3}\pi wr^3$, and if $\bar{x}$ is the distance of its centre of gravity from O,

$$\frac{2}{3}\pi wr^3\bar{x} = \frac{1}{4}w\pi r^4$$

$$\therefore \qquad \bar{x} = \frac{3}{8}r.$$

16.21. Centre of gravity of a thin hollow hemisphere

Let ACB (Fig. 16.23) be a section of a hemisphere perpendicular to its plane base, of which AB is a diameter and O the centre.

Let r be the radius, w the weight per unit area of the surface, and C the highest point so that OC is perpendicular to AB.

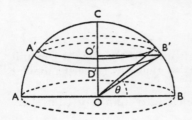

Fig. 16.23

Suppose the surface divided into infinitely narrow bands, such as A'D'B', by planes parallel to the base.

If O' is the centre of A'D'B' and $\angle BOB' = \theta$ the radius of the band O'B' is equal to $r\cos\theta$.

It is clear from symmetry that the centres of gravity of all the bands lie in OC.

The angle subtended by the arc of the band at O is $\delta\theta$, and its breadth is therefore $r\,\delta\theta$.

The whole surface of the band is therefore $2\pi r\cos\theta\, r\,\delta\theta$, and its weight is $2\pi wr^2\cos\theta\,\delta\theta$.

This weight may be supposed to act at O', and its moment about O is therefore

$$r\sin\theta\,2\pi wr^2\cos\theta\,\delta\theta.$$

The sum of the moments of all the bands about O is

$$2\pi wr^3\int_0^{\frac{\pi}{2}} \sin\theta\cos\theta\,d\theta$$

$$= 2\pi wr^3\left[\frac{\sin^2\theta}{2}\right]_0^{\frac{\pi}{2}} = \pi wr^3.$$

The weight of the whole surface is $2\pi r^2 w$, and if $\bar{x}$ is the distance of its centre of gravity from O,

$$2\pi r^2 w \times \bar{x} = \pi w r^3$$

$$\therefore \qquad \bar{x} = \frac{r}{2}.$$

16.22. The centre of gravity of a portion or zone of the surface between two planes parallel to the base in positions such that $\theta = \alpha$, $\theta = \beta$ can be obtained by evaluating the weight and moment integrals of the last paragraph between the limits α and β instead of 0 and $\pi/2$.

The weight of an elementary zone is $2\pi w r^2 \cos\theta\,\delta\theta$.

The weight of the zone between $\theta = \alpha$ and $\theta = \beta$ is

$$2\pi w r^2 \int_\alpha^\beta \cos\theta\,d\theta = 2\pi w r^2(\sin\beta - \sin\alpha).$$

But $r(\sin\beta - \sin\alpha)$ is the distance between the cutting planes, i.e. h, the height of the zone.

$$\therefore \qquad \text{the weight is } 2\pi w r h.$$

The moment about O of the weight of an elementary zone is $2\pi w r^3 \sin\theta\cos\theta\,\delta\theta$.

The sum of these moments is

$$2\pi w r^3 \int_\alpha^\beta \sin\theta\cos\theta\,d\theta = \pi w r^3\,(\sin^2\beta - \sin^2\alpha),$$

$$= \pi w r^2 h(\sin\beta + \sin\alpha).$$

Hence, if x is the distance of the centre of gravity of the zone from O

$$x = \frac{\pi w r^2 h(\sin\beta + \sin\alpha)}{2\pi w r h},$$

$$= \tfrac{1}{2}r(\sin\beta + \sin\alpha).$$

Now $r\sin\beta + r\sin\alpha$ is the sum of the distances of the cutting planes from the base, so that $\tfrac{1}{2}r(\sin\beta + \sin\alpha)$ is the distance of the plane half-way between them.

The centre of gravity of the zone is therefore half-way between the planes which cut it off from the sphere.

16.23. The position of the centre of gravity of a complete hemispherical surface, and of a zone bounded by planes parallel to the base, can both be deduced from the known geometrical fact that the area of each elementary band or zone cut off by planes parallel to the base is equal to the corresponding band which they cut off from the circumscribing cylinder. The centre of gravity of the spherical surfaces is therefore at the same height as that of the circumscribing cylinder, i.e. half-way between the base and vertex in the case of the complete hemisphere, and half-way between the bounding planes in the case of a zone.

16.24. EXAMPLE

Find the centre of gravity of a uniform parabolic plate whose boundary consists of the curve $y^2 = ax$ and the line $x = b$. Find also the position of the centre of gravity of the solid formed by revolution of the above area about the axis of x.

Let ABMC (Fig. 16.24) represent the plate, AX the axis of the parabola (also the axis of x), and $AM = b$.

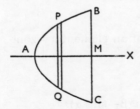

Fig. 16.24

It is clear from symmetry that the centre of gravity lies in AM. The area of a strip PQ parallel to BC, of breadth δx and distant x from A, is $2y\ \delta x$ or $2a^{\frac{1}{2}}x^{\frac{1}{2}}\ \delta x$, and its weight is $2wa^{\frac{1}{2}}x^{\frac{1}{2}}\ \delta x$, where w is the weight per unit area.

In this case we cannot write down the weight of the whole plate, but the value is obtained by integrating $2wa^{\frac{1}{2}}x^{\frac{1}{2}}\ \delta x$ between $x = 0$ and $x = b$. If W is the weight of the plate,

$$W = 2wa^{\frac{1}{2}}\int_0^b x^{\frac{1}{2}}\ \mathrm{d}x = \tfrac{4}{3}wa^{\frac{1}{2}}\left[\ x^{\frac{3}{2}}\ \right]_0^b = \tfrac{4}{3}wa^{\frac{1}{2}}b^{\frac{3}{2}}.$$

The weight of each strip acts at its mid-point, and the moment of the weight of PQ about A is

$$2wa^{\frac{1}{2}}x^{\frac{3}{2}}\ \delta x.$$

The sum of the moments about A is

$$2wa^{\frac{1}{2}}\int_0^b x^{\frac{3}{2}}\,dx = \tfrac{4}{5}wa^{\frac{1}{2}}\left[x^{\frac{5}{2}}\right]_0^b = \tfrac{4}{5}wa^{\frac{1}{2}}b^{\frac{5}{2}}.$$

If $\bar{x}$ is the distance of the centre of gravity from A,

$$\tfrac{4}{3}wa^{\frac{1}{2}}b^{\frac{3}{2}}\times\bar{x} = \tfrac{4}{5}wa^{\frac{1}{2}}b^{\frac{5}{2}},$$
$$\therefore \qquad \bar{x} = \tfrac{3}{5}b.$$

When the area is rotated about AX, the section of the solid so formed by a plane perpendicular to AX will be circular. Dividing the solid into circular slices by planes perpendicular to AX, the volume of a slice distant x from A will be

$$\pi y^2\,\delta x = \pi a x\,\delta x$$

and its weight $= \pi w a x\,\delta x$.

The weight of the whole solid, W, is given by

$$W = \pi w a\int_0^b x\,dx = \tfrac{1}{2}\pi w a b^2.$$

The weight of each slice acts at its centre, and the moment about A of the weight of the slice distant x from A is

$$\pi w a x^2\,\delta x.$$

Hence, the sum of the moments about A is

$$\pi w a\int_0^b x^2\,dx = \tfrac{1}{3}\pi w a b^3.$$

If $\bar{x}$ is the distance of the centre of gravity from A,

$$\tfrac{1}{2}\pi w a b^2\times\bar{x} = \tfrac{1}{3}\pi w a b^3$$
$$\therefore \qquad \bar{x} = \tfrac{2}{3}b.$$

EXAMPLES 16.5

1. Find the centre of gravity of a uniform semicircular disc.

2. A piece of metal, of uniform thickness, consists of a semicircular portion ABC with diameter AC, and a triangular portion ACD having AD = CD. Find the ratio of the height of the triangle to the radius of the semicircle in order that, when placed on a smooth horizontal plane with the plane ABCD vertical, the metal may rest in equilibrium whatever point of the circular arc may be in contact with the horizontal plane.   (Ex.)

3. Find the centre of gravity of a thin wire in the form of a circular arc. A thin strip of metal of uniform width and thickness has part of it bent into the form of a semi-cylinder of radius r, leaving a plane piece of length l tangential to the semi-cylinder along one of its edges. Show that the body can rest with the plane piece in contact with a horizontal plane provided that l is greater than $2r$.   (I.E.)

4. A solid body consists of a solid hemisphere surmounting a cylinder of the same radius whose height is three times the radius of its base. It is placed with its plane face in contact with a rough plane, and the inclination of the plane to the horizontal is gradually increased. Prove that it will slide down the plane without toppling over, provided that the coefficient of friction between the body and the plane is less than $\frac{44}{81}$.   (I.E.)

5. A uniform solid circular cylinder is cut in two by a plane through its axis. One half is placed with its curved surface in contact with an inclined plane rough enough to prevent slipping. The line of contact is perpendicular to the line of greatest slope. Show that there are two positions of equilibrium if the inclination of the plane to the horizontal lies between $\sin^{-1}(4/3\pi)$ and $\tan^{-1}(4/3\pi)$, and one position if it is less than the latter angle.   (H.C.)

6. A chimney of brickwork 45 cm thick has an external diameter of 3·9 m at the base, and 2·7 m at the top, which is 30 m above the base. Show that the centre of gravity of the chimney is about 1·05 m below the mid-point of the axis.   (C.S.)

7. Show that the centre of gravity of a uniform semicircular rod is at a distance from the centre equal to $2/\pi$ times the radius. A circular disc, whose weight per unit area is σr, where σ is a constant and r the distance from the centre, is divided into two by a diameter. Find the centre of gravity of either half.   (C.S.)

8. Find by integration the position of the centre of gravity of a uniform solid right circular cone.

9. Prove that the centre of gravity of a uniform thin hemispherical cup of radius r is at a distance $r/2$ from the centre. Such a cup stands on a circular base of the same material, thickness, and radius as the cup, while the intervening stem is of length equal to the radius of the cup, and its weight is one-quarter of that of the hemisphere. Find the height of the centre of gravity above the base.   (I.S.)

10. Show that the centre of mass of a semicircular lamina of radius r is at a distance $4r/3\pi$ from the centre. A solid right circular cylinder is cut into two equal parts by a plane through its axis.

One of these parts is placed with its curved surface on a rough plane, which is inclined to the horizontal at an angle θ, with its generators horizontal. What will be the inclination of the rectangular plane face of the solid to the horizontal when it rests in equilibrium, assuming the plane to be rough enough to prevent slipping? (H.S.D.)

11. Assuming that the centre of gravity of a uniform circular arc subtending an angle 2θ at the centre of a circle of radius a is at a distance $(a \sin \theta)/\theta$ from the centre, find the centre of gravity of the uniform sector bounded by that arc and the radii to its extremities. Find the centre of gravity of the segment cut off by a chord equal to the radius. (I.E.)

12. Find the centre of gravity of a hemispherical surface. A hemispherical bowl of weight W is placed with its spherical surface on a smooth horizontal plane; what weight must be placed on the rim in order that the bowl may rest with its plane surface inclined at $\alpha°$ to the horizontal? (H.S.D.)

13. A uniformly tapering circular spar is 15 m long. The butt diameter is 35 cm and the top diameter is 25 cm. Find the mass of the spar and the position of the centre of mass, assuming the wood has a mass of 700 kg m^{-3}.

14. A uniform wire bent in the form of a semicircle hangs in a vertical plane over a rough horizontal peg and is just on the point of slipping when the line joining its ends makes an angle of 30° with the horizontal. Find the coefficient of friction for the wire and the peg.

15. A solid uniform hemisphere rests with its convex surface in contact with a rough inclined plane; show that the greatest possible inclination of the plane to the horizontal is $\sin^{-1} \frac{3}{8}$.

16. If a solid uniform hemisphere rest in equilibrium with its curved surface in contact with a rough plane inclined to the horizontal at an angle $\sin^{-1} \frac{1}{8}$, find the inclination of the plane base of the hemisphere to the horizontal.

REVISION EXAMPLES E

1. ABCDE is a chain formed of four uniform equal heavy rods freely jointed at B, C, and D. The ends A and E of the chain are hinged to two fixed points in the same horizontal line so that the chain hangs symmetrically with C as its lowest point. If θ is the angle of inclination of the upper pair of rods to the horizontal in the equilibrium position and ϕ the corresponding angle for the lower pair, prove that $\tan \theta = 3 \tan \phi$.

If, instead of being hinged, A and E are attached to small rings able to slide along a fixed rough horizontal rod, determine the coefficient of friction given that in limiting equilibrium $\theta = 60°$.

(L.A.)

2. Two equally rough parallel bars are each fixed horizontally, the distance between them being l and their plane being inclined to the horizontal at an angle θ. A uniform heavy rod rests in contact with both bars passing over the upper and under the lower one. If the rod is at right angles to the bars and in limiting equilibrium, show by consideration of force moments, or otherwise, that the centre of gravity of the rod must be higher than the upper bar. Deduce that the length of the rod is at least

$$l(\mu+\tan\theta)/\mu$$

where μ is the coefficient of friction.

(L.A.)

3. Two small rings, each of mass m, are threaded on a rough straight rod which is fixed at an inclination α to the horizontal. The rings are connected by a light inelastic string to the mid-point of which is attached a particle of mass m. The system is in equilibrium, the angle between the two parts of the string being $2\theta(>2\alpha)$. By considering the equilibrium of the higher ring and of the particle show that, if μ is the coefficient of friction between either ring and the rod,

$$\mu \geqslant \left(\frac{3\tan\alpha+\tan\theta}{\tan\alpha+3\tan\theta}\right)\tan\theta.$$

(L.A.)

4. A uniform rod of length $2l$ and weight W is smoothly hinged at one end to a horizontal plane. It is supported in an inclined position by a cylinder of radius r which has one generator on the plane and at right angles to the vertical plane through the rod, the point of contact being the mid-point of the rod. The coefficient of friction between the rod and the cylinder is μ and the horizontal plane is sufficiently rough to prevent the cylinder sliding on it. Prove that if the cylinder is about to roll, $\mu = r/l$. Find the reaction at the hinge.

(L.A.)

5. A uniform ladder AB, of weight W, leans at an angle α to the vertical against a rough wall BC with its other end on a rough horizontal floor AC, the coefficient of friction at each point of contact being $\mu(<\tan\frac{1}{2}\alpha)$. The mid-point of the ladder is attached to the point C by means of a taut string. If the ladder is on the point of slipping, prove that the tension in the string is

$$\frac{W}{2\mu}\left\{(1-\mu^2)\sin\alpha-2\mu\cos\alpha\right\}$$

and find the normal components of the reactions at A and B.

(C.W.B.)

6. Explain the term 'angle of friction'. A rectangular block rests in limiting equilibrium with one edge on the floor and another edge in contact with a vertical wall, the angle of friction λ being the same at both contacts. Prove that, if the cross-section at right angles to the wall is a rectangle, ABCD, with the corner A on the floor and B on the wall, then the inclination θ of AB to the vertical is given by

$$\tan \theta = \tan 2\lambda + \frac{BC}{AB} \sec 2\lambda. \qquad (H.C.)$$

7. Explain the terms coefficient of limiting friction, angle of limiting friction, and the relation between them. Two equal light rods AB, BC, of length $2a$, rigidly joined at right angles to each other at B, are placed astride a fixed rough horizontal circular cylinder of radius a, so that they are equally inclined to the vertical. Weights w, $W(W>w)$ are hung from A and C respectively, W being adjusted so that slipping is about to take place. Find the normal reactions of the cylinder on the rods and prove that

$$W/w = (1+\mu+\mu^2)/(1-\mu+\mu^2),$$

where $\mu(<1)$ is the coefficient of limiting friction.   (H.S.D.)

8. The diagram (Fig. 16.25) shows a smoothly jointed framework of light rods AB, BC, AC, CD smoothly pivoted at A and D to a vertical wall. A weight of mass 100 kg is suspended at B and the

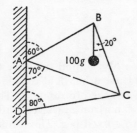

Fig. 16.25

system is at rest in a vertical plane. Find the stresses in all the rods, distinguishing tension from compression, and find also the forces exerted on the wall at A and D.   (I.S.)

9. The framework shown in the diagram (Fig. 16.26) consists of five light rods freely jointed at their ends. A load of 2 units is hung from D and the framework is kept in equilibrium, with AD horizontal and AB vertical, by a horizontal force at A and a force at B.

Calculate these forces and determine, graphically or otherwise, the forces in the rods, stating which rods are in tension and which in compression.   (L.A.)

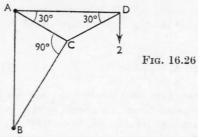

Fig. 16.26

10. The diagram (Fig. 16.27) shows a framework of five freely jointed light rods AB, BC, CD, DA, AC in the form of a parallelogram ABCD in a vertical plane with AB horizontal, and acted on by vertical forces, as shown, at the four corners. Prove that the frame is in equilibrium, and find graphically the stresses in all the rods, distinguishing tension from compression.   (I.S.)

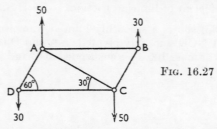

Fig. 16.27

11. Six light rods of equal length are smoothly jointed together to form a regular hexagon OABCDE, and three other light rods join OB, OC, OD. Particles of weight w are attached to A and E. The system rests in a vertical plane with OC horizontal (A vertically above E), the point O being fastened to a fixed peg. The framework is kept in position by means of a string attached to B, whose line of action is along CB produced. Find the tension of the string. Find the stresses in AO, OB, OC, OD, OE, and state whether these rods are struts or ties.   (H.C.)

12. ABCD is a rhombus of smoothly jointed light rods suspended from a point O by a light vertical rod OA smoothly jointed at A and equal strings OB, OD, the diagonal AC being vertical, and ABC = 120°, BOD = 30°. Find graphically, or calculate, the stresses in the rods and strings when a weight W is suspended from C, and indicate which of them are tensions.   (H.C.)

13. The diagram (Fig. 16.28) represents a framework of seven smoothly jointed light rods hinged to a fixed point at A. The outer rods form a square, and A, C, B are collinear, with AC = 3CB. Determine, graphically or otherwise, the stress in each rod when a force P is applied at B as shown, distinguishing between tensions and thrusts.   (H.C.)

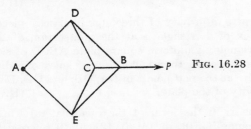

Fig. 16.28

14. Three light rods equal in length are smoothly jointed together at their ends to form an equilateral triangle ABC. The frame hangs freely at rest from A and supports loads of mass 30 kg and 10 kg at B and C respectively. Find graphically or otherwise the inclination of BC to the horizontal and the forces in the rods.

                                              (L.A.)

15. Six equal light uniform rods AB, BC, CD, DE, EF, FA are freely hinged together and suspended from the point A. Light rods FB, BE, EC, of such lengths that ABCDEF is a regular hexagon, are inserted and are freely hinged to the hexagon at their ends. By drawing, find the force in each of the nine rods when weights of mass 10 kg are suspended from each of C, D, E.   (L.A.)

16. The framework shown in the diagram (Fig. 16.29) consists of seven equal light rods freely jointed together. It is in equilibrium in a vertical plane with AB horizontal, there being vertical supports at A and B and vertical loads, as indicated, at D and E.

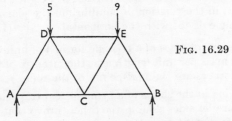

Fig. 16.29

Find the reactions at the supports and the forces in the rods CD, CE, and DE, stating which of these rods are in tension and which in compression.

                                              (L.A.)

17. Find the centres of gravity of: (i) a uniform triangular lamina; (ii) a uniform thin hollow right circular cone. The cone has a base made of the same material. When it is suspended from a point O on the rim the diameter of the base and the generator through O make equal angles with the vertical. Find the vertical angle of the cone. (H.C.)

18. Show that the centre of gravity of three equal particles placed one at each vertex of a triangle is at the intersection of the medians of the triangle. A uniform square plate ABCD of side $2a$ and centre O is pierced by three small circular holes, of radius b, whose centres are at the mid-points of OA, OB, and OD. Find the centre of gravity of the plate. (H.C.)

19. A uniform lamina is in the form of the quadrilateral whose vertices are the points $(4, 0)$, $(5, 0)$, $(0, 12)$, $(0, 3)$ referred to rectangular axes. Find the coordinates of the centre of mass of the lamina.

Find also the coordinates of the centre of mass of a uniform wire bent into the form of the perimeter of the quadrilateral. (L.A.)

20. Prove that the centre of gravity of a uniform semicircular lamina of radius a is at a distance $4a/3\pi$ from its centre.

AOB is the base of a uniform semicircular lamina of radius $2a$, O being its centre. A semicircular lamina of radius a and base AO is cut away and the remainder suspended freely from A. Find the inclination of AOB to the vertical in the equilibrium position. (L.A.)

21. Show that the centre of gravity of a thin uniform hemispherical shell is at the mid-point of the radius of symmetry. A thin hemispherical shell of weight W rests with its curved surface on a horizontal plane. To a point on the rim a particle of weight $\frac{1}{2}W$ is attached. Show that, in the position of equilibrium the plane of the rim makes an angle of $45°$ with the horizontal. (I.S.)

22. (i) Show that the centre of mass of a triangle formed of uniform rods of the same mass per unit length is at the incentre of the triangle whose corners are the mid-points of the rods.

(ii) If a uniform lamina in the shape of a symmetrical trapezium has one of its parallel sides double the other, prove that its centre of mass is distant from the centre of mass of four equal particles situated at the corners of the trapezium, by a distance equal to one-eighteenth of that between the two parallel sides. (H.S.D.)

23. Show that the centre of gravity of a uniform solid hemisphere of radius a is at a distance $3a/8$ from the centre of the base. A uniform cube is attached by one of its faces to the base of a uniform hemisphere, a diagonal of this face of the cube being a diameter of the base of the hemisphere. If ρ_1 be the density of the material of the hemisphere and ρ_2 of the material of the cube, show that the combined solid will be in equilibrium with any point of the curved surface of the hemisphere in contact with a horizontal plane if $\pi\rho_1 = 8\rho_2$. (I.S.)

24. The central cross-section of a solid right prism is a trapezium ABCD in which A and D are right angles, $AD = CD = a$ and $AB = b$. Find the distances of the centre of mass of the solid from AB and AD.

    Show that if the solid can stand at rest with the face through AB on a horizontal plane, then the least possible value of b/a is $\frac{1}{2}(\sqrt{3}-1)$. (L.A.)

25. A hollow vessel made of uniform material of negligible thickness is in the form of a right circular cone of surface density ρ mounted on a hemisphere of surface density σ whose radius is equal to that of the circular rim of the cone. If the vessel can just rest with a generator of the cone in contact with a smooth horizontal plane, prove that the semi-vertical angle α of the cone is given by the equation

    $$\rho(\cot^2\alpha+3) = 3\sigma(\cos\alpha-2\sin\alpha). \qquad \text{(L.A.)}$$

26. Show that the centroid of a thin hollow hemispherical shell is at the mid-point of the radius of symmetry.

    If this hemisphere rests in equilibrium with its curved surface in contact with a plane inclined to the horizontal at an angle α and sufficiently rough to prevent sliding, prove that α must be less than or equal to $30°$. (L.A.)

27. A solid consists of a uniform right circular cone of density ρ, radius r, and height $4r$, mounted on a uniform hemisphere of density σ and radius r, so that the plane faces coincide. Show that the distance of the centre of mass of the whole solid from the common plane face is

    $$\frac{r}{8}\left[\frac{16\rho-3\sigma}{2\rho+\sigma}\right].$$

    If $\rho = \sigma$ and the solid is suspended freely by a string attached to a point on the rim of the common plane face, find the inclination of the axis of the cone to the vertical. (L.A.)

28. A uniform solid consists of a cylinder of radius r and height r surmounted by a hemisphere of radius r, the centre of the plane face of the hemisphere being on the axis of the cylinder. The solid rests with its plane face on a rough plane which is slowly tilted from a horizontal position until equilibrium is broken. Show that the body will slide and not topple if the coefficient of friction is less than 20/17. (L.A.)

29. Prove that if a rigid body is in equilibrium under the action of three coplanar forces, then the lines of action of these forces are either parallel or concurrent.

A hollow conical vessel, of internal height h and vertical angle 90°, is fixed with its axis vertical and vertex downwards. A smooth uniform rod rests in equilibrium with one end inside and the other end outside the vessel. If the rod is inclined at an angle θ ($<45°$) to the horizontal, show that its length is

$$\frac{4h}{\cos \theta(\cos \theta + \sin \theta)^2}.$$ (L.A.)

30. Find the position of the centre of mass of a uniform solid hemisphere of radius a.

Prove that the centre of mass of a uniform hemispherical shell, whose inner and outer radii are a and b, is at a distance

$$\frac{3}{8}\frac{(a+b)(a^2+b^2)}{a^2+ab+b^2}$$

from the centre and deduce the position of the centre of mass of a thin hemispherical shell. (L.A.)

31. A uniform solid sphere is divided into two parts by a spherical surface of the same radius, the centre of the spherical surface being on the surface of the solid sphere. Find the position of the centre of mass of the larger portion into which the solid sphere is divided.

Show that, when this portion hangs at rest from a point on its circular rim, its axis of symmetry is inclined at an angle θ to the horizontal, where $\tan \theta = 16\sqrt{3}/33$. (L.A.)

32. There are three pulleys in each block of a 'block and tackle'. The rope is attached to the fixed block, passes round each pulley, and the free end comes off a pulley of the fixed block. Find the effort needed to raise a load of 60 N if the weight of the movable block is negligible and the efficiency is 63 per cent. (I.S.)

33. In a machine of velocity ratio r, the applied force P is connected with the load W by the equation $P = a+bW$, where a and b are positive constants. Prove that the efficiency increases with the

load from 0 to $1/br$ as a limit. If the efficiency for an applied force P_2 is double that for an applied force P_1, prove that

$$\frac{2}{P_1} - \frac{1}{P_2} = \frac{1}{a}.$$ (H.S.C.)

34. The diagram (Fig. 16.30) indicates a system of frictionless pulleys by means of which an effort P raises a load W; pulleys A, B are movable and of mass 2 and 3 kg respectively, while C is fixed. What is the *velocity ratio* of this system? Find the *mechanical advantage* and the *efficiency* when a load of mass 50 kg is being raised. If there were n movable pulleys, each of weight w, what effort would raise a load W?   (I.S).

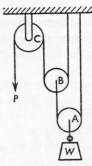

Fig. 16.30

35. When lifting a load the mechanical advantage of a machine is given by the formula $4 - 4w/(W+w)$, where w is a constant and W the load. If the velocity ratio of the machine is 5, find expressions in terms of w and W for the effort and the efficiency and show that the latter approaches the value $\frac{4}{5}$ as W increases. If the machine consists of two suitable pulley blocks, draw a clear diagram to show their arrangement and the run of the connecting rope. Suggest an interpretation of w.   (H.S.C.)

36. The screw of a screw-jack is rotated by an arm, the end of which describes a circle of radius 90 cm, and the load is raised 0·6 cm by one complete turn of the screw. It is found that to lift a load of 500 kg a force of 20 N must be applied to the end of the arm, while to lift 1000 kg a force of 36 N must be applied. Assuming the law of the machine is of the form $P = aW + b$, where a and b are constants, find the force, P, required to raise a load, W, of 2000 kg. Calculate the efficiency of the jack when W equals the weight of 1, 2, 3 Mg, and show that it is always less than $49/48\pi$. Sketch the graph of the efficiency against the load.

CHAPTER SEVENTEEN

VECTORS

17.1. Throughout this book use has been made of vector notation and in some measure of vector methods. We shall now collect together in this chapter all the vector algebra that has been used earlier, and develop it further.

17.2. A *scalar* quantity is one which is completely determined by a single number, its magnitude. It has no intrinsic reference to direction in space. For example, mass, length, time, energy, temperature are all scalars.

A *vector* has magnitude, in the ordinary algebraic sense, as well as direction in space. Two quantities, its magnitude and direction, are needed to specify it completely. For example, force, velocity, acceleration, momentum are all vectors.

The simplest vector is a displacement of a particle, or a displacement of translation of a rigid body, in space. If a particle is displaced from a point P to a point P' the displacement is specified by the vector **PP'**; its magnitude is PP' and its direction from P to P'.

All vectors can be represented by a line such as PP'. It is often convenient, however, to denote a vector by a single letter such as **a**, in which case we denote its magnitude by a.

The magnitude of any vector **AB** is sometimes called its modulus and is denoted by $|AB|$.

There is a vector algebra analogous to the ordinary scalar algebra of positive and negative numbers. This we will now develop formally.

17.3. Equality of vectors

Two vectors **a** and **b** are said to be equal if they have the same magnitude *and* the same direction in space.

We write $\mathbf{a} = \mathbf{b}$, and this implies that $a = b$ and that the vectors are parallel and similiarly directed. Strictly this definition of equality refers only to free vectors, and not to vectors localised in a line (such as forces acting on a rigid body).

17.4 Addition and subtraction of vectors

The sum of any two vectors of the same kind represented by **OP** and **PQ** is defined as a vector represented by **OQ**. We write **OP+PQ = OQ**.

This addition can always be done graphically, that is, by drawing the triangle OPQ (Fig. 17.1).

It will be noted that OP+PQ $\geqslant$ OQ.

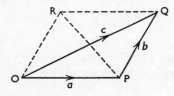

FIG. 17.1

Denoting **OP** by **a**, **PQ** by **b** and **OQ** by **c** we write

$$a+b = c.$$

Complete the parallelogram OPQR. Then from the definition of equality we have

$$OR = PQ = b$$

and $$RQ = OP = a.$$

But, $$OR+RQ = OQ$$

$\therefore$ $$b+a = c.$$

Hence, $$b+a = a+b$$

which establishes the *commutative law* of addition for vectors.

The special case when **a** and **b** are such that Q and O coincide is of some importance. In this case OQ is zero, and hence

$$a+b = OQ = 0.$$

A zero vector has zero magnitude; strictly it is represented by a point and has no direction.

If **a+b = 0** we write **b** = −**a**, that is, −**a** is a vector of magnitude a, parallel to the vector **a** but in the opposite direction.

Similarly, since
$$OP+PO = 0$$
we write
$$PO = -OP.$$
Quite generally
$$LM = -ML.$$

From Fig. 10.1 we may write
$$RP = RO+OP$$
$$= -OR+OP$$
$$= -b+a$$
$$= a-b.$$
Similarly,
$$PR = b-a.$$

We note that the two diagonals of a parallelogram represent the sum and difference of the vectors represented by the adjacent sides.

The consistency of these rules of addition and subtraction might be illustrated in various ways. We shall show later that some geometrical proofs may be based on them.

17.5. The addition of any number of vectors **a**, **b**, **c**, **d**, . . . may be carried out by a repeated application of the above law of addition. This is indicated in Fig. 17.2.

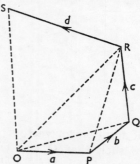

FIG. 17.2

We draw OP, PQ, QR, . . . to represent the vectors **a**, **b**, **c**, . . . respectively.

Then
$$a+b = OQ$$
∴
$$(a+b)+c = OQ+QR$$
$$= OR$$
and so on until the whole addition has been completed.

It is clear that

$$OR = OP + PR$$
$$= a + (b + c)$$

and hence

$$(a + b) + c = a + (b + c).$$

This shows that the order in which the vectors are added does not affect the sum, and so the brackets are unnecessary. This is referred to as the *associative law* of addition.

We write the sum of the vectors simply as

$$a + b + c + d + \dots$$

It also follows from the commutative law that the order in which the vectors are written does not matter.

17.6. In the special case when $a = b = c = d = \dots$

we get $a + b = a + a$, which we write $2a$.

Also, $a + b + c = a + a + a$, which we write $3a$.

Indeed, na, where n is a positive scalar quantity, is defined as a vector in the same direction as a but of magnitude na (Fig. 17.3).

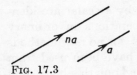

FIG. 17.3

If n is negative, say $-m$ where m is a positive scalar quantity, then $na = -ma$ which is the vector ma reversed in direction, that is, a vector in the opposite direction to a and of magnitude ma.

It follows that a unit vector in the direction of a can be written as $\dfrac{1}{a} a$. The notation $\hat{a}$ is sometimes used for this unit vector. Thus

$$\hat{a} = \frac{1}{a} a \quad \text{or} \quad a = a\hat{a}.$$

17.7. Further, we can show, if **a** and **b** are any two vectors and n is a scalar quantity, that

$$n(\mathbf{a}+\mathbf{b}) = n\mathbf{a}+n\mathbf{b}.$$

If OP (Fig. 17.4) represents **a**, then $OP_1 = nOP$ represents $n\mathbf{a}$. Also if PQ represented **b** and if P_1Q_1 is drawn parallel to PQ and such that $P_1Q_1 = nPQ$, then P_1Q_1 represents $n\mathbf{b}$.

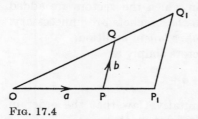

FIG. 17.4

Thus, $OP_1/OP = P_1Q_1/PQ = n$, and hence Q_1 lies on OQ produced and is such that $OQ_1/OQ = n$.

$\therefore$ $$OQ_1 = nOQ$$

$\therefore$ $$OP_1+P_1Q_1 = n(OP+PQ)$$

$\therefore$ $$n\mathbf{a}+n\mathbf{b} = n(\mathbf{a}+\mathbf{b}).$$

Figure 17.4 has been drawn corresponding to a positive value of n, but the proof holds for negative values of n too.

17.8. It will be noted that the rules for vectors which govern addition, subtraction, and multiplication by a scalar are identical with the rules governing these operations in ordinary algebra. They are easy to apply to vectors, for no new methods of manipulation have to be learnt. They have been used from time to time as seemed appropriate throughout this book, and numerous examples of their usefulness have been given. They have, however, a wider range of application: in geometry, for instance, vector methods lead to concise and even elegant proofs. A simple example was given earlier in paragraph 1.12; others are given below.

EXAMPLE (i)

Prove that the diagonals of a parallelogram bisect one another.

Let S be the point of intersection of the diagonals of the parallelogram OPQR (Fig. 17.5). Let **OP** = **a** and **OR** = **b**.

Then,
$$\mathbf{OS} = k\mathbf{OQ} \text{ where } k = \text{OS/OQ}$$
$$= k(\mathbf{a}+\mathbf{b}).$$

Hence,
$$\mathbf{SP} = \mathbf{SO}+\mathbf{OP}$$
$$= -k(\mathbf{a}+\mathbf{b})+\mathbf{a}$$
$$= (1-k)\mathbf{a}-k\mathbf{b}.$$

But,
$$\mathbf{SP} = m\mathbf{RP} \text{ where } m = \text{SP/RP}$$
$$= m(\mathbf{a}-\mathbf{b}).$$

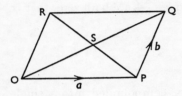

FIG. 17.5

Comparing these two expressions for **SP**, it follows that
$$1-k = m = k$$

Hence,
$$k = m = \tfrac{1}{2}.$$

Hence,
$$\mathbf{OS} = \tfrac{1}{2}\mathbf{OQ} \text{ and } \mathbf{SP} = \tfrac{1}{2}\mathbf{RP},$$

that is, the diagonals bisect one another.

EXAMPLE (ii)
Prove vectorially that if PQ *is drawn parallel to the side* BC *of a triangle* ABC *and cuts* AB, AC *at* P, Q, *then* AP/AB = AQ/AC.

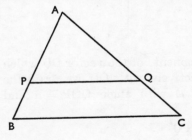

FIG. 17.6

Since PQ, Fig. 17.6, is parallel to BC, we can write
$$\mathbf{PQ} = k\mathbf{BC}$$
where
$$k = \text{PQ/BC}.$$

But $\mathbf{PQ} = \mathbf{PA} + \mathbf{AQ}$

and $\mathbf{BC} = \mathbf{BA} + \mathbf{AC}$

∴ $\mathbf{PA} + \mathbf{AQ} = k\mathbf{BA} + k\mathbf{AC}$

∴ $\mathbf{PA} - k\mathbf{BA} = k\mathbf{AC} - \mathbf{AQ}$

∴ $\left(\dfrac{\mathrm{PA}}{\mathrm{BA}} - k\right)\mathbf{BA} = \left(k - \dfrac{\mathrm{AQ}}{\mathrm{AC}}\right)\mathbf{AC}.$

But $\mathbf{BA}$ and $\mathbf{AC}$ are *any* two vectors, and hence this result is only possible if the coefficients $\dfrac{\mathrm{PA}}{\mathrm{BA}} - k$ and $k - \dfrac{\mathrm{AQ}}{\mathrm{AC}}$ are both zero, that is, $k = \mathrm{PA}/\mathrm{BA} = \mathrm{AQ}/\mathrm{AC}.$

Hence $\mathrm{AP}/\mathrm{AB} = \mathrm{AQ}/\mathrm{AC}.$

17.9. Components of a vector

Since two vectors can be added or compounded into a single vector, so conversely any vector can be split up, or resolved, into two vectors; they are known as its *components*.

Any vector represented by OQ can be resolved into two vectors, **OP** and **PQ**, merely by drawing any triangle of which OQ is one side, or by drawing a parallelogram OPQR, of which OQ is a diagonal. This can be done in an infinite number of ways.

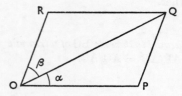

Fɪɢ. 17.7

Thus if we require the components of the vector **OQ** which make angles of α and β respectively with OQ we draw the parallelogram OPQR (Fig. 17.7) with angle QOP = α and angle QOR = β.

Then $\mathbf{OQ} = \mathbf{OP} + \mathbf{PQ}$

and $\dfrac{\mathrm{OP}}{\sin\beta} = \dfrac{\mathrm{PQ}}{\sin\alpha} = \dfrac{\mathrm{OQ}}{\sin(\alpha+\beta)}$

∴ $\mathrm{OP} = \mathrm{OQ}\,\sin\beta/\sin(\alpha+\beta)$

and $\mathrm{PQ} = \mathrm{OQ}\,\sin\alpha/\sin(\alpha+\beta).$

These are the magnitudes of the components of the vector in the specified directions.

The special case when the components of the vector are perpendicular frequently occurs and should be noticed.

If $\alpha+\beta = 90°$, then

$$OP = OQ \cos \alpha \text{ and } PQ = OQ \sin \alpha.$$

17.10. Since each component of a vector can in turn be resolved into two components, it follows that by repeated application of the addition law a vector can be resolved into any number of components.

Thus a vector **OQ** can be divided into n components by drawing a polygon of $(n+1)$ sides, of which OQ is one side. Moreover, the polygon need not be a plane polygon. There is an infinite number of sets of components of this kind.

17.11. It is sometimes convenient to use components of a vector parallel to certain chosen axes of coordinates.

If P is a point with coordinates (x, y) (Fig. 10.8) the position

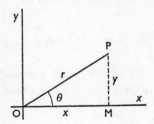

FIG. 17.8

of P relative to the origin may be denoted by the vector **OP**. It is called the position-vector of P and is often denoted by **r**.

If PM is drawn perpendicular to Ox we have

$$\mathbf{OP} = \mathbf{OM} + \mathbf{MP}.$$

But **OM** may be written as $x\mathbf{i}$, where **i** is a vector of unit magnitude parallel to Ox, and **MP** may be written as $y\mathbf{j}$, where **j** is a vector of unit magnitude parallel to Oy.

We have $\mathbf{r} = x\mathbf{i} + y\mathbf{j}$.

If the angle POM $= \theta$, then

$$x = r \cos \theta \text{ and } y = r \sin \theta.$$

For any vector **r** the components x and y can be uniquely determined. We note that $r^2 = x^2 + y^2$, that is,

$$r = |\mathbf{r}| = (x^2 + y^2)^{\frac{1}{2}}.$$

17.12. More generally, suppose **a** and **b** are any two non-parallel vectors in a plane. Then any vector **r** coplanar with **a** and **b** can be resolved into components parallel to **a** and **b** respectively.

If OR (Fig. 17.9) represents **r** we complete the parallelogram OARB with sides parallel to **a** and **b**.

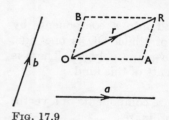

FIG. 17.9

Then, $\qquad\qquad\mathbf{r} = \mathbf{OA} + \mathbf{OB}$
$$= x\mathbf{a} + y\mathbf{b}$$

where x and y are scalar quantities. In fact, $x = OA/a$ and $y = OB/b$.

Similarly, if $\mathbf{r}_1$, $\mathbf{r}_2$, $\mathbf{r}_3$, ... are any set of coplanar vectors they can be resolved into components parallel to the vectors **a** and **b** as follows:

$$\mathbf{r}_1 = x_1\mathbf{a} + y_1\mathbf{b}$$
$$\mathbf{r}_2 = x_2\mathbf{a} + y_2\mathbf{b}$$
$$\mathbf{r}_3 = x_3\mathbf{a} + y_3\mathbf{b}$$

and so on. We note that their vector sum is

$$\mathbf{r}_1 + \mathbf{r}_2 + \mathbf{r}_3 + \ldots = (x_1 + x_2 + x_3 + \ldots)\,\mathbf{a} + (y_1 + y_2 + y_3 \ldots)\mathbf{b}.$$

It follows that the components of the sum of any set of vectors are the sums of the components of the separate vectors.

Further, if the vector sum is zero then

$$x_1 + x_2 + x_3 + \ldots = 0$$
and $\qquad\qquad y_1 + y_2 + y_3 + \ldots = 0.$

The converse of this statement is also true.

17.13. If a vector **r** is not in the plane of the vectors **a** and **b** (or in a plane parallel to this plane) it may be resolved into a component in this plane and a component not in this plane.

It follows that any vector **r** can be resolved into components parallel to any three non-coplanar vectors **a**, **b**, and **c**, and we can write

$$\mathbf{r} = x\mathbf{a} + y\mathbf{b} + z\mathbf{c}$$

where x, y, z are scalar quantities.

In particular, if **i**, **j**, **k** are unit vectors parallel to a set of mutually perpendicular axes Ox, Oy, Oz the position-vector **r** of any point (x, y, z) in space may be written

$$\mathbf{r} = x\mathbf{i} + y\mathbf{j} + z\mathbf{k}.$$

We note that
$$r = |\mathbf{r}| = (x^2 + y^2 + z^2)^{\frac{1}{2}}.$$

The direction of the vector in space is given by the direction-cosines x/r, y/r, and z/r.

17.14. Vector-equation of a line

If OA and OB (Fig. 17.10) represent the vectors **a** and **b**, and

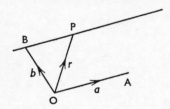

FIG. 17.10

P is any point on the line through B parallel to OA, then the position-vector **r** of P with respect to O is given by:

$$\mathbf{r} = \mathbf{OB} + \mathbf{BP}$$
$$= b + m\mathbf{a}$$

where $m = \text{BP/OA}$, a scalar quantity.

This equation $\mathbf{r} = \mathbf{b} + m\mathbf{a}$ is the vector-equation of the line that passes through the point B (defined by **b**) and is parallel to the vector **a**.

Any particular value of m gives a particular point on the line; m can have any value from minus infinity to plus infinity.

Similarly, if P is any point on the line BA its position vector **r** is given by

$$\mathbf{r} = \mathbf{OB} + \mathbf{BP}$$

$$= \mathbf{b} + m\mathbf{BA} \text{ where } m = BP/BA$$

$$= \mathbf{b} + m(\mathbf{a} - \mathbf{b})$$

$$= m\mathbf{a} + (1-m)\mathbf{b}$$

This is the vector-equation of the line through the two points whose position vectors are **a** and **b**.

The point A corresponds to $m = 1$ and the point B to $m = 0$. Any other point on AB or AB produced corresponds to some particular value of m. The mid-point of AB corresponds to $m = \frac{1}{2}$; for this point $\mathbf{r} = \frac{1}{2}\mathbf{a} + \frac{1}{2}\mathbf{b}$.

17.15. EXAMPLE (i)

ABC *is any triangle and the bisector of the angle ACB meets AB in M. Prove vectorially that* CA/CB = AM/MB.

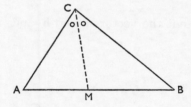

FIG. 17.11

For *any* point M in AB we have (Fig. 17.11)

$$\mathbf{CM} = \mathbf{CA} + \mathbf{AM}$$

$$= \mathbf{CA} + \frac{AM}{AB} \times \mathbf{AB}$$

$$= \mathbf{CA} + \frac{AM}{AB} (\mathbf{AC} + \mathbf{CB})$$

$$= \left(1 - \frac{AM}{AB}\right)\mathbf{CA} + \frac{AM}{AB} \mathbf{CB}$$

$$= \frac{MB}{AB} \times \mathbf{CA} + \frac{AM}{AB}\mathbf{CB}$$

giving the components of **CM** alone CA and CB.

But if CM bisects the angle ACB the components of **CM** along CA and CB must be equal in magnitude.

$$\therefore \qquad \frac{MB}{AB} \times CA = \frac{AM}{AB} \times CB$$

$$\therefore \qquad \frac{CA}{CB} = \frac{AM}{MB}.$$

EXAMPLE (ii)

Express the vector $\mathbf{r} = 10\mathbf{i} - 3\mathbf{j} - \mathbf{k}$ *as a linear function of the vectors* **a**, **b**, *and* **c**, *given that* $\mathbf{a} = 2\mathbf{i} - \mathbf{j} + 3\mathbf{k}$, $\mathbf{b} = 3\mathbf{i} + 2\mathbf{j} - 4\mathbf{k}$, *and* $\mathbf{c} = -\mathbf{i} + 3\mathbf{j} - 2\mathbf{k}$.

r is a linear function of **a**, **b**, and **c** if it can be written in the form

$$\mathbf{r} = m_1\mathbf{a} + m_2\mathbf{b} + m_3\mathbf{c}$$

where m_1, m_2, m_3 are scalars.

Assuming this relation, we have

$$10\mathbf{i} - 3\mathbf{j} - \mathbf{k} = m_1(2\mathbf{i} - \mathbf{j} + 3\mathbf{k}) + m_2(3\mathbf{i} + 2\mathbf{j} - 4\mathbf{k}) + m_3(-\mathbf{i} + 3\mathbf{j} - 2\mathbf{k}).$$

Hence equating components we get

$$2m_1 + 3m_2 - m_3 = 10$$

$$-m_1 + 2m_2 + 3m_3 = -3$$

and
$$3m_1 - 4m_2 - 2m_3 = -1.$$

These lead to $m_1 = 1$, $m_2 = 2$, and $m_3 = -2$.

Hence, $\mathbf{r} = \mathbf{a} + 2\mathbf{b} - 2\mathbf{c}$.

EXAMPLE (iii)

Find the foot of the perpendicular from the origin on to the line $\mathbf{r} = 3m\mathbf{i} + 4(1 - m)\mathbf{j}$.

The line with the vector-equation

$$\mathbf{r} = 3m\mathbf{i} + 4(1 - m)\mathbf{j}$$

is shown in Fig. 17.12. It passes through the point A on the axis of x where **OA** = 3**i**, and the point B on the axis of y where **OB** = 4**j**. A and B correspond to $m = 1$ and $m = 0$ respectively.

If P is the foot of the perpendicular from O on to AB, then the angle POA, denoted by θ, equals the angle ABO.

But $\qquad$ $\tan \text{POA} = \text{MP}/\text{OM} = 4(1-m)/3m$

and $\qquad$ $\tan \text{ABO} = \text{OA}/\text{OB} = 3/4.$

Hence, P corresponds to that value of m for which

$$\frac{4(1-m)}{3m} = \tfrac{3}{4}$$

$\therefore \qquad\qquad 16(1-m) = 9m$

$\therefore \qquad\qquad\qquad m = 16/25.$

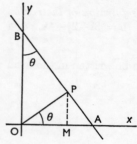

FIG. 17.12

Hence, the position vector of P is

$$\frac{48}{25}\,\mathbf{i} + \frac{36}{25}\,\mathbf{j}$$

that is, $\text{OM} = 48/25$ and $\text{MP} = 36/25.$

We note that the length of the perpendicular OP is

$$\left\{\left(\frac{48}{25}\right)^2 + \left(\frac{36}{25}\right)^2\right\}^{\frac{1}{2}},$$

that is, $12/5.$

17.16. Areas as vectors

Any plane areas has magnitude and orientation in space; the latter can be specified by the direction of the normal to the area. Any plane area can therefore be represented by a vector normal to the area, say $\mathbf{An}$, where A is the magnitude of the area and $\mathbf{n}$ is unit vector in the direction of the normal. $\mathbf{An}$ is sometimes written $\mathbf{A}$, it being understood that $\mathbf{A}$ is normal to the area A.

There is an ambiguity as to the positive direction of the normal; it has, therefore, to be specified carefully in any particular case. Sometimes the positive direction of the normal is taken to be related to positive movement round the boundary of the area by the right-hand screw rule (Fig. 17.13). In turn, movement round the boundary is taken as positive if the area is always on the left-hand side. If, however, the area forms part of a closed surface the *outward* normal is usually taken as positive. For example, the surfaces of a rectangular parallelepiped can be represented (Fig. 17.14) by six vectors normal to the surfaces outwards; they are equal and opposite in pairs.

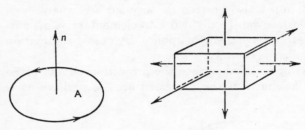

FIG. 17.13   FIG. 17.14

If a surface S is *not* plane it may be divided into elements of area dS_1, dS_2, dS_3, . . . each sufficiently small to be regarded as plane. Then the vector **S** representing the whole surface is the vector-sum of $dS_1\mathbf{n}_1$, $dS_2\mathbf{n}_2$, . . . where $\mathbf{n}_1$, $\mathbf{n}_2$, . . . are unit vectors normal to the surface at the positions of the various elements.

For any closed surface this vector-sum is zero, that is, the representative vector of any closed surface is zero. This is obvious in the particular example of a rectangular parallelepiped, as shown in Fig. 17.14. It can be proved generally.

17.17. An area vector can be resolved into components like any other vector. It can be shown that the component of an area vector in any direction equals in magnitude the projection of the area on a plane perpendicular to the given direction.

For if a triangle ABC is projected orthogonally on to a plane its projection is a triangle abc such that

$$\text{area of } \triangle abc = (\text{area of } \triangle ABC) \cos \theta$$

where θ is the angle between the planes of ABC and abc. If $90° < \theta < 180°$, the area of $\triangle abc$ is negative.

This result can be extended to apply to any plane rectilinear figure, for such a figure consists of a set of triangles. Similarly, the result applies to a plane area bounded by any curve, since this area may be regarded as the limit of that of a plane rectilinear figure as the number of sides of the figure increases indefinitely.

Thus, the orthogonal projection of a plane area upon any plane can be represented by the component of the representative vector of the area in a direction normal to the plane of projection.

This result must also be true for any surface whatsoever, since such a surface can be divided into elementary plane surfaces to which the above theorem applies. By vector-summation the theorem follows generally.

In the case of a closed surface the projection on *any* plane is zero, since as much of the projected area is positive as is negative.

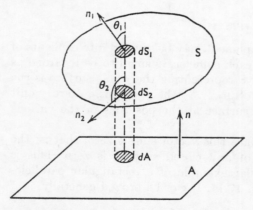

FIG. 17.15

This is clear from Fig. 17.15, where dS_1 is any element of a closed surface S. If the projection of dS_1 on any plane A is denoted by dA, and if $\mathbf{n}_1$ is unit vector normal to the element dS_1, outwards from the surface, then dA equals the component of $dS_1\mathbf{n}_1$ perpendicular to the plane A, that is, in the direction of the unit vector $\mathbf{n}$ shown in the figure. Now the cylinder of which dS_1 and dA are the ends cuts the surface S again in some element of area dS_2. If $\mathbf{n}_2$ is unit vector normal to the element

dS_2 outwards from the surface, then the component of $dS_2\mathbf{n}_2$ in the direction of the normal to A, that is, in the direction of the unit vector $\mathbf{n}$, is $-dA$.

This is true for all pairs of elements dS_1 and dS_2. Hence, summing for the whole surface, it follows that the representative vector of any closed surface is zero.

17.18. The application of the results discussed above to plane sections of certain solids is obvious.

For instance, a right section of a cube of side x is a square of area x^2. A section ADFE (Fig. 17.16) at an angle θ to the face

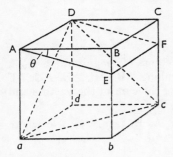

FIG. 17.16

ABCD is a rectangle of sides x and $x \sec \theta$, that is, of area $x^2 \sec \theta$. Hence, area of ABCD = (area of AEFD) $\cos \theta$ in keeping with the general result stated in 17.17 above.

If the six faces of the solid AEFDabcd are represented by vectors, normally outwards from each face, it can easily be shown that their vector sum is zero. This may also be done for the five faces of the wedge ADCBEF.

Similarly, the section Dca of the cube (Fig. 17.16) is an equilateral triangle of side $x\sqrt{2}$, and therefore of area $\frac{1}{2}(x\sqrt{2})^2 \sin 60° = \frac{1}{2}x^2\sqrt{3}$. Its projection on the face abcd of the cube is the triangle dca of area $\frac{1}{2}x^2$. Hence if α is the angle which the section Dca makes with the face abcd we have

$$\tfrac{1}{2}x^2 = (\tfrac{1}{2}x^2\sqrt{3}) \cos \alpha$$

$\therefore \qquad\qquad \cos \alpha = 1/\sqrt{3}.$

This could also be found by representing the areas of the faces of the tetrahedron Ddca by vectors normally outwards from each face. These have magnitudes $\frac{1}{2}x^2$, $\frac{1}{2}x^2$, $\frac{1}{2}x^2$, and

$\frac{1}{2}x^2\sqrt{3}$ respectively, and their vector-sum is zero provided $(\frac{1}{2}x^2\sqrt{3})\cos\alpha = \frac{1}{2}x^2$, that is, $\cos\alpha = 1/\sqrt{3}$. Conversely, we can prove $\cos\alpha = 1/\sqrt{3}$ geometrically, and then verify that the sum of the vectors representing the four faces is zero.

Again, the right section of a solid cylinder of radius a is a circle of area πa^2. A section at an angle θ to the right section has an area A where

$$A \cos\theta = \pi a^2$$

$\therefore$ $$A = \pi a^2 \sec\theta.$$

This section is, in fact, an ellipse with semi-axes a and $a \sec\theta$, and can be represented by a vector of magnitude $\pi a^2 \sec\theta$ at an angle θ to the axis of the cylinder.

EXAMPLES 17.1

1. ABCDEF is a regular hexagon. Vectors of magnitude 2, $4\sqrt{3}$, 8, $2\sqrt{3}$, and 4 units are directed along AB, AC, AD, AE, AF respectively. Find the magnitude of the sum of the vectors and the inclination of its direction to AB.

2. The position vectors of the points A, B, C, are $\mathbf{a}$, $\mathbf{b}$, $\mathbf{c}$ where $\mathbf{a} = a_1\mathbf{i}+a_2\mathbf{j}$, $\mathbf{b} = b_1\mathbf{i}+b_2\mathbf{j}$, $\mathbf{c} = c_1\mathbf{i}+c_2\mathbf{j}$.
   Find the lengths of AB, BC, and CA.

3. (i) If $\mathbf{a} = 2\mathbf{i}+3\mathbf{j}$, $\mathbf{b} = 3\mathbf{i}-4\mathbf{j}$, and $\mathbf{c} = -2\mathbf{i}+5\mathbf{j}$, write down $\mathbf{a}+\mathbf{b}+\mathbf{c}$, $2\mathbf{a}-\mathbf{b}+3\mathbf{c}$, and $\mathbf{a}+2\mathbf{b}-7\mathbf{c}$.
   (ii) Find values of m and n such that $m\mathbf{a}+n\mathbf{b}$ is parallel to $\mathbf{c}$.
   (iii) Find the unit vectors $\hat{\mathbf{a}}$, $\hat{\mathbf{b}}$, and $\hat{\mathbf{c}}$.

4. Show that the vectors $a_1\mathbf{i}+a_2\mathbf{j}$ and $b_1\mathbf{i}+b_2\mathbf{j}$ are perpendicular if $a_1b_1+a_2b_2 = 0$. Find a vector perpendicular to the vector $3\mathbf{i}-4\mathbf{j}$.

5. Show that the position vector $\mathbf{r}$ of the point P which divides the line AB in the ratio $m : n$ is given by $(m+n)\mathbf{r} = n\mathbf{a}+m\mathbf{b}$, where $\mathbf{a}$ and $\mathbf{b}$ are the position vectors of A and B.

6. Prove that the three points, whose position vectors are $\mathbf{a}$, $\mathbf{b}$, $\mathbf{c}$ are collinear if $m_1\mathbf{a}+m_2\mathbf{b}+m_3\mathbf{c} = 0$ where $m_1+m_2+m_3 = 0$.

7. Show that a triangle may be constructed whose sides are parallel and equal to the medians of any given triangle.

8. Prove vectorially that if the medians AD and BE of any triangle ABC intersect at G, then G divides AD and BE in the ratio $2 : 1$. Show also that the three medians are concurrent.

9. Prove that if the mid-points of the sides of any quadrilateral be joined in order the figure formed is a parallelogram.

10. The diagonals of a given quadrilateral bisect one another; prove that the quadrilateral is a parallelogram.

11. If the points A_1, A_2, ... A_n have position vectors r_1, r_2, ... r_n with respect to 0, show that the position of the point G defined by the relation

$$(m_1+m_2+ \ldots +m_n)\mathbf{OG} = m_1\mathbf{r_1}+m_2\mathbf{r_2}+ \ldots +m_n\mathbf{r_n},$$

where m_1, m_2, ... m_n are scalar quantities, is independent of the position of O.

12. Prove vectorially that if a transversal cuts the sides BC, CA, AB of a triangle ABC, in D, E, F respectively, then

$$\frac{BD}{DC} \times \frac{CE}{EA} \times \frac{AF}{FB} = -1.$$

13. Prove vectorially that the internal bisectors of the angles of a triangle are concurrent.

14. Find the point of intersection of the lines of which the vector equations are $\mathbf{r} = k\mathbf{i}+2(1-k)\mathbf{j}$ and $\mathbf{r} = 3(1-m)\mathbf{i}-m\mathbf{j}$.

 Draw these lines on a diagram, and find the angle between them. Find also the area enclosed by the lines and the axis of x.

15. If A and B have position vectors $\mathbf{a}$ and $\mathbf{b}$, and a parallelogram OACB is constructed with OA and OB as adjacent sides, find the vector equation of the line through C parallel to the diagonal AB. Verify that if this line meets OA produced in D, then $\mathbf{OD} = 2\mathbf{a}$.

16. ABCD is a parallelogram and E is the mid-point of BC. AE cuts the diagonal BD at F. Find the ratio in which F divides BD.

17. Show that the lines of which the vector equations are

$$\mathbf{r} = k\mathbf{a}+(1-k)\mathbf{b} \text{ and } \mathbf{r} = 2(1+m)\mathbf{a}-(1+2m)\mathbf{b}$$

are coincident.

18. The vectors $\mathbf{a}$, $\mathbf{b}$, $\mathbf{c}$ form the adjacent sides of a parallelepiped. Find the vector equations of the four diagonals of the parallelepiped and show that these diagonals are concurrent and bisect one another.

19. If the position vectors of the vertices of a tetrahedron are $\mathbf{r_1}$, $\mathbf{r_2}$, $\mathbf{r_3}$, $\mathbf{r_4}$, show that the position vector of the centre of mass of the tetrahedron is $\frac{1}{4}(\mathbf{r_1}+\mathbf{r_2}+\mathbf{r_3}+\mathbf{r_4})$.

20. Show that the three straight lines which join the mid-points of opposite edges of a tetrahedron are concurrent and bisect one another.

21. Find the vector equation of the line which passes through the points whose coordinates are (1, 2, 3) and (4, −1, 5). Find where the line cuts the (x, y) plane.

22. Show that the four points A, B, C, D lie in a plane if their position vectors r_1, r_2, r_3, r_4 are such that $m_1r_1+m_2r_2+m_3r_3+m_4r_4 = 0$ and $m_1+m_2+m_3+m_4 = 0$. Find m_1, m_2, m_3, m_4 when: (i) ABCD is a parallelogram; (ii) D is the mid-point of BC; and (iii) D is the centroid of the triangle ABC.

Show that the equation of the plane through the points whose position-vectors are r_1, r_2, r_3 can be written in the form

$$r = m_1r_1+m_2r_2+(1-m_1-m_2)r_3.$$

23. If the position-vectors of A, B, C are $2i-j+3k$, $3i+2j-4k$ and $-i+3j-2k$, find: (i) the equation of the line through A parallel to BC, and (ii) the equation of the plane through A, B, and the origin O.

24. If $a = 2i-j+3k$, $b = 3i+2j-4k$ and $c = -5i-j+k$, find the unit vectors $\hat{a}$, $\hat{b}$, $\hat{c}$.

Show that if three vectors a, b, c are such that $a+b+c = 0$, then in general $\hat{a}+\hat{b}+\hat{c}$ is not zero. Find the conditions that must be satisfied if $a+b+c$ and $\hat{a}+\hat{b}+\hat{c}$ are both zero.

25. A cube has adjacent sides along the coordinate axes Ox, Oy, Oz. It is divided into two equal parts by a diagonal plane. Write down the vectors which represent the five faces of one of these parts, and verify that their vector-sum is zero.

26. Write down the vectors which represent the four faces of a regular tetrahedron, and verify that their vector sum is zero.

27. A tetrahedron OABC has its vertices A, B, C on Ox, Oy, Oz respectively. Assuming that the sum of the vectors representing the four faces is zero, find the area of the face ABC and the direction of its normal.

28. A regular pentagon ABCDE of side a is projected orthogonally on to a plane through the side AB that makes an angle θ with the plane of ABCDE. If the projection of the triangle ADB is an equilateral triangle, find θ. Find also the area of the projection of the triangle BDC.

29. An equilateral triangle of sides 6 cm has its vertices at height of 7, 9, 11 cm above a horizontal plane. Find the dimensions of the projection of the triangle on the horizontal and the inclination of the equilateral triangle to the horizontal.

30. A regular hexagon ABCDEF of side 2 cm is projected orthogonally on to the plane through the side AB, which makes an angle of 30° with the plane of the hexagon. Find the lengths of the sides of the projected figure, and the angle between BC and its projection.

CHAPTER EIGHTEEN

ELEMENTARY STATISTICS

18.1. Numerical data, if they are sufficiently numerous, are often represented graphically as an aid to their appreciation.

The first step in dealing with such data is to arrange them in some convenient order. This is often done by grouping them into classes according to their magnitude or according to suitable intervals of a variable on which they depend.

For instance, the height of a barometer might be recorded on 100 occasions. Instead of writing down successively the 100 observations, it might for some purposes be more convenient to count the number of times each observation occurred and to record these as follows:

Height (mm)	740	741	742	743	744	745	746	747	748	749	750
Frequency	1	5	9	23	20	17	12	6	4	2	1

The frequency of an observation is the number of times it occurs, that is, the height of the barometer was 743 mm on 23 of the 100 occasions, whereas it was 750 mm only once.

Again, the heights of a collection of women, measured to 0·5 cm, could be grouped by counting the number of women who had heights between 150 and 151·5 cm, 152 and 153·5 cm, ... 172 and 173·5 cm. The data could then be tabulated as follows:

Height in cm	Frequency
150–151·5	1
152–153·5	2
154–155·3	7
156–157·5	8
158–159·5	18
160–161·5	20
162–163·5	18
164–165·5	11
166–167·5	8
168–169·5	4
170–171·5	2
172–173·5	1

The heights of the 100 women have thus been grouped into
12 classes, and the 'width' of each class is 2 cm. They could
have been grouped into a different number of classes; for example, we could have counted the number of women with
heights between 150 and 153·5 cm, 154 and 157·5 cm, . . . 170
and 173·5 cm giving 6 classes each of 'width' 4 cm.

18.2. Classification of data in this sort of way is obviously
helpful. We can see at a glance from the above table, for
instance, how many of the women are not more than 156 cm
tall and how many of them are 170 cm or over. Again, it is clear
that 56 per cent of the women have a height between 158 and
163·5 cm. A graphical representation can possibly be even
more useful. There are two graphical methods in common use.

In Fig. 18.1 the heights of the women are represented along
the horizontal axis and the frequencies along the vertical axis.
The points are obtained by plotting the frequency against the
mid-value of the corresponding class, namely, 150·75, 152·75,
. . . 172·75. These points are joined by straight lines. The resulting figure is known as a *frequency polygon*. The variations of
height among the women are thus made clear.

Another kind of graphical representation may be used, as
shown in Fig. 18.2.

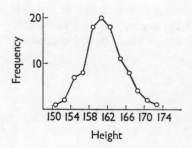

FIG. 18.1.   Frequency polygon of
heights of women.

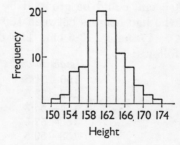

FIG. 18.2. Histogram of heights
of women.

Heights are again represented along the horizontal axis, but
a series of rectangles are constructed, each of width equal to the
class-width and of *area* equal to the frequency of the corresponding class. The resulting figure is known as a *Histogram*. The total

area of the histogram is equal in magnitude to the sum of all the frequencies, in this case 100 units, equal in magnitude to the number of women.

It will be noted that when the class widths of the data are equal the heights of the rectangles forming the histogram are proportional to the corresponding frequencies, and represent these frequencies on a certain scale. If the class-widths are unequal the ordinates do *not* represent the frequencies.

18.3. Some terms and definitions

For clarity, we collect together the terms in common use, some of which have already been introduced.

Class. Data are usually grouped into classes; that is, in the example given in 18.1 the women of height between 154 and 155·5 cm are placed in the same class. Usually two numbers are needed to specify a class, but sometimes one is sufficient.

Class-width. The width of any class is the difference between the first number specifying that class and the first number specifying the next class, that is, 2 cm for all the classes given in the Table in 18.1. Class-widths may be equal or unequal. Their specification obviously depends upon the accuracy of the measurements. If the heights of the women referred to in 18.1 were measured to the nearest 0·5 cm the class 154–155·5 might include all the women with recorded heights of 154, 154·5, 155, and 155·5 cm; strictly in that case it would include all those with heights between 153·75 and 155·75 cm and the mid-value of the class would be 154·75 cm. On the other hand, in the class 154–156 there might be included the women with recorded heights of 154·5, 155, 155·5 cm and half of those with recorded heights of 154 and 156 cm; the mid-value of the class would then be 155 cm. Similarly, a class-width of 0·5 cm might be used, in which case all the women of recorded height 154·5 cm would be put in the class 154·5; this class would include all women with heights between 154·25 and 154·75 cm. In the same way, in grouping the barometer heights referred to in paragraph 18.1 the class 744 includes all the heights between 743·5 mm and 744·5 mm; these are the class *boundaries*. It is important that there should be no doubt as to where the boundaries of the classes are, and that there should be no overlapping or gaps between successive classes.

Class limits. The pairs of numbers used to specify a class are called the lower and upper class limits. As explained above, these are not necessarily the class boundaries.

Frequency. The number of data in each class is called the frequency corresponding to that class.

Frequency distribution. A table of data showing the variation of frequency with class is called a frequency distribution. Sometimes this variation may be expressed in mathematical form. A frequency distribution may be represented graphically by means of a *frequency polygon* and/or a *histogram*.

When the number of data is very large the frequency polygon and the histogram approximate closely to a continuous curve which is known as a *frequency curve*.

There are certain important characteristics of frequency distributions which we shall now discuss.

18.4. The mean

The arithmetic mean of any set of numbers x_1, x_2, ... x_n is defined as $(x_1+x_2+ \ldots +x_n)/n$.

If the numbers occur with frequencies $f_1, f_2, \ldots f_n$ it follows that their arithmetic mean is given by

$$(f_1x_1+f_2x_2+ \ldots +f_nx_n)/(f_1+f_2+ \ldots +f_n).$$

Thus the mean of 10, 11, 12 is $(10+11+12)/3 = 11$, and the mean of 10, 10, 10, 11, 11, 12, 12, 12, 12 is

$$(3 \times 10+2 \times 11+4 \times 12)/(3+2+4) = (30+22+48)/9 = 11\tfrac{1}{9}.$$

We extend this definition to the *mean* of any set of data. If $f_1, f_2, \ldots f_n$ are the frequencies corresponding to the various classes of which x_1, x_2, ... x_n are the mid-values of the variable the mean value of the variable is defined as

$$(f_1x_1+f_2x_2+ \ldots +f_nx_n)/(f_1+f_2+ \ldots +f_n)$$

It is usually denoted by $\bar{x}$ and may be written as

$$\bar{x} = \sum_{s=1}^{n} f_sx_s / \sum_{s=1}^{n} f_s = [fx]/[f].$$

To evaluate $\bar{x}$ in any particular case we may proceed directly as shown below.

x_s	f_s	$f_s x_s$
2·5	1	2·5
3·5	4	14·0
4·5	10	45·0
5·5	12	66·0
6·5	8	52·0
7·5	3	22·5
Sum	38	202·0

Hence, the mean $\bar{x} = 202/38 = 5\frac{12}{38} = 5\cdot3$.

In some cases the arithmetic might be heavy, as it would if we attempted to find directly in this way the mean height of the 100 women whose heights are tabulated in 18.1. The amount of arithmetic, and consequently the likelihood of error can be reduced by using what is called an *assumed* or *working* mean. It is effectively a change of origin of the variable.

18.5. The working mean

The mean of the numbers 41, 42, 44, 47, 50 is obviously 40 plus the mean of the numbers 1, 2, 4, 7, 10, that is,

$$40+(1+2+4+7+10)/5 = 44\cdot8.$$

In this case, 40 has been used as a working mean. Or again, the mean of the given numbers is 44+the mean of the numbers -3, -2, 0, 3, 6, that is, $44+(-3-2+0+3+6)/5$, which equals 44·8.

We can establish the validity of this method algebraically as follows:

Writing $x_s = m+x'_s$ we have

$$f_1 x_1 + f_2 x_2 + \ldots + f_n x_n = f_1(m+x'_1) + f_2(m+x'_2) + \ldots + f_n(m+x'_n)$$

$$= m(f_1 + f_2 + \ldots + f_n) + f_1 x'_1 + f_2 x'_2 + \ldots + f_n x'_n$$

$$\frac{f_1 x_1 + f_2 x_2 + \ldots + f_n x_n}{f_1 + f_2 + \ldots + f_n} = m + \frac{f_1 x'_1 + f_2 x'_2 + \ldots + f_n x'_n}{f_1 + f_2 + \ldots + f_n}$$

that is, $\bar{x} = m + \overline{x'}$.

where $\overline{x'}$ is the mean of the quantities x'_1, x'_2, $\ldots x'_n$.

The calculation of $\overline{x'}$ can be made easier than that of $\bar{x}$ by choosing m conveniently.

In the example given in 18.4 the evaluation of $\bar{x}$ could have proceeded as follows. Choosing $m = 4\cdot5$, we get:

x_s	f_s	$x'_s = x'_s - 4\cdot5$	$f_s x_s$
2·5	1	−2	−2
3·5	4	−1	−4
4·5	10	0	0
5·5	12	1	12
6·5	8	2	16
7·5	3	3	9
sum	38		31

Hence, $\qquad\qquad \overline{x'} = 31/38$

and, therefore, $\qquad \bar{x} = 4\cdot5 + 31/38 = 5\frac{12}{38} = 5\cdot3$

as found directly. The calculation is obviously simpler than the direct method, even in this case, but in many other cases the economy is considerable.

As a further example we will find the mean of the heights of the 100 women given in 18.1.

Class boundaries	x_s	f_s	x'_s	$f_s x'_s$
149·75–151·75	150·75	1	−10	−10
151·75–153·75	152·75	2	−8	−16
153·75–155·75	154·75	7	−6	−42
155·75–157·75	156·75	8	−4	−32
157·75–159·75	158·75	18	−2	−36
159·75–161·75	160·75	20	0	0
161·75–163·75	162·75	18	2	36
163·75–165·75	164·75	11	4	44
165·75–167·75	166·75	8	6	48
167·75–169·75	168·75	4	8	32
169·75–171·75	170·75	2	10	20
171·75–173·75	172·75	1	12	12
	sum	100		56

In the table the values of x_s are the mid-values of the variable in each class. A working mean of $m = 160\cdot75$ has been used, and so the values of x'_s equal those of $x_s - 160\cdot75$.

It follows that $\bar{x}' = 56/100$ and hence $\bar{x} = 160{\cdot}75 + 0{\cdot}56$, which equals $161{\cdot}31$, that is, $161{\cdot}3$ correct to one decimal place.

This is clearly much simpler than the direct method of finding $\sum f_s x_s / 100$.

18.6. The median

The *Median* of any set of data is the middle one of the set arranged in *ascending* or *descending* order of magnitude.

If the number in the set is odd, say $2n+1$, where n is an integer, the median is the $(n+1)$th in ascending order of magnitude. If the number in the set is even, say $2n$, the middle values of the set are the nth and $(n+1)$th, and the arithmetic mean of these two is taken as the median.

For example, the numbers 9, 16, 13, 4, 7, 8, 20 when arranged in ascending order of magnitude are 4, 7, 8, 9, 13, 16, 20, of which the median is 9. If the value 8 had not been present the median would have been the mean of 9 and 13, that is, 11.

To find the median of the 100 heights of women given in 18.1, we note that if the women had been set out in ascending order of height the two women in the middle would have been the 50th and the 51st. The median may be taken as the height of the fictitious 'individual' number 50·5 in the group. On examining the table it will be found that there are 36 women in the first five classes and 56 in the first six classes, and hence the 50·5 woman is in the sixth class with boundaries 159·75 and 161·75 cm. The median may be taken to be

$$159{\cdot}75 + \frac{50{\cdot}5 - 36}{20} \times 2 = 161{\cdot}20 \text{ cm.}$$

If any set of data, arranged in order of magnitude, is divided into four equal parts the corresponding values of the variables are known as the *quartiles*. It follows that the second quartile is the same as the median. Also half the data must lie between the lower quartile and the upper quartile. Similarly, if the data are divided into ten equal parts the corresponding values of the variable are called the *deciles*.

Another term that is sometimes used is the *Mode*. It is the value of the variable which occurs most frequently, that is, in the set of heights quoted in 18.1 it is between 160 and 161·5 of the class with the greatest frequency, a little above 160·75.

For a symmetrical distribution the mean, the median and the mode are coincident. For asymmetrical (or skew) distributions the following relation is often approximately satisfied:

$$\text{Mean} - \text{Mode} = 3(\text{Mean} - \text{Median}).$$

A method of finding the mean, mode and median of continuous distributions is given later.

18.7. Cumulative frequency

It is sometimes convenient, as for instance when dealing with the quartiles or the median, to use the total number of data in all the classes above or below a particular value of the variable.

If $f_1, f_2, \ldots f_n$ are the frequencies of the various classes of which $X_1, X_2, \ldots X_n$ are the upper class-boundaries of the variable, what is known as the *cumulative frequency* corresponding to the class of which the upper boundary is X_e is the sum of all the frequencies up to and including f_e. If it is denoted by F_e we have

$$F_1 = f_1, \; F_2 = f_1 + f_2, \; F_3 = f_1 + f_2 + f_3$$

and

$$F_e = f_1 + f_2 + \ldots + f_e.$$

Again using the heights given in 18.1 the cumulative frequencies can be tabulated as shown in the following table,

X_s	f_s	F_s
151·75	1	1
153·75	2	3
155·75	7	10
157·75	8	18
159·75	18	36
161·75	20	56
163·75	18	74
165·75	11	85
167·75	8	93
169·75	4	97
171·75	2	99
173·75	1	100

and represented as in Fig. 18.3, where the values of F_s have been plotted against the values of the upper class boundaries.

A curve such as that in Fig. 18.3 is known as an *Ogive* curve.

The median is the value of X corresponding to $F = 50$, and this can be read off the curve in Fig. 18.3. Similarily the lower and upper quartiles correspond to $F = 25$ and $F = 75$ respectively.

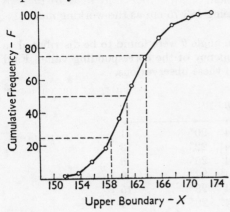

FIG. 18.3

EXAMPLES 18.1

1. Find the mean of 5, 7, 9, 10, 13, 17, 20 using (*a*) 5, (*b*) 10 as the working mean.

2. The mean of 100 observations is 4·2 and the mean of a further 50 is 3·9. Find the mean of the two sets of observations taken together.

3. If the mean of 500 data is 6·7, and the mean of a sample of 100 taken from these is 6·3, find the mean of the remaining 400.

4. Find the mean of the numbers 5, 7, 9, 10, 13, 17, 20 when they occur with frequencies 2, 3, 4, 10, 7, 3, 1 respectively. Use: (*a*) 10; (*b*) 13 as the working mean. Find also the median.

5. (*a*) Find the mean and the median of the following:

   15, 21, 19, 20, 18, 17, 22, 23, 16, 25.

   (*b*) If when these numbers are arranged in ascending order they occur with frequencies 1, 4, 7, 12, 13, 9, 6, 4, 3, 1, find the mean and the median.

6. Find the mean of the heights tabulated in 18.5 by using 162·75 as the working mean.
Draw the frequency polygon and the histogram.

7. Group the heights of women given in 18.1 into six classes each of width 4 cm. Draw a frequency polygon and a histogram to represent this classification.
Find the mean height using 163·75 cm as the working mean.

8. Forty observations of an angle θ were found to be distributed as follows, f being the frequency of the corresponding value. Find the mean and median of these observations.

θ			f
45°	24′	20″	1
45°	24′	22″	3
45°	24′	25″	5
45°	24′	27″	9
45°	24′	28″	15
45°	24′	29″	4
45°	24′	30″	3

9. Find the median of the variable x which occurs with frequency f as shown:

x	10	20	30	40	50	60	70	80	90
f	35	52	74	95	81	62	48	32	21

Find also the mean using (i) 40 and (ii) 50 as the working mean. Draw the frequency polygon. Draw also a smooth curve to fit the data as closely as possible, and from it find the mode.

10. Observations on the scattering of electrons led to the following results, which give the relative intensity of electrons in tracks of given radii of curvature. Find the mean radius of curvature of the tracks.

Radius of curvature (cm)	5·4	5·5	5·6	5·7	5·8	5·9	6·0
Relative intensity	0	11	36·5	40·5	31	9·5	0

11. The heights of a barometer as recorded on 100 occasions were as follows:

Height (mm)	740	741	742	743	744	745	746	747	748	749	750
Frequency	1	5	9	23	20	17	12	6	4	2	1

Find the mean height, and draw the histogram representing the heights.

12. Draw the histogram of the following observations and calculate the mean value of x:

x	0–19	20–39	40–49	50–59	60–69	70–79	80–99	100–119
f	1	3	7	19	27	23	12	8

13. The weights of a group of men are as given in the following distribution. Calculate the mean weight, and draw the histogram. The unit of weight is 1 lb. wt or 4·45 N.

Weight	Frequency
100–109·5	1
110–119·5	5
120–129·5	7
130–139·5	30
140–149·5	47
150–159·5	41
160–169·5	31
170–179·5	18
180–189·5	11
190–199·5	7
200–209·5	1
210–219·5	1

14. Form a frequency table and draw the frequency polygon of the following data:

330	341	358	348	386
379	395	384	316	375
349	337	340	355	326
359	369	353	338	354
382	352	323	341	334
321	347	344	328	349
342	355	333	352	343
312	305	362	368	353
351	365	357	374	358
360	370	377	383	367

Calculate the mean. Draw a smooth curve to fit the data as closely as possible, and from it find the mode.

15. Form a frequency table and plot a frequency polygon of the following data:

86	114	81	72	97	110	87	106	118
92	103	132	108	107	80	91	84	98
120	70	110	96	82	99	110	117	83
85	92	83	86	125	87	104	57	46
92	86	92	110	110	66	148	80	
109	95	107	99	94	108	89	118	
83	102	70	88	163	89	131	98	
104	130	88	75	91	97	76	94	
151	89	108	97	87	107	117	100	
74	108	106	103	104	80	134	92	
115	91	123	97	84	106	96	65	
100	87	86	110	102	96	94	161	

Find the mean value and the median. Draw a smooth curve to fit the data as closely as possible, and from it find the mode.

16. The following table shows the distribution of ages of a group of husbands and their wives. Determine the median age of each group and for that obtained by combining the figures irrespective of sex. Draw a cumulative frequency curve for each group.

Age last birthday	Wives	Husbands
Under 22	6	3
22–24	11	5
25–29	25	24
30–34	19	21
35–39	22	20
40–44	20	19
45–49	18	12
50–54	7	17
55–59	6	10
60–64	3	7
65 and over	1	0

17. Tabulate the cumulative frequencies for the data given in question 5 (b) above, and represent them graphically.

18. Tabulate the cumulative frequencies for the data given in question 13 above, and represent them graphically. Estimate the first and third quartiles from the graph and check these by calculation.

19. The heights of 120 men are recorded in the following table. Find the mean height.

Height (cm)	142–149	150–157	158–165	166–173	174–181	182–189
No. of men	3	14	39	46	16	2

Find also the median, and the lower and upper quartiles.

20. The following table gives the results of measurements of the height of 1000 specimens of a new strain of wheat. Draw the frequency polygon, and calculate the mean height. Find also the median.

Height (cm)	56	58	60	62	64	66	68	70	72	74	76
Frequency	12	40	170	206	240	190	70	38	22	10	2

18.8. Dispersion about the mean

The mean of a group of data is a useful quantity, but often it is more important to have a measure of the way in which the data are distributed or dispersed about the mean. In general, different sets of data have different means and different dispersions.

The three numbers 24, 25, 26 have a mean of 25, and so have the numbers 5, 25, 45. The first group are within the limits indicated by 25 ± 1, whereas the second group are within the limits 25 ± 20. Again, the numbers 12, 16, 19, 23, 25 have a mean of 19; they range from $19 - 7$ to $19 + 6$.

The word *Range* when applied to a distribution of data is used to mean the difference between the least and greatest values. Thus the range of the numbers 12, 16, 19, 23, 25 is 13. It is a very simple measure of dispersion and has limitations because of its simplicity. The numbers 12, 13, 14, 23, 25 have the same range as 12, 22, 23, 24, 25, but the two sets have a different mean and are very differently distributed about their means.

On the other hand, the term *interquartile range* is used to indicate the difference between the lower and upper quartiles (18.6). By definition, half the data lie between these limits, and usually they include those that occur most frequently.

Two other parameters are often used as measures of dispersion and are known as the *mean deviation* and the *standard deviation*.

18.9. The mean deviation

Suppose $x_1, x_2, \ldots x_n$ are a set of values of a variable. Denoting their mean by $\bar{x}$, the deviations of these values from the mean (Deviations are sometimes measured from the median rather than from the mean.) are $x_1 - \bar{x}, x_2 - \bar{x}, \ldots x_n - \bar{x}$ respectively, which we will write as $d_1, d_2 \ldots d_n$. Some of these deviations are positive and some negative; in fact, their sum is zero.

For, $d_1 + d_2 + \ldots + d_n = x_1 + x_2 + \ldots + x_n - n\bar{x} = 0$.

Hence, the mean of these deviations is zero. However, the mean of the *numerical values* of the deviations is a positive quantity which is sometimes used as a measure of dispersion. It is known as the *mean deviation* (sometimes the *mean absolute deviation*) of the set of quantities. It is given by

$$\frac{|d_1| + |d_2| + \ldots + |d_n|}{n} = \frac{1}{n} \sum_{s=1} |d_s|.$$

Thus the numbers 12, 16, 19, 23, 25 have a mean of 19 and a mean deviation of $(7 + 3 + 0 + 4 + 6)/5 = 4$.

If a distribution of data has frequencies $f_1, f_2, \ldots f_n$, corresponding to the various classes of which $x_1, x_2, \ldots x_n$ are the mid-values of the variable, the mean deviation of the distribution is defined as

$$\frac{f_1|d_1| + f_2|d_2| + \ldots + f_n|d_n|}{f_1 + f_2 + \ldots + f_n} = \frac{\sum f_s |x_s - \bar{x}|}{\sum f_s}.$$

As an example we will take the table used in 18.4. The mean was found to be 5·3; hence the values of $|d_s|$ equal $|x_s - 5\cdot3|$ and are as shown below.

x_s	f_s	$|d_s|$	$f_s|d_s|$
2·5	1	2·8	2·8
3·5	4	1·8	7·2
4·5	10	0·8	8·0
5·5	12	0·2	2·4
6·5	8	1·2	9·6
7·5	3	2·2	6·6
sum	38		36·6

Hence, the mean deviation = 36·6/38 = 0·96.

18.10. The standard deviation

The most important measure of dispersion is the *standard deviation*, usually denoted by σ. It is defined in terms of the squares of the deviations from the mean as follows.

If $x_1, x_2, \ldots x_n$ are a set of values of a variable and $d_1, d_2, \ldots d_n$ denote their deviations from the mean, then

$$\sigma^2 = (d_1^2 + d_2^2 + \ldots + d_2^n)/n$$

that is, σ^2 is the mean of the squares of the deviations, or σ is the root-mean-square-deviation measured from the mean.

We have

$$\sigma = \left[\frac{1}{n}\sum_{s=1}^{n} d_s^2\right]^{\frac{1}{2}} = \left[\frac{1}{n}\sum_{s=1}^{n}(x_s - \bar{x})^2\right]^{\frac{1}{2}}.$$

If $x_1, x_2, \ldots x_n$ have frequencies $f_1, f_2, \ldots f_n$ it follows that

$$\sigma^2 = \frac{f_1 d_1^2 + f_2 d_2^2 + \ldots + f_n d_n^2}{f_1 + f_2 + \ldots + f_n}$$

$$= \sum_{s=1}^{n} f_s(x_s - \bar{x})^2 / \sum_{s=1}^{n} f_s.$$

σ^2 is known as the *variance* of the distribution. (It should be noted here that the sum $\sum f_s$ in the denominator of the expression for σ^2 should, in most practical cases, be replaced by $\sum f_s - 1$. This is known as Bessel's correction, as explained in 18.21.)

EXAMPLE (i)
Find the standard deviation of the numbers 12, 16, 19, 23, 25.

The mean of this set is 19, and so the deviations from the mean are $-7, -3, 0, 4, 6$ respectively. We note that the sum of the deviations is zero.

Hence $\quad \sigma^2 = (49 + 9 + 0 + 16 + 36)/5 = 110/5 = 22$

$\therefore \quad\quad\quad \sigma = 4 \cdot 7.$

EXAMPLE (ii)

Find the standard deviation of 10, 10, 10, 10, 11, 11, 12, 12, 12, 13.

The mean of this set is $10+(0+2+6+3)/10 = 11\cdot1$. The deviations from the mean are $-1\cdot1$, $-1\cdot1$, $-1\cdot1$, $-1\cdot1$, $-0\cdot1$, $-0\cdot1$, $0\cdot9$, $0\cdot9$, $0\cdot9$ and $1\cdot9$.

Hence
$$\sigma^2 = \{4(1\cdot1)^2+2(0\cdot1)^2+3(0\cdot9)^2+1\cdot9^2\}/10$$
$$= \{4\cdot84+0\cdot02+2\cdot43+3\cdot61\}/10 = 1\cdot090$$
$$\therefore \qquad\qquad \sigma = 1\cdot04.$$

18.11. The standard deviation and a working mean

The evaluation of the standard deviation by direct application of the definition (18.9) can in many cases involve much unwieldy arithmetic. This can be avoided in great measure by using a suitable working mean. We can establish the basic relation as follows:

If x_1, x_2, . . . x_n have frequencies f_1, f_2, . . . f_n respectively, and $\bar{x}$ is the mean, then for any working mean m we have

$$\sum f_s(x_s-m) = \sum f_s x_s - m\sum f_s$$
$$= \bar{x}\sum f_s - m\sum f_s$$
$$= (\bar{x}-m)\sum f_s.$$

Hence $\qquad \sum f_s(x_s-m)/\sum f_s = \bar{x}-m$

as we proved earlier in 18.5. The expression on the left-hand side, which we denoted earlier by $\bar{x}'$, involves deviations from the working mean m (denoted earlier by x'_s) and is often much easier to calculate than $\bar{x}$.

Similarly, the standard deviation σ is given by

$$\sum f_s(x_s-\bar{x})^2 = \sigma^2\sum f_s.$$

But we can write

$$\sum f_s(x_s-\bar{x})^2 = \sum f_s[(x_s-m)+(m-\bar{x})]^2$$
$$= \sum f_s(x_s-m)^2+2(m-\bar{x})\sum f_s(x_s-m)$$
$$\qquad\qquad +(m-\bar{x})^2\sum f_s$$
$$= \sum f_s(x_s-m)^2+2(m-\bar{x})(\bar{x}-m)\sum f_s$$
$$\qquad\qquad +(m-\bar{x})^2\sum f_s$$
$$= \sum f_s(x_s-m)^2-(m-\bar{x})^2\sum f_s.$$

Dividing by $\sum f_s$ this can be written

$$\sigma^2 = \mu^2 - (m - \bar{x})^2$$

where μ^2 denotes $\sum f_s(x_s - m)^2 / \sum f_s$, and is the mean of the squares of the deviations *from the working mean m*. To calculate σ^2 it is often much easier to calculate μ^2 using a suitable working mean m, and then to subtract $(m - \bar{x})^2$ from μ^2.

We can illustrate this by using the data in the table in 18.9. The mean was found to be 5·3; hence the values of d_s equal $x_s - 5\cdot3$ and are as shown below.

x_s	f_s	d_s	d_s^2	$f_s d_s^2$
2·5	1	−2·8	7·84	7·84
3·5	4	−1·8	3·24	12·96
4·5	10	−0·8	0·64	6·40
5·5	12	0·2	0·04	0·48
6·5	8	1·2	1·44	11·52
7·5	3	2·2	4·84	14·52
sum	38			53·72

Hence, $\sigma^2 = 53\cdot72/38 = 1\cdot41.$

Alternatively, we could have used a working mean $m = 5.5$. Writing $d'_s = x_s - 5\cdot5$ we get

x_s	f_s	d'_s	$f_s d'_s{}^2$
2·5	1	−3	9
3·5	4	−2	16
4·5	10	−1	10
5·5	12	0	0
6·5	8	1	8
7·5	3	2	12
sum	38		55

Hence, $\mu^2 = 55/38$

∴ $\sigma^2 = 55/38 - (5\cdot5 - 5\cdot3)^2 = 55/38 - 0\cdot04$

         $= 53\cdot48/38 = 1\cdot41$

as found by the direct method. The arithmetic is clearly simpler.

It might be noted that the difference between 53·72 and 53·48 found by the two methods results from taking the mean as 5·3, whereas it is $5\frac{12}{38}$, which equals 5·316. But usually it is not necessary to find σ^2 more accurately.

The relation

$$\sigma^2 = \mu^2 - (m-\bar{x})^2$$

is important. We note that putting $m = 0$ gives

$$\sigma^2 = \mu^2_0 - \bar{x}^2$$

where μ_0 is the value of μ when $m = 0$. Again, putting $m = \bar{x}$ gives $\sigma^2 = \mu^2$, as is obvious, but more importantly, we note that $\mu^2 \geqslant \sigma^2$ whatever the value of m.

Indeed, μ^2 exceeds σ^2 by the quantity $(m-\bar{x})^2$, or in other words, the least value of μ^2 is σ^2, and this arises when $m = \bar{x}$. This means that *the sum of the squares of the deviations of any set of data, measured from any value m, is least when m equals the mean of the data.*

This relation between σ^2 and μ^2 corresponds directly to the Parallel Axis Theorem for moments of inertia which was proved in paragraph 9.10.

EXAMPLE (i)

Find the standard deviation of the heights of the group of women tabulated in 18.5.

We use again a working mean of 160·75 so that the values of d'_s in the table equal those of $x_s - 160·75$.

x_s	f_s	d'_s	$f_s d'_s$	$f_s d'^2_s$
150·75	1	−10	−10	100
152·75	2	−8	−16	128
154·75	7	−6	−42	252
156·75	8	−4	−32	128
158·75	18	−2	−36	72
160·75	20	0	0	0
162·75	18	2	36	72
164·75	11	4	44	176
166·75	8	6	48	288
168·75	4	8	32	256
170·75	2	10	20	200
172·75	1	12	12	144
sum	100		56	1816

The mean of the distribution is $160 \cdot 75 + 56/100 = 161 \cdot 31$ and from the column five of the table we get

$$\mu^2 = 1816/100 = 18 \cdot 16$$

and hence $\sigma^2 = 18 \cdot 16 - 0 \cdot 56^2 = 18 \cdot 16 - 0 \cdot 31 = 17 \cdot 85$

so that $\sigma = 4 \cdot 2$.

EXAMPLE (ii)

The mean of 200 measurements is $65 \cdot 56$ cm and the standard deviation is $1 \cdot 12$ cm; the mean of another 300 measurements of the same quantity is $67 \cdot 24$ cm and the standard deviation is $1 \cdot 34$ cm. Find the mean of the 500 measurements and the standard deviation.

The mean of 500 measurements is

$$(65 \cdot 56 \times 2 + 67 \cdot 24 \times 3)/5 \text{ cm}$$

$$= 65 + \frac{1 \cdot 12 + 6 \cdot 72}{5} \text{ cm}$$

$$= 66 \cdot 57 \text{ cm}.$$

Using the relation $\mu^2 = \sigma^2 + (m - \bar{x})^2$, which was established in 18.10, we get:

For the first 200 measurements, the sum of the squares of the deviations from the mean of the whole

$$= \{1 \cdot 12^2 + (66 \cdot 57 - 65 \cdot 56)^2\} \times 200 = 2 \cdot 275 \times 200.$$

For the other 300 measurements, the sum of the squares of the deviations from the mean of the whole

$$= \{1 \cdot 34^2 + (66 \cdot 57 - 67 \cdot 24)^2\} \times 300 = 2 \cdot 245 \times 300.$$

Hence, for the 500 measurements the standard deviation is given by

$$\sigma^2 = \{2 \cdot 275 \times 200 + 2 \cdot 245 \times 300\}/500 = 2 \cdot 257$$

$$\therefore \qquad \sigma = 1 \cdot 50.$$

EXAMPLE (iii)

The observation x occurs with the frequency f as shown below; calculate the mean and standard deviation of the observations.

x	0	1	2	3	4	5	6	7	8	9	10
f	10	40	72	85	78	55	32	18	7	2	1

From inspection it would seem that the mean is somewhere between 3 and 4. We therefore choose a working mean of 3. The working is tabulated below; the values of d equal those of $x - 3$.

The last two columns are included to check the arithmetic, as explained in 18.12.

x	f	d	fd	fd^2	$f(d+1)$	$f(d+1)^2$
0	10	−3	−30	90	−20	40
1	40	−2	−80	160	−40	40
2	72	−1	−72	72	0	0
3	85	0	0	0	85	85
4	78	1	78	78	156	312
5	55	2	110	220	165	495
6	32	3	96	288	128	512
7	18	4	72	288	90	450
8	7	5	35	175	42	252
9	2	6	12	72	14	98
10	1	7	7	49	8	64
sum	400		228	1492	628	2348

The mean of the data is therefore $3 + \dfrac{228}{400} = 3\cdot57$.

Also $\mu^2 = 1492/400 = 3\cdot73$ and hence

$$\sigma^2 = 3\cdot73 - (0\cdot57)^2 = 3\cdot73 - 0\cdot32 = 3\cdot41$$

$$\therefore \qquad \sigma = 1\cdot85.$$

18.12. Charlier's checks

Certain checks, due to Charlier, may be used to check the arithmetic in the calculation of the mean and standard deviation. They depend on the simple expansions

$$\sum f(d+1) = \sum fd + \sum f$$
and
$$\sum f(d+1)^2 = \sum fd^2 + 2\sum fd + \sum f.$$

In example (iii) above in 18.11 $\sum f(d+1)$ and $\sum f(d+1)^2$ were calculated; the values obtained agree with the above results, for these give

$$\sum f(d+1) = 228 + 400 = 628$$
and
$$\sum f(d+1)^2 = 1492 + 2(228) + 400 = 2348.$$

These checks are only partial, but are usually worthwhile.

18.13. Correction for class-width

Data can be classified in groups of which the widths may be variously chosen; for example, the heights of women given in 18.1 in classes of width 2 cm could have been grouped in classes of width 4 cm or 6 cm or some other suitable measure. In practice, the class-width is dictated by the nature of the data, in particular by their number as well as their accuracy; classes either too wide or too narrow do not reveal the general characteristics of the data. For example, in dealing with examination marks expressed as percentages, the smallest possible class-width is one mark, since fractional marks are not given, but in fact a class-width of less than five marks is probably meaningless, as few examiners would claim to be able to mark within 5 per cent. On the other hand, the maximum class-width is 100, in which case the histogram would consist of a single rectangle from which no useful information could be derived. The class-width, however chosen, will in general affect the values of the mean and the standard deviation, since these are defined in terms of the mid-values of the classes; the effect on the mean is usually negligible, but Sheppard has shown that to allow for the class-width, c, the value of μ^2 (and therefore of σ^2) should, under certain conditions, be reduced by $c^2/12$.

In example (iii) in 18.11 the class-width $c = 1$, and hence applying Sheppard's correction we get

$$\mu^2 = 3\cdot73 - 0\cdot08 = 3\cdot65.$$

Hence, $$\sigma^2 = 3\cdot65 - 0\cdot32 = 3\cdot33$$

$\therefore$ $$\sigma = 1\cdot82.$$

EXAMPLES 18.2

1. (a) Find the mean deviation and the standard deviation of the following:

    15, 21, 19, 20, 18, 17, 22, 23, 16, 25.

   (b) Find the mean deviation and the standard deviation of the set of numbers in (a) if their frequencies are 1, 11, 12, 14, 9, 6, 9, 5, 3, 1 respectively.

2. Calculate the standard deviation σ of the distribution consisting of the integers 1 to 5 inclusive.

Samples are taken from these integers, each sample consisting of three different integers (there being ten samples in all) and a second distribution is formed from the means of these samples. If s is the standard deviation of this second distribution, prove that $s/\sigma = 1/\sqrt{6}$. (L.A.)

3. Find the mean and standard deviation of the following distribution:

x	0	1	2	3	4	5	6	7	8
f	1	3	8	12	20	18	16	8	4

4. The following table gives the number of boys in a class of 100 who obtain various marks between 0 and 10 in a test.

Mark	0	1	2	3	4	5	6	7	8	9	10
Number	1	4	7	8	10	20	15	12	11	8	4

Calculate the mean mark and the standard deviation. (L.A.)

5. The heights of 100 men of a certain regiment are given in the following table:

Height in cm	Frequency
151–152	1
153–154	2
155–156	7
157–158	8
159–160	18
161–162	20
163–164	18
165–166	11
167–168	8
169–170	4
171–172	2
173–174	1

Draw the frequency polygon and calculate the mean and the standard deviation of this distribution.

6. The mean of 100 observations is 2·96 and the standard deviation is 0·12, and the mean of a further 50 observations is 2·93 with a standard deviation of 0·16. Find the mean and standard deviation of the two sets of observations taken together.

7. The mean of 500 observations is 4·12 and the standard deviation is 0·18. One hundred of these observations are found to have a mean of 4·20 and a standard deviation of 0·24. Find the mean and standard deviation of the other 400 observations.

8. If n_1 quantities have a mean $\bar{x}$ and standard deviation σ_1 and another n_2 quantities have a mean $\bar{y}$ and standard deviation σ_2, show that the aggregate of (n_1+n_2) quantities has a variance given by

$$\frac{n_1\sigma_1^2+n_2\sigma_2^2}{n_1+n_2}+\frac{n_1n_2(\bar{x}-\bar{y})^2}{(n_1+n_2)^2}.$$

9. The following values of a quantity x were obtained experimentally:

x	18	19	20	21	22	23	24	25	26
Frequency	1	5	8	12	10	7	4	1	2

Calculate the mean and the standard deviation and draw the histogram for this distribution. (L.A.)

10. The following table gives the estimates of 100 individuals of the interpolation of the readings of a scale instrument:

Reading	6·2	6·3	6·4	6·5	6·6	6·7	6·8
No. of individuals	4	11	18	24	21	14	8

Draw the cumulative frequency curve, and calculate the mean, the mode, the median, and the standard deviation from the mean.

11. In testing the weight of ball-bearings weighings were made to the nearest tenth of a unit. Draw a frequency polygon of the following distribution:

Weight	2·7	2·8	2·9	3·0	3·1	3·2	3·3	3·4	3·5
Frequency	1	2	6	17	27	26	13	5	3

Calculate the mean value and the standard deviation from the mean.

12. The following table gives the electrical resistance of 138 carbon rods tested at the same temperature:

Resistance in ohms	310	311	312	313	314	315	316	317	318	319	320
Frequency	1	2	6	21	25	32	24	18	5	3	1

Calculate the mean resistance $\bar{x}$ and the standard deviation σ. Check whether the data lie roughly between $\bar{x}-3\sigma$ and $\bar{x}+3\sigma$.

13. The following table gives the frequencies f of the measured length L cm of 50 rods; calculate the mean value of L and the standard deviation:

L	8·60	8·59	8·58	8·57	8·56	8·55	8·54	8·53	8·52
f	2	4	6	9	12	8	5	3	1

14. The acceleration due to gravity was determined by 24 students using the same method with the following results:

982	995	966	980	982
995	985	964	967	984
972	962	989	987	975
982	987	985	985	976
989	979	980	974	

Arrange the results in order of magnitude and determine the quartiles. Calculate also the mean and the standard deviation.

15. A batch of 200 metal rods are made to a specified length of 50 cm. On measurement the number n of bars of length l cm was found to be as follows:

l	49·6	49·7	49·8	49·9	50·0	50·1	50·2	50·3	50·4
n	4	7	25	43	60	36	19	4	2

Calculate the mean length of the rods, and the standard deviation from the mean.

16. A batch of 80 resistors were manufactured to a supposed resistance of 150 ohms. The resistance of each was then measured to the nearest ohm and the following results obtained:

Resistance in ohms	142	144	145	147	148	149	150	151	152	153	154	157
Frequency	1	2	3	6	10	17	19	13	5	3	2	1

Calculate the mean resistance and the standard deviation. Apply the three standard deviations check (see question 12 above) to your results.

17. In a test on a rifle a hundred rounds were fired at a fixed elevation, and their ranges beyond the 1000-metre mark from the firing point are shown in the following table. Draw the frequency polygon, and from a smooth curve drawn to fit the data estimate the mode. Calculate the mean range and the standard deviation.

Distances (m)	10	20	30	40	50	60	70	80	90	100
Frequency		1	3	6	13	24	26	17	7	2	1

18. A number of electric lamps rated at 100 watts were tested and their power consumption determined. The results were as follows:

Power in watts	99·3	99·4	99·5	99·6	99·7	99·8	99·9	100·0
Frequency	3	4	6	13	26	74	103	105

	100·1	100·2	100·3	100·4	100·5
	91	45	18	8	4

Calculate the mean, median, and standard deviation of the distribution. Draw the cumulative frequency curve.

19. To check a machine filling tins with orange juice, 100 tins were chosen at random and the contents carefully weighed. The following results were obtained. Calculate the mean weight and the standard deviation of the batch.

Weight	0·94	0·95	0·96	0·97	0·98	0·99	1·00	1·01	1·02	1·03
Frequency	1	0	3	4	12	19	24	17	12	8

20. Calculate the mean and standard deviation of the following distribution of weights of a group of men (the unit of weight is 4·45 N):

Weight	Frequency
100–109·5	5
110–119·5	4
120–129·5	7
130–139·5	42
140–149·5	57
150–159·5	51
160–169·5	36
170–179·5	25
180–189·5	13
190–199·5	8
200–209·5	1
210–219·5	1
Total	250

Draw the frequency polygon, and a smooth curve to represent the distribution as closely as possible; find the mode from this curve.

21. Calculate the mean and standard deviation of the following frequency distribution of weekly expenditure on certain items of food:

Expenditure (units of cost)	Frequency of families
3·5–5·4	18
5·5–7·4	107
7·5–9·4	255
9·5–11·4	245
11·5–13·4	173
13·5–15·4	101
15·5–17·4	38
17·5–19·4	17
19·5–21·4	9
21·5–23·4	7
Total	970

22. Apply Bessel's correction and Sheppard's correction to the calculation of σ in Example (i) of 18.11.

23. Discuss the relative importance of the Bessel and Sheppard corrections as applied to question 14 above.

24. The given table shows the number of letters in 40 consecutive lines of a column of print. Form a frequency table from these figures.

36	32	33	31	33	36	33	33	30	29
35	35	32	31	34	29	35	33	32	32
30	29	30	32	32	34	32	33	31	34
27	34	36	36	35	35	30	33	32	31

Calculate:

  (i) the mean number of letters per line;
  (ii) the standard deviation;
  (iii) the mean deviation;
  (iv) the ratio of the mean deviation to the standard deviation.
                                                                    (C.A.)

25. The following table shows the marks obtained by the same 150 candidates in two different papers in a recent examination:

	0–10	11–20	21–30	31–40	41–50
No. of candidates (Paper 1)	2	6	20	28	31
No. of candidates (Paper 2)	3	12	12	2	31

	51–60	61–70	71–80	81–90	91–100
No. of candidates (Paper 1)	20	17	11	8	7
No. of candidates (Paper 2)	15	14	9	9	2

Estimate the mean and median marks for Paper 1 only. If you were told that the true median mark for Paper 1 was in fact 48, what conclusion could you draw about the grouping of the marks?

Comment on the relative difficulty of the two papers. (C.A.)

18.14. Some other terms and definitions

It will be helpful at this stage to add to the terms and definitions explained in 18.3.

Coefficient of variation. The coefficient of variation of any distribution is defined as $100\sigma/\bar{x}$, where $\bar{x}$ and σ are the mean and standard deviation of the distribution; it is expressed as a percentage.

Relative frequency. If f_1, f_2, . . . f_n are the frequencies of the various classes of which x_1, x_2, . . . x_n are the mid-values of the variable, the relative frequency with which x_c occurs is defined as $f_c/\sum f_s$. Denoting this by r_c, it follows that $\sum_{s=1}^{n} r_s = 1$ and that the mean of the data can be written as

$$\bar{x} = \sum_{s=1}^{n} r_s x_s.$$

Also if a histogram is drawn to represent the frequency distribution, then r_c equals the area of the rectangle corresponding to the class of which x_c is the mid-value divided by the total area of the histogram.

If values of r_c are plotted against values of x_c the *relative* frequency polygon or the *relative* frequency histogram can be drawn.

Sample and population. The number of data associated with any particular process or system of measurement is necessarily limited; in some cases the process could be continued indefinitely, but practical considerations rule this out. It is usual to regard a finite set of data as a *sample* taken from a much larger, or infinite, set known as the *population*. For example, 100 measurements of a physical quantity, such as a length or a time-interval, may be thought of as a sample selected from the very large number of measurements which could be made and which are referred to as the population. The term population is used generally in this way, and not limited to the biological examples to which it was first applied. The importance in statistics of this concept of population cannot be over-emphasised.

Sampling. The process of choosing or using a limited group of data from a much larger population is known as sampling. It is the statistician's job to draw conclusions about the population as a whole from the characteristics of the sample. The way the sample is chosen is therefore important; to permit good generalisations to be made a random sample has to be selected. This is difficult, perhaps impossible, to achieve, but may be defined as follows:

Random sampling is defined as such that in selecting an individual from a population each individual in the population has the same chance of being chosen. To approximate to this ideal various devices may be used, including the use of *random numbers*, collections of which are available.

Probability. On tossing a coin there are two possibilities: we get either heads or tails. We therefore say that the probability of getting heads on any one toss is $\frac{1}{2}$, as is the probability of getting tails. The scale of probability ranges from 0 to 1; a probability of 1 means that the event will certainly happen, and a probability of zero that it will not happen. If the probability that an event will happen is p and the probability that it will not happen is q, then $p+q = 1$. For instance, if a die in the form of a uniform cube is thrown, the numbers 1 to 6 are equally probable, and hence the probability of throwing a 2, say, is 1/6 and of not throwing a 2 is 5/6. The phrase 'the odds against an event is m to n' means that the probability of the event happening is $n/(m+n)$.

18.15. Discrete frequency distributions

The variable associated with some measurements or processes has only a certain number of discrete values; for others it may

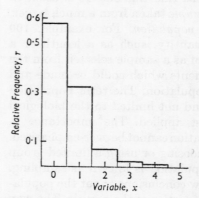

FIG. 18.4

vary continuously over a certain range. Sometimes it is restricted to integral values, as for example, the number of children in a family. Similarly, if a large batch of screws were inspected by taking samples at random five at a time the number x of defective screws in each sample could have any one of the six values 0, 1, 2, 3, 4, 5 *but no others*; x could not be fractional or negative or greater than 5.

A histogram could be drawn in the usual way, the area of each rectangle representing the frequency of each class. The total area would thus equal the total number of samples inspected.

If, however, the area of each rectangle represented the *relative* frequency r of each class, as in Fig. 18.4, then whatever the number of samples inspected, the total area of the histogram would be unity, since by definition the sum of the relative frequencies is always unity.

18.16. Continuous frequency distributions

The variable x may in other cases vary continuously from some value a to another value b. For example, the lengths of certain rods cut by a machine might have any value between, say, 29 and 30 cm. Similarly, the heights of a group of men might have any value between, say, 125 and 225 cm, although actually we might be able to measure them only to the nearest

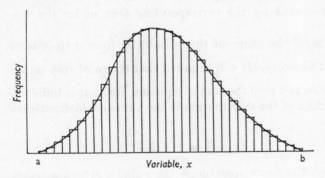

Fig. 18.5

0·5 cm. If we collected a very large number of measurements of this kind and grouped them into classes of small uniform width, say 0·5 cm, the resulting histogram would be as illustrated in Fig. 18.5, and its outline would approximate to a continuous curve.

To find the limiting form of the outline of the histogram as the number of measurements increases indefinitely (and therefore as the area of the histogram increases indefinitely), it is necessary to use the relative frequency. In this case the total area of the histogram remains unity, whatever the number of measurements. The limit of the outline of the relative frequency histogram as the number of measurements tends to infinity is a continuous curve, the area under which is unity. The histogram might be regarded as relating to a sample drawn from the infinite population represented by the continuous curve.

A *continuous* frequency distribution is usually represented mathematically by a *frequency function*, denoted by f, which is some specified function of the variable x. The graph of the function is known as the *frequency curve*.

The frequency function f is defined so that it has the property that the relative frequency of the measurements or observations that lie between x and $x+\delta x$ is $f\,\delta x$. It follows that the relative frequency of the measurements that lie between x_1 and x_2 is given by the integral

$$\int_{x_1}^{x_2} f\,dx,$$

and is represented by the corresponding area under the frequency curve.

Of course, if the range of the variable is from a to b, then $\int_a^b f\,dx$ must be unity. (It will be noted that the total area under the curve does not give the total frequency, for that is infinite.)

The median of the distribution is the value c which satisfies the relation

$$\int_a^c f\,dx = \tfrac{1}{2} = \int_c^b f\,dx.$$

Similarly, the lower quartile is the value d which satisfies the relation

$$\int_a^d f\,dx = \tfrac{1}{4}.$$

The fundamental property of the frequency curve is sometimes interpreted in terms of probabilities, namely, that the probability that any measurement or observation x will lie between x_1 and x_2 is equal to the area under the frequency curve between these limits, that is, is given by the integral

$$\int_{x_1}^{x_2} f\,dx.$$

The frequency function f is therefore sometimes known as the *probability density function*.

The *mean value* $\bar{x}$ and the *standard deviation* σ of a variable x, of which the frequency function f is given, can be expressed in terms of integrals.

In fact, using the definition of the mean given in 18.4, we get

$$\bar{x} = \int_a^b xf \, \mathrm{d}x \bigg/ \int_a^b f \, \mathrm{d}x$$

$$= \int_a^b xf \, \mathrm{d}x,$$

where a and b define the range of x.

This should be compared with the expression for the x-coordinate of the position of the centre of mass of a body, which was discussed in Chapter 16.

Similarly, in keeping with the definition of the standard deviation given in 18.10, we have

$$\sigma^2 = \int_a^b (x-\bar{x})^2 f \, \mathrm{d}x \bigg/ \int_a^b f \, \mathrm{d}x$$

$$= \int_a^b (x-\bar{x})^2 f \, \mathrm{d}x.$$

For example, for the distribution such that f is given by $2/\pi(x^2+1)$ from $x = -1$ to $x = +1$, the factor $2/\pi$ has been chosen to ensure that the area under the frequency curve is unity, that is,

$$\int_{-1}^1 f \, \mathrm{d}x = \frac{2}{\pi} \int_{-1}^1 \frac{\mathrm{d}x}{x^2+1} = \frac{2}{\pi} \left[\tan^{-1} x \right]_{-1}^1 = 1.$$

Also, the mean value of the variable is

$$\bar{x} = \frac{2}{\pi} \int_{-1}^1 \frac{x \, \mathrm{d}x}{x^2+1} = \frac{1}{\pi} \left[\log (x^2+1) \right]_{-1}^1 = 0.$$

This is obvious from the symmetry of the curve about the axis $x = 0$. The median and mode are also $x = 0$.

Similarly, the standard deviation σ is given by:

$$\sigma^2 = \frac{2}{\pi}\int_{-1}^{1} \frac{x^2}{x^2+1}\,dx$$

$$= \frac{2}{\pi}\int_{-1}^{1}\left(1 - \frac{1}{x^2+1}\right)dx$$

$$= \frac{4}{\pi} - 1 = 0.27$$

so that $\sigma = 0.52.$

What is sometimes known as the *second moment* of a distribution about the value $x = m$ is given by

$$\mu^2 = \int_a^b (x-m)^2 f\,dx \bigg/ \int_a^b f\,dx$$

$$= \int_a^b (x-m)^2 f\,dx$$

$$= \int_a^b x^2 f\,dx - 2m\bar{x} + m^2.$$

Similarly, on replacing m by $\bar{x}$, we get

$$\sigma^2 = \int_a^b x^2 f\,dx - 2\bar{x}^2 + \bar{x}^2.$$

Hence $\sigma^2 - \mu^2 = -(\bar{x}-m)^2$

or $\mu^2 = \sigma^2 + (\bar{x}-m)^2$

which agrees with the result proved for a finite distribution in 18.11 (the parallel-axis theorem analogue).

The *mode* of a distribution is the value of the variable for which f has a maximum value; there may be more than one maximum and therefore more than one mode.

18.17. Approximations to continuous distributions

When the number of data is large, that is, when the total frequency is large, the distribution may approximate closely to a continuous one. It is often possible to find the equation of a curve that fits the observations well; the process is known as curve-fitting.

From the equation of the curve the mean, mode, median,

and standard deviation of the population can be found using the methods explained in 18.16.

EXAMPLE (i)

If $f = C(3x - x^2)$, find C so that f might be a frequency function. Find also the mean, the mean deviation, and the standard deviation of the distribution it represents.

We note that f is positive from $x = 0$ to $x = 3$ and is a frequency function if $\int_0^3 f \, dx$ is unity.

$$\therefore \qquad \int_0^3 C(3x - x^2) dx = 1$$

$$\therefore \qquad C\left[\frac{3x^2}{2} - \frac{x^3}{3}\right]_0^3 = 1$$

$$\therefore \qquad C = \tfrac{2}{9}.$$

The mean of the distribution is given by

$$\bar{x} = \int_0^3 xf \, dx$$

$$= \frac{2}{9}\int_0^3 (3x^2 - x^3) \, dx$$

$$= \frac{2}{9}\left[x^3 - \frac{1}{4}x^4\right]_0^3 = \frac{3}{2}$$

as is obvious from symmetry.

The standard deviation is given by

$$\sigma^2 = \int_0^3 \left(x - \frac{3}{2}\right)^2 \times \frac{2}{9}(3x - x^2) dx$$

which reduces to

$$\sigma^2 = 0.45 \text{ or } \sigma = 0.67.$$

Alternatively, we can find the second moment about the origin given by

$$\mu^2 = \int_0^3 x^2 \times \frac{2}{9}(3x - x^2) dx = 2.7$$

and hence

$$\sigma^2 = 2.7 - \left(\frac{3}{2}\right)^2 = 0.45.$$

Similarly, the mean deviation is given by

$$\int_0^3 |x-\bar{x}| f \, dx$$

$$= \frac{2}{9} \int_0^{\frac{3}{2}} \left(\frac{3}{2}-x\right)(3x-x^2) dx + \frac{2}{9} \int_{\frac{3}{2}}^3 \left(x-\frac{3}{2}\right)(3x-x^2) dx$$

$$= 9/16.$$

EXAMPLE (ii)

Find the median and the mode of the distribution given by $f = 12x^2 (1-x)$ *from* $x = 0$ *to* $x = 1$.

The area under the frequency curve from $x = 0$ to $x = 1$ is

$$\int_0^1 12x^2(1-x) dx = 12\left[\frac{x^3}{3} - \frac{x^4}{4}\right]_0^1 = 1.$$

The function f has a stationary value when $\dfrac{df}{dx} = 0$, that is, when

$$2x - 3x^2 = 0$$

$$\therefore \qquad x = 0 \text{ or } \tfrac{2}{3}.$$

There is a maximum value when $x = \tfrac{2}{3}$ and this is the mode of the distribution.

The median of the distribution is $x = c$ where

$$\int_0^c 12x^2(1-x) dx = \tfrac{1}{2}$$

$$\therefore \qquad 12\left(\frac{c^3}{3} - \frac{c^4}{4}\right) = \tfrac{1}{2}$$

$$\therefore \qquad 4c^3 - 3c^4 = \tfrac{1}{2}.$$

The appropriate root of this equation is $c = 0.61$ approximately.

EXAMPLES 18.3

1. For the following frequency distribution find (*a*) the relative frequencies and (*b*) the cumulative frequencies, and draw the corresponding histograms.

x	0	1	2	3	4	5	6	7	8	9	10
f	1	4	7	8	10	20	15	12	11	8	4

2. For the following frequency distribution draw the relative frequency histogram. Draw also a continuous curve which approximates to it. Show roughly the area under the middle portion of the curve which equals one-half.

x	60	61	62	63	64	65	66	67	68	69	70	71
f		1	2	7	8	18	20	18	11	8	4	2	1

3. A sample of 20 data is found to have a mean of 10·3 and standard deviation 2·1; another sample of 30 data has a mean of 11·3 and standard deviation 2·6. Assuming that the two samples were taken from the same population, use the 50 data to estimate the mean and standard deviation of the population. Find also the coefficient of variation.

4. Sketch the frequency curve given by $f = C(1-x^2)$ from $x = -1$ to $x = 1$. Find the value of the parameter C in order that the area under the curve should be unity. Find also the mean value of x, the standard deviation, and the lower and upper quartiles.

5. Draw the frequency curve given by $f = x$ from $x = 0$ to $x = 1$ and $f = 2-x$ from $x = 1$ to $x = 2$. (This is known as the triangular distribution.) What is the mean value of x?

   Find also the median and the standard deviation.

   Obtain the range of x, symmetrical about $x = 1$, for which the area under the curve is $\frac{1}{2}$.

6. Sketch the frequency curve given by $f = Cx^2(2-x)$. Choose the constant C so that the area under the curve, for which f and x are both positive, is unity. Find the mean value of x over this range.

   Find the standard deviation, and the second moment about $x = 0$. Find also the probability that x lies between 0·5 and 1·5.

7. Sketch the frequency curve for the distribution given by $f = 2/\pi(x^2+1)$ from $x = -1$ to $x = 1$. Find approximately the standard deviation of this distribution by using the values of f from $x = 0$ to 1 at intervals of 0·2.

8. The median law is defined by $f = (1/2a)e^{-|x|/a}$ for all values of x. Sketch the frequency curve and show that the area under it is unity. Find the standard deviation.

9. Sketch the frequency curve $f = \frac{1}{8}\pi \sin \frac{1}{4}\pi x$ from $x = 0$ to $x = 4$. Find the area under the curve from $x = 1$ to $x = 3$.

   Calculate the mean deviation of the distribution.

10. A population has the frequency function $f = xe^{-x}$ for all positive values of x. Sketch the frequency curve.

Find the mean and mode of the distribution, and show that the median approximately satisfies the relation

$$\text{Median} - \text{Mode} = 2 \, (\text{Mean} - \text{Median}).$$

11. Calculate the mean deviation of the distribution represented by $f = 12x^2(1-x)$ from $x = 0$ to $x = 1$. Check your result by using only the values of f from $x = 0$ to 1 at intervals of 0.2. Draw the corresponding histogram.

12. A population has the frequency function $f = 4x(x-1)(x-2)$ for $0 \leqslant x \leqslant 1$. Determine the mean and the mode. Determine the median from the relation

$$\text{Median} - \text{Mode} = 3 \, (\text{Mean} - \text{Median}),$$

and check the result by direct calculation.

18.17. Certain special frequency distributions

Observational data are distributed in various ways, but many approach closely to one or other of three specially important types of frequency distributions. These are known as the *binomial*, *Poisson*, and *normal* (or *Gaussian*) distributions. The first two are discontinuous, the variable having only integral values, but the third is a continuous distribution of wide application in science.

18.18. The binomial distribution

A set of data which for integral values of the variable ($x = 0, 1, 2, 3, \ldots n$) has relative frequencies given by the terms of the expansion of $(q+p)^n$, where $p+q = 1$, is known as a *binomial* distribution.

The sum of the relative frequencies is unity, as it should be, since $p+q = 1$.

If, for example, $p = \frac{1}{3}$, $q = \frac{2}{3}$, and $n = 6$ the relative frequencies are given by the successive terms of the expansion of $(\frac{2}{3}+\frac{1}{3})^6$, namely,

$$\frac{1}{3^6}\left[2^6, \; \frac{6}{1}\times 2^5, \; \frac{6.5}{1.2}\times 2^4, \; \frac{6.5.4}{1.2.3}\times 2^3, \; \frac{6.5}{1.2}\times 2^2, \; \frac{6}{1}\times 2, \; 1 \right]$$

that is, $\dfrac{1}{3^6}$ [64, 192, 240, 160, 60, 12, 1].

These are represented as a histogram in Fig. 18.6.

It is instructive to draw histograms for different values of p (and q) and n. They are symmetrical when $p = q = \frac{1}{2}$. It can be shown that the mean of the binomial distribution $(q+p)^n$ is np and the standard deviation $\sqrt{(npq)}$.

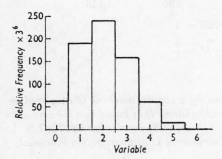

FIG. 18.6. Binomial distribution of $(\frac{2}{3} + \frac{1}{3})^6$

EXAMPLE (i)

Verify that the following frequency distribution is of binomial type and find the mean and standard deviation.

x	0	1	2	3	4
f	81	108	54	12	1

Since the first and last terms of $(q+p)^n$ are q^n and p^n, if the above frequencies are distributed binomially, then $(p/q)^4$ must equal $1/81$, that is, p/q must equal $\frac{1}{3}$. It follows that q must equal $\frac{3}{4}$ and p equal $\frac{1}{4}$.

Now the expansion of $(\frac{3}{4} + \frac{1}{4})^4$ is

$$\frac{1}{4^4}(81 + 108 + 54 + 12 + 1)$$

which verifies that the above distribution is binomial.

Hence the mean of the distribution is $np = 1$ and the standard deviation is $\sqrt{(npq)} = \frac{1}{2}\sqrt{3}$.

We can, however, calculate the mean and the standard deviation from first principles as follows, using $x = 0$ as the working mean.

x	f	fd	fd^2
0	81	0	0
1	108	108	108
2	54	108	216
3	12	36	108
4	1	4	16
sum	256	256	448

Hence, the mean $\bar{x} = 256/256 = 1$

and
$$\sigma^2 = \frac{448}{256} - 1^2 = \frac{3}{4}.$$

EXAMPLE (ii)

A large batch of articles produced by a certain machine is inspected by taking 100 samples of 5 articles at random. It is found that the numbers of samples containing 0, 1, 2, 3, 4, 5 defective articles are 58, 32, 7, 2, 1, 0 respectively. Show that this distribution is approximately binomial.

The mean of the above distribution is
$$(0+32+14+6+4+0)/100 = 0·56.$$

If we equate this to np with $n = 5$ we get $p = 0·112$. Taking $p = \frac{1}{9}$ for simplicity, the binomial expansion of $(\frac{8}{9}+\frac{1}{9})^5$ gives

$$\frac{1}{9^5}[8^5+5\times8^4+10\times8^3+10\times8^2+5\times8+1]$$

$$= 0·5549+0·3468+0·0867+0·0108+0·0007+0·0000$$

Hence if the distribution were of this binomial type we should expect the 100 samples to be distributed as follows: 55, 35, 9, 1, 0, 0. These agree well with the numbers actually found.

Note. $p = \frac{1}{9}$ means that the proportion of defectives in the batch is likely to be about 11 per cent. Or put another way, the probability that any article chosen at random is defective is $\frac{1}{9}$ or 11 per cent.

Further, if two articles are chosen from the batch at random the terms of the expansion of $(\frac{8}{9}+\frac{1}{9})^2$, namely, $\frac{64}{81}$, $\frac{16}{81}$, $\frac{1}{81}$, give in turn the probabilities that neither of the two articles is defective, that one of them is defective, and that both are defective.

This is a special case of Bernoulli's Theorem, which states that if the probability of an event happening is p and the probability that it will not happen is q (so that $q+p = 1$) the probabilities that it will happen on 0, 1, 2, 3, ... n out of n occasions are given by the successive terms of the binomial expansions of $(q+p)^n$.

Thus in tossing pennies the probability of getting heads is $\frac{1}{2}$ and of getting tails is also $\frac{1}{2}$; if therefore a penny is tossed 8 times the probability of getting heads 5 times is

$$\frac{8 \times 7 \times 6 \times 5 \times 4}{1 \times 2 \times 3 \times 4 \times 5} (\tfrac{1}{2})^5 (\tfrac{1}{2})^3 = \frac{7}{32}.$$

18.19. The Poisson distribution

In this distribution the relative frequencies are related to successive terms of the exponential series

$$1 + \frac{m}{1} + \frac{m^2}{1 \times 2} + \frac{m^3}{1 \times 2 \times 3} + \cdots + \frac{m^n}{n!} + \cdots$$

A distribution is defined to be of the Poisson type if for integral values of the variable ($x = 0, 1, 2, 3, \ldots n$) the relative frequencies are proportional to $1, \dfrac{m}{1}, \dfrac{m^2}{1 \times 2}, \dfrac{m^3}{1 \times 2 \times 3}, \cdots \dfrac{m^n}{n!}$ respectively.

The actual relative frequencies are obtained by dividing each of these terms by their sum, which if n is large enough equals e^m approximately, where $e = 2 \cdot 718\,28$ correct to five decimal places.

The relative frequencies r of a Poisson distribution may therefore be written as in the following table:

x	0	1	2	3	... n
$e^m r$	1	m	$\dfrac{m^2}{1 \times 2}$	$\dfrac{m^3}{1 \times 2 \times 3}$	$\cdots \dfrac{m^n}{n!}$

The mean of such a distribution can be shown to be m and the standard deviation m^2 when n is infinite.

The histogram of a Poisson distribution for which $m = 3$ is shown in Fig. 18.7.

Data conforming approximately to Poisson distributions occur widely in science, particularly in biology. They also arise in many industrial situations, when the particular event recorded is such that the probability that it will happen is small. See note below.

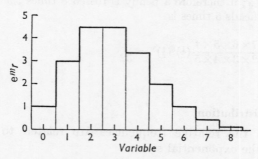

FIG. 18.7.   Poisson distribution having mean $= 3$

EXAMPLE (i)

A large batch of articles produced by a certain machine is inspected by taking 100 *samples of* 5 *articles at random. It is found that the numbers of samples containing* 0, 1, 2, 3, 4, 5 *defective articles are* 58, 32, 7, 2, 1, 0 *respectively. Show that this is approximately a Poisson distribution.*

The mean number of defective articles is 0·556, that is, $\frac{5}{9}$ approximately, and the terms of the Poisson series with $m = \frac{5}{9}$ are

$$\mathrm{e}^{-\frac{5}{9}}\left[1+\frac{5}{9}+\frac{25}{162}+\frac{125}{4374}+\frac{625}{157\,464}+\cdots\right]$$

$$= 0\cdot574+0\cdot319+0\cdot089+0\cdot016+0\cdot002+\cdots$$

If the distribution were of the Poisson type we should therefore expect the 100 samples to be distributed as follows: 57, 32, 9, 2, 0, 0. These agree well with the actual values.

Note. It was shown in Example (ii) of 18.18 that this particular distribution is also approximately binomial. For some values of p, n, and m binomial and Poisson distributions are almost identical, but in other cases they are very different. It can be shown that if p is small while n is large, and such that $np = m$, the binomial expansion of $(q+p)^n$ approximates closely to the series

$$\mathrm{e}^{-m}\left(1+\frac{m}{1}+\frac{m^2}{1\times2}+\frac{m^3}{1\times2\times3}+\cdots+\frac{m^n}{n!}\right).$$

EXAMPLE (ii)

The number of dust particles in a small sample of air can be estimated by using a dust counter. The following values were found in a set of 400 samples. Find the mean and standard deviation. Verify that the distribution is roughly Poissonian.

No. of particles	0	1	2	3	4	5	6	7	8
Frequency	23	56	88	95	73	40	17	5	3

The mean number of particles and the standard deviation are calculated below, using a working mean of 3.

x	f	d	fd	fd^2
0	23	-3	-69	207
1	56	-2	-112	224
2	88	-1	-88	88
3	95	0	0	0
4	73	1	73	73
5	40	2	80	160
6	17	3	51	153
7	5	4	20	80
8	3	5	15	75
sum	400		-30	1060

Hence, the mean $= 3 - \dfrac{30}{400} = 2\cdot93$

and $\qquad \sigma^2 = \dfrac{1060}{400} - \left(\dfrac{3}{40}\right)^2 = 2\cdot64.$

The terms of the Poisson series with $m = 2\cdot9$ are

$$e^{-2\cdot9}[1 + 2\cdot9 + 2\cdot9^2/2 + 2\cdot9^3/6 + \dots]$$

$$= 0\cdot055 + 0\cdot160 + 0\cdot231 + 0\cdot224 + 0\cdot163 + 0\cdot094 + 0\cdot046 + 0\cdot019$$

$$+ 0\cdot007 + \dots$$

On multiplying by the total frequency the successive terms become 22, 64, 92, 90, 65, 38, 18, 8, 3, which agree fairly well with the observed values. The degree of departure from the Poisson distribution is indicated by the value of σ^2 (2·64), which should equal the mean (2·93).

18.20. The normal distribution

The frequency function of the *normal* or *Gaussian* distribution is

$$f = \frac{h}{\sqrt{\pi}}\, e^{-h^2(x-m)^2}.$$

It involves two parameters h and m. It can be shown that the mean of the distribution is m (this is obvious from the symmetry of the curve, as shown in Fig. 18.8), and also the standard deviation of the distribution is given by $\sigma^2 = 1/2h^2$.

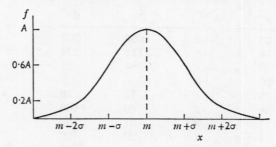

Fig. 18.8

We can therefore write

$$f = \frac{1}{\sigma\sqrt{(2\pi)}} e^{-(x-\bar{x})^2/2\sigma^2}.$$

This represents a normal distribution of which the mean is $\bar{x}$ and the standard deviation is σ. The range of the distribution includes all values of x, positive and negative, and the constant $1/\sigma\sqrt{(2\pi)}$ is chosen to ensure that $\displaystyle\int_{-\infty}^{\infty} f\, dx = 1$.

The shape of the normal frequency curve for the same value of $\bar{x}$ and for different values of σ is shown in Fig. 18.9.

It can be shown that the histogram of a binomial distribution for which n is large approximates closely to a normal frequency curve.

We might use as an example the binomial distribution corresponding to $(\frac{1}{2}+\frac{1}{2})^{10}$, the mean of which is 5 and the standard deviation is $\frac{1}{2}\sqrt{10}$. The normal frequency distribution with the same mean and standard deviation is given by

$$f = \frac{1}{\sqrt{(5\pi)}} e^{-(x-5)^2/5}.$$

The normal frequency curve and the histogram of the binomial distribution drawn on the same diagram fit well, even though in this case n is not very large.

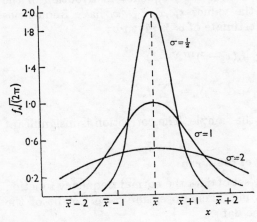

FIG. 18.9

The normal distribution was first derived by Demoivre in 1733 when dealing with problems associated with the tossing of coins. It was also obtained independently by Laplace and Gauss later, and applied to the distribution of accidental errors in astronomical and other scientific data. It is the basis of what is called the theory of errors.* It has other important applications in physics.

We can find the normal frequency curve which best fits any set of data by finding the mean and standard deviation of the data, using the methods explained earlier. If, for example, we consider the observations quoted in Example (iii) of 18.11 it was found that $\bar{x} = 3\cdot57$ and $\sigma = 1\cdot82$, after Sheppard's corrections had been applied. The corresponding frequency function is therefore

$$f = \frac{1}{1\cdot82\sqrt{(2\pi)}} e^{-(x-3\cdot57)^2/6\cdot66}.$$

* See *Errors of Observation*, by J. Topping.

It is instructive to draw this frequency curve and the corresponding relative frequency histogram on the same diagram.

The standard deviation of a sample of N data is often denoted by s to distinguish it from the standard deviation σ of the infinite population from which the sample is drawn. It can be shown that the best estimate we can make of σ^2 is not s^2 but $Ns^2/(N-1)$. This factor $N/(N-1)$ is often called Bessel's correction. It follows that if the frequency distribution of the sample is such that the values x_1, x_2, ... x_n have frequencies $f_1, f_2, \ldots f_n$ the best estimate of σ^2 is given by

$$\sum_{s=1}^{n} f_s(x_s - \bar{x})^2/(N-1)$$

where
$$N = \sum_{s=1}^{n} f_s$$

and $\bar{x}$ is the mean of the sample. The correction is insignificant when N is large.

18.21. Standard error of the mean

It is clear that for any set of data the normal frequency function found in this way is not likely to ensure a perfect fit of the frequency curve to the data.

In any case the frequency function refers to an infinite population, of which the set of data is merely a sample. However, $\bar{x}$ and σ calculated for the sample are the best values of the parameters that can be found for the population as a whole.

It is important to know how $\bar{x}$ and σ vary with the size of the sample. If we select at random a sample of N data from an infinite population it is obvious that, in general, the mean of the sample will not be the same as the mean of the whole population; if N is large the two means may not differ very much, but if N is small they may. It is possible to express mathematically the manner in which the means of different samples of given size, taken from a normal population, are distributed. In fact, it can be shown that this distribution is itself normal, and such that its mean equals the true mean of the whole population, while its standard deviation equals $\sigma/\sqrt{N}$, where N is the number of data in each sample and σ is the standard deviation of whole population. Figure 18.9 illustrates how the distribution of the means of samples retains its normal form but decreases in dispersion as the size of the samples increases.

It is therefore usual to write the mean of any set of data in the form $\bar{x} \pm \alpha$, where $\alpha = \sigma/\sqrt{N}$ and is called the *standard error of the mean*.

Similarly, the standard error of the standard deviation is $\sigma/\sqrt{\{2(N-1)\}}$.

Thus for Example (iii) of 18.11 the mean of the observations could be written as $3{\cdot}57 \pm 1{\cdot}82/\sqrt{400}$, that is, $3{\cdot}57 \pm 0{\cdot}09$.

18.22. Area under the normal frequency curve

For a normal distribution the relative frequency of the observations that lie between any two values x_1 and x_2 is

$$\frac{1}{\sigma\sqrt{(2\pi)}} \int_{x_1}^{x_2} e^{-(x-\bar{x})^2/2\sigma^2} dx$$

and equals the area under the normal frequency curve between the ordinates x_1 and x_2.

Writing $(x-\bar{x})/\sigma = t$, this integral becomes

$$\frac{1}{\sqrt{(2\pi)}} \int_{t_1}^{t_2} e^{-\frac{1}{2}t^2} dt$$

where $t_1 = (x_1-\bar{x})/\sigma$ and $t_2 = (x_2-\bar{x})/\sigma$. It can be expressed as the difference of two integrals of the type

$$\frac{1}{\sqrt{(2\pi)}} \int_0^T e^{-\frac{1}{2}t^2} dt.$$

This integral has been evaluated for different values of T and is given in mathematical tables. When $T = 1$ its value is $0{\cdot}3413$; when $T = 2$ it equals $0{\cdot}4772$, and when $T = 3$ it equals $0{\cdot}4987$. It equals $\frac{1}{2}$ when T is infinite, and it equals $\frac{1}{4}$ when $T = 0{\cdot}6745$.

It follows that for a normal distribution the relative frequency of the observations that lie within the range $\bar{x}-2\sigma$ to $\bar{x}+2\sigma$ is $2(0{\cdot}4772)$ or $0{\cdot}9543$, and of the observations that lie within the range $\bar{x}-3\sigma$ to $\bar{x}+3\sigma$ it is $2(0{\cdot}4987)$ or $0{\cdot}9973$. This is the justification for the three standard deviations check referred to in Examples 18.2; the probability that an observation will lie outside this range is $0{\cdot}27$ per cent or about 1 in 370.

Similarly, if α is the standard error of the mean $\bar{x}$ of any set of data it may be inferred that if a much larger number of measurements had been made the probability that their mean would lie between $\bar{x}-\alpha$ and $\bar{x}+\alpha$ is 0·68, that it would lie between $\bar{x}-2\alpha$ and $\bar{x}+2\alpha$ is 0·95, and between $\bar{x}-3\alpha$ and $\bar{x}+3\alpha$ is 0·9973. This is the significance of the standard error of the mean.

EXAMPLES 18.4

1. Draw the histogram of the binomial distribution corresponding to $(q+p)^n$ when $p = \frac{1}{3}$ and $n = 5$. Calculate the mean and standard deviations.

2. Draw the histogram of the binomial distribution corresponding to $(q+p)^n$ when $q = \frac{4}{5}$ and $n = 6$. Calculate the mean and standard deviation.

3. A penny is tossed 10 times; calculate the probability that there will be: (a) 3 heads, (b) 7 heads and (c) more than 2 heads.

4. A man throws a die 4 times. What is the probability that he will get four sixes? What number of sixes is he most likely to get?

5. The production of a radar component is checked by examining samples of 4. The following table shows the number of defectives found in 200 samples; calculate the mean number of defectives per sample:

No. of defectives	0	1	2	3	4
No. of samples	62	85	40	11	2

Show that the distribution is roughly binomial.

6. Find the frequencies of the Poisson distribution of which the mean is 3. Calculate the standard deviation of the distribution. Draw the histogram.

7. Find the frequencies of the Poisson distribution of which the mean is 4·5. Calculate the standard deviation of the distribution. Draw the histogram.

8. The number of stoppages on 400 consecutive shifts in an industrial firm were recorded as follows:

Stoppages per shift	0	1	2	3	4	5
Number of shifts	245	119	30	4	2	0

Show that the distribution is approximately of the Poisson type.

9. A number of large boxes of eggs are tested and it is found that the average number of broken eggs is two per box. What is the probability that a box will contain more than: (a) three broken eggs; (b) four broken eggs?

10. Results of a count of warp breakages during the weaving of particular lengths of cloth are given below. Show that the distribution is approximately Poissonian.

Warp breakages	0	1	2	3	4	5	6
Frequency	15	26	21	19	8	3	0

11. Tests made on electrical contacts to examine how often the contacts failed to interrupt the circuit due to their welding together yielded the following results:

No of welds per test	0	1	2	3	4	5
Frequency	10	13	13	8	4	2

Show that the distribution is roughly Poissonian, and find its standard deviation.

12. The following table gives the frequencies f of the number n of successes in a set of 500 trials. Find the mean of the distribution and verify that the distribution is roughly of the Poisson type. Calculate also the standard deviation.

n	0	1	2	3	4	5	6	7	8	9
f	24	77	110	112	84	50	24	12	5	2

13. Show that the following distribution is roughly of the Poisson type and find its standard deviation:

n	0	1	2	3	4	5
f	21	29	22	12	5	1

Show also that the binomial distribution of which the mean equals the mean of the data does not fit them very well.

14. The number of α-particles emitted per unit time by polonium were counted, and the results are given below where f is the number of times n particles were observed. Show that the mean number of particles emitted is 3·87 and find the Poisson distribution corresponding to this mean.

n	0	1	2	3	4	5	6	7	8	9	10	11	12
f		57	203	383	525	532	408	273	139	45	27	10	4	2

15. Write down the binomial distribution corresponding to $(\frac{1}{2}+\frac{1}{2})^{10}$ and find the mean and standard deviation. Write down the normal frequency function corresponding to this mean and this standard deviation. Draw the histogram of the distribution and the normal curve on the same diagram.

16. Find the equation of the normal frequency curve to fit the following distribution:

x	25	26	27	28	29	30	31	32	33	34
f	1	5	17	49	85	52	25	11	4	1

17. The diameters of the spores of lycopodium can be found by an interference method. The results of an experiment are given below, where $k = 5880$ when the diameters are measured in cm.

$k \times$ diameter	14	15	16	17	18	19	20	21	22	23
No. of spores	1	1	8	24	48	58	35	16	8	1

Find the mean diameter of the spores and the standard error of the mean. Represent the results by a histogram and draw the corresponding normal error curve.

18. The results of examining 213 discharge tubes and noting the voltage associated with a particular operating characteristic are given below. Find the corresponding normal frequency function.

Voltages	97	98	99	100	101	102	103	104	105	106	107	108	109
No. of tubes	1	8	10	25	32	42	42	27	15	4	3	3	1

19. The results of certain measurements on the breakdown voltages of 100 insulators are given below; n is the number of insulators with a breakdown voltage less than E kV.

Breakdown voltages, E	110	120	130	140	150	160	170	180	190	200	210
Number of insulators, n	0	3	7	15	26	55	78	92	96	99	100

Find the mean and standard deviation, and verify that the distribution is roughly normal. Apply the three standard deviations check to your results.

20. The heights of a population are normally distributed with mean 168·95 cm and standard deviation 5·28 cm; find the probability that any individual taken at random will be: (a) between 163·68 and 174·25 cm in height, and (b) more than 180 cm in height.

21. A sample of 100 taken from a population is roughly normally distributed and has a mean of 9·35 and standard deviation 2·1. What is the probability that the mean of the population will be between: (i) 9·14 and 9·56; (ii) 8·93 and 9·77; (iii) 9·14 and 9·77. If the probability that the mean of the population lies between $9·35 - \beta$ and $9·35 + \beta$ is $\frac{1}{2}$, find the value of β.

22. From a large number of standard 10-ohm resistances, thirty were taken at random and their resistances in ohms measured ac-

curately at 18°C, with the results shown below. Calculate the
mean and standard deviation of the results, the standard error
of the mean, and state two values between which the mean
resistance of the complete batch may be assumed to be with
reasonable certainty.

10·02	10·02	10·00	10·02	10·01	10·01
10·00	10·01	10·02	10·00	10·00	10·00
10·01	9·99	10·01	10·00	10·03	10·00
10·00	10·00	9·98	10·01	10·00	10·05
9·99	10·01	10·01	9·99	10·00	10·01

23. Twenty-five measurements of the surface tension of water have
a mean value of $0·07247$ N m^{-1} with a standard deviation of
$0·00055$. Find the standard error of the mean.

Given that the accepted value of the surface tension at the
temperature of the laboratory is $0·07305$ N m^{-1}, show that
there is likely to be a systematic error in the measurements.

24. A penny is tossed 100 times. Write down the normal frequency
function which corresponds roughly to the distribution of heads.
From this function find the probability that there will be more
than 55 heads.

25. Eleven independent determinations of the percentage of nitrogen
in a fertiliser gave the following values: 16·0, 17·0, 16·8, 16·3,
17·2, 16·1, 16·4, 16·7, 17·1, 17·0, 16·3. Estimate the mean
nitrogen content of the fertiliser and its standard error.

How many more observations would be required to reduce
the standard error of the mean to 0·1 ?   (C.A.)

26. Explain what is meant by a frequency distribution for measurements which take only integral values and describe conditions
under which the distribution would be binomial.

Before a consignment of potatoes may be exported as seed
potatoes a random sample of 300 has to be inspected and found
free of infection. Show that if the average rate of infection in
the consignment is 1 per cent, then there is approximately a
95 per cent chance that it will not be passed.   (C.A.)

27. A critical length is determined experimentally a hundred times
by an observer A, with the following results:

Length (mm)	540	541	542	543	544	545	546	547	548	549	550
Frequency	1	5	9	23	20	17	12	6	4	2	1

Draw a histogram for this distribution, and, using a working
origin of 544 mm, determine the mean and the standard deviation, giving each to one place of decimals.

Another observer B performs the same experiment a hundred times with a consequent mean of 543·4 and standard deviation 2·4. Which observer is the more consistent and why?

28. The numbers 1, 2, 3, 4, 5, 6 are printed one on each of six cards. Three cards are drawn at random and the numbers on them are added together. In 100 trials the following distribution is obtained:

Total	6	7	8	9	10	11	12	13	14	15
Frequency	3	6	9	16	15	11	17	12	5	6

Calculate the mean and the standard deviation from the mean of this distribution. Would you expect the mean to rise or fall if the number of trials were greatly increased, assuming that every selection is equally probable?   (L.A.)

29. A set of 200 data has a mean of 4·56. Examine whether this set may be regarded as a random sample drawn from a normal population of which the mean is 4·76 and the standard deviation 0·96.

30. Measurements of a physical quantity yielded a mean of 200 with a standard deviation of 12. A year later a further 25 measurements were made which had a mean of 195. May it be concluded that the quantity had changed in the interval?

31. A hen may be expected to lay five eggs a week. If six hens are kept, calculate the chance of getting: (a) six eggs in one day; (b) four eggs in one day.

32. In the theory of samples drawn from a population the proofs of two theorems are needed; first, that the mean of the means of the samples is the same as the mean of the population; secondly, that the standard error of these means is $\sigma/\sqrt{n}$, where σ is the standard deviation of the population and n is the sample size. Prove the *first* of these theorems.

A machine is intended to make insulators 3 cm long. These are satisfactory provided their standard deviation is not more than 0·01 cm. As the machine gets older its accuracy is tested by finding the mean lengths of sample batches of 20 insulators. It is found that the standard deviation of the means of a number of batches is 0·005 cm. State, with reasons, what conclusions you draw about the condition of the machine.   (C.A.)

33. In a certain test 100 valves were run until they failed. The table gives the numbers of valves still working after various periods of time:

No. of hours (in thousands)	1	2	3	4	5	6	7	8	9	10
No. of valves still working	68	57	50	42	32	23	16	10	5	0

   Obtain a new table showing the estimated probability of a valve failing within the next thousand hours against the numbers of hours for which it has already worked. Hence show that it is unwise to replace a valve which is still working by a new one until it has worked for 7000 hours.   (C.A.)

34. Ten pennies, supposed to be equally likely to come down 'heads' or 'tails' are tossed together 1024 times, and at each tossing the numbers of heads and tails are recorded. Find the probability of a toss resulting in 3 heads and 7 tails.

   In the actual result this combination appeared 152 times out of the 1024. Discuss the discrepancy between this and the 'expected' value, and say whether you consider this divergence has any significance.

   Find the number of times out of 1024 in which this combination of heads and tails might be expected if all the pennies were equally untrue and if the odds on tails are 8 to 7.   (C.A.)

35. Prove that, in a distribution whose standard deviation is σ, the standard error of the mean of n independent observations is $\sigma/\sqrt{n}$.

   It is found that light bulbs have a mean life of 1120 hours with a standard deviation of 70 hours. How large a sample is required to be reasonably certain that the mean life in the sample shall exceed 1100 hours?   (C.A.)

36. (a) In a binomial distribution where the frequencies of occurrence of an event are given by the terms of the expansion of $N(p+q)^m$, the mean μ and the standard deviation σ of the distribution are given by the formulae

$$\mu = mp, \quad \sigma = \sqrt{(mpq)}.$$

Prove these formulae in the case where $m = 3$.

   (b) Two men A and B play a game in which A should win 8 games to every 7 won by B. If they play 3 games, show that the probability that A will win at least two games is approximately 0·55.   (C.A.)

ANSWERS TO THE EXAMPLES

EXAMPLES 1.1 (p. 11)

1. 72, 20.
2. 9, 4·5, 6 kmh⁻¹.
3. $8\frac{1}{3}$ minutes.
5. 300 km; 2·6 s.
6. $a.\ s = 4t$.
   $b.\ s = 2t$, then $s = 6$.
   $c.\ s = 3t+1$.
   $d.\ s = t(t+1)$.
7. $a.$ 3, 1·8, $1\frac{7}{8}$ ms⁻¹;
   3, 0, 2 ms⁻¹.
   $b.$ 1, 1·6, 1·5 ms⁻¹;
   2, 2, 0 ms⁻¹.
8. $a.$ 14·09; 20·9 km.
   $b.$ 13·58.
   $c.$ 31 minutes.
9. 5, 5, 8, 8 ms⁻¹; 5, 7, 8, 9 ms⁻¹.
10. 40, 19, 29 kmh⁻¹.

11. (i) 48 kmh⁻¹; (ii) 96 kmh⁻¹;
    (iii) 20 and 50 minutes approximately.
12. (i) 4, 4; (ii) 4t, 0.
13. (a) $30-10t-5\delta t$;
    (b) $30-10t$;
    (c) $t = 3$, $s = 45$ m.
14. (a) 2, 0, 3 ms⁻¹; (b) 4, 0, 4 ms⁻¹; (c) 0, 8, 0 ms⁻¹.
15. 8 cms⁻¹. 42 cm.
16. (i) 3 hours 39 minutes and 18·2 km; (ii) 1 hour 27 minutes and 2 hours 42 minutes from start.
17. $112\frac{1}{2}$ minutes; $10\frac{2}{3}$ kmh⁻¹.
18. $(3t-1)$ ms⁻¹, $\frac{1}{3}$ s.
19. 12 ms⁻¹, 2 s, 10 s.
20. 4t, 16, $80-8t$ ms⁻¹.

EXAMPLES 1.2 (p. 20)

1. 7 km.
2. 50·3 km; 28° 40′ W. of N.; 1·006 hours.
3. 600 km, 60° E. of N.
4. 62 minutes 30° W. of N.
6. (a) $9\sqrt{2}/2$, $9\sqrt{2}/2$; (b) 4·5, $9\sqrt{3}/2$; (c) $-6\sqrt{3}$, 6; (d) $-6\sqrt{2}$, $-6\sqrt{2}$.
7. (i) 17·85 km, $37\frac{1}{2}°$ E. of N.;
   (ii) 15 km, 23° 8′ W. of N.;
   (iii) 3 km S.W.
8. (i) 2·35 km, $37\frac{1}{2}°$ S. of W.;
   (ii) 15 km, 6° 52′ N. of E.;
   (iii) 21 km N.E.

9. 5.18, 7.32.
10. 5°, 110°.
11. 17·1 units at 95° 16′.
12. 7·7 units, 29°.
13. (i) $\sqrt{29}$ at 21° 48′ to $0x$;
    (ii) $6\sqrt{2}$ at 45°; (iii) $\sqrt{10}$ at $-18°$ 26′; (iv) $\sqrt{74}$ at 54° 28′;
    (v) $7\sqrt{2}$ at 45°; (vi) $\sqrt{85}$ at 220° 36′.
14. (i) $m = 3$; (ii) $n = 2$;
    (iii) $m = 6/5$, $n = -7/5$.

EXAMPLES 1.3 (p. 27)

1. 10 ms⁻¹.
2. 12·16 ms⁻¹.
3. 34 ms⁻¹ at 62° to the direction of motion.

4. $6\sqrt{3}$, $8\sqrt{3}$ ms⁻¹.
5. 10 ms⁻¹; 17·32 ms⁻¹.
6. $5/\sqrt{2}$, $-5/\sqrt{2}$ kmh⁻¹.
7. $8\sqrt{3}$, 8 kmh⁻¹.

8. 5 ms^{-1} at tan^{-1}($\frac{3}{4}$) to horizontal.

9. 6, 6$\sqrt{3}$ kmh^{-1}.

10. 7·3, 5·2 ms^{-1}.

11. 5$\sqrt{2}$; 2$\sqrt{5}$, 4$\sqrt{5}$ ms^{-1}.

12. 5·35, 10·7 ms^{-1}.

13. 2$\sqrt{5}$, 4$\sqrt{5}$ ms^{-1}.

14. 6$\frac{1}{2}$; 2$\frac{1}{4}$, 6 units s^{-1}.

15. 3π ms^{-1}; −3π, 0;
−3$\sqrt{3}\pi/2$, −3$\pi/2$; 3$\sqrt{3}\pi/2$,
−3$\pi/2$; 3$\pi/2$, 3$\sqrt{3}\pi/2$ ms^{-1}.

16. 10π ms^{-1} tangential;
(a) 20$\sqrt{2}$ ms^{-1} at 45° to initial velocity; (b) 20 ms^{-1} perpendicular to initial velocity; (c) 0.

17. (a) 2, 3 ms^{-1}; (b) 2, 4 ms^{-1}; (c) 2, 4 ms^{-1}.

18. 2, 4, 2$\sqrt{5}$ ms^{-1}; 2, 6, 2$\sqrt{10}$ ms^{-1}.

19. 15, 0 ms^{-1}; 5$\sqrt{13}$ ms^{-1}; 1 s.

20. 0·4, 1·6 s; 3$\sqrt{29}$ ms^{-1};
tan^{-1} ($\pm$0·4).

EXAMPLES 1.4 (p. 33)

1. 72 m.

2. At cos^{-1} $\frac{1}{3}$ with the bank upstream.

3. At 123° 45′ with his direction of motion.

4. The one who swims north; 0·27 minute sooner.

5. 80° 25′.

6. 12 nearly; about 79° N. of E.

9. (i) straight across; 1·8 minutes; 240 m; (ii) at cos^{-1} 5/8 with bank upstream; 2·3 minutes; 187 m.

10. 18° 42′ E. of N.;
41° 18′ E. of N.

11. 7 ms^{-1}; 38° to velocity 12.

13. 3·9 kmh^{-1} along XO.

14. 3v parallel to AD; $v\sqrt{3}$.

15. v, 120°.

EXAMPLES 1.5 (p. 38)

1. 64·03 kmh^{-1} at 38° 40′ with direction of second.

2. 28·85 kmh^{-1} at 33° 41′ with direction of bus.

3. tan^{-1} 0·45 with horizontal; 7·3 ms^{-1}.

4. tan$^{-1}\dfrac{2+\sqrt{2}}{2}$ S. of W.

5. 40 kmh^{-1}; tan^{-1} $\frac{3}{4}$ W. of N.

6. After 0·47 hour; 11·9 km.

7. sin^{-1} $\frac{1}{40}$ in front of ship.

8. 7·5 kmh^{-1}; tan^{-1} $\frac{3}{4}$ with A's direction.

9. 28 kmh^{-1}; 40·4 and 7·3 m.

10. 19·8 kmh^{-1}; 41° 31′ W. of N.; $\sqrt{2}$ km.

11. 25° 26′ E. of N.

12. 30° 22′ N. of E.; 28 kmh^{-1}.

13. 90·16 kmh^{-1}; 27° 28′ N. of E.; about 4$\frac{1}{2}$ minutes.

14. 0·39 km.

15. 20 kmh^{-1}; 5·5 minutes.

16. 6·93 minutes.

17. 48° 36′ with FW.

18. 24·2 km; 48° 4′ E. of N.

19. 16·8 kmh^{-1}; 12° 7′ E. of N.; 10° 11′ W. of N.; 16·1 kmh^{-1}.

21. 0·12 km.

EXAMPLES 1.6 (p. 47)

1. 10π rads^{-1}; 62·8 cms^{-1}.

3. 114·5 kmh^{-1} at 26° 33′ above and below the horizontal.

4. 32·7 ms^{-1}.

5. 18 : 1.

6. 5 rads^{-1}; 8·5 ms^{-1} at 45° above and below the horizontal.

7. 20 kmh^{-1}; 12 kmh^{-1}; 32 kmh^{-1}; zero.

8. $u+v$; $\sqrt{(u^2+v^2+\sqrt{2}uv)}$; $\sqrt{(u^2+v^2)}$; where u is the velocity of the wheel and v that of the point.

9. 4$\sqrt{(37+12\cos\theta)}$ kmh^{-1}.

EXAMPLES 2.1 (p. 54)

1. 36 ms^{-1}, 540 m.
2. 1·5 ms^{-2}, 75 m.
3. 3 ms^{-2}, 37·5 m.
4. 50 s, 2500 m.
5. 1 ms^{-2}, 12·5 m.
6. 6 ms^{-1}, 2 ms^{-2}.
7. 3·75 ms^{-2}, 14·6 ms^{-1}.
8. 667·4 m.
9. 10$\sqrt{7}$ kmh^{-1}, 4 minutes, 2·58 minutes.
10. $\frac{4}{75}$ ms^{-2}, 0·82 km.
11. 132 m, 5 ms^{-1}.
12. $\frac{2}{3}$ ms^{-2}, 1$\frac{2}{3}$ ms^{-1}, 2$\frac{1}{12}$ m.
13. 22·5 ms^{-1}.
14. 0·1 ms^{-2}; 0·2 ms^{-2}.
15. 65 m; 1·875 ms^{-2}.

16. $2b = a+c$; $f = \dfrac{c-b}{t^2}$;
    $u = \dfrac{3a-b}{2t}$.
18. $u = 0·9$ ms^{-1}; $f = 0·15$ ms^{-2}; 216 m.
19. 260 m. 17·7 ms^{-1}.
20. $\frac{5}{72}$ ms^{-2}.
23. 300 m.
26. $\dfrac{3u+v}{4(u+v)}$.
27. $u = \dfrac{4b-c-3a}{2n}$.
28. 13·1 km.
29. 0·5 ms^{-2}; 0·25 ms^{-2}.
30. 3 s more.
31. $\frac{6}{7}$.
32. 166$\frac{2}{3}$ s; 2$\frac{7}{9}$ km.

EXAMPLES 2.2 (p. 61)

1. (i) 15·6 m; (ii) $\frac{5}{7}$ s, and 2$\frac{6}{7}$ s.
2. (i) After 2 s; (ii) 5 s; (iii) 1 s and 4 s.
3. (i) 490 m; (ii) 4·5 s; (iii) 44·3 ms^{-1}.
4. 164·1 m.
5. (i) 3$\frac{4}{7}$ s; (ii) 10·5 m.
6. 122·5 m.
7. 96·8 ms^{-1}; 19·8 s.

8. 14·4 m.
9. 0·3 m above the top of the window.
10. 12·5 m; 2$\frac{6}{7}$ s.
13. 87·5 m; 92·5 m; 10 s.
14. 40 m, 4·9 s after first body started; 20, 7·4 ms^{-1}.
18. 45 m, 29·7 ms^{-1}, 4·5 s.

EXAMPLES 2.3 (p. 66)

1. 40·8 m; 4·1 s.
2. 30° 40′.
3. 7·27 ms^{-1}; 3·3 s.
5. $\dfrac{l^2-h^2}{l}\sqrt{\dfrac{g}{2h}}$.
6. $\frac{1}{2}gt^2 \sin\alpha \cos\beta$.
   A circle of diameter $\frac{1}{2}gt^2 \sin\alpha$ with A as highest point.

7. Let the bisector of $\angle$BCA cut BA in D, and let the circle with centre D and radius BD touch CA at E, then BE is the required line.
10. 1 : 3 : 5.

EXAMPLES 2.4 (p. 76)

1. Uniform speed for the first 10 s, then an acceleration of $\frac{3}{2}$ ms^{-2}; 275 m.

2. 12 ms^{-1}; 0·6 ms^{-2}.
4. 11·2 ms^{-1}.
5. The increase in $\frac{1}{2}v^2$.

6. $\frac{3}{8}$ ms^{-2}; 27 ms^{-1}; 3240 m.

7. 25 ms^{-1}.

8. 1571 m; 38 s.

9. 2·8 ms^{-2}.

11. 23·2 ms^{-1}; 25 ms^{-1}.

12. 5·4 km; 0·12 ms^{-2}.

13. 57 m; 9 ms^{-2}.

14. 0·75 ms^{-2}; 1 ms^{-2}.

15. 35 ms^{-1}; 20 ms^{-2}.

16. 16, 16.

17. $180t - 135t^2$, $180 - 270t$, $\frac{4}{3}$ hour; $53\frac{1}{3}$ km, 60 kmh^{-1}.

18. 4 m; 20 m; $1\frac{2}{3}$ ms^{-1}.

19. 5 ms^{-2}; 15 s; $56\frac{1}{4}$ ms^{-1}.

20. 30 ms^{-1}; 42 ms^{-2}; $6\frac{3}{4}$ m.

EXAMPLES 3.1 (p. 95)

1. $\frac{1}{2}$ ms^{-2}; 500 ms^{-2}.

2. $\frac{5}{6}$ N.

3. 6 s nearly.

4. $1·9 \times 10^5$.

5. 71·4 m.

6. $\frac{5}{18}$ N; 1 minute.

7. 225 cms^{-1}; 561·9 cm.

8. 0·8 N.

9. 1·6 km.

11. 0·0615 N.

12. 0·058 N.

13. 5·88 ms^{-1}; 8·82 m.

14. (i) 98 N; (ii) 148 N.

15. (i) 966 N; (ii) 406 N.

16. 0·2 ms^{-2}.

17. $g/13$ downwards.

18. (i) 109 s; (ii) 22·2 s; (iii) 546 s.

19. 379 s.

20. 9 kg; $g/9$.

21. 2 : 1.

22. $75\sqrt{2}$ ms^{-1}.

23. 1323 N.

EXAMPLES 3.2 (p. 104)

1. (i) 2·45 ms^{-2}; (ii) $7\frac{1}{2}g$ N; (iii) $15g$ N.

2. (i) 1·63 ms^{-2}; (ii) $5\frac{5}{6}g$ N.

3. (i) 1·22 ms^{-2}; (ii) 0·077 N.

4. (i) 196 cms^{-2}; (ii) 0·24 N.

5. (i) 4·3 ms^{-2}; (ii) $3\frac{15}{16}g$ N; (iii) $63\sqrt{2}/16 \, g$ N.

6. (i) 1 s; (ii) $\frac{1}{2}$ s.

7. (i) 1 s; (ii) 1 s.

8. (i) 2·45 ms^{-2}; (ii) $2\frac{1}{4}g$ N.

9. (i) 1·81 s; (ii) 4·52 s.

10. (i) 2·2 s; (ii) 1·1 s.

11. 4 m.

12. $\frac{1}{14}g$ ms^{-2}; $2\frac{1}{7}g$ N.

13. $\frac{1}{4}g$ ms^{-2}; $2\frac{1}{4}g$ N.

14. 9·8 ms^{-1}; 34·3 m.

16. 2·2 ms^{-2}.

17. 7·67 ms^{-1}; 3·91s.

18. 1·96 ms^{-2}; 3·5 m.

19. 8·8 ms^{-1}.

20. 5195 N.

EXAMPLES 3.3 (p. 113)

1. 6·5 ms^{-2}; $\frac{5}{3}mg$ N.

2. 12 kg; 20g N.

3. $5\frac{5}{7}$ kg; 4·2 ms^{-2}; $2\frac{6}{7}$ g N.

4. For M, $\dfrac{4m_1m_2 - M(m_1+m_2)}{4m_1m_2 + M(m_1+m_2)}g$;

for m_1, $\dfrac{4m_1m_2 + M(m_1-3m_2)}{4m_1m_2 + M(m_1+m_2)}g$;

for m_2, $\dfrac{M(3m_1-m_2) - 4m_1m_2}{4m_1m_2 + M(m_1+m_2)}g$.

5. $\dfrac{2Mmg}{(m+4M)(m+M)}$;

$\dfrac{m^2g}{(m+4M)(m+M)}$.

6. $\frac{9}{13}mg$ N; A, $\frac{5}{13}g$; B, $\frac{10}{13}g$.

7. $\dfrac{2wg}{3W+2w}$ for $(W+w)$;

$\dfrac{wg}{3W+2w}$ for $2W$.

8. $g/4$.

9. (i) $2g$ N; (ii) $1\frac{5}{7}g$ N; (iii) $1\frac{1}{8}g$ N.

11. 2 : 1.

14. $\dfrac{M(M+m)g \cos \alpha}{M+m \sin^2 \alpha}$.

16. $\frac{13}{72}g$; $\frac{1}{8}g$.

17. 4 ms^{-2}.

REVISION EXAMPLES A (pp. 117)

1. $\sqrt{(u^2-v^2)} : v$.
2. 12·12, 1·13 km, 24 minutes.
3. $768\sqrt{2}$ km.
4. u from 2θ E. of N.
6. 20 kmh^{-1} from 54° W. of N.
9. 4 s; 35·1 ms^{-1}; 89 m; 47 m.
10. $V/(1+p+q)$.
11. 120 s.

12. 16.35; $\frac{1}{15}$ ms^{-2}.
13. 3·5 km; $2\frac{2}{3}$ minutes; 3 minutes 8 seconds.
15. 8/9.
16. $m/21$; $5g/21$.
17. $6\frac{6}{13}$ g N; 1·6 s; $7\frac{7}{26}$ g N, 1·5 s.
19. 2·45 ms^{-2}; 0·1125g, 0·075g, 0·090g, 0·045g N.

EXAMPLES 4.1 (p. 128)

1. 11 000 J.
2. 2000 J.
3. 13·1 kW.
4. 8000 J; 27 600 J; 0·11 kW, 0·38 kW.
5. 370·2 kW.
6. 112·5 N.
7. $75g$ N; 9·8 kW.
8. 446·4 kW, 99·2 kmh^{-1}.
9. 25 162 N; 335·5 kW.
10. 25·6 kmh^{-1}.
11. 0·21.
12. 2598 N; 11·55 kW.
13. $1·2 \times 10^5$ J.
14. 20·6 kW.
15. 68·3 m; 60·5 m.
16. 2 N; 200 J; 40 W.
17. 51 m.

18. 9·4 kmh^{-1}.
19. 1 in $\dfrac{mgV}{H-VR}$; $\dfrac{Hn}{V}$; 1 in 27; 450 N.
20. (i) 21·2 kmh^{-1}; (ii) 14·8 kmh^{-1} $7\frac{7}{8}g$ N.
21. 428·7 kW.
22. 588 kW; 86·4 kmh^{-1}.
23. 7·4 s; 178·2 kW.
24. 1403 kW.
25. 0·092 ms^{-2}; 92·6 kmh^{-1}.
26. (i) 408 kW; (ii) 817 kW.
27. 1350 N; 59·3 minutes; 19·75 km; 214 km.
28. $65·5 \times 10^3$ N.
29. 2946 N; 9·8 cm.
31. 10·2 kW.

EXAMPLES 4.2 (p. 138)

1. (i) 1 : 6; (ii) 125 : 36.
2. $81\frac{2}{3}$ m; 4001 J.
3. 964·5 J; 17·4 ms^{-1}.
4. 1649 J; 6·1 kW.
5. 11·28 J; 3·76 W.
6. 16·8 kW.
7. 10·53 kW.
8. 1·43 kW.
9. 132 kJ; 78·8 kJ; 210·8 kW.

10. 8·25 kW.
11. 596 kW.
12. 2·04 kW.
13. 3640 J; 13·2 N.
14. 287·5 kW; 1·76 hour.
15. 0·4430; 0·55; 4·6 kW.
16. 5° 8′.
17. 0·1568 J; 0·8 ms^{-1}.
18. $1·18 \times 10^6$ J; $\frac{1}{8}$; $1·03 \times 10^6$ J.

EXAMPLES 4.3 (p. 149)

2. (i) $1\cdot65\times10^5$ J;
   (ii) $0\cdot67\times10^5$ J; (iii) $3\cdot2$ ms^{-1}.
3. Nearly $13\cdot0$ ms^{-1}.
4. Nearly $12\cdot9$ ms^{-1}.
5. 64 kmh^{-1}.
6. $\frac{1}{2}\,mg/(\cot\theta-\cos\theta)$.
8. $0\cdot3$ J.
9. $(1+2m/M)e$.
10. $3\cdot13$ ms^{-1}.

11. $2mga(\sin\theta-\mu\cos\theta)/\lambda$.
13. $1\cdot14$ cm.
14. $\frac{11}{12}mga$.
16. (i) $32\cdot65$; (ii) $32\cdot8$ km.
17. $15\cdot7$ ms^{-1}.
18. $4\cdot95$ ms^{-1}.
19. $\sqrt{(5ga/2)}$.
20. $2:1$.

EXAMPLES 4.4 (p. 156)

1. 1 N; 100 J.
3. $9\cdot8^2$ J.
4. J; (i) $\times1000$; (ii) $\times10^5$;
   (iii) $\times10^4$; (iv) $\times10^6$.
6. 2,319,000.

7. L^3/MT^2; $6\cdot482\times10^{-11}$.
9. 0, $\frac{1}{2}$, $-\frac{1}{2}$.
10. $\frac{1}{2}$, $-\frac{1}{2}$.
11. $\frac{1}{2}$, 0, $\frac{1}{2}$.

EXAMPLES 5.1 (p. 165)

1. $5\cdot01$ ms^{-1}.
2. 20 cms^{-1}.
3. 4 ms^{-1}; $\frac{2}{3}\times10^6$ N.
4. $5\cdot45$ ms^{-1}; $3\cdot03$ m.
5. $0\cdot12$ N m^{-2}.
6. $15\cdot9\times10^5$ N.
7. $122\cdot5\times10^3$ g N.
8. $5\cdot82$ ms^{-1}; $2\cdot91$ per cent; $0\cdot0086$ s; 705 N.
9. $R-2W+\dfrac{\sqrt{(R^2+400RW-400W^2)}}{202}$.
10. m/M; $4\cdot84\times10^5$ N.
12. 8 ms^{-1}; $1\cdot016\times10^6$ J; $4\cdot83\times10^5$ N; $3\cdot3$ cm.
13. $v\sqrt{\dfrac{M}{M+m}}$; $\dfrac{mv}{M}\sqrt{\dfrac{M}{M+m}}$; $\dfrac{m^2v^2}{2Mg(M+m)}$.

14. $8333g$ N.
15. 1102 kg ms^{-1}.
17. (i) $11\cdot1$ ms^{-1}; (ii) $15\cdot7$ m;
   (iii) $12\cdot5:1$.
19. $1\cdot71$ m.
20. $171\cdot9$ ms^{-1}.
21. $1\cdot45\times10^3$ N.
22. $54\cdot1$ kW.
23. $101\cdot5$ N.
24. $0\cdot87$ m.
25. $4\cdot2\times10^4$ N; $0\cdot13$ s.
26. 625 kW.
27. MV/mv; $\frac{1}{2}\dfrac{Mm(V+v)^2}{(M+m)}$.
28. $3\cdot7\times10^4$ kg m units.
29. 288 N.

EXAMPLES 5.2 (p. 174)

2. $2\sqrt{\left(\dfrac{2\mathrm{d}(m_1-m_2)}{g(m_1+m_2)}\right)}$ s;
   $\dfrac{m_2}{m_1+m_2}\sqrt{\left(\dfrac{2g\mathrm{d}(m_1-m_2)}{m_1+m_2}\right)}$.
3. $3\cdot07$ m; $6\cdot5$ s.

5. $0\cdot9$ m; $1\frac{5}{7}$ s.
7. $1\cdot05\sqrt{3}$ ms^{-1}; $3\sqrt{3}/7$ s.
8. $0\cdot45$ s.
10. 12 ms^{-1}; 378 J; $3\cdot5$ kg.
11. (i) $\frac{1}{2}mu\sqrt{3}$; $\frac{1}{2}u$;
   (ii) $\frac{1}{4}mu\sqrt{3}$; $\frac{1}{4}u\sqrt{7}$.

12. Perpendicular to the original direction of the first particle at $10\sqrt{3}/9$ ms^{-1}; 10 ms^{-1} at 60° to its direction before the blow.

13. A, $2\sqrt{13}I/15m$; B, $7I/15m$; C, $2I/15m$.

14. $\frac{17}{60}$ s; 1·8 ms^{-1}; 0·3645 J.

15. 2·4 ms^{-1}; 94 J; 2·22 ms^{-1}.

EXAMPLES 5.3 (p. 185)

1. 3 ms^{-1}; $3\frac{1}{2}$ ms^{-1}.
2. 6 ms^{-1}; $7\frac{1}{2}$ ms^{-1}.
3. $\frac{8}{9}$ms^{-1}; $4\frac{8}{9}$ ms^{-1} reversed.
7. $\dfrac{v_1(m_1-em_2)}{m_1+m_2}$;

   $\dfrac{m_1v_1(m_2-m_3e')(1+e)}{(m_1+m_2)(m_2+m_3)}$;

   $\dfrac{m_1m_2v_1(1+e)(1+e')}{(m_1+m_2)(m_2+m_3)}$.

8. 10·9 ms^{-1} and 2·6 ms^{-1}, both reversed; 2·55 J.

11. $\frac{35}{51}$ s.
12. 9000 J.
13. 2 ms^{-1}; 3 ms^{-1}; 45 J.
15. 0·6 ms^{-1}; 1·5 ms^{-1}; 1350 J.
17. $\frac{13}{64}u$; $\frac{15}{64}u$; $\frac{36}{64}u$.
18. 0·3 ms^{-1}; 3600 J.
23. $\frac{5}{22}$; $2\frac{1}{2}$ ms^{-1}.
25. 11·9ms^{-1}; 6·7ms^{-1}, reversed; 42 per cent.
26. $\dfrac{m_1m_2(1+e)(v_1-v_2)}{m_1+m_2}$.

EXAMPLES 5.4 (p. 193)

1. 0·4 m; $\frac{4}{7}$ s; 0·56 ms^{-1}.
2. $\frac{4}{5}$.
3. $3\sqrt{13}$ ms^{-1} at tan^{-1} $(1/2\sqrt{3})$ with the plane.
4. (i) $2\cdot8\sqrt{13}$ ms^{-1} at tan^{-1} $(\frac{2}{3})$ below the horizontal.
   (ii) $2\cdot8\sqrt{19}$ ms^{-1} at tan^{-1} $(7\sqrt{3}/9)$ below the horizontal.
5. 0·035 J.
6. 0·866.

7. 0·36 m from the corner at tan^{-1} $(\frac{3}{2})$.
8. (i) $u\sqrt{(\cos^2\alpha+e^2\sin^2\alpha)}$ at tan^{-1} $(e\tan\alpha)$;
   (ii) $m(1+e)\,u\sin\alpha$ normal to plane;
   (iii) $\frac{1}{2}mu^2\sin^2\alpha(1-e^2)$.
10. 5·75 cm.
11. $u(1-e)/2$ towards the wall; $u(1+e)e'/2$ away from the wall.
12. 32 000 N; 4368 J.

EXAMPLES 5.5 (p. 200)

1. 8·66 ms^{-1} perpendicular to the line of centres; $2\frac{1}{2}$ ms^{-1} along the line of centres.
2. 3·7 ms^{-1} at cot^{-1} $5\sqrt{3}/12$ to line of centres; 6·1 ms^{-1} along the line of centres.
3. 4·62 ms^{-1} at 60° to the line of centres; 4·16 ms^{-1} at tan^{-1} $(\sqrt{3}/7)$ to the line of centres.
4. 4·07 ms^{-1} at tan^{-1} $(-3\sqrt{3})$ to the line of centres; 2·34 ms^{-1} at tan^{-1} $(3\sqrt{3}/11)$ to the line of centres.

5. $\frac{1}{2}u\sqrt{2}$ and $\frac{1}{2}u\sqrt{6}$, each at 45° to the line of centres.
6. 0·8u and 1·16u at 40° 12′ and 48° 12′ to the line of centres.
10. $\frac{1}{2}u\sqrt{(4\sin^2\alpha+\cos^2\alpha(1-e)^2)}$; $\frac{1}{2}u\cos\alpha(1+e)$; at

    tan$^{-1}\left[\dfrac{2\tan\alpha}{1-e}\right]$ to, and

    along the line of centres.
12. Along the line of centres; at tan^{-1} $(10\sqrt{3}/3)$ to the line of centres.

EXAMPLES 6.1 (p. 210)

1. (i) 11·5 m; (ii) 3·06 s, 79·5 m;
   (iii) 28·66 ms^{-1} at tan^{-1} 0·466
   to the horizontal.
2. (i) 40·8 m; (ii) 33·1 m;
   (iii) 91·8 m.
3. 14$\sqrt{3}$ ms^{-1}; 3·5 s.
4. 2100 m.
5. 1800$\sqrt{3}$ m.
6. 25·6 ms^{-1} at tan^{-1} ($\frac{3}{4}$) to the
   horizontal.
7. 960 m.
8. 31·3 ms^{-1}; 4·5 s.
10. 48$\sqrt{3}$ m.
11. 960 m; 9° 16′ to the horizontal.
12. 28·1 km.

13. 117·1 m.
14. 4 m.
15. tan^{-1} ($\frac{4}{3}$); 64 ms^{-1}; 10·4 s.
16. 2·1 s.
18. 16·1 ms^{-1}.
19. 495 ms^{-1}.
20. Horizontal and vertical distances from O are 367 m;
    367 m; 459 m; 229·5 m.
21. tan^{-1} 0·49; 111·8 ms^{-1}.
24. 1257 ms^{-1}; 40·3 km.
26. $a/2\sqrt{(g/2b)}$; $\sqrt{(2gb)}$.
28. 32·8 m; 18$\sqrt{3}$ m.
29. a tan $\alpha - (ga^2/2V^2 \cos^2 \alpha) - b$.

EXAMPLES 6.2 (p. 220)

1. 10·6 s; 550·8 m.
2. (i) Nearly 7·8 km;
   (ii) nearly 13·5 km.
3. 217·5 m.
4. 2000 m; 6000 m.

5. 24·5 km; 19·0 km.
   24·5 km; 21·5 km.
12. 18·8 km; 566 ms^{-1} at
    tan^{-1} (1·6) to the horizontal.
13. 47 km; 98 s.

EXAMPLES 6.3 (p. 223)

3. $\tan^{-1}\left[\dfrac{bc}{a(c-a)}\right]$; $\dfrac{bc^2}{4a(c-a)}$.

4. A little under 1°; about
   0·7 m.
5. 15° and 75°; $\dfrac{2-\sqrt{3}}{2+\sqrt{3}}$.

EXAMPLES 6.4 (p. 231)

1. $\dfrac{9v^2 \sin \alpha \cos \alpha}{256}$; $\dfrac{v \sin \alpha}{64}$.
3. 48 m horizontally from A.
5. $\frac{1}{3}$.

7. 8h sin α, where α is the inclination of the plane.
12. 0·211.

REVISION EXAMPLES B (pp. 232–240)

1. 122·5 W; 375 kW.
2. 0·079 ms^{-2}; 10·2 ms^{-1}.
3. 25·5 ms^{-1}; 392 N; 458·6 N.
4. 45·9 ms^{-1}; 905 N.
5. 0·122 ms^{-2}; 72 000 N.
6. 1306·7 kW.
7. $5V(V^2+U^2)Mg$ sin $\alpha/18U^2$;
   13·15 kW.

8. 11·7 ms^{-1}.
9. 13·1 cm.
13. $mu^2/2c$; $\frac{1}{2}u$; c/u.
14. 0·57 ms^{-1}; 0·69 m.
15. $Mu/(M+m)$.
16. $\frac{1}{3}(v^2-2\mu ga)^{\frac{1}{2}}$.
18. $(1-e)$: 1;
    (I/m) cos α, (I/m) sin α.

20. $1 \cdot 8$ m; $3\frac{1}{3}$ s.
21. $2ev/g$.
23. $\{(m_1+m_2)gh/(m_1-m_2e)\}^{\frac{1}{2}}$.
24. $\tan^{-1}$
$$\left\{\frac{(m_1+m_2)v_1 \tan \alpha}{(m_1-em_2)v_1-(1+e)m_2v_2}\right\}.$$
25. $\frac{1}{2}$.
26. $\frac{7}{4}\sqrt{(gh)}$.
27. $\frac{1}{2}a\sqrt{3}$.

28. $\frac{1}{2}u(1+e^2)$; $2\pi a/eu$.
33. $\tan^{-1} 2$.
36. (i) a straight line in direction of projection of A; (ii) $2u^2/g$.
37. $1 \cdot 22$ m.
38. $45°$; $71° \, 34'$; $\sqrt{5}$ to 1.
40. $(2ag+bg)^{\frac{1}{2}}$ at $\tan^{-1}(1+4a/b)^{\frac{1}{2}}$ to horizontal.

EXAMPLES 7.1 (p. 244)

1. $9 \cdot 6$ N.
2. 122.
3. $1 \cdot 78 \times 10^5$ N.
4. $1 \cdot 78 \times 10^3$ N.

5. $0 \cdot 13$ m.
6. $2\pi\sqrt{(l/g)}$.
7. $77 \cdot 2$.
10. $1 \cdot 92$ ms^{-1}; $18 \cdot 4$ ms^{-2}.

EXAMPLES 7.2 (p. 251)

1. $\pi^2 n^2 a/900g$.
4. 8 cm approximately.
5. $1 \cdot 493$ m; 53 N.
6. $g(\lambda-ma\omega^2)/\lambda a\omega^2$.
7. $3 \cdot 6\pi^2$ N.

11. $\cos^{-1}\left(\dfrac{m}{M}\right)$; $\dfrac{1}{2\pi}\sqrt{\left(\dfrac{Mg}{m(l-a)}\right)}$.
14. $ma\left(4\pi^2n^2-\dfrac{g}{b}\right)$.
15. 49 N.

EXAMPLES 7.3 (p. 260)

1. $7 \cdot 2$ cm.
2. $12 \cdot 1$ ms^{-1}.
3. bv^2/gr.
4. $2 \cdot 8$ cm.
5. $80 \cdot 2$ kmh^{-1}; $\frac{9}{8}$.
6. $48° \, 36'$; $2 \cdot 27 \times 10^3$ g N.
7. $81 \cdot 6$ kmh^{-1}.
8. $23 \cdot 6$ cm.
9. $7° \, 40'$; $0 \cdot 1345$.
10. $11° \, 24'$; $0 \cdot 52$.

11. $61 \cdot 7$ kmh^{-1}.
12. $41° \, 25'$.
13. $28 \cdot 9 \times 10^3$ g N.
15. $0 \cdot 06$ of wt.
16. $0 \cdot 15 \times 10^4$ N nearly.
18. $0 \cdot 47 \times 10^3$ g N.
19. $29 \cdot 8$ kmh^{-1}.
20. $14 \cdot 4$ ms^{-1}.
21. $\tan^{-1}(v^2/gR)$.

EXAMPLES 7.4 (p. 273)

1. $7 \cdot 67$ ms^{-1}; $2 \cdot 65$ N.
3. 239 cms^{-2}; $1 \cdot 24 \times 10^{-3}$ g N.
4. $3 \cdot 07$ ms^{-1}.
5. $4 \cdot 2\sqrt{(\sin \theta)}$ ms^{-1}; $0 \cdot 6$ g N; $0 \cdot 4$ m; $0 \cdot 3\sqrt{3}$ g N.
6. $1 \cdot 89$ m; $2 \cdot 07$ m.
7. 1 m.
8. $1 \cdot 916 \times 10^3$ N.

9. $12 \cdot 12$ ms^{-1}.
11. $8 \cdot 37$ ms^{-1}; $1 \cdot 5$ nearly; $5 \cdot 09$ ms^{-1}.
12. 135 g N; just.
13. $mg(3\cos\theta-2)$ outwards; $3g/4$.
15. $0 \cdot 43$ of its wt.
17. $5 \cdot 14$ ms^{-1}; $0 \cdot 446$ m.
20. 15 cm.

EXAMPLES 8.1 (p. 286)

1. $\pi\sqrt{2}$; $\pi/2$.
2. $1 \cdot 5\sqrt{2}$ ms^{-1}; $0 \cdot 9\sqrt{2}$ ms^{-1}.
3. $0 \cdot 9$ m; π s.
4. 2π s; $1 \cdot 5$ ms^{-2}.
5. $1 \cdot 2$ m; $0 \cdot 6\sqrt{7}$ ms^{-2}.
6. $0 \cdot 9\pi$ ms^{-1}; $0 \cdot 9\pi^2$ ms^{-2}.
8. 8 s; $28\sqrt{2}$ cm.
9. $3/5\pi$ ms^{-1}; $6/25\pi^2$ m.
11. a; $2\pi/k$.
13. $2\pi\sqrt{\left(\dfrac{x_2{}^2-x_1{}^2}{v_1{}^2-v_2{}^2}\right)}$;

$\sqrt{\left(\dfrac{v_1{}^2 x_2{}^2-v_2{}^2 x_1{}^2}{v_1{}^2-v_2{}^2}\right)}$;

$\sqrt{\left(\dfrac{v_1{}^2 x_2{}^2-v_2{}^2 x_1{}^2}{x_2{}^2-x_1{}^2}\right)}$;

$\dfrac{\sqrt{(v_1{}^2-v_2{}^2)}}{x_2{}^2-x_1{}^2}\sqrt{(v_1{}^2 x_2{}^2-v_2{}^2 x_1{}^2)}$;

$\frac{2}{3}\pi\sqrt{5}$; $0 \cdot 1\sqrt{161}$; $0 \cdot 3\sqrt{(161/5)}$;
$0 \cdot 18\sqrt{161}$.

14. Nearly 196
16. $\pi/3\omega$ s; $(\sqrt{3}/2)a\omega$.
17. $6 \cdot 8$ cm; $0 \cdot 095$ s.
18. $3\pi/10$ ms^{-1}; 18 ms^{-2};
    $0 \cdot 15\pi\sqrt{3}$ ms^{-1}; 9 ms^{-2}.
22. (i) $2\pi n\sqrt{(a^2-x^2)}$;
    (ii) $2\pi na \sin 2\pi nt$.
27. (i) $0 \cdot 6/\pi$ ms^{-1};
    (ii) $1 \cdot 2/\pi^2$ ms^{-1}.
28. $2 \cdot 4\sqrt{10}/5$ m; $0 \cdot 6\pi\sqrt{\frac{3}{5}}$ s;
    $0 \cdot 080$ s.
29. $2 \cdot 7/\pi$ m; (i) $2 \cdot 25\sqrt{3}$ ms^{-1};
    (ii) $2 \cdot 25\sqrt{2}$ ms^{-1}.

EXAMPLES 8.2 (p. 297)

1. 15 cm; $\pi\sqrt{30}/35$ s.
2. $\pi\sqrt{10}/35$ s; $0 \cdot 19$ ms^{-1};
   $2 \cdot 45$ ms^{-2}.
3. $0 \cdot 022$ m.
4. (i) $3/2\pi$; (ii) $9\pi/16$ W.
8. $\pi/8\sqrt{(9-2l)}$;
   $\dfrac{0 \cdot 4}{\sqrt{(9-2l)}}$ ms^{-1}.
9. $0 \cdot 59$ m; $\frac{1}{5}\pi\sqrt{3}$.
11. $140\sqrt{6}/\pi$ per minute;
    $7\sqrt{6}/30$ ms^{-1}.
12. $\pi\sqrt{5/7}$ s; $7\sqrt{15}/200$ m;
    $4 \cdot 5g$ N.

13. $2\pi/7$ s; $6 \cdot 75g$ N; $0 \cdot 3$ ms^{-1}.
15. $5\sqrt{3}\pi/42$ s; 42 cms^{-1};
    $2 \cdot 35$ ms^{-2}.
16. 20 cm; $2 \cdot 5g$ N; $\pi\sqrt{3/7}$ s.
17. 3 cm; $4\sqrt{10}\pi/70$ s;
    $21\sqrt{10}/2$ cms^{-1}.
18. 35 cms^{-1}; $\pi/7$ s.
19. $\pi\sqrt{2}/14$ s.
20. $3\sqrt{3}\pi/14$ s; $56/5\sqrt{3}$ cms^{-1}.
24. 10 cm; $0 \cdot 64$ ms^{-1}.
25. $T = 2\pi a/V$; $V^2 b/a^2$;
    $\frac{21}{11}$ nearly.

EXAMPLES 8.3 (p. 305)

1. Gains 265 s.
2. $99 \cdot 4$ cm; $1 \cdot 775$ mm shorter.
4. 440 s.
5. $100/197$.
6. 110 s.

7. $0 \cdot 046$ cm; $1 \cdot 5$ km.
8. $1 \cdot 0005 : 1$; $2 \cdot 97$ km.
9. $30 \cdot 2$.
11. $4 \cdot 59$ cm; $4 \cdot 9$ N; $1 \cdot 90$ s.

EXAMPLES 9.1 (p. 317)

1. $2Ma^2$.
3. $\frac{8}{3}Ma^2$.

4. $\frac{4}{3}M(a^2+b^2)$.
5. $\frac{1}{2}Ma^2$.

8. $\frac{3}{2}Ml^2$.

11. (i) $\frac{117}{800}M$, where M = mass of remainder of plate; (ii) $\frac{441}{3200}M$.

12. $0\cdot266M$, where M is the total mass.

13. $\frac{1}{3}Ml^2 \sin^2\theta$.

14. $\frac{1}{3}Ma^2 \sin^2\theta$.

15. $\frac{1}{2}Mp^2$, $\frac{1}{18}Mp^2$ where p is the perpendicular height.

17. $\frac{3}{5}Ma^2$.

18. $\frac{2}{5}Mr^2$.

19. $\frac{1}{4}Mr^2$; $\frac{1}{4}Mr^2$.

21. $0\cdot056M$, where M is the mass of wheel and shaft.

23. $1\cdot938$ kg m^2.

24. (i) $\frac{2}{3}Ma^2$; (ii) $\frac{5}{12}Ma^2$.

EXAMPLES 9.2 (p. 322)

1. $8\cdot08$ rad s^{-1}.

2. $0\cdot6$ kgm^2 nearly.

3. $1\cdot8\sqrt{7}$ ms^{-1}; $29\cdot4$ J.

4. $4\frac{2}{3}$ rad s^{-1}.

5. $\frac{48}{170}\sqrt{102}$ ms^{-1}.

6. 866 kgm^2.

7. $\frac{3}{2}ml^2$; $\sqrt{(2\sqrt{3}g/3l)}$.

9. $\sqrt{(V^2+4ga)/2a}$.

10. $\sqrt{(g/a)}$ rad s^{-1}.

12. 3813 J.

13. $\sqrt{(10\cdot8g)}$; $\sqrt{(9g)}$.

14. $M\dfrac{a^2+2b^2}{4}\omega^2$.

15. $7\cdot9$.

16. $12\cdot6\pi$.

EXAMPLES 9.3 (p. 336)

1. $2\pi\sqrt{13l/15g}$.

3. $0\cdot65\pi$ s.

4. $4\pi/7$ s.

6. 4440 J approx.; 30π N.

7. $16\frac{2}{3}$ revolutions; $\sqrt{(3/\pi)}$ m.

8. 150 revolutions; 20π Nm.

9. $16250\pi^2$ J; $21\cdot3$ Nm; 1200 revolutions.

10. $76\cdot8\pi^2$ J; $1\cdot01$ N m.

13. $\sqrt{\{2mgx/(M+m)\}}$.

15. $0\cdot005\pi$ N m; $37\cdot8$ g.

16. $1\cdot29$; $0\cdot21$ m.

17. $2\cdot7$ m.

18. $100g/972$; $0\cdot98$ N cm.

19. 4 cm.

20. $0\cdot091$ N m.

EXAMPLES 9.4 (p. 349)

4. 100 mh^{-1}; $1\cdot72$ J.

5. $3\cdot615\times10^5$J; 502 N.

8. $\frac{11}{20}\,Mg$ N on back; $\frac{9}{20}\,Mg$ N on front.

REVISION EXAMPLES C (pp. 351–357)

2. $2\sqrt{ag}$ at $\tan^{-1}(5\sqrt{2}/2)$ to horizontal.

7. $9\cdot4$ N; $50°\ 15'$.

9. $\sqrt{(a^2+b^2)}:b$; $\sqrt{(g/b)}$; $a\sqrt{(1+(gt^2/b))}$; $d-b$.

10. OA; $(m_1+m_3)a\omega^2$; OB, $(m_2+m_3)a\omega^2$; BC, $m_3a\omega^2$; AC, $m_3a\omega^2$; AB, $m_3a\omega^2$. AB in thrust.

11. $(3gr/\sqrt{2})^{\frac{1}{2}}$; $(gr/\sqrt{2})^{\frac{1}{2}}$. Midpoint of BC.

12. $7a/3$.

13. 8 s; $3\cdot6\sqrt{2}/\pi$ m; $0\cdot9\sqrt{2}$ ms^{-1}; $3+2\sqrt{2}:1$.

16. $\sqrt{2}:1$; $1:\sqrt{2}$.

18. $\frac{1}{6}$ AB.

21. $50\pi^2$ J.

22. $4mg/a(M+2m)$; $8mg/a(M+2m)$.

23. $\sqrt{7}:\sqrt{2}$.

24. $4:3$.

25. $2\pi\sqrt{\{(3M+16m)a/(2M+8m)g\}}$

29. $g\sin\alpha\times(m+4M)/(m+6M)$; $m=M$.

30. $0\cdot1275$ kg m^2; $13\cdot8$ N; $10\cdot4$ N.

EXAMPLES 10.1 (p. 366)

1. (i) 15; (ii) 12; (iii) 13; (iv) 10;
   (v) $\cos^{-1}(-\frac{2}{5})$; (vi) $\sqrt{58}$.
3. (i) 120°; (ii) 60°.
4. $Q = \sqrt{3}P$.
5. 15 N, 9 N, $\cos^{-1}(-\frac{3}{5})$.
6. 10 g N on each peg.
7. $5\sqrt{3}$ g N on the upper peg;
   5 g N on the lower peg.
8. $\cos^{-1}(\frac{7}{15})$.
10. 120°.
11. 4 N, $\cos^{-1}(-\frac{3}{8})$.

12. $\sqrt{76}$ N.
13. 10·3 N.
14. $4\sqrt{3}$ N, at 90° to the 4 N force.
16. 20 N, $\tan^{-1}\frac{3}{4}$.
17. $5\sqrt{2}$; $3\sqrt{10}$ and $\sqrt{10}$ N.
18. $\cos^{-1}\frac{1}{4}$ to P.
19. 8·8 N; 43° with 3 N.
20. 353·5 N; 234·5 N.
21. 8·7, 22·0 g N.

EXAMPLES 10.2 (p. 376)

1. 16 g N and 12 g N.
2. 72 g N and 54 g N.
3. 24 g N and 10 g N.
5. 7·8 g N and 6·6 g N.
6. 4·8 g N and 1·4 g N.
7. $a.$ $5\sqrt{3}$ g N.
   $b.$ $10\sqrt{3}$ g N.
8. 8·1 g N and 5·5 g N.
9. $M = 3$; $3\sqrt{3}$ g N.
10. 9·03 g N in AC; 7·1 g N in BC.
12. (i) $7\frac{1}{2}$ g N, 6 g N;
    (ii) 60 g N, 36 g N;
    (iii) $2·89 \times 10^3$ g N, $2\frac{1}{2} \times 10^3$ g N.

13. 5 g N, $5\sqrt{3}$ g N.
14. At right angles to the first string; $2·5\sqrt{3}$ g N and 2·5 g N.
15. 30·1 g N.
16. $5\sqrt{2}(\sqrt{3}-1)$ g N and $10(\sqrt{3}-1)$ g N.
17. 3·6 g N; 67° 58', 44° 3'.
18. $5\sqrt{2}$; 5 g N.
19. 63·9 N; 23°; 80 g N; 54°.
21. $5\sqrt{2}$, $5\sqrt{2}$, 10, $5(\sqrt{2}-1)$.
23. 10 g.

EXAMPLES 10.3 (p. 385)

1. 7·7 N, 29°.
2. 10 N at $\tan^{-1}(\frac{3}{4})$ with the 4 N force.
3. 7 N, between the 13 and 10 N forces at $\tan^{-1}(5\sqrt{3}/11)$ with the former.
4. 9·198 N.
5. 64·5 N, 13° 57' S. of W.
6. 20 N at 60° to AB.
7. 228·8 N, 49° 39' S. of E.
8. 23·9 g N on A; 10 g N on B and C; $10\sqrt{3}$ g N on D.
9. $\sqrt{3}F$; $\tan^{-1}(3-2\sqrt{2})$.
10. 112·8 N, $\tan^{-1} 3(\sqrt{2}-)1$ S. of E.

11. 12·17 N, $25\frac{1}{4}°$.
12. 6·3 N at $\tan^{-1}(7\sqrt{3}/3)$, with the 2 N force.
13. $\sqrt{281}$ N at $\tan^{-1}(\frac{16}{5})$ with AB.
14. 8 N along GA.
15. 30 N, 34 N.
16. 10 N, 53° 8'; 10 N, 36° 52' E. of N.
17. 2·91 N, 290° 6'.
18. $2\sqrt{2}$ N parallel to DB through E.
19. $\sqrt{3}$ N perpendicular to BC, 7·5 cm from B.

EXAMPLES 10.4 (p. 390)

1. 8 N; 15 N.
2. $12\sqrt{5}$; $4\sqrt{2}$.
3. $31\frac{1}{4}$ N; $P = 25$ N.
4. 0·0726 g N.

5. 13 N; $\tan^{-1}\frac{12}{5}$ to BA.
6. 16 N opposite to 5 N.
7. 3·77 N at 142°.
9. $\frac{1}{2}\sqrt{3}$, $-\frac{1}{2}$.

EXAMPLES 10.5 (p. 399)

1. 10 g N, 8·96 g N.
2. 0·25.
3. 4·85 g N.
5. $\frac{1}{8}$.
6. $10\sqrt{3}/3$ g N.
7. (i) 8·8 g N; (ii) 15·2 g N.
8. $1/\sqrt{39}$.
9. 12 g N, 213 g N.
10. 73·57 g N.
13. $\tan^{-1}(\frac{1}{4})$ with the plane; 56 g N.
14. $\sin \alpha = \sin \beta + \mu \cos \beta$, where μ is the coefficient of friction, and α the inclination of the smooth plane.

16. (i) 0·536; (ii) 170·9 N.
17. $P = W\dfrac{\sin \alpha + \mu \cos \alpha}{\cos \beta + \mu \sin \beta}$;

$Wl \cos \beta \dfrac{\sin \alpha + \mu \cos \alpha}{\cos \beta + \mu \sin \beta}$;

608 J.
18. $\cos \lambda = \dfrac{PW}{Q\sqrt{(P^2 + W^2)}}$.
19. 52° 30′, 7° 30′, $W/\sqrt{2}$ at $7\frac{1}{2}$° to plane.
20. $2R\alpha$, where α is in radians.
21. 0·3535; 1·096 g N.
22. 10 g N, 14·33 g N.

EXAMPLES 11.1 (p. 409)

1. 110 N, 14 cm from A; 30 N, $51\frac{1}{3}$ cm, from A beyond B.
2. 21 N, 24 cm from A; 3 N, 168 cm from A beyond B.
3. 4 N, 24 cm from A on BA produced.
4. 12 N, 10 cm from the 8 N force.

5. 75 N, 25 N, the 75 N force being 1 m from the resultant.
11. 2 units; cuts diagonal BD distance $\frac{1}{10}$ (diagonal) from centre.
12. If D is on CA such that CD = 2 cm resultant bisects BD.

EXAMPLES 11.2 (p. 416)

1. 32 N cm, 64 N cm, 16 N cm about A, B, C respectively.
2. 180 N cm, 180 N cm.
3. $5\sqrt{3}$ N m.

4. 18 N m, zero.
5. 5 N m, 3 N m.
6. $21\sqrt{3}$ N cm, $21\sqrt{3}$ N cm.

EXAMPLES 11.3 (p. 419)

1. 7 g N on the support nearer the 3 kg; 6 g N on the other.
2. 20 g N at A; 40 g N on the the other.

3. 62·5 g N on the nearer; 37·5 g N on the other.
4. 37·5 kg.
5. $7\frac{1}{3}$ g N at A; $10\frac{2}{3}$ g N at B.

6. 0·865 m from the end from which distances are measured.

7. 5 units at 14 m from A on DA produced.

8. 2·1 m from A.

9. 0·6 m.

10. 7·35 g N at C; 4·65 g N at D; 51·5 g N cm.

11. $\frac{9}{34}$ m on either side of the centre.

13. Not nearer than 17·5 cm to either string.

14. A couple of moment 37 units, 10 g N — 3·7 m from O.

16. $4\frac{2}{3}$ g N on the prop further from the 2 kg; $7\frac{1}{3}$ g N on the nearer one.

17. 26 g N and 14 g N.

18. 12·5 kg.

19. $p+q$.

20. AC = 0·6 m, DB = 0·3 m.

21. 202 N, 1·78 m.

22. At B, $\dfrac{48+9M_1-3M_2}{7}g$,

   At C, $\dfrac{36+10M_2-2M_1}{7}g$;

   each equal to 6 kg.

23. 0·46 m.

24. 60°.

25. 25 g N at 2·4 m from the end from which distances are measured; 15 g N at this end, 10 g N at the other end.

EXAMPLES 11.4 (p. 429)

1. $\frac{1}{8}$.

3. Mark off distances a, $2a$, etc., from M towards A, a being the distance of the mid-point of BD from C.

5. x must not be less than 7 kg. $x = 7\sqrt{2}$ kg.

7. 14 g N; $\frac{3}{14}$ m from centre.

9. $\frac{1}{2}$ cm; $W_0 = 4W_1$.

EXAMPLES 12.1 (p. 441)

1. 45°.

2. $\tan^{-1}\left(\frac{3}{2}\right)$; $1\frac{1}{4}$ times weight of rod at $\tan^{-1}\left(\frac{4}{3}\right)$ to the horizontal.

4. $W \sin 15°$; $W \cos 15°$, at 15° to the vertical.

8. $4\frac{3}{8}$ g N.

9. 5 g $\tan 40° = 4\cdot2$ g N nearly. 10·8 g N at 67° 14′ to horizontal.

10. $\frac{1}{6}W$; $W\sqrt{37/6}$; at $\tan^{-1}6$ to the horizontal.

11. $W\sqrt{3}/3$; $2W\sqrt{3}/3$; at 60° to horizontal.

12. $2W\sqrt{3}/3$; $W\sqrt{3}/3$.

15. $7\frac{1}{4}$ g N.

16. 77·1 g N; 163·4 g N, 63° 39′ to the horizontal.

18. 0·46 m each.

19. ACB = 90°, and B is below C. Least pressure = $W \sin \alpha$.

21. $3\frac{1}{8}$ g N.

22. 20·5 g N, 4·5 g N.

24. Perpendicular to AB; $\frac{1}{2}w\sqrt{(4-3\sin^2\theta)}$.

25. 10 N; $5\sqrt{3}$ N.

26. $10\sqrt{3}$ g N on 30° plane; 10 g N on 60° plane; at 30° to horizontal.

EXAMPLES 12.2 (p. 455)

1. 33 g N; 30·5 g N, at $\tan^{-1}\frac{25}{56}$ to the horizontal.

2. 1·5 g N; 9·1 g N nearly, at $\tan^{-1}6$ to the horizontal.

4. 11·4 g N.

6. $\frac{1}{8}$ of the length of the beam from the end on the 30° plane.

8. 5·25 g N, 7 g N, vertically.

9. $R_1 = \frac{67}{56}W$; $R_2 = \frac{45}{56}W$.

10. $\sin^{-1}\left(\dfrac{m+n}{m}\sin\theta\right)$; $0\cdot73$.

11. Perpendicular to the line joining the centre of roller to edge of kerb.

12. Perpendicular to the line joining the centre of roller to edge of step, $1:2$. There is a tendency to slip at the step, but not at the ground.

14. 1476 N, 75° S. of E.; 4400 N.

15. $(8-\sqrt3)$ g N.

EXAMPLES 12.3 (p. 466)

1. $W\sqrt3/6$ horizontal at the lowest joint; $W\sqrt{39}/6$ at $\tan^{-1}2\sqrt3$ to the horizontal at each of the upper joints.

2. $2W$ in AC; $W/2$ horizontal at B and D.

3. Tension in string $= 2W$. Reaction at B and D $= W\sqrt3/6$ horizontal.

4. W; W vertical at A and C; W horizontal at B.

5. $\frac34W$.

6. Horizontal and vertical components of reactions are at B,
$\dfrac{ab(a+b)}{2(a^2+b^2)}Mg$, $\dfrac{a^3-b^3}{2(a^2+b^2)}Mg$;
at C.;
$\dfrac{ab(a+b)}{2(a^2+b^2)}Mg$, $\dfrac{a^3+2a^2b+b^3}{2(a^2+b^2)}Mg$;
at A.
$\dfrac{ab(a+b)}{2(a^2+b^2)}Mg$, $\dfrac{a^3+2ab^2+b^3}{2(a^2+b^2)}Mg$.

7. $W\left(1+\dfrac{b}{2a}\right)$; $W\left(2-\dfrac{b}{2a}\right)$;
$\dfrac{c(a+b)}{2a\sqrt{(a^2-c^2)}}W$.

9. $2W$; the horizontal and vertical components of the reaction at the hinge are $2W$ and $\frac53W$.

12. Horizontal and vertical components of the reaction at B or E are
$\dfrac{W}{4\cos18}$ and $W\left(\dfrac{1}{4\sin18}-\tfrac12\right)$.

13. $w\sqrt7/2$ at A and D; $w\sqrt{19}/2$ at B and C.

14. $0\cdot05$ m on side nearer B. The horizontal and vertical components of the stresses are:
at A, $0\cdot84$, and $1\cdot63$ g N;
at B, $0\cdot84$, and $1\cdot87$ g N;
at C, $0\cdot84$, and $0\cdot37$ g N.

15. $W\cot\alpha$; $W\operatorname{cosec}\alpha$.

16. $\frac12W(\tan\alpha+(a/c)\operatorname{cosec}^2\alpha)$.

17. 2 g N, 2 g N.

20. 200 g N horizontal and vertical at both D and B.

23. $11\cdot74$ g N.

24. $0\cdot6$ m from B; $2\cdot5$ g N.

25. $2\cdot5$ g N horizontal.

26. $\cos^{-1}\{M/(2M+m)\}$.

EXAMPLES 12.4 (p. 476)

1. $0\cdot74a$ from A on the side opposite to B.

2. At C.

3. $0\cdot75$ m.

4. $6\cdot05$ at 70° 42′ to AB on the side opposite to the square.

5. Divides BC in the ratio $1:2$.

6. $24\sqrt2$ N.

7. 30 N.

8. $57\cdot6$.

9. $2\cdot37$ P, it cuts BC at $\frac79$BC from B, and makes an angle $\tan^{-1}\sqrt{15}/5$ with BC.

10. 1 from C to D, 1 from C to B, 1 from A to D.
(i) 2 along BC; (ii) a couple of moment twice the side of the square.

11. A force of 21 from B to A; 54·5 nearly.

13. $5\sqrt{2}/4$ N; $5\sqrt{2}$ n.

14. 2 N from D to A.

15. 13, $\sqrt{173}$.

16. $2P$ parallel to AB bisecting AD.

EXAMPLES 12.5 (p. 482)

8. Another circle.

9. 6DG where D is the mid-point of AB, and G the point of trisection of BC which is nearer to C.

10. The line bisecting AC at right angles, where C is the mid-point of AB.

11. The centre is at G, the mid-point of the line joining the mid-points of opposite sides of the quadrilateral; the radius is PG.

12. CF = AE.

16. $\sqrt{10}$ N at $\tan^{-1} \frac{1}{3}$ with AB, cutting AB produced at 1·36 AB from A.

21. Through mid-point of AB.

22. $l = 3-m$; $2:1$.

EXAMPLES 12.6 (p. 489)

1. $\frac{1}{2}Wa$.

2. Vertical force 7·5 N; couple 18 N m.

5. Reactions on BC at B: vertical force $2W$, horizontal force $2W$, couple $5Wa$; and at C vertical force W, horizontal force $2W$, couple Wa where W = weight of AB, $2a$ = length of AB.

6. Two equal forces $12P/5$ forming a couple.

8. $k = -4$.

10. kb parallel to AD, $\frac{3}{2}a$ from A; couple kab.

EXAMPLES 12.7 (p. 498)

1. $3\frac{3}{4}$; 5.

2. $(21\sqrt{3}/2)a$; where a is a side of the hexagon; 6 parallel to the force of 5.

3. $6F$, $\tan^{-1} (5\sqrt{5}-9/8)$ to AB; $3\cdot17$ of AB beyond A, $0\cdot27$ of BC beyond C.

5. $G/a\sqrt{3}$ where G^2 equals $G_1{}^2+G_2{}^2+G_3{}^2-G_2G_3-G_3G_1-G_1G_2$.

6. $N-xY+yX = 0$.

7. 50; 0·047 m on BA produced, 0·094 m between A and D.

8. 1 N; $\sqrt{3}x-y-\sqrt{3}a = 0$.

10. $\sqrt{74}$ N at $\tan^{-1} (-\frac{7}{5})$ to AB; 36 units counter-clockwise.

11. 19·05 units at 1° 36′ with the horizontal sides of square; 23·11 units anticlockwise.

12. 6N in direction CO; 90·9 N cm.

13. 10, $5\sqrt{2}$, $5\sqrt{2}$ N.

14. $4\sqrt{5}/5$ N along BC, $16\sqrt{5}/15$ N along AC, $8\sqrt{5}/15$ N along AB.

15. 6 N inwards at mid-point of BC; 8 N outwards at mid-point of AC.

17. (i) $\sqrt{10}$ N at $\tan^{-1} 3$ with AB;
    6 N m anticlockwise.
    (ii) $\sqrt{160}$ N at B; $\sqrt{90}$ N
    at C.

20. 1·59 N m.
22. $\sqrt{194}$; $5x + 13y - 17a = 0$.
24. $2P$, perpendicular to BD at a
    distance $\frac{1}{2}$ BD from D.

EXAMPLES 12.8 (p. 505)

1. 120·7 g N.
2. $\frac{40}{3} + 6\sqrt{3}$, $\frac{40}{3} + 10\sqrt{3}$,
   $\frac{220}{3} - 16\sqrt{3}$ N at A, B, C
   respectively.
4. 20 g N.

5. $16\frac{2}{3}$ g N; 100 g N.
6. 14·93 g N.
7. 58·8π N; 34·8π N.
8. 20π, 20$\pi - \pi^2$ J.

REVISION EXAMPLES D (pp. 507–512)

1. 6, $3\sqrt{3}$.
3. $P \cos(\pi - \theta)$, $P \sin(\pi - \theta)$.
7. $\tan^{-1}\{(2 - \sqrt{3})/\sqrt{3}\}$.
8. $(\sqrt{3} - 1)/2$;
   $\tan^{-1} \sqrt{3}/(2\sqrt{3} - 1)$.
11. 4 : 3.
12. $w/2\sqrt{3}$.
13. $W + wd/4b$; $W + w(1 - d/4b)$.
14. $5W/2 \cos \pi/5$.
17. $\frac{1}{2}W$, $\frac{3}{2}W$.
18. 553 g N.
19. Ties: DA 117 g N, AC 224 g N.
    Struts: CD 168 g N, CB
    280 g N.

22. kb parallel to AD, $\frac{3}{2}a$ from A;
    kab.
23. $(P+Q) \cos \alpha$, $(P-Q) \sin \alpha$.
24. $\sqrt{2}$.
25. $5M/12a$.
26. 1 N parallel to AB; $1\cdot2\sqrt{3}$ m;
    $1\cdot2\sqrt{3}$ N m; 1 N parallel to
    BA.
27. $10a$ in the sense DCBA; $3\sqrt{2}$
    from C to A.
28. $10\sqrt{(4-\sqrt{3})}$ N at
    $\tan^{-1}(2-\sqrt{3})/\sqrt{3}$ with BA;
    10 N m.
29. $(4 \cos 36° - 1)(6 \cos 36° + 1)$.
30. 4, $-8\sqrt{3}$; $18a\sqrt{3}$.

EXAMPLES 13.1 (p. 520)

1. Between the 5 and 4 N forces;
   0·08 m from the former.
2. $9\cdot7 \times 10^3$ g N at the left-hand
   end; $9\cdot3 \times 10^3$ g N at the other
   end.
3. Between the 7 and 4 N forces,
   at 0·24 m from the former.
4. 1·08 m from the end.
5. 7·2 g N at end from which
   distances are measured, 7·8
   g N at the other end.
6. 10·5 g N, and 8·5 g N.
7. 2·66 m from the 2 N force.

8. 4·8 m from the first 10-Mg
   load.
9. 6·3 m from the end nearer to
   the 4 kg; 8·2 g N on the end
   nearer the 4 kg, and 13·8 gN
   on the other end.
10. 5·46 m.
11. 44·375 g N at A; 105·625 g N
    at the support near B.
13. 2·5, 5·5, 2·8, 3·9 g N.
14. 6·2 N at 76° 6′ to AB, cutting
    AB between A and B at $\frac{6}{7}$ cm
    from A.
15. 5·9 N at 13° with 3 N force.

EXAMPLES 13.2 (p. 531)

1. 14·5 N; BC and CD, +12·2; AB and AD, +8·45.

2. 90 g N; 64 g N at 100° 36′ with DB.

4. AB, $-w$; BC, $-w$; CD, $-0·62w$; DE, $-0·38w$; EA, $-0·62w$; BE, $+0·6w$; BD, $+0·62w$.

5. 2·19 g N; 4·8 g N.

6. P = 25 g N; AB, +43·3; AC, −50; BC, +86·5.

7. AB and DC, −0·38; AD and BC, −0·76; BD, +0·66.

8. AB and AD, +18·75; BC and CD, +25; AE, −22·5; BE and ED, −31·25.

9. AB, −15; BC, −9; CD, −5·5; AC, +9·25 N.

10. BD, +10; BC and AD, −8·3; AB and CD, −5·5.

11. YD and YC, −1·73; AD and BC, −1·5; XD and XC, +0·86; XA and XB, −1·15; AB, −0·86.

12. Each force = 10, AB, BC, CD, DE, +20; AC and CE, −11·55; AE, +5·77.

13. 21·21 in each supporting string; 17·32 in AB and AC; 6·34 in BC.

14. AE, +358; AD, −320; EC, +134; ED, +223; CD, −150; CF, +268; FD, +56; FB, +324; DB, −145. Reactions, 160 at A, 290 at B.

15. Reactions, 27·7 at A, 22·3 at B; AC, −28·3; AD, −7·7; CD, +20; AB, −20; BD, +3·6; DE, +17·3; BE, −15; BF, −20; EF, +17·3.

16. Reactions, 27·5 at A, 22·5 at B; AC, +55; AF, −48; CD, +25; CF, +30; DF, −25; DE, +25; EF, +20; EB, +45; FB, −39·0.

17. Reaction at D = 22·4; at A = 20; AB, −20; BD, +14; BC, 14; DC, +10.

18. AB, +11·5; BD, +34·5; DE, +11·5; DF, +23·0; CD, +11·5; EF, −11·5; CE, −11·5; AC, −23; CD, −11·5.

19. OB, −60; AB, +42·3; AC, +30; BD, −20; BC, −14·2; CD, +14·2; CE, +10; DE, −14·2. Reaction at A = 66·9.

20. AF, −40; AB, −20; BC, +20; BF, +28·3; FE, −20; CE, +14·1; CD, +10; ED, −14·1; CF, −20.

21. Reaction at A = 126; AC, +56·5; BC, −120; AD, +80; CD, −56·5; CE, −40; DE, +28·2; DF, +20; EF, −28·2.

22. AB, $-0·5W$; AC, $+1·12W$; BC, $+W$; EB, $-1·12W$; CD, $+3·3W$; EC, $-1·4W$.

23. TB, 1·03; TC, 1·10; TD, 1·25; TE, 1·4.

24. AC, −4·62; BC, +2·3; BD, +5·63; CD, −4.

25. AB, +18; BF, +18; BG, −11·3; FG, −18; CG, +15.

26. AF and BG zero; AD, +0·66; DF, −0·94; DE, +0·66; FE, −0·37; ED, +0·37; FG, −0·5; EC, +0·34; CG, −0·47; BC, +0·34.

27. Reaction, 0·6 at A, 0·72 at B; AD, −1·1; AC, +1·32; DE, −1; CD, −0·20; EC, −0·20; BC, +0·5; EB, −1·1.

28. CE, −2; EF, zero; AD, +14; DC, +10; AE, −12·1; DE, +4; EB, −8·7; CF, +10; BF, +10.

29. 33°, +2·6.

30. AC, +4·18; AE, +14·26; ED, +15·7; CD, −11·83; BC, −16·01; CE, −3·53.

EXAMPLES 14.1 (p. 550)

1. $\tan^{-1}(\frac{3}{2})$.
3. $\frac{2}{5}$ of the weight of the ladder.
11. $3\frac{1}{3} g$ N.

12. Zero; $\frac{1}{4}W$. The friction will be limiting at both wall and ground.
13. $\sqrt{3}W/6$; 50 g N.
15. The thirteenth rung.

EXAMPLES 14.2 (p. 554)

2. $2\tan^{-1}(\frac{1}{16})$.
4. $a/2h < \mu$.
9. (i) by sliding; (ii) by tilting.

11. $\mu \not< \frac{1}{2}(w/W)$; $\sqrt{2(a/b)}$.
12. $\frac{2}{3}$, $7a/2$.

EXAMPLES 14.3 (p. 557)

1. $\frac{30}{59}$; the longer rod will slip.
2. $\frac{1}{2}$.

4. At A, $\dfrac{W(3+\cos 2\alpha)}{4\cos\alpha}$;

   at C, $\dfrac{W(3\cos 2\alpha+1)}{4\cos\alpha}$;

   at A, $5\sqrt{3}/7$.

EXAMPLES 14.4 (p. 561)

1. $\dfrac{\mu}{\cos\alpha+\mu\sin\alpha}$.
2. $P = W\sqrt{(\mu^2-n^2)}$,
   $\tan^{-1}\dfrac{n}{\sqrt{(\mu^2-n^2)}}$.
6. $W_1/W = \dfrac{\mu}{\cot 2\theta-\mu}$.

7. $\frac{1}{7}$.
8. $\dfrac{m(\sin\alpha-\mu\cos\alpha)}{(M+m)(\mu\sin\alpha+\cos\alpha)}$.
17. $P = W/\sqrt{(2-1)}$; not.
18. $\mu = 1/(3\mu'+4)$.

EXAMPLES 15.1 (p. 574)

1. $32\cdot875 g$ N.
2. $9\cdot5 g$ N.

4. 25 g N, 25 g N, 50 g N, 100 g N, 200 g N. Difference is the effort, 25 g N.

EXAMPLES 15.2 (p. 581)

1. 10 g N.
2. $7\frac{1}{2} g$ N.

3. 50 g N.
4. 50; $16\frac{2}{3} g$ N.

EXAMPLES 15.3 (p. 583)

1. 4 strings; 2 units.
2. 3 units, M.A. = 6.
3. 5; 24 N.
4. 85·4 units, 31·74 per cent, 38·09 per cent, 40·82 per cent.

5. $W = 15P+11w$.
6. 672 N.
7. 7 g N.
8. 129 g N, 129 g N.
9. 50·8 g N.

10. $P/Q = \frac{1}{2}$.
11. 187·5 N.
12. 0·68.
13. The side wound on the 30 cm drum.
14. $\frac{9}{8}W$.
15. $\frac{1}{11}$.

16. 0·23.
17. 4000π N.
18. 1·88 cm.
19. 0·10.
20. $Wb/4a$; $b/4an$.
21. 40 g N, 196 g N.
22. $\mathrm{Pc} = \frac{1}{2}W(a-b)$; 864 N.

EXAMPLES 16.1 (p. 592)

1. 3·1 cm.
2. 2·5 m.
3. 2·828 cm from BC; $\frac{1}{3}$ cm from AD.
4. 5·6 cm; 4 cm.
5. $\sqrt{171}/2$ cm.
6. 21·9 cm nearly.
7. $2\frac{2}{3}$ m.

9. Half the length of a side on the line joining the 15 kg and 3 kg masses.
10. 4 cm, towards the 5 kg mass on the line joining this mass to the 2 kg mass.
11. 3·15 cm.
12. 8·4 m; 3 m.

EXAMPLES 16.2 (p. 601)

1. $9\frac{1}{3}$ cm.
2. $\frac{6}{35}$ cm on diameter through hole.
3. $3\sqrt{2}/17$ cm from centre on diameter bisecting line joining centres of holes.
4. $6\frac{2}{3}$ cm; $3\frac{1}{9}$ cm.
5. $5\frac{2}{7}$ cm; $6\frac{2}{7}$ cm.
7. On AC at 6·07 cm from A.
9. $\tan^{-1}\left(\frac{16}{33}\right)$.
11. $\frac{16}{45}$ of its length up the median.
12. 46·4 cm.
13. 15·05 cm, 15·07 cm.
15. 72 cm.
18. $55\sqrt{3}/18$ cm.
20. 2·0 cm.
21. 3·12 m.
22. In each case $\frac{1}{4}$ of the way up the line joining the vertex to the centre of gravity of the base.

24. $26\sqrt{2}/9$ cm up the median drawn to the side of 8 cm.
28. 13 : 54.
31. $\tan^{-1}[\frac{3}{10}(5+\sqrt{5})]$.
33. At the point (2, 3) taking the outer edges as axes.
34. $\frac{185}{376}$ of an edge.
35. $\frac{11}{56}\sqrt{\frac{2}{3}}a$ from the base.
36. $\frac{1}{3}b\frac{3a+c}{2a+c}$; $\frac{3a^2+3ac+c^2}{3(2a+c)}$.
37. 3·15 m from the free end of the first plank, and at the height of the upper surface of the second plank.
38. $0\cdot52a$ from the top.
39. At a distance $2mca^2/Mb^2$ from the axis.
$$\frac{m}{M} \gtrless \frac{b^2(a-b)}{2a^2c}.$$

EXAMPLES 16.3 (p. 607)

3. $\dfrac{(a^2+ab+b^2)\sqrt{[4c^2-(b-a)^2]}}{6c(a+b)}$ from DA;
$\dfrac{4ac^2+2bc^2-a^3+b^3}{6c(a+b)}$ from the other axis.

4. 0·50, 2·69.
6. $\frac{5}{3}$ cm from each diagonal.

EXAMPLES 16.4 (p. 615)

2. 24 cm from C.

3. $\dfrac{(a^2+ab+b^2)\sqrt{[4c^2-(b-a)^2]}}{6c(a+b)}$ from DA;
   $\dfrac{4ac^2+2bc^2-a^3+b^3}{6c(a+b)}$ from the other axis.

5. $\frac{1}{2}(3-\sqrt{5})$.

6. $\dfrac{a^2+ax+x^2}{3(a+x)}$ and $\dfrac{a(2a+x)}{3(a+x)}$, where $x = $ AE. AE not less than $\frac{1}{2}(\sqrt{3}-1)a$.

EXAMPLES 16.5 (p. 625)

2. $\sqrt{2}:1$.

7. $3a/2\pi$ from the centre along the middle radius, a being the radius of the disc.

9. $\frac{13}{14}r$.

10. $\sin^{-1}(\frac{3}{4}\pi \sin \theta)$.

7. With BC or DE in contact with the plane; with BD or EC in contact with it if DE is above BC.

10. Yes.

11. Not less than $3:1$.

12. 1·59.

13. $(n-1)c/2$ from the centre of lowest block and at a vertical height of $na/2$.

14. $r\sqrt{3}$.

15. 53·9 cm; 29°.

11. At $a/(2\pi-3\sqrt{3})$ from the centre.

12. $\frac{1}{2}W \tan \alpha$.

13. 749 kg, 6·7 m from the butt.

14. $(\pi^2-1)^{-\frac{1}{2}}$.

16. $\sin^{-1} \frac{1}{3}$.

REVISION EXAMPLES E (pp. 627–635)

1. $\frac{1}{4}\sqrt{3}$.

4. μW.

5. $W/2\mu \sin \alpha (\sin \alpha - \mu \cos \alpha)$; $W/2\mu \sin \alpha (\mu \sin \alpha + \cos \alpha)$.

7. $(W-w)(1-\mu)/\sqrt{2}\mu$; $(W-w)(1+\mu)/\sqrt{2}\mu$.

8. AB, compression $= 35$ g N; BC, compression $= 88$ g N; CA, tension $= 173$ g N; CD, compression $= 135$ g N; force at A $= 153$ g N; at 60° to AD.

9. $\sqrt{3}$ (A), $\sqrt{7}$ (B); AD (tension) $2\sqrt{3}$, CD (compression) 4, AC (compression) 2, BC (compression) $2\sqrt{3}$, AB (tension) 1.

10. AB, CD compression $= 10\sqrt{3}$; BC, DA, tension $= 20\sqrt{3}$; AC, tension $= 40$.

11. Tension in string $= w/\sqrt{3}$; OA, thrust $= 2w/\sqrt{3}$; OB, tension $= \frac{1}{2}w$; OC, thrust $= w/2\sqrt{3}$; OD, thrust $= \frac{1}{2}w$; OE, tension $= 2w/\sqrt{3}$.

12. Stress in rods $= W/\sqrt{3}$, $W(1+1/\sqrt{3})$, $W(\sqrt{3}+1)$; tension $= W(\sqrt{6}+\sqrt{2})/2$; BC, CD in tension.

13. AD, AE tension $= P/\sqrt{2}$; BD, BE, tension $= 3P/\sqrt{2}$; CD, CE thrust $= P\sqrt{5}$; CB, thrust $= 2P$.

14. 16° 6′; BC (thrust) 8·3 g N, CA (tension) 11·1 g N, AB (tension) 33·3 g N.

15. DC 10, DE 10, EC 8·7, EF 15, CB 15, EB 0, BA 30, FA 30, FB 26·0, in g N to 1 dp.

16. 6, 8, $2\sqrt{3}$ tension, $2/\sqrt{3}$ compression, $7/\sqrt{3}$ compression.

17. $2 \sin^{-1}(\frac{1}{3})$.

18. On AC, distant $\pi ab^2\sqrt{2}/2(4a^2-3\pi b^2)$ from O.

19. $(\frac{7}{4}, \frac{19}{4})$, $(\frac{47}{28}, \frac{153}{28})$.

20. $\tan^{-1}(4/3\pi)$.

24. $(2a^2+ab)/(3a+3b)$, $(a^2+ab+b^2)/(3a+3b)$.

27. $\tan^{-1}\left(\frac{24}{13}\right)$.

32. 15·9 N.

34. 4; 3·45; 0·86.

$\{W+(2^n-1)w\}/2^n$.

35. $\frac{1}{4}(W+w)$; $4W/5(W+w)$.

36. 68 N; $49/54\pi$, $49/51\pi$, $49/50\pi$.

EXAMPLES 17.1 (p. 652)

1. 20 units at 60° to AB.

2. $AB^2 = (a_1-a_2)^2+(b_1-b_2)^2$.

3. (i) $3i+4j$, $-5i+25j$, $22i-40j$.
   (ii) 7, -16. (iii) $(2i+3j)/\sqrt{13}$, $(3i-4j)/5$, $(-2i+5j)/\sqrt{29}$.

4. $4i+3j$.

14. $\tan^{-1} 7$, $-4/7$.

15. $r = (1+m)a+(1-m)b$.

16. 2 : 1.

21. $r = (1+3m)i+(2-3m)j+(3+2m)k$; $(-3\frac{1}{2}, 6\frac{1}{2})$.

23. (i) $(2-4m)i+(m-1)j+(3+2m)k$, (ii) $(2m_1+3m_2)i+(2m_2-m_1)j+(3m_1-4m_2)k$.

24. $(2i-j+3k)/\sqrt{14}$; $a = b = c$.

27. $\frac{1}{2}(b^2c^2+c^2a^2+a^2b^2)^{\frac{1}{2}}$; $bc : ca : ab$.

28. 55° 45′, $0·27a^2$.

29. $4\sqrt{2}$, $4\sqrt{2}$, $2\sqrt{5}$ cm, 41° 29′.

30. 2, $\frac{1}{2}\sqrt{13}$ cm, 25° 38′.

EXAMPLES 18.1 (p. 663)

1. $11\frac{4}{7}$.

2. 4·1.

3. 6·8.

4. 10·97, 10.

5. (a) 19·6, 19·5.
   (b) 19·15, 19.

6. 161·31 cm.

7. 161·39 cm.

8. 45° 24′ 27″, 45° 24′ 28″.

9. 44·42, 45·98.

10. 5·59.

11. 744·3 mm.

12. 68·5.

13. 154·05.

14. 351·9.

15. 98·7, 97.

16. 36, 39, 37.

18. 141·2, 165·9.

19. 165·8, 167·2, 161·2, 172·4 cm.

20. 63·76 cm, 63·6 cm.

EXAMPLES 18.2 (p. 675)

1. (a) 2·6, 3·04.
   (b) 1·6, 2·02.

2. $\sqrt{2}$.

3. 4·5, 1·76.

4. 5·56, 2·35.

5. 162·06, 4·2 cm.

6. 2·95, 0·135.

7. 4·10, 0·15.

9. 21·6, 1·8.

10. 6·52, 6·5, 6·52, 0·156.

11. 3·14, 0·15.

12. 315·0, 1·77 ohms.

13. 8·56, 0·018 cm.

14. 974·5, 985·5, 980·1, 9·1.

15. 49·98, 0·15 cm.

16. 149·4, 2·3 ohms.

17. 1057, 1055·6, 16·2 m.

18. 99·97, 99·97, 0·19 watt.

19. 0·999, 0·018.

20. 153·75, 19·1.

21. 10·70, 3·21.

24. $32\frac{1}{2}$, 2·20, 1·8, 0·82.

25. 49·5, 46·3; grouped nearer to 50 than 41; Paper II harder.

EXAMPLES 18.3 (p. 688)

3. $10 \cdot 9$, $2 \cdot 5$, 23 per cent.
4. $\frac{3}{4}$, 0, $1/\sqrt{5}$; $\pm 0 \cdot 35$.
5. 1, 1, $1/\sqrt{6}$; $0 \cdot 7$ to $1 \cdot 3$.
6. $\frac{3}{4}$, $1 \cdot 2$, $0 \cdot 4$, $1 \cdot 6$, $11/16$.
8. $a\sqrt{2}$.

9. $1/\sqrt{2}$; $(\pi - 2)/\pi$.
10. 2, 1, $5/3$.
11. $0 \cdot 166$.
12. $\frac{7}{15}$, $0 \cdot 42$, $0 \cdot 46$.

EXAMPLES 18.4 (p. 700)

1. $5/3$, $\frac{1}{3}\sqrt{10}$.
2. $1 \cdot 2$, $0 \cdot 98$.
3. $120/1024$, $120/1024$, $968/1024$.
4. $1/1296$, 0.
5. $1 \cdot 03$, $p = \frac{1}{4}$ nearly.
6. $1 \cdot 73$.
7. $2 \cdot 12$.
9. $0 \cdot 143$, $0 \cdot 042$.
12. $3 \cdot 01$, $\sqrt{3 \cdot 05}$.
15. 5, $\frac{1}{2}\sqrt{10}$.
16. $\bar{x} = 29 \cdot 22$, $\sigma^2 = 2 \cdot 03$.
17. $18 \cdot 83$, $0 \cdot 099$.
18. $\bar{x} = 102 \cdot 23$, $\sigma^2 = 4 \cdot 01$.
19. $162 \cdot 9$, $17 \cdot 0$.

20. $0 \cdot 68$, $0 \cdot 02$.
21. $0 \cdot 68$, $0 \cdot 95$, $0 \cdot 82$, $0 \cdot 14$.
22. $10 \cdot 007$, $0 \cdot 013$, $0 \cdot 0024$, $10 \cdot 000$ to $10 \cdot 014$.
23. $0 \cdot 000\ 11$.
24. $0 \cdot 16$.
25. $16 \cdot 63$, $0 \cdot 12$. At least another 5, possibly 9.
27. $544 \cdot 3$ mm, $1 \cdot 9$ mm, A.
28. $10 \cdot 67$, $2 \cdot 29$. Fall.
31. $0 \cdot 133$, $0 \cdot 319$.
32. Significantly inaccurate.
34. $15/128$, significant, $153 \cdot$
35. A sample of around 50 would suffice.